ELECTRICITY AND MAGNETISM

ELECTRICITY
AND MAGNETISM

EDSON RUTHER PECK

Associate Professor of Physics, Northwestern University

New York   Toronto   London

McGRAW-HILL BOOK COMPANY, INC.

1953

ELECTRICITY AND MAGNETISM

Library of Congress Catalog Card Number: 53-6048

XI

49142

PREFACE

This book is a rethinking of the classical subject of electromagnetism which stems from two convictions. The first is that the subject itself challenges the mind to really careful thought. It repays close reasoning by unfolding to the mind an elegant combination of experimental observation and mathematical analysis, whereas it repays superficial attention rather by bewilderment and a sense of dissatisfaction with its logical foundations. A simple example of bewilderment is found in the common failure to understand the purpose of defining a pair of electric field vectors, the force field **E** and the electric displacement **D**. The second conviction is, however, that an adequate and rewarding grasp of the entire fundamental structure of electromagnetic theory can be achieved on the intermediate level. This volume is dedicated to the student with a background of general physics and calculus as an aid in mastering the fundamental concepts of electromagnetism.

One justification for another book on electromagnetism is the need for a modern presentation. The atomic nature of matter and electricity is constantly borne in mind, even as a background for purely macroscopic theory. There is a systematic effort throughout the work to reconcile microscopic and macroscopic pictures with each other. Magnetism is presented as arising in connection with the motion of electric charge, whether on a macroscopic or microscopic scale. The magnetic pole takes its place with the concept of equivalent current distributions as a representation of the properties of magnetic matter, rather than as a physical entity. Rationalized mks units are used exclusively.

It is not expected that every reader will agree with the author's notion of the limits of an intermediate treatment of electromagnetism. In particular, some rather elaborate proofs are given, which may give the book a formidable appearance. It will be found, however, that it is generally possible to take up these proofs or to leave them alone. The instructor of the course may find it useful to be able to say to the student, "The proof is there, if you care to read it; otherwise we shall simply use the result." The inclusion of proofs, wherever possible, is important so that the reader may not feel that he is asked to take theorems on faith. It seems better to show how much work is involved in a mathematical demonstration than simply to remark, "It can be shown." This must, of course, still be done for some proofs which clearly belong to more advanced books, as, for example, proof of the uniqueness theorem for the electrostatic field and solving of the wave equations with sources.

v

The mathematical background required of the reader has been kept at a minimum. This has necessitated including some purely mathematical matters such as vector analysis and material on line and surface integrals. Such topics are so essential to the presentation of electromagnetism that they have been presented in the text itself rather than in an appendix. To allow flexibility in order of presentation, cross references are made to these mathematical demonstrations.

An effort has been made to render the book as serviceable as possible to the reader. This has been done by careful discussion of points which, according to the author's teaching experience, are likely to be misunderstood; by the abundance of cross references; and by making the demonstration of theorems sufficiently full to be read easily, without imposing on the reader the necessity of filling in essential steps of the reasoning.

This volume is not intended to serve as a laboratory manual. For a course with laboratory work, it should be supplemented by a good set of experiment notes or a textbook on electrical measurements. The reader is assumed to have the familiarity with common apparatus, such as the voltmeter and the electroscope, which comes from any elementary physics course or elementary electricity laboratory. It should be noted, however, that the needs of a laboratory course have been borne in mind and met within the scope of the work. After Secs. 1.1 to 1.5 inclusive, Chap. 1, which are preliminary to all that follows, the reader may proceed to parts of Chap. 5 (Secs. 5.1, 5.4 to 5.14), and thence enter upon d-c circuit theory without stopping for the bulk of electrostatics. Then, he may read only the earlier parts of Chaps. 7, 8, and perhaps 9 to prepare him for transient and a-c circuit analysis without stopping for the bulk of the work on magnetism. Such an order of sections has been successfully followed at Northwestern University, where two quarters of electrical measurements precede a quarter of theory. The material on circuit analysis is unusually thorough for a general textbook, and provides adequate background for laboratory work. Problems throughout the text frequently refer to experimental applications.

Some topics will be notable for their absence. This is a time of such specialization that it seems right to avoid a shallow coverage of many related fields which are properly discussed as distinct branches of physics, physical chemistry, or engineering. Thus there is no treatment of electronic tubes and their applications; of filters or transmission lines; of the physical electronics proper to atomic or nuclear physics; of thermoelectricity; of electrolytic and voltaic cells; of kinetic theory; of the detailed applications of the quantum mechanics to atomic structure.

Considerable attention has been given to the problem sets. Most of the material in the text has been illustrated with problem material. It is the author's belief that the working of problems is indispensable to a firm grasp of any field of physics. The problems are intended to take the place of a great number of worked examples. Why should an author take credit for making numerous simple applications of the theory, when their discovery is both profitable and pleasurable for the student?

The author is glad to acknowledge his great indebtedness to many of the standard textbooks in the field for their contributions to his own understanding of electromagnetic theory. Nevertheless, the book is in no sense merely a collection of conventional methods of presentation. It is hoped that any innovations which it contains may prove their worth in mental stimulation and help to the reader.

Edson Ruther Peck

"Lo, these are parts of His ways"
Job

CONTENTS

CHAPTER 1

ELECTROSTATICS

1.1. Electric Charge. Electric charge was first observed in experimental science as a property of matter producing force actions between unlike substances which had been rubbed together. If, for example, hard rubber is rubbed with fur, then the rubber and the fur are found to attract each other, and both have the power to attract dust particles. In more modern physics, electric charge may be defined as a basic and characteristic property of elementary particles of matter in terms of which certain force interactions and interaction energies may be described. The subject matter belonging under the heading of Electricity and Magnetism is the description and analysis of those fundamental phenomena related to electric charge. Detailed applications of the basic phenomena are worked out in related fields of study, as, for example, study of electric discharges or of electronic instruments. Our concern will be the basic analysis, and mention of applications will serve primarily for illustration.

1.2. Coulomb's Law, and Conservation of Charge. Simple experiments with charged bodies indicate the following facts concerning electric charges and their static reactions; and these facts have been confirmed directly and indirectly in many ways.

1. There exist two and only two kinds of electric charge, called positive and negative, respectively; and quantities of charge are given a positive or a negative algebraic sign in analysis according to their kind. By tradition, negative electricity is the kind which hard rubber acquires when rubbed with fur. The electron has a negative charge. The fur acquires a positive charge, which is of the same kind as the charge of the proton. Qualitative electrostatic experiments show the existence of the two classes of charge by the direction of the force action between charges, according to the traditional rule: Two charges of the same kind repel one another, while two charges of different kinds attract one another.

2. When two charges have spatial dimensions small compared to their distance apart, we shall refer to them as *point charges* so far as their interactions are concerned. The static interaction force between two point charges acts along the straight line joining them and is proportional to the inverse square of their distance apart.

1

3. Charge is a scalar quantity. We may agree that the total charge in a region is the algebraic sum of the separate charges in it. Then without yet defining a unit of charge, we may show experimentally that the interaction force between point charges is proportional to the magnitude of each charge. Thus the separate parts of one point charge are affected by another point charge in the same way when grouped together as if they were alone; and conversely the forces on a point charge due to several other point charges grouped together to make a point charge add independently according to vector rules. These are special cases of a general principle of independence: The mutual interaction of a pair of charges is unaffected by the presence of other charges.

4. Net charge is conserved under all conditions; that is, the algebraic sum of the charges within a closed system is constant.

The first three of the foregoing statements constitute Coulomb's law,[1] and may be combined as follows: Between every pair of point charges relatively at rest there is a force

$$\mathbf{F}_{kj} = C \, \frac{q_j q_k}{r_{jk}{}^3} \, \mathbf{r}_{jk} \tag{1.1}$$

where q_j and q_k are the algebraic magnitudes of the two charges, $\mathbf{F}_{kj}$ is the force on q_k due to q_j, r_{jk} is the scalar distance between the charges, $\mathbf{r}_{jk}$ is the vector distance directed from q_j to q_k, and C is a constant of proportionality whose value depends on the units employed. It must be remembered that any matter in the vicinity of the pair of charges under consideration will in general exert additional forces on q_k. For example, if the pair of charges is embedded in an infinite homogeneous isotropic dielectric, we shall see later on that the total force on q_k, which is now due not only to q_j but also to charges induced in the dielectric, has the form of Eq. (1.1) but with a constant C which depends on the dielectric material. Equation (1.1) is universally true, however, in any electrostatic system and with a universal constant C appropriate to empty space, when it is understood to apply solely to the direct interaction of the pair of charges. Its validity is not affected by intervening or surrounding matter of any kind.

By convention, and to simplify other equations later, we shall write for the universal constant

$$C = \frac{1}{4\pi\epsilon_0} \tag{1.2}$$

where ϵ_0 is a constant called the permittivity of free space. If in Eq. (1.1) r_{jk} is in meters, F_{kj} in newtons, and the q's in coulombs (which we shall define later), then experimentally

$$\epsilon_0 = 8.854 \times 10^{-12} \text{ coulomb}^2/\text{newton m}^2 \tag{1.3}$$

---

[1] In honor of Charles Augustin de Coulomb (1736–1806).

The Coulomb law for a pair of charges now takes the form

$$\mathbf{F}_{kj} = \frac{q_j q_k}{4\pi\epsilon_0 r_{jk}{}^3} \mathbf{r}_{jk} \tag{1.4}$$

The total electrostatic force on q_k is the vector sum of the forces on it due to all charges in the universe which are at rest relative to q_k, including those in the constitution of matter:

$$\mathbf{F}_k = \frac{q_k}{4\pi\epsilon_0} \sum_{j=1}^{n} \frac{q_j}{r_{jk}{}^3} \mathbf{r}_{jk} \tag{1.5}$$

For completeness, we repeat in equation form the principle of conservation of electric charge:

$$\sum_j q_j = \text{constant} \tag{1.6}$$

for any closed system.

1.3. Charge Density. All matter is composed of elementary particles of only a few kinds; and these particles have been found to be either uncharged or else to have exact multiples of the quantity of charge of one electron, which is 1.602×10^{-19} coulomb. It follows that electric charge occurs in nature only in multiples of the electronic charge, and thus from a microscopic viewpoint it is discontinuously distributed unless we are dealing with the internal structure of an elementary particle. Nevertheless, the electronic charge is extremely small, and very large numbers of elementary particles are present in charges of ordinary, macroscopic magnitude. In addition, the charged particles in matter are not actually at rest, but in continual motion. This would seem to invalidate all our statements of the principles of electrostatics, for we have been careful to limit them to truly static systems. This limitation is necessary for rigor, since the force equation for moving charges is much more complex than for static charges. However, the time average of force upon a fixed charge due to the moving charges in matter may be correctly computed by averaging over the motion; and this averaging results analytically in a smearing out of charge into a continuous distribution. The same averaging may be carried out for force on charges moving relative to the observer, provided the motion is sufficiently random. In this way it is possible to interpret electrostatic experiments and develop electrostatic theory without detailed reference to the discontinuous structure and the internal motions of matter.

We conclude that from a macroscopic viewpoint it is possible to treat electric charge as continuously distributed in space. This is somewhat analogous to treating a fluid as continuous in hydrodynamics, even though we are well aware of its molecular structure. In this way we may define charge densities as continuous scalar point functions. There are three kinds of charge density:

1. Volume density of charge ρ:

$$\rho \equiv \lim_{\substack{\Delta x \to 0 \\ \Delta y \to 0 \\ \Delta z \to 0}} \frac{\Delta q}{\Delta x \, \Delta y \, \Delta z} = \lim_{\Delta V \to 0} \frac{\Delta q}{\Delta V} \tag{1.7}$$

where Δq is the net charge enclosed by $\Delta V = \Delta x \, \Delta y \, \Delta z$ and ΔV shrinks about the point at which ρ is to be evaluated.

2. Surface density of charge σ is conveniently used when charge is spread over a surface in a layer whose thickness Δt is small compared to the other dimensions of the problem:

$$\sigma \equiv \lim_{\Delta S \to 0} \frac{\Delta q}{\Delta S} \tag{1.8}$$

where Δq is the net charge on an element of surface ΔS and ΔS shrinks about the point where σ is to be evaluated. Note that if we let $\Delta t \to 0$, as will be done later, while requiring σ to be finite, the result is the introduction into our analysis of an infinite volume density of charge; for then in the layer of charge

$$\rho = \lim_{\substack{\Delta S \to 0 \\ \Delta t \to 0}} \frac{\Delta q}{\Delta S \, \Delta t} = \lim_{\Delta t \to 0} \frac{\sigma}{\Delta t} \to \infty$$

This infinity of ρ is of course not physically significant, since Δt need only be small compared with other dimensions of the problem; but it does introduce discontinuities into our analysis.

3. Linear density of charge λ is occasionally useful, when charge is distributed along a curve in a filament whose cross section is negligible compared to other dimensions of a problem:

$$\lambda \equiv \lim_{\Delta l \to 0} \frac{\Delta q}{\Delta l} \tag{1.9}$$

where Δq is the net charge in length Δl of the filament and Δl shrinks about the point where λ is to be evaluated.

Differential elements of charge are, in the three cases,

$$\begin{aligned} dq &= \rho \, dV \\ &= \sigma \, dS \\ &= \lambda \, dl \end{aligned} \tag{1.10}$$

If the differentials dV, dS, and dl are small in extent compared with the other dimensions of a problem, the dq may be treated as point charges. Total charge in a finite region is found by integration over the region:

$$q = \int_V \rho \, dV + \int_S \sigma \, dS + \int_l \lambda \, dl \tag{1.11}$$

1.4. Electric Field. Electric field is defined as a vector point function, *i.e.*, a vector function of position in space, in terms of which the force on a charge at rest at that point of space may be determined. Specifically, if a test charge q is placed at rest at the point (x,y,z) where the electric field is to be determined and the test charge at that point experiences a force **F**, then the field at the point, exclusive of the field directly produced by the test charge itself, is defined to be

$$\mathbf{E}(x,y,z) \equiv \frac{\mathbf{F}}{q} \tag{1.12}$$

The unit of the electric field vector in the mks-coulomb system is the newton per coulomb.

We shall not philosophize upon the question of what the electric field "is." Our job is simply to define it precisely and to use it. The justification of the definition is its utility in analysis. Note, however, that the concept of the electric field as a property of space relieves us of the necessity for the concept of "action at a distance."

One point about the definition (1.12) which needs examination is the possibility that **E** as defined depends on the magnitude of q. If the sources of the field are entirely independent of q, which means for an electrostatic system that they are charges fixed in location and in magnitude, then the force **F** is proportional to q, and hence **E** as defined is independent of q. This follows from statement 3 or Eq. (1.5), Sec. 1.1, so far as an electrostatic system is concerned. However, if there are material bodies in the vicinity of q, then q may induce charges in them which are dependent in magnitude on q, and in this case **E** as given by Eq. (1.12) depends on the magnitude of q. When q is not itself a part of the problem, we shall exclude this possibility by taking the limiting value of Eq. (1.12) as q becomes indefinitely small, for then the charges induced by it also must become indefinitely small, with the result that q does not alter the problem by its presence:

$$\mathbf{E} \equiv \lim_{q \to 0} \frac{\mathbf{F}}{q} \tag{1.13}$$

On the other hand, Eq. (1.12) will still be correct and useful for the field experienced by a finite point charge which is part of a problem; and it will then define the actual field at that charge, exclusive of its own field but including fields due to charges which it induces. Therefore the force on any point charge q in an electrostatic field is given in terms of the actual field by

$$\mathbf{F} = q\mathbf{E} \tag{1.14}$$

The foregoing definition of electric field and hence Eq. (1.14) will be considered to hold even in the interior of matter, whether from a microscopic or macroscopic point of view.

It is now easy to write down the electric field produced by a point charge or a distribution of charge. From Eq. (1.4) the field of a point charge q_j at a point k is

$$\mathbf{E}_{kj} \equiv \frac{\mathbf{F}_{kj}}{q_k} = \frac{q_j}{4\pi\epsilon_0 r_{jk}{}^3}\, \mathbf{r}_{jk}$$

only now the notation is redundant, and we may write

$$\mathbf{E} = \frac{q}{4\pi\epsilon_0 r^3}\, \mathbf{r} \tag{1.15}$$

where $\mathbf{r}$ is the vector distance from q to the point at which $\mathbf{E}$ is evaluated and r is the scalar distance.

The total field due to a set of charges is found similarly from Eq. (1.5):

$$\mathbf{E} = \frac{1}{4\pi\epsilon_0} \sum_{j=1}^{n} \frac{q_j}{r_j{}^3}\, \mathbf{r}_j \tag{1.16}$$

where $\mathbf{r}_j$ is the vector distance from the charge q_j to the point at which $\mathbf{E}$ is evaluated, and r_j is the scalar distance.

Likewise, using the definitions of Sec. 1.3, if charge is continuously distributed, its resulting field is

$$\mathbf{E} = \frac{1}{4\pi\epsilon_0} \int \frac{\mathbf{r}\, dq}{r^3} \tag{1.17}$$

where the integral is to be evaluated over all volume, surface, and linear charge distributions; $\mathbf{r}$ is the vector distance from the element of integration dq to the point at which $\mathbf{E}$ is evaluated; and r is the scalar distance.

These formulas, like the ones for $\mathbf{F}$ in Sec. 1.2, are only complete when all charges are considered, including those induced in neighboring matter.

Note that the integral (1.17) is a vector integral, that is, it is a sum of infinitesimal elements each of which has a direction as well as a magnitude. One way of evaluating such an integral is to express the vector factor in terms of its cartesian components. In Eq. (1.17) we may write

$$\mathbf{r} = r_x \mathbf{i} + r_y \mathbf{j} + r_z \mathbf{k}$$

where $\mathbf{i}$, $\mathbf{j}$, and $\mathbf{k}$ are unit vectors along the fixed coordinate directions. After this substitution, Eq. (1.17) becomes

$$\mathbf{E} = \frac{\mathbf{i}}{4\pi\epsilon_0} \int \frac{r_x\, dq}{r^3} + \frac{\mathbf{j}}{4\pi\epsilon_0} \int \frac{r_y\, dq}{r^3} + \frac{\mathbf{k}}{4\pi\epsilon_0} \int \frac{r_z\, dq}{r^3} \tag{1.18}$$

where each integral is now scalar and the unit vectors, being constant in both direction and magnitude, have been taken outside the integral signs.

1.5. Electrostatic Potential. Since an electric charge experiences a force in an electric field, the field may do work on it, or conversely work may have to be done on it by an agent external to the field, to move it from one place to another. During an infinitesimal vector displacement $d\mathbf{l}$ of the charge q the work which has to be done on the charge by an external agent is

$$dW = -\mathbf{F} \cdot d\mathbf{l} \tag{1.19}$$

if $\mathbf{F}$ is the force on q due to the electric field; for if the charge is not to be accelerated, the agent must exert a force $-\mathbf{F}$. But the force due to the electric field is

$$\mathbf{F} = q\mathbf{E}$$

and therefore

$$dW = -q\mathbf{E} \cdot d\mathbf{l}$$

or

$$\frac{dW}{q} = -\mathbf{E} \cdot d\mathbf{l} \tag{1.20}$$

This quantity dW/q is a differential scalar which, for a given point of space and differential vector $d\mathbf{l}$, is characteristic of the particular system of charges and matter which produces the field $\mathbf{E}$. The field may or may not depend on q, as discussed in Sec. 1.4, and accordingly dW/q may or may not depend on q. In the present connection, however, q will ordinarily be considered a test charge of infinitesimal size, so that dW/q will be independent of q. We shall now write

$$\frac{dW}{q} = dU \tag{1.21}$$

so that

$$dU = -\mathbf{E} \cdot d\mathbf{l} \tag{1.22}$$

and we shall proceed to establish the properties of a function U whose differential is (1.22). Either Eq. (1.21) or Eq. (1.22) may serve to define dU, and then the other will be an immediate deduction in view of Eq. (1.20).

The finite change of the quantity U when the test charge traverses a finite path L from a reference point $G(x_0,y_0,z_0)$ to a point $P(x,y,z)$ is

$$(\Delta U)_L = -\left(\int_G^P \mathbf{E} \cdot d\mathbf{l} \right)_L \tag{1.23}$$

The notation here suggests the important fact that we may not assume a priori that ΔU for a given field depends only upon the terminal points of L. It is, however, one of the basic theorems of electrostatics that the line integral

$$\int_G^P \mathbf{E} \cdot d\mathbf{l}$$

for an electrostatic system does actually depend only upon the terminal points of the path. We shall prove this theorem for a general electrostatic field produced by a distribution of point charges, which may of course include induced charges in matter. Such a system has at any point (x,y,z) a field which may be expressed by Eq. (1.16):

$$\mathbf{E}(x,y,z) = \frac{1}{4\pi\epsilon_0} \sum_{j=1}^{n} \frac{q_j}{r_j^3} \mathbf{r}_j \qquad (1.16)$$

where

$$r_j = [(x - x_j)^2 + (y - y_j)^2 + (z - z_j)^2]^{\frac{1}{2}} \qquad (1.24)$$

The cartesian components of the field vector are

$$E_x = \frac{1}{4\pi\epsilon_0} \sum_{j=1}^{n} \frac{q_j(x - x_j)}{r_j^3}$$

$$E_y = \frac{1}{4\pi\epsilon_0} \sum_{j=1}^{n} \frac{q_j(y - y_j)}{r_j^3} \qquad (1.25)$$

$$E_z = \frac{1}{4\pi\epsilon_0} \sum_{j=1}^{n} \frac{q_j(z - z_j)}{r_j^3}$$

Now it is a well-known analytical theorem of mathematics that a line integral such as

$$\int_G^P \mathbf{E} \cdot d\mathbf{l} = \int_G^P (E_x\, dx + E_y\, dy + E_z\, dz)$$

is independent of path L between two given terminal points, provided

$$\frac{\partial E_y}{\partial x} = \frac{\partial E_x}{\partial y} \qquad \frac{\partial E_z}{\partial y} = \frac{\partial E_y}{\partial z} \qquad \frac{\partial E_x}{\partial z} = \frac{\partial E_z}{\partial x} \qquad (1.26)$$

These conditions are fulfilled by the electric field vector (1.25); for we may write Eqs. (1.25) in the form:

$$E_x = \sum_{j=1}^{n} q_j(x - x_j)f(r_j)$$

$$E_y = \sum_{j=1}^{n} q_j(y - y_j)f(r_j) \qquad (1.27)$$

$$E_z = \sum_{j=1}^{n} q_j(z - z_j)f(r_j)$$

where $f(r_j)$ is put for $1/4\pi\epsilon_0 r_j^3$. Therefore

$$\frac{\partial E_y}{\partial x} = \sum_{j=1}^{n} q_j(y - y_j) \frac{df(r_j)}{dr_j} \frac{\partial r_j}{\partial x}$$

$$\frac{\partial E_x}{\partial y} = \sum_{j=1}^{n} q_j(x - x_j) \frac{df(r_j)}{dr_j} \frac{\partial r_j}{\partial y}$$

(1.28)

But

$$\frac{\partial r_j}{\partial x} = \frac{x - x_j}{r_j} \qquad \frac{\partial r_j}{\partial y} = \frac{y - y_j}{r_j}$$

(1.29)

By substitution, we have at once

$$\frac{\partial E_y}{\partial x} = \frac{\partial E_x}{\partial y}$$

as required; and similarly the other conditions (1.26) are shown to hold. A similar proof may be written out immediately if the charge is assumed to be distributed so that the field is given by Eq. (1.17).

We have therefore established that if $\mathbf{E}$ is a fixed electrostatic field, then $\int_G^P \mathbf{E} \cdot d\mathbf{l}$ depends only upon $\mathbf{E}$ and upon the terminal points P and G. Thus we may define uniquely the difference of potential between P and a reference point G as

$$\Delta U = - \int_G^P \mathbf{E} \cdot d\mathbf{l}$$

(1.30)

where the path of integration is arbitrary. Now $-\mathbf{E} \cdot d\mathbf{l}$ was defined as the differential dU. Therefore

$$\Delta U = + \int_G^P dU = U(P) - U(G)$$

so that

$$U(P) = U(G) + \Delta U$$

(1.31)

Our final result is the definition of a scalar point function U, characteristic of a given electrostatic field and called the electrostatic potential function. This function has the property of being single-valued and uniquely defined except for an arbitrary reference value at an arbitrary point of space. It is the electrostatic analogue of the potential function of the gravitational field used in mechanics.

The fact that U is a scalar function gives it advantages both for computation and for analysis over the vector function $\mathbf{E}$. If U is known for a particular electrostatic system, $\mathbf{E}$ may immediately be deduced from it by use of Eq. (1.22). For, in cartesian coordinates,

$$\mathbf{E} = E_x\mathbf{i} + E_y\mathbf{j} + E_z\mathbf{k}$$

and
$$d\mathbf{l} = \mathbf{i}\,dx + \mathbf{j}\,dy + \mathbf{k}\,dz$$

Therefore
$$-dU = E_x\,dx + E_y\,dy + E_z\,dz \tag{1.32}$$

so that
$$-\frac{\partial U}{\partial x} = E_x \qquad -\frac{\partial U}{\partial y} = E_y \qquad -\frac{\partial U}{\partial z} = E_z \tag{1.33}$$

These equations are readily extended to other orthogonal coordinate systems. In general, if ds_1 is a differential displacement corresponding to a coordinate differential dx_1 and in the direction of a unit vector $\mathbf{i}_1$, then the rectangular component E_1 of the field in this direction at any point of space is given by

$$E_1 = -\frac{\partial U}{\partial s_1} \tag{1.34}$$

evaluated at that point. In vector analysis, the relationship between $\mathbf{E}$ and U is described by saying that $\mathbf{E}$ is the negative gradient of U:

$$E = -\,\mathbf{grad}\;U \tag{1.35}$$

A field whose line integral is independent of path is called *conservative*. The electrostatic field is therefore a conservative field. The fact that the field can be derived from a scalar potential function by Eqs. (1.33) or (1.35) is one mathematical expression of the conservative nature of the field. Another expression of the same property, this time in integral form, is that the line integral of the field taken around any closed path C must be zero:

$$\oint_C \mathbf{E} \cdot d\mathbf{l} = 0 \tag{1.36}$$

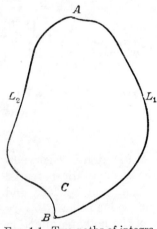

FIG. 1.1. Two paths of integration between a pair of points.

If we consider two points A and B on the closed curve C, as in Fig. 1.1, Eq. (1.36) may readily be seen to follow from the statement that the integral between any two points is independent of path. Call the two sections of C between A and B L_1 and L_2. Then by hypothesis

$$\left(\int_A^B \mathbf{E} \cdot d\mathbf{l}\right)_{L_1} = \left(\int_A^B \mathbf{E} \cdot d\mathbf{l}\right)_{L_2}$$

Therefore
$$\left(\int_A^B \mathbf{E} \cdot d\mathbf{l}\right)_{L_1} - \left(\int_A^B \mathbf{E} \cdot d\mathbf{l}\right)_{L_2} = 0$$

Thus

$$\left(\int_A^B \mathbf{E} \cdot d\mathbf{l}\right)_{L_1} + \left(\int_B^A \mathbf{E} \cdot d\mathbf{l}\right)_{L_2} = 0$$

which is identical with the statement (1.36). Q.E.D.

The mks unit of electric potential is, from the definition (1.21), the joule per coulomb. This quantity is used so much that it has received its own name, the volt. Frequently the volt is also used for expressing the unit of electric field strength by means of the relationship (1.33) between potential and field. The resulting unit for electric field strength is the volt per meter.

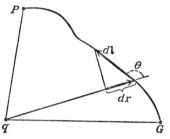

FIG. 1.2. Path of integration for potential of a point charge.

1.6. Potential of a Point Charge. Let us compute the potential difference ΔU between an arbitrary point $P(x,y,z)$ and a reference point $G(x_0,y_0,z_0)$ in the field of a point charge q at the origin (see Fig. 1.2). Take $d\mathbf{l}$ as an element of the path L of integration, and let $d\mathbf{l}$ make an angle θ with the vector $\mathbf{r}$ from q to $d\mathbf{l}$. The potential increment in $d\mathbf{l}$ is, by definition (1.22),

$$dU = -\mathbf{E} \cdot d\mathbf{l}$$

and the electric field $\mathbf{E}$ is

$$\mathbf{E} = \frac{q}{4\pi\epsilon_0 r^3} \mathbf{r}$$

so that

$$dU = -\frac{q}{4\pi\epsilon_0 r^3} \mathbf{r} \cdot d\mathbf{l} \tag{1.37}$$

But

$$\mathbf{r} \cdot d\mathbf{l} = r \, dl \cos \theta = r \, dr \tag{1.38}$$

where the correct sign is given automatically by the factor $\cos \theta$. Thus

$$dU = -\frac{q}{4\pi\epsilon_0 r^3} r \, dr = -\frac{q}{4\pi\epsilon_0 r^2} \, dr \tag{1.39}$$

We may now integrate immediately:

$$\Delta U = U(P) - U(G) = -\int_{R_0}^{R} \frac{q \, dr}{4\pi\epsilon_0 r^2} = \frac{q}{4\pi\epsilon_0}\left[\frac{1}{R} - \frac{1}{R_0}\right] \tag{1.40}$$

where $R = (x^2 + y^2 + z^2)^{1/2}$ and $R_0 = (x_0^2 + y_0^2 + z_0^2)^{1/2}$.

From Eq. (1.40) we deduce that if we are to define a potential function for a single point charge, it must have the form

$$U = \frac{q}{4\pi\epsilon_0 R} + \text{constant}$$

The simplest choice of the constant is to make it zero, which implies that we choose $U = 0$ at $R = \infty$. Then our potential function is

$$U = \frac{q}{4\pi\epsilon_0 R} \tag{1.41}$$

1.7. Potential of a Charge Distribution. Suppose the electrostatic field is produced by a set of point charges q_j. The field is the vector sum of the fields of the separate point charges, as given in Eq. (1.16). Substitution of this sum for **E** in the differential of potential, and integration term by term, as was done for a single charge in Sec. 1.6, leads to

$$\Delta U = \frac{1}{4\pi\epsilon_0} \sum_j q_j \left(\frac{1}{R_j} - \frac{1}{R_{0j}} \right) \tag{1.42}$$

for the potential difference between point P, at which the radii from the charges are R_j, and a reference point G, at which the radii are R_{0j}.

As in Sec. 1.6, we may now define the potential function as

$$U = \frac{1}{4\pi\epsilon_0} \sum_j \frac{q_j}{R_j} \tag{1.43}$$

only now, if this expression is to have meaning, we must be sure that it has a finite value. This will be the case, except at the points where $R_j = 0$, for a system in which the total charge is finite. Comparison with Eq. (1.41) shows that if a finite system is made up of charges q_j each having a potential function U_j, then the potential function of the system is simply

$$U = \sum_j U_j \tag{1.44}$$

If a finite quantity of charge is continuously distributed in volume, surface, or line densities, the summation (1.43) may be replaced by the integrals

$$U = \frac{1}{4\pi\epsilon_0} \int \frac{\rho \, dV}{r} + \frac{1}{4\pi\epsilon_0} \int \frac{\sigma \, dS}{r} + \frac{1}{4\pi\epsilon_0} \int \frac{\lambda \, dl}{r} \tag{1.45}$$

Infinite distributions of charge density are often of importance in analysis. In such cases, even though the expressions (1.43) and (1.45) may become infinite, it is possible to compute ΔU between two finite points and hence to define a potential function by use of Eq. (1.31). For this purpose, Eq. (1.42) may be used in the form of an integral:

$$\Delta U = \frac{1}{4\pi\epsilon_0} \int\limits_{\text{all space}} \left(\frac{1}{R_j} - \frac{1}{R_{0j}} \right) dq \tag{1.46}$$

It may be easier, however, to compute the electric field first in these cases, and from it to obtain the potential.

1.8. Convergence of Improper Integrals. The basic integrals for electric field and potential, Eqs. (1.17) and (1.45), are improper if charge density exists at the point of observation, where $r = 0$, for then the integrand becomes infinite at this point. It is important to examine whether these integrals converge in such cases. We shall briefly investigate the integral for the electric field at a point at which the volume density of charge is finite, and we shall see that the integral converges in this case. The electric field will in general be indeterminate at a point where the ρ function is infinite. The integral for potential will also be convergent at a point where ρ remains finite; but in addition it will converge for a point of observation located on a surface density of charge.

The statements concerning the volume integrals are readily proved without entering into involved demonstrations by simply writing the integrals in a spherical coordinate system with origin at the point of observation. In spherical coordinates, the element of volume is $dV = r^2 \sin \theta \, d\phi \, d\theta \, dr$; therefore element of charge is

$$dq = \rho \, dV = \rho r^2 \sin \theta \, d\phi \, d\theta \, dr \tag{1.47}$$

We may rewrite Eq. (1.17) by using the unit vector $\mathbf{r}^0$ from dq to the observer, defined as $\mathbf{r}^0 \equiv \mathbf{r}/r$. Then

$$\mathbf{E} = \frac{1}{4\pi\epsilon_0} \int \mathbf{r}^0 \frac{dq}{r^2} \tag{1.48}$$

When expression (1.47) is substituted into this integral, it is evident that the radius r cancels, and hence the integrand remains finite at all points. The integral is therefore no longer improper; thus our proposition is proved. It might be thought, however, that some difficulty would be caused by the indeterminate direction of $\mathbf{r}^0$ at the origin. This causes no trouble in evaluating the integral; for if a small sphere V_0 of radius R about the origin is considered to be cut out of the field of integration, the integral splits into two parts, one over V_0 and the other over the region outside V_0. In the latter integral, $\mathbf{r}^0$ is uniquely determined at all points, while the value of the former integral approaches zero at least as fast as R when R approaches zero. This may be seen if the trouble is taken to expand the ρ function in a Taylor's series in the neighborhood of the observation point.

The integral for electrostatic potential at an observation point where a finite volume density of charge exists is still more easily seen to converge. The pertinent part of this integral is, from Eq. (1.45),

$$U = \frac{1}{4\pi\epsilon_0} \int \frac{\rho \, dV}{r} \tag{1.49}$$

When Eq. (1.47) is substituted into this integral, the integrand becomes well behaved at the origin, and in fact vanishes there. Thus (1.49) converges.

The case of an observation point on a surface density of charge is readily handled by a similar method in two dimensions. In a small enough neighborhood of a point on a smooth surface the surface may be considered plane, and in fact to depart as little as we please from its tangent plane at the point. Let us then cut out from the surface S on which charge is spread a disk D of infinitesimal radius R with center at the point of observation. The integral for potential

$$U = \frac{1}{4\pi\epsilon_0} \int_S \frac{\sigma \, dS}{r} \tag{1.50}$$

can then be divided into an improper integral over D and a proper integral over the part of S exterior to D. An element of area in D in polar coordinates may be written

$$dS = r\, d\theta\, dr \qquad (1.51)$$

When this is substituted into Eq. (1.50), the integral over D becomes proper, so that the integral (1.50) is seen to converge.

We conclude that the integrals (1.48) to (1.50) all converge and may be used when the point of observation lies in the field of integration, so long as ρ in (1.48) and (1.49) and σ in (1.50) remain finite. For discussion of the electric field at a surface density of charge, see Sec. 4.13.

1.9. Flux of the Electric Field. Gauss' Law. An important analytical theorem of electrostatics concerns the surface integral of the electric field vector.

Consider first a plane surface of area A in a uniform electric field $\mathbf{E}$. Let $\mathbf{n}$ be a unit vector normal to A (see Fig. 1.3). The quantity $\mathbf{E} \cdot \mathbf{n}A$ is defined as the flux of $\mathbf{E}$ through the area in the sense of $\mathbf{n}$. The word

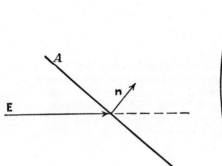

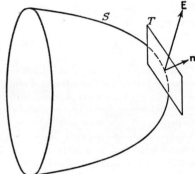

FIG. 1.3. Electric flux through a plane area.

FIG. 1.4. Computation of electric flux through a curved surface.

flux comes by analogy from the hydrodynamics of an incompressible fluid, for if $\mathbf{E}$ were replaced by a flow velocity vector, the flux would then be the rate of flow of fluid across A in the sense of $\mathbf{n}$.

The idea of flux can be extended easily to curved surfaces, and to nonuniform electric fields. If da is an infinitesimal area element of a surface S, that is, an element such that its dimensions are all infinitesimal, and if S is continuous, then da approaches indefinitely near to the plane T tangent to S at a point x, y, z enclosed by da (see Fig. 1.4). Thus da has a definite normal direction $\mathbf{n}$, namely, that of T, with a positive sense to be established by definition. Further, the electric field $\mathbf{E}$ at da has a definite value and direction if $\mathbf{E}$ is continuous, namely, the value $\mathbf{E}(x,y,z)$. The flux of the electric field through da is then defined as

$$d\Phi_E \equiv \mathbf{E}(x,y,z) \cdot \mathbf{n}\, da \qquad (1.52)$$

This is a scalar quantity, so the flux through the surface will be the scalar integral

$$\Phi_E = \int_S \mathbf{E}(x,y,z) \cdot \mathbf{n}\, da \qquad (1.53)$$

Let us now compute the value of Φ_E due to a static point charge. Let surface element da be at distance r from q, and let $\mathbf{r}$ be the vector distance directed from q to da (see Fig. 1.5). Then

$$\mathbf{E} = \frac{q}{4\pi\epsilon_0}\frac{\mathbf{r}}{r^3} \qquad (1.54)$$

and

$$d\Phi_E = \frac{q}{4\pi\epsilon_0}\frac{\mathbf{r}\cdot\mathbf{n}}{r^3}\, da \qquad (1.55)$$

Now

$$\frac{\mathbf{r}\cdot\mathbf{n}}{r^3}\, da \equiv d\Omega \qquad (1.56)$$

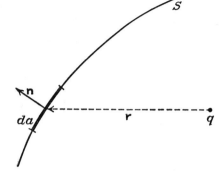

FIG. 1.5. Computation of electric flux from a point charge.

the solid angle in steradians subtended by da at q, and considered positive if q is on the side of da opposite to $\mathbf{n}$. Thus

$$d\Phi_E = \frac{q}{4\pi\epsilon_0}\, d\Omega \qquad (1.57)$$

and at once by integration

$$\Phi_E = \frac{q}{4\pi\epsilon_0}\, \Omega \qquad (1.58)$$

if Ω is the total solid angle at q subtended by S. This simple result leads to important consequences; but to appreciate them we must digress for a moment to consider Ω in some detail.

Consider again the infinitesimal area da at distance r from q. We may rewrite the equation for its solid angle in terms of the angle θ between $\mathbf{r}$ and $\mathbf{n}$:

$$d\Omega = \frac{da\cos\theta}{r^2} = \frac{da'}{r^2} \qquad (1.59)$$

FIG. 1.6. Projected area in determination of solid angle.

where $da' = da\cos\theta$ is the projection of da on a plane perpendicular to the radius r (see Fig. 1.6). Since da' is infinitesimal, it may be considered as an infinitesimal element of a spherical surface of radius r about q. Now think of $d\Omega$ as specifying the angular magnitude of a cone of lines intersecting at q and cutting out da' on the surface of the sphere of radius r with center at q. This same cone of lines cuts out on a sphere of arbitrary radius R about q an area da'' which is always proportional to R^2; so that

$$\frac{da''}{R^2} = \frac{da'}{r^2} \qquad (1.60)$$

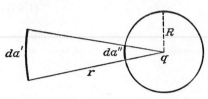

da' da'' r R q

FIG. 1.7. Solid angle element referred to a standard sphere.

(See Fig. 1.7.)   The solid angle element may now be written in terms of the area it cuts out on the arbitrary sphere about q:

$$d\Omega = \frac{da''}{R^2} \qquad (1.61)$$

This may serve as the simplest definition of the solid angle of a given cone of lines.   It follows that the solid angle around a point is 4π steradians, for the total surface of the sphere of radius R is $4\pi R^2$.

Now consider the solid angle subtended by a closed surface S which does not intersect itself.   Let the unit normal be taken always outward from the volume enclosed by S.   It is then certainly reasonable that for any point q inside S, the total solid angle subtended by S is 4π steradians, since S goes all the way around q.   Nevertheless, it takes a bit of demonstration to show that

$$4\pi = \oint \frac{\mathbf{n} \cdot \mathbf{r}}{r^3} \, da \qquad (1.62)$$

regardless of the shape of the surface; for a given infinitesimal cone of lines from q may cut S in more than one area element, as in Fig. 1.8.

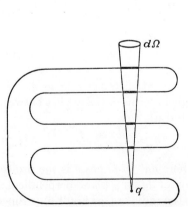

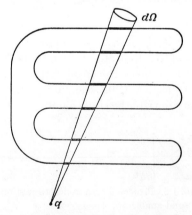

FIG. 1.8. An element of solid angle about an interior point cutting the surface an odd number of times.

FIG. 1.9. An element of solid angle about an exterior point cutting the surface an even number of times.

To emerge from S, the cone must eventually cut S in an odd number of areas, however, and the contributions to the integral vanish for successive pairs of area elements, since at successive elements the cosine of θ has opposite signs. Thus only one unpaired area element is left to contribute to the computation of a given element of solid angle, and the result is the same as for a simpler surface in which all lines from q cross S only once.

In a similar way, it may be seen that the total solid angle of S for a point outside S is zero. For any area element through which an infinitesimal cone from q emerges from S, giving a positive contribution to Ω, there is a paired element which gives an equal negative contribution where the same cone again cuts S in entering V (see Fig. 1.9). Since there is always a total number of crossings of S which is even for a given infinitesimal cone from q, the resulting total solid angle is zero.

Thus we have for any closed surface S which does not intersect itself:

$$\begin{aligned} \Omega &= 4\pi \quad &\text{for a point inside} \\ \Omega &= 0 \quad &\text{for a point outside} \end{aligned} \tag{1.63}$$

Substituting these results into Eq. (1.58), we have for the flux of a point charge through a closed surface S

$$\begin{aligned} \Phi_E &= \frac{q}{\epsilon_0} \quad &\text{for } q \text{ inside } S \\ \Phi_E &= 0 \quad &\text{for } q \text{ outside } S \end{aligned} \tag{1.64}$$

Now for an electrostatic system it follows that the total flux through a closed surface S is given by

$$\Phi_E \equiv \oint_S \mathbf{E} \cdot \mathbf{n} \, da = \frac{1}{\epsilon_0} \times (\text{total net charge inside}) \tag{1.65}$$

For systems of point charges,

$$\Phi_E \equiv \oint_S \mathbf{E} \cdot \mathbf{n} \, da = \frac{1}{\epsilon_0} \sum_k q_k \tag{1.66}$$

summed over all charges q_k within S only, excluding all charges outside S. When we are dealing with volume charge density, this important equation may be written

$$\oint_S \mathbf{E} \cdot \mathbf{n} \, da = \frac{1}{\epsilon_0} \int_V \rho \, dv \tag{1.67}$$

where S is the boundary of V.

It will be important for future reference to note that the q_k in Eq. (1.66) and ρ in Eq. (1.67) must include charges in the constitution of the matter enclosed in V, as well as free charges in V.

1.10. Computation of Electric Field by Gauss' Law. An immediate application of Gauss' law is the easy calculation of the magnitude of the electric field in cases of sufficient symmetry. A few examples will make the method clear, as well as yielding some important results.

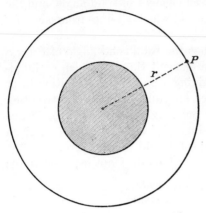

Field of a Spherically Symmetrical Charge Distribution of Net Total Charge Q at a Point outside the Whole Distribution (see Fig. 1.10). By symmetry, **E** is everywhere radial. To find the magnitude of **E** at point P whose distance is r from the center of the distribution, describe a spherical surface S of radius r about the charge distribution and concentric with it. S is called a Gaussian surface, since it is constructed for the purpose of applying Gauss' law. By symmetry again, **E** has the same magnitude at all points of S, for E can only be a function of r. There-

Fig. 1.10. Gaussian surface outside a spherical charge distribution.

fore the flux of the electric field is

$$\Phi_E = \oint \mathbf{E} \cdot \mathbf{n} \, da = 4\pi r^2 E$$

Gauss' law then gives

$$4\pi r^2 E = \frac{Q}{\epsilon_0}$$

Thus the electric field has the magnitude

$$E = \frac{Q}{4\pi\epsilon_0 r^2} \qquad (1.68)$$

just as if all the charge were concentrated in a point at the center of the distribution.

Suppose the spherical charge distribution to have an inner boundary. Let us compute the field within this boundary B (see Fig. 1.11). By sym-

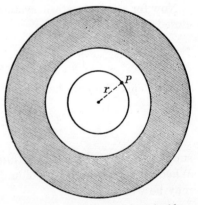

Fig. 1.11. Gaussian surface inside a hollow spherical charge distribution.

metry, any field in the region inside B is radial in direction. Describe a Gaussian surface of radius r about the center of the distribution, through a point P where the field is desired. By symmetry, E has the same value at all points of S, and the flux is, as before,

$$\Phi_E = 4\pi r^2 E$$

Now, however, there is no charge within S. Gauss' law then requires that

$$4\pi r^2 E = 0$$

Thus

$$E = 0 \qquad (1.69)$$

completely inside a spherical charge distribution.

Field of a Line Charge. Suppose charge is distributed along an infinite straight line L with a constant linear density λ. Then by symmetry the electric field at a point P is always directed along a radius perpendicular to L (see Fig. 1.12). Select a Gaussian surface S through P in the form of a right circular cylinder about L. The entire electric flux due to L through S is through the curved surface of S, which has the area $2\pi rl$,

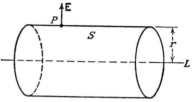

Fig. 1.12. Gaussian surface about an infinite line charge.

where r is the radius and l the length of S. Furthermore, E is everywhere constant on this curved surface, and $\mathbf{E}$ is normal to it, so that the flux through S is

$$\Phi_E = 2\pi rlE$$

The charge inside the surface is $l\lambda$; therefore, according to Gauss' law,

$$2\pi rlE = \frac{1}{\epsilon_0} l\lambda$$

$$E = \frac{\lambda}{2\pi \epsilon_0 r} \qquad (1.70)$$

Notice that this field falls off only as the inverse first power of the distance.

Field of an Infinite Plane Sheet of Charge. Suppose a surface layer of surface density σ is in the form of an infinite plane sheet F (see Fig. 1.13). To find the field at a point P, construct a Gaussian surface having plane faces of area a parallel to F and having sides entirely perpendicular to F. This is appropriate to the symmetry of the problem, which implies that the field $\mathbf{E}$ at every point not on F is perpendicular to F. The flux through the surface is then $2Ea$, the enclosed charge is σa, and Gauss' law yields

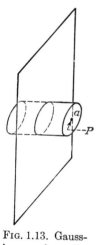

Fig. 1.13. Gaussian surface for an infinite plane sheet of charge.

$$2Ea = \frac{1}{\epsilon_0} \sigma a$$

Therefore

$$E = \frac{\sigma}{2\epsilon_0} \tag{1.71}$$

which is independent of the distance from the sheet.

Gauss' theorem has enabled us to determine the electric field in certain simple cases, in some of which the charge distribution is infinite. Once the field is known, the potential may be found by line integration of the field. For example, consider the case of the infinite line charge. Here the field is along the cylindrical radius; thus the potential depends only on this cylindrical radius. The potential difference between two points of radii R and R_0 is thus

$$\Delta U = - \int_{R_0}^{R} E \, dr = - \int_{R_0}^{R} \frac{\lambda}{2\pi\epsilon_0 r} \, dr$$

Therefore

$$\Delta U = - \frac{\lambda}{2\pi\epsilon_0} \ln \frac{R}{R_0} \tag{1.72}$$

The potential function itself for the point of radius R is

$$U = \frac{\lambda}{2\pi\epsilon_0} \ln \frac{R_0}{R} \tag{1.73}$$

if the zero of the potential is defined to be at $r = R_0$.

1.11. Lines of Force and Equipotential Surfaces. The electrostatic field is capable of being mapped by a family of lines and a family of surfaces in space. The lines are those whose direction is always that of the electric field, and are called lines of electric force. The surfaces are those defined by $U(x,y,z) = $ constant, and are called equipotential surfaces. It is easy to label equipotential surfaces, for the value of the potential, relative to some agreed reference value, is a parameter by which the equipotential surfaces of a given electrostatic system may be uniquely labeled. The labeling of lines of force would be more difficult, for a line in space is the intersection of two surfaces, and thus two parameters would be needed to specify a line in a given electrostatic system. It is possible to build up a fairly extensive analysis of field mapping, but we shall limit ourselves to the following remarks:

1. Lines of force always cut equipotential surfaces perpendicularly. This is easy to prove; for supposing it were not true, then there would be a component of electric field parallel to the equipotential surface. But then it would require force, and hence work, to move a test charge about from one point of the surface to another; and the surface would by definition not be equipotential. Q.E.D.

2. A single equipotential surface (*i.e.*, defined by a particular value of

potential) cannot cut across itself except at a point where the electric field intensity vanishes or is indeterminate. For, supposing that this were possible, there would be more than one perpendicular direction to the surface at a point of such an intersection, and hence, by (1), more than one direction of electric field at this point. But this is only possible when the direction of the electric field is indeterminate.

3. Equipotential surfaces of different potential can never intersect. For potential is uniquely defined once the reference point is agreed upon; thus one point of space cannot have more than one potential.

4. The spacing between equipotential surfaces, as measured along a line of force, is inversely proportional to the space average of the electric field along this line of force between the two surfaces. Thus, where equipotential surfaces crowd together, we have regions of high electric field, and where they become widely separated, regions of low electric field. The proof is simple. Let s be a coordinate corresponding to arc length along a line of force L between two equipotentials U_1 and U_2 (see Fig. 1.14). Since the electric field is everywhere in the direction of L,

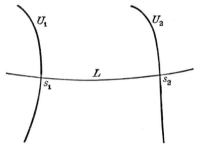

FIG. 1.14. A line of force between two equipotentials.

the integral for the potential difference between points s_1 and s_2 where L intersects the equipotential surfaces is simply

$$U_2 - U_1 = - \int_{s_1}^{s_2} E \, ds \tag{1.74}$$

But the space average of E over the line is defined as

$$\bar{E} \equiv \frac{1}{s_2 - s_1} \int_{s_1}^{s_2} E \, ds \tag{1.75}$$

Thus

$$\bar{E}(s_1 - s_2) = U_2 - U_1$$

Therefore, as was to be proved,

$$s_1 - s_2 = \frac{U_2 - U_1}{\bar{E}} \tag{1.76}$$

5. Define a tube of force as a region bounded on the sides by a surface containing lines of force, but not cut by them. Let the tube cut off areas A_1 and A_2 on two equipotential surfaces U_1 and U_2, and let the volume V enclosed by the tube be free of net electric charge density

(see Fig. 1.15). The flux out of V must be zero, and must occur over the areas A_1 and A_2 only. Let $\bar{E}_1$ be the average magnitude of the electric field over A_1 and $\bar{E}_2$ the average over A_2. The flux through A_1 is $\bar{E}_1A_1$, since E_1 must be everywhere normal to A_1. This flux must equal that through A_2, so that

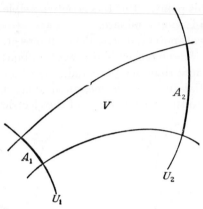

$$\bar{E}_1A_1 = \bar{E}_2A_2$$

Therefore

$$\frac{\bar{E}_2}{\bar{E}_1} = \frac{A_1}{A_2} \qquad (1.77)$$

FIG. 1.15. A tube of force cutting equipotentials U_1 and U_2 in areas A_1 and A_2.

or in words, the average electric field is inversely proportional to the area cut out by the tube in an equipotential surface. Thus, where a tube of force is constricted, the electric field is larger, and where the tube enlarges, the field is smaller.

1.12. Conductors in Electrostatic Systems. Conductors are bodies in whose material there are elementary charged particles free to migrate under the action of a macroscopic electric field. This freedom implies the absence of macroscopic force on the particles due to their location in the material, but does not deny the existence of resistive forces of the viscous type due to velocity. Migration must be distinguished from the slight relative motions of the positively and negatively charged particles of atomic, molecular, or crystalline systems which result in dielectric polarization. Macroscopic electric charge due to migration of elementary particles is called free charge. Free charge is found not only on conductors, but also on insulators. There the term implies that migration has occurred previously, either an addition or subtraction of elementary charges having been made relative to the uncharged constitution of the matter. Free charge may be characterized in other terms as the net excess of charge of either sign occurring in a macroscopic region.

The important part that conductors play in the study of electrostatics is due to two circumstances. First, a metallic conductor is often used to bear a net positive or negative charge, according to whether some of its electrons have been removed entirely from it or whether some excess electrons have been added to it. This net charge may thus be considered a primary cause of the electrostatic field being studied. Second, the entire volume occupied by conducting material is from a macroscopic viewpoint a space completely free from electric field, provided the system is truly electrostatic, that is, supposing all macroscopic charges are at rest and in equilibrium. For by definition of the conductor, there exist throughout it charged particles free to migrate, and the definition of electric field is force per unit charge. Therefore if the macroscopic field should exist, there would be a macroscopic drift of charged particles, either accelerated or experiencing a balancing force due to their acquiring a drift velocity. This would constitute a macroscopic motion of charge, and the system would not then be static. Q.E.D. Now if the space occupied by conducting material is free from electric field, it follows that it is a region of constant electrostatic potential. In particular also, the surface of a conductor is an equipotential surface.

It should be emphasized that these properties of a conducting material are true only from the macroscopic point of view. Thus, there certainly are intense local fields about the electrons and atomic nuclei in a conductor, but the space average over a volume containing many atoms, which would still be infinitesimal from the macroscopic point of view, is always zero in the electrostatic case.

Some interesting consequences result from the statement that conducting material is field-free in an electrostatic system. These we state as theorems, with their immediate deductions.

Theorem 1. *The space completely enclosed within the outer bounding surface of a conductor, or within any surface, every point of which lies in conducting material, contains a zero total net electric charge.*

Thus, for example, the charge density ρ must vanish at all interior points of conducting material; for only so will $q = \int_V \rho \, dV$ over every arbitrary volume V in the conductor be zero. Therefore, if a conductor in an electrostatic system bears any charge, it must be as a surface density σ over its boundaries. Further, if a net free charge q be located within a closed cavity of a conductor, a charge totaling exactly $-q$ must appear as surface charge on that part of the conductor boundary which forms the cavity. Such surface charge is said to be induced by the presence of the free charge q.

The proof of this theorem rests upon Gauss' law. This tells us that

$$\oint_S \mathbf{E} \cdot \mathbf{n} \, da = \frac{q}{\epsilon_0}$$

where q is the total net charge inside the surface S. But if E is everywhere zero over S, as it is if every point of S lies in conducting material, then q inside every such surface S must be zero. Q.E.D. Physically, what this means is that if we start out with a distribution of charge in which this condition is not fulfilled, there will be a motion of charges (nonstatic system) until it is fulfilled.

Theorem 2.   In the space outside but just at the boundary of conducting material, the electric field intensity is everywhere normal to the boundary.

Thus lines of electric force are perpendicular to conductor surfaces where the lines touch them.   Incidentally, the lines of force which do touch a conductor end there, since there is no electric field inside the conductor.

The proof of this theorem follows immediately from the statement in Sec. 1.11 that lines of force are normal to equipotential surfaces, for a conductor surface is equipotential.

A qualitative deduction may now be made concerning electric field intensities at the surface of a conducting body.   Suppose the cross-hatched region in Fig. 1.16 represents a charged conductor.   Consider tubes of force terminating at A, B, and C on the conductor surface,

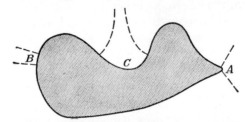

FIG. 1.16. Regions of different curvature on a conductor surface.

such that the outward curvature of the conductor surface is greatest at A, less at B, and negative (inward) at C.   Evidently the tube at A expands its cross section rapidly as we follow it out from the conductor, while the tube at B expands less rapidly, and the tube at C actually contracts at first.   Now at a great distance R from the conductor, it should appear like a point charge, so that at this distance from the conductor, regardless of direction, the field will have the same intensity, say E_0.   Between the conductor and the sphere at distance R, the tube starting at A will expand greatly which by Eq. (1.77) means that the field intensity E_A, at the point A on the conductor, is much greater than E_0. Likewise we should expect $E_0 < E_B < E_A$, since the tube at B begins to expand less rapidly than the tube at A.   We cannot say that $E_C < E_0$, since all tubes starting from the conductor will at large distance be bounded by straight radial lines, and hence will expand alike in cross section; but it is reasonable that $E_C < E_B$, since the tube at C will expand less than that at B, having started by actually contracting.

In this qualitative way, we have seen that over the surface of a charged conductor the electric field is most intense at points of greatest convex curvature, and least intense at points of greatest concave curvature.   An important application of this fact is the use of sharply pointed conductors to raise the field intensity to a value so high that the air about the points is rendered conducting.   Electric charge may then be "sprayed" off from sharp points. Use is made of this principle in lightning rods and in electrostatic generators. Conversely, where electrical leakage into the surrounding air is to be minimized, as in terminals of high-voltage equipment, or high-voltage transmission lines, sharp points must be avoided.

It should be remembered that such qualitative statements cannot be made precise, for the field intensity cannot be quantitatively computed just from the curvature of the equipotential surfaces. In addition, the word "curvature" has not been used with precision, for in general there are two curvatures to a surface at a given point.

Theorem 3. If a closed cavity in conducting material is empty of electric charge density, it is a region free from electric field.

This theorem is the basis of electrostatic shielding. The zero field in an enclosure completely surrounded by conducting material is automatically maintained by the charge distribution induced on the conductor, no matter what the electric field outside the conductor may be.

A partially enclosed space will often be shielded approximately, as appears from the foregoing consideration of the field intensity over conductor surfaces of concave curvature; but the shielding is complete when the enclosure is complete. The theorem is proved as follows: let U_1 in Fig. 1.17 be the boundary of a cavity in a conductor. U_1 is therefore an equipotential surface. Now suppose the potential at some interior point P near the wall of the cavity could differ from U_1. Let the equipotential surface through P be U_2. U_2, being different in potential from

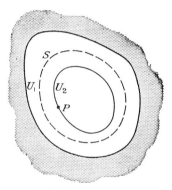

FIG. 1.17. A cavity in a conductor.

U_1, can never intersect U_1, and hence lies entirely inside U_1. If U_2 is near enough to U_1, the electric field between them must be always directed from U_2 to U_1, or from U_1 to U_2, depending on which potential is higher, since the potential function is continuous in space. But then there must be a net electric flux across any surface S between U_1 and U_2, either inward or outward, and this implies, from Gauss' law, the existence of net charge within S, which is contrary to hypothesis. Thus the space between U_1 and U_2 is field free. In the same manner, we may work inward from U_2 and thus show that the entire space in the cavity is necessarily field free. Q.E.D.

Theorem 4. The charge density on a boundary between conducting material and empty space is everywhere proportional to the electric field intensity in the space just outside the conductor.

Gauss' law proves this theorem directly, and also gives us the proportionality constant. S in Fig. 1.18 represents an infinitesimal part of a conductor-space boundary. We have seen that the electric field is zero inside the conducting material and that the lines of force outside are normal to S. Construct a Gaussian pillbox having an end of area dA parallel to S and in the space outside the conductor, infinitesimal sides everywhere perpendicular to S, and

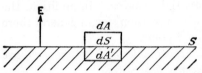

another end dA' in the conducting material. Supposing the positive sense of the electric field to be outward from the conductor, the net electric flux out from the box is $E\ dA$, and the charge enclosed is that residing on an element of surface area $dS = dA$ of the conductor. If

FIG. 1.18. Gaussian surface for determination of surface charge density on a conductor.

the surface charge density function is σ, then the charge enclosed is $\sigma\ dA$, so that $\epsilon_0 E\ dA = \sigma\ dA$, from Gauss' law. Therefore

$$\sigma = \epsilon_0 E \qquad \text{Q.E.D.} \qquad (1.78)$$

This theorem, combined with the discussion under Theorem 2, leads to a qualitative description of the distribution of charge density over the surface of a charged conductor. Since the electric field intensity is greater at points of greater convex curvature, the electric charge density is higher at points of greater convex curvature. This tendency may be visualized as the natural result of the mutual repulsion of like charges, which causes greater charge density at places in the conductor which have least conductor surface in the near vicinity.

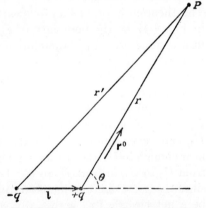

FIG. 1.19. A pair of charges which in the limit becomes a dipole.

1.13. The Electric Dipole. A particularly important type of electric field is that produced by a pair of equal and opposite point charges close together in comparison with the distance to the observer. Let l be the vector distance from the charge $-q$ to the charge $+q$ in Fig. 1.19, and consider the field observed at a point P. Let r be the distance from P to $+q$, let $\mathbf{r}^0$ be the unit vector directed from $+q$ to P, and let $\mathbf{r}^0$ make an angle θ with l. The distance r' from $-q$ to P is then given by the cosine law as

$$r'^2 = r^2 + l^2 + 2rl \cos \theta \qquad (1.79)$$

The electric potential at P is

$$U = \frac{q}{4\pi\epsilon_0} \left(\frac{1}{r} - \frac{1}{r'} \right) \qquad (1.80)$$

Let us allow l to decrease relative to r and find the limiting expression for U:

$$r'^2 = r^2 \left(1 + \frac{2l}{r} \cos \theta + \frac{l^2}{r^2} \right)$$

Therefore

$$r' = r \sqrt{1 + \left(\frac{2l}{r} \cos \theta + \frac{l^2}{r^2} \right)}$$

Hence

$$\frac{1}{r'} = \frac{1}{r} \left[1 + \left(\frac{2l}{r} \cos \theta + \frac{l^2}{r^2} \right) \right]^{-\frac{1}{2}} \qquad (1.81)$$

Use the binomial expansion:

$$\left[1 + \left(\frac{2l}{r} \cos \theta + \frac{l^2}{r^2} \right) \right]^{-\frac{1}{2}} = 1 - \frac{1}{2} \left(\frac{2l}{r} \cos \theta + \frac{l^2}{r^2} \right) + \cdots$$

Drop terms above the first degree in l/r:

$$\left[1 + \left(\frac{2l}{r} \cos \theta + \frac{l^2}{r^2} \right) \right]^{-\frac{1}{2}} \doteq 1 - \frac{l}{r} \cos \theta \qquad (1.82)$$

Therefore

$$\frac{1}{r'} \doteq +\frac{1}{r} - \frac{l}{r^2} \cos \theta \qquad (1.83)$$

Substitute into (1.80):

$$U \doteq \frac{ql \cos \theta}{4\pi\epsilon_0 r^2} \qquad (1.84)$$

The next term in the expansion for U would be of the form

$$\frac{ql^2}{4\pi\epsilon_0 r^3} f(\theta)$$

which is of the order l/r times the first nonzero term, that of Eq. (1.84); and succeeding terms involve still higher powers of l/r. Thus as $l/r \to 0$, the potential at P approaches (1.84) as its limit.

Let us define

$$q\mathbf{l} \equiv \mathbf{p} \qquad (1.85)$$

the vector dipole moment of the pair of charges, and

$$ql \equiv p \qquad (1.86)$$

the scalar magnitude of the dipole moment. Then Eq. (1.84) becomes, written as an exact equation for the limiting value of U as $l/r \to 0$,

$$U = \frac{p \cos \theta}{4\pi\epsilon_0 r^2} \tag{1.87}$$

This equation can also be written in the vector form

$$U = \frac{\mathbf{p} \cdot \mathbf{r}^0}{4\pi\epsilon_0 r^2} \tag{1.88}$$

Notice that in these limiting forms, there is no distinction any more between the lines r and r' in Fig. 1.19; but r now represents the distance between the dipole and the observer, while θ is the angle between $\mathbf{p}$ and $\mathbf{r}^0$. Also, as a matter of terminology, we shall call an actual pair of charges an electric dipole only when the observer's distance is such that the limiting forms represent the electric field to whatever order of accuracy is required. There are infinitely many other charge distributions, in addition to the pair of equal and opposite point charges, yielding a potential of the dipole form, either for all distances sufficiently great, or in a particular range of values of r. In such a case, the value of $\mathbf{p}$ for which Eq. (1.88) correctly represents the given dipole potential is called the dipole moment of the charge distribution.

It is an easy matter now to deduce the components of the electric field of a dipole. Since the radial component of electric field is in general

$$E_r = -\frac{\partial U}{\partial r} \tag{1.89}$$

by use of Eq. (1.34), the radial component of the dipole field is

$$E_r = \frac{2p \cos \theta}{4\pi\epsilon_0 r^3} \tag{1.90}$$

Likewise, the field component in the direction of increasing θ is found from

$$E_\theta = -\frac{\partial U}{r \, \partial \theta} \tag{1.91}$$

Thus

$$E_\theta = \frac{p \sin \theta}{4\pi\epsilon_0 r^3} \tag{1.92}$$

1.14. Expansion of the Potential of a System of Charges. Consider an arbitrary system A of static electric charges in space. Let us describe the charge distribution of the system by differential elements dq whose spatial dimensions are small compared with their distances from an observer. These elements of charge may result from volume, surface, or line densities, or even from point charges. This notation allows us to combine Eqs. (1.43) and (1.45) into a single integral for the electrostatic potential at the observer, without regard to the manner in which the charge is distributed:

$$U = \frac{1}{4\pi\epsilon_0} \int_A \frac{dq}{r} \tag{1.93}$$

where r is the distance from dq to the observer. Suppose now that an origin 0 is specified in the system, with respect to which the observer's coordinates are x, y, z while the coordinates of the element dq are x', y', z'. Then

$$U = \frac{1}{4\pi\epsilon_0} \int_A \frac{dq}{\sqrt{(x - x')^2 + (y - y')^2 + (z - z')^2}} \tag{1.94}$$

Let us now postulate that the observer's distance from the origin,

$$R = \sqrt{x^2 + y^2 + z^2} \tag{1.95}$$

is much larger than the maximum dimension of the system, so that

$$x' \ll R \qquad y' \ll R \qquad z' \ll R \tag{1.96}$$

The binomial theorem leads then to an important expansion for the potential U in terms of certain characteristics of the system A and in ascending inverse powers of R. Consider the integrand of Eq. (1.94):

$$\frac{1}{\sqrt{(x - x')^2 + (y - y')^2 + (z - z')^2}}$$
$$= (x^2 + y^2 + z^2 - 2(xx' + yy' + zz') + x'^2 + y'^2 + z'^2)^{-\frac{1}{2}}$$
$$= R^{-1}\left(1 - \frac{2}{R^2}(xx' + yy' + zz') + \frac{x'^2 + y'^2 + z'^2}{R^2}\right)^{-\frac{1}{2}} \tag{1.97}$$

To first degree terms in x'/R, y'/R, or z'/R, the binomial expansion yields

$$\frac{1}{\sqrt{(x - x')^2 - (y - y')^2 - (z - z')^2}} = \frac{1}{R} + \frac{1}{R^3}(xx' + yy' + zz') \tag{1.98}$$

To this first order of approximation, the potential function far from the system is therefore

$$U = \frac{1}{4\pi\epsilon_0 R} \int_A dq + \frac{1}{4\pi\epsilon_0 R^3}\left(x \int_A x'\, dq + y \int_A y'\, dq + z \int_A z'\, dq\right) \tag{1.99}$$

Now the first integral of Eq. (1.99) is the total charge of the system:

$$q = \int_A dq \tag{1.100}$$

The zero-degree term of Eq. (1.99) thus represents the potential of a point charge having the net total charge of the system and located at the point chosen as origin. We shall label this term U_0:

$$U_0 = \frac{q}{4\pi\epsilon_0 R} \tag{1.101}$$

The second term of Eq. (1.99), to be designated by U_1, is complex in appearance, but when expressed in vector notation it is seen to be simply the potential of an electric dipole located at the origin [see Eq. (1.88)]:

$$U_1 = \frac{\mathbf{p} \cdot \mathbf{R}^0}{4\pi\epsilon_0 R^2} \tag{1.102}$$

Here $\mathbf{R}^0$ is the unit vector from the origin toward the observer,

$$\mathbf{R}^0 = \frac{x\mathbf{i} + y\mathbf{j} + z\mathbf{k}}{R} \tag{1.103}$$

and the dipole moment vector $\mathbf{p}$ is identified by its cartesian components,

$$p_x = \int_A x'\, dq \qquad p_y = \int_A y'\, dq \qquad p_z = \int_A z'\, dq \tag{1.104}$$

Equations (1.104) may be combined into a single vector equation in terms of the position vector $\mathbf{r}' = x'\mathbf{i} + y'\mathbf{j} + z'\mathbf{k}$ from the origin to the element dq of charge:

$$\mathbf{p} = \int_A \mathbf{r}'\, dq \tag{1.105}$$

We have shown that when the potential function of a static system of charges is expanded in ascending powers of x'/R, y'/R, and z'/R, the first two terms of the expansion are, respectively, a point-charge potential and a dipole potential. We have defined the dipole moment of the system, Eq. (1.105), by means of the dipole term of this expansion. It should be remembered that the expansion can be continued to terms of higher than the first degree in ratios x'/R, etc. As the observer's distance increases so that the inequalities (1.96) become stronger, only the lowest nonvanishing term of the expansion eventually remains significant. For a sufficiently distant observer, the system is then entirely characterized as a point charge if $q \neq 0$; as a dipole if $q = 0$ but $\mathbf{p} \neq 0$; and as a multipole of higher order if some higher-degree term in the expansion is the first to exist. Sometimes it is convenient at moderate distances to retain more than the first nonzero term of the expansion, so that, for example, a system having finite values of both q and $\mathbf{p}$ is considered a combination of a point charge and a dipole. The second-degree term of the expansion, which contains the second-degree terms in the ratios

x'/R, etc., is important in correcting the point-charge approximation to the electric field of atomic nuclei, which may be aspherical in their charge distribution.

PROBLEMS

1.1. Point charges of $+6$, $+12$, and -0.5 millimicrocoulomb are located in empty space on the x axis at positions of 0, $+20$, and $+50$ cm, respectively. (One millimicrocoulomb is 10^{-9} coulomb.) Find the direction and the magnitude in newtons of the force on each charge.

1.2. Given three point charges. When q_1 and q_2 are placed close enough together to form a single point charge, the force on q_3 at a distance L from this combination is a repulsion of 2 units magnitude. When q_3 and q_1 are so combined, the force on q_2 at the same distance L is an attraction of 18 units; and when q_2 and q_3 are combined, the force on q_1 at the distance L is an attraction of 4 units. Deduce the algebraic ratios of the charges. *Ans.* $q_1:q_2:q_3 = 4: -3:2$.

1.3. A point charge of $+20 \times 10^{-3}$ microcoulomb is located at $(3,4,5)$ cm in empty space. Find the cartesian components of the force on it due to point charges of -40×10^{-3} and $+50 \times 10^{-3}$ microcoulomb, respectively, at the origin and at $(-6,-1,2)$ cm; and find the magnitude of the total force on it.

1.4. Two small pith balls weighing $\frac{1}{4}$ g apiece are suspended from a fixed point, each by a weightless thread 30 cm in length. What electric charge, divided equally between the balls, will cause them to separate to an equilibrium position 10 cm apart?

1.5. Three small pith balls of the same mass m are suspended by equal, weightless threads of length l from a common point. A charge q is divided equally between the balls, and they come to equilibrium at the corners of a horizontal, equilateral triangle whose sides are d. Show that

$$q^2 = 12\pi\epsilon_0 mgd^3 \Big/ \sqrt{l^2 - \frac{d^2}{3}}$$

where g is the acceleration of gravity.

1.6. Two equal point charges q are fixed at a distance $2b$ apart, and a third similar point charge q is constrained to remain on the line joining them. Show that if x is the displacement of the third charge from the point midway between the other two, there is a restoring force for small displacements $x \ll b$ which is approximately linear:

$$F \doteq -\frac{q^2}{\pi\epsilon_0 b^3} x$$

1.7. Coulomb's law is found to hold for the electrostatic repulsion between atomic nuclei at very short distances. Compute the electrostatic force between an alpha particle of atomic number 2 and a gold nucleus of atomic number 79 at a separation of 3×10^{-12} cm. (The atomic number gives the positive charge on the nucleus in units of the magnitude of the electronic charge which is -1.60×10^{-19} coulomb.)

1.8. *a.* Suppose an excess of 10^{10} electrons to be evenly distributed throughout the volume of a sphere of 10 cm radius. How many electrons are there per cubic millimeter? What is the charge density in mks units?

b. If these electrons are all on the surface of the sphere and evenly distributed, what are the number of electrons per square millimeter and the charge density in mks units?

1.9. *a.* Find the electric field on the axis of a plane circular disk of charge having uniform surface density σ. Let a be the radius of the disk and x the distance from the center of the disk to the observer. Use direct integration.

b. Show that for $x \gg a$, this field becomes that of a point charge whose magnitude equals the total charge on the disk.

1.10. Given point charges $+q$ at $(a/2,0,0)$ and $-q$ at $(-a/2,0,0)$ in empty space.

a. Find the cartesian components of the electric field at a general point (x,y,z).

b. Show that for a general point in the xy plane at distance r from the origin, the limiting form of the electric field components when $r \gg a$ is

$$E_x = \frac{aq}{4\pi\epsilon_0 r^3}\left(\frac{3x^2}{r^2} - 1\right)$$

$$E_y = \frac{aq}{4\pi\epsilon_0 r^3}\frac{3xy}{r^2}$$

1.11. A small pith ball having a mass of $\frac{1}{10}$ g and hanging on a weightless thread is given an electric charge of 10^{-9} coulomb. At a certain place in an electrostatic system, the ball is in equilibrium when the thread makes an angle of $20°$ with the vertical. Using the standard acceleration of gravity, find the magnitude of the electric field to which the ball is subjected if the field is horizontal.

1.12. Find by direct integration the electric field of an infinite, plane sheet of charge of uniform density σ, for a point of observation not on the sheet.

1.13. Find by direct integration the electric field due to an infinite line charge of uniform linear density λ. A symmetry argument showing the direction of the field may be used first.

Ans. $E = \dfrac{\lambda}{2\pi\epsilon_0 r}$, where r is the distance of the observation point from the line. Direction is radial.

1.14. Find by direct integration the electric field at the center of a hemispherical surface of charge having uniform density σ. The polar angle θ and azimuth angle ϕ of spherical coordinates are suitable variables. Generalize this result for any incomplete spherical surface whose polar angle runs from 0 to θ_0.

Ans. For hemisphere: $E = \dfrac{\sigma}{4\epsilon_0}$ along the polar axis.

1.15. Given the electric field of an infinite straight line charge of uniform linear density λ to be radial with the magnitude

$$E = \frac{\lambda}{2\pi\epsilon_0 r}$$

where r is the radial distance to the observer. Show that this field has a single-valued scalar potential function, without finding that function.

1.16. Given the electric field of an infinite straight line charge of uniform linear density λ:

$$E = \frac{\lambda}{2\pi\epsilon_0 r}$$

outward along the cylindrical radius r from the line charge. Let the line charge lie along the z axis, and find by integration in cartesian coordinates the potential difference between points (x_0,y_0,z_0) and (x,y,z). Check against Eq. (1.72).

1.17. *a.* Test the vector function $\mathbf{f} = xy\mathbf{i} + x^2/2\mathbf{j}$, $\mathbf{i}$ and $\mathbf{j}$ being the unit vectors along the x and y axes, respectively, to see whether its line integral should be independent of path.

b. Check by integrating this function between the origin and the point (1,2,0), over the following three paths in the xy plane:

Path A: Straight from $(0,0)$ to $(1,0)$, and thence straight to $(1,2)$
Path B: Straight from $(0,0)$ to $(0,2)$, and thence straight to $(1,2)$
Path C: Straight from $(0,0)$ to $(1,2)$
See the figure.

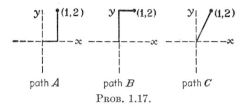

path A path B path C

PROB. 1.17.

1.18. *a.* Test the vector function $f = xy\mathbf{i} + y^2/2\mathbf{j}$ to see whether its line integral is independent of path.

b. Check by integration over the paths A, B, and C of Prob. 1.17 between the origin and the point $(1,2,0)$.

1.19. Find the work which must be done against the electrostatic force in order to separate the electron and the proton of a normal hydrogen atom. The electron has a charge of -1.60×10^{-19} coulomb, the proton has a charge of $+1.60 \times 10^{-19}$ coulomb, and their separation is 0.529×10^{-10} m.

1.20. Given two point charges, q_1 of $+10^{-3}$ microcoulomb at the origin and q_2 of $-\frac{1}{2} \times 10^{-3}$ microcoulomb at $x = 2.0$ m on the x axis.

a. Find the potential function U for points on the x axis.

b. Plot this function roughly.

c. At what points on the x axis does U vanish?

d. At what points on the x axis does the electric field vanish?

e. At what points on the x axis does U have extreme values, finite or otherwise?

1.21. Given the two point charges of the preceding problem: q_1 of $+1 \times 10^{-3}$ microcoulomb at the origin and q_2 of $-\frac{1}{2} \times 10^{-3}$ microcoulomb at $(2,0,0)$ m. Find the potential function in space, and show that the finite extreme value of this function which occurs on the x axis is not an absolute maximum or minimum, so that a point charge of neither sign could be in stable equilibrium at that place under the electrostatic force alone. This is a special case of a theorem called Earnshaw's.

1.22. Given a plane circular disk of surface charge with uniform density σ and radius a.

a. Find the electrostatic potential function for a general point on the axis of the disk at distance x from its center.

b. Use this potential function, together with symmetry considerations, to compute the electric field on the axis of the disk.

c. Show that for $x \gg a$, the potential function of the disk approaches as its limit the potential of a point charge whose magnitude is that of the total charge on the disk.

1.23. Given a finite, straight line charge of uniform linear density λ and length b. Find the work required to carry a point charge q from a point on the perpendicular bisector and at distance $c > b/2$ from the center of the line charge to a point colinear with the line charge and at the same distance c from its center.

1.24. Set up an integral for the electrostatic potential of a thin spherical shell of charge having a uniform surface density σ and radius R, for a general point inside or outside the shell. Integrate to find the potential function both inside and outside.

Ans. Inside: $U = \dfrac{R\sigma}{\epsilon_0}$. Outside: $U = \dfrac{\sigma}{\epsilon_0} \dfrac{R^2}{r}$.

1.25. From the result of Prob. 1.24, find the potential function of a spherical distribution of charge with density $\rho(r)$ and radius R, for an exterior point at distance r from the center. Express the result in terms of the total charge Q of the distribution.

1.26. From the result of Prob. 1.24, find the potential function at a general point inside a spherical charge distribution of uniform volume density ρ and radius R.

1.27. Given a finite straight line charge of variable linear density $\lambda = kx$ where k is a constant, lying along the x axis and extending from $x = -b/2$ to $x = +b/2$.

a. For a general point of observation (x',y',z'), set up an integral for the electrostatic potential function of the line charge. Integrate.

b. Use the potential function to find the cartesian components of the electric field at the observer.

1.28. Given a spherical distribution of electric charge with radius R and volume density of charge $\rho = kr^2$, where r is the distance from the center and k is a constant. Find the electrostatic potential at the center by direct integration.

1.29. Given a plane circular disk of surface charge with uniform density σ and radius a. Find by direct integration the electrostatic potential (a) at a point on the rim of the disk; (b) at the center of the disk.

1.30. Show that the integral for the electrostatic potential of a line charge diverges for any point on the line, even though the line is finite in extent.

1.31. Use Gauss' law to find the flux of the electric field through a square surface of side b due to a point charge q located on the normal to the square through its center, at a distance $b/2$ from the center. Evaluate this flux when $q = 10^{-8}$ coulomb.

1.32. Find by integration the flux of the electric field through a circular disk of radius a due to a point charge q located at a distance b from the center of the disk on

its axis.   *Ans.* $\Phi_E = \dfrac{q}{2\epsilon_0}\left(1 - \dfrac{b}{\sqrt{b^2 + a^2}}\right).$

1.33. Use the result of the preceding problem together with Gauss' law to find the flux of the electric field through the curved surface only of a circular cylinder of radius a and length l due to a point charge q at the center of the cylinder.

1.34. *a.* Find the electric field at general points inside and outside an infinitely long, circular cylinder of electric charge, having uniform volume density ρ and radius R.

b. Repeat for a cylindrically symmetrical charge distribution of radius R in which the volume density of charge is $\rho = kr^3$, where r is the cylindrical radius and k is a constant.

1.35. Find what spherically symmetrical distribution of charge density $\rho(r)$ will produce within itself an electric field in the radial direction having a magnitude $E = kr^2$, where k is a constant.   *Ans.* $\rho(r) = 4k\epsilon_0 r.$

1.36. *a.* Use Gauss' law to find the electric field at a general point at distance r from the center of a spherical ball of uniform charge density ρ and radius R. Consider both $r < R$ and $r > R$.

b. Integrate this field from $r = \infty$ to $r = 0$ to find the potential at the center of the ball.

c. Verify the result by using an integral over the charge distribution to find the potential at the center of the sphere.

1.37. Show that the zero-potential surface in the field of a pair of point charges of opposite sign is spherical. In what special case does it become plane?

1.38. Given an isolated point charge of 10^{-10} coulomb:

a. Draw to scale the traces in a plane containing the charge of the equipotential surfaces of 1,000, 2,000, 3,000, and 4,000 volts. Draw some lines of force in this plane.

b. What is the average electric field along a line of force between the 1,000- and 2,000-volt equipotentials?

1.39. Given two point charges, $q_1 = +4q$ at the origin and $q_2 = -q$ at $x = 5$ units, on the x axis:

a. Draw the traces in the xy plane of a family of equipotential surfaces by the following method: Let a series of concentric circles be drawn about q_1 or use polar graph paper. Represent a given value of the potential U by the parameter $k \equiv 4\pi\epsilon_0 U/q$, and let r_1 and r_2 be the distances from the observation point to q_1 and q_2, respectively. For each k, make a table of values of r_2 corresponding to the r_1 values of the circles. Then, with compass, locate points on the given equipotential.

b. Sketch some lines of force in this field map, in dotted lines, using the equipotentials as a guide.

1.40. Given two equal point charges q on the x axis at $(-a,0,0)$ and $(+a,0,0)$, respectively.

a. Write the electrostatic potential function in cartesian coordinates.

b. Expand this function in the neighborhood of the origin by the binomial theorem. Let $x \ll a$, $y \ll a$, and $z \ll a$, and carry to whatever degree in x/a, y/a, and z/a is necessary to obtain a variable function.

c. Describe the equipotential surface which passes through the origin. What can be said of the direction of its normal at the origin?

$$Ans. \ (b) \quad U = \frac{q}{4\pi\epsilon_0}\left[\frac{2}{a} + \frac{1}{a^3}(2x^2 - y^2 - z^2)\right].$$

1.41. Given the two equal point charges of the preceding problem, sketch the trace in the xy plane of a family of equipotential surfaces. Use qualitative considerations together with result (b) of the preceding problem. Dot in some lines of force, using the equipotential surfaces as a guide.

1.42. A downward electric field of 120 volts/m exists on the average in the atmosphere near the earth. Find the average charge density and the total charge on the earth's surface.

1.43. In the Faraday ice-pail experiment, a charged metal ball is suspended by an insulating string inside a closed metal pail which is initially uncharged and is insulated except for a wire connecting it to an electroscope indicating the potential of the pail. Use the material of Sec. 1.12 to predict and explain the results of the following experiments:

a. The ball is moved about in the pail without touching it. What is the effect on the electroscope?

b. The ball is touched to the inside of the pail. What effect is noted on the electroscope?

c. The ball, after touching the inside of the pail, is removed and tested for electric charge. What is the result?

1.44. A spherical shell of metal with inner and outer radii a and b, respectively, is made with a removable cap from which a metal ball is suspended on an insulating string so as to hang at the center of the shell. The shell is insulated and initially uncharged; and then the ball, bearing a charge q, is inserted.

a. What are the electric fields at general points in all regions of the system?

b. What are the charge densities of the shell?

c. Check Eq. (1.78) for this system.

1.45. Given an electric dipole whose vector moment **p** lies along the y axis, and which is located at the origin. Find the cartesian components of the electric field at an observation point (x,y,z).

1.46. For the field of an electric dipole, plot the trace in a plane containing the dipole of a family of equipotential surfaces. Use polar coordinate paper if desired. Dot in a family of lines of force, using the equipotentials as a guide.

1.47. Two point charges of $+10^{-10}$ coulomb and -10^{-10} coulomb are located, respectively, at the origin and at $(-1,-3,+2)$ cm.

    a. What is the vector dipole moment of the pair of charges?

    b. What is the electrostatic potential at the point $(80,-60,120)$ cm, to the dipole approximation?

1.48. Show that the absolute value of the electric field of a dipole decreases monotonically as the angle θ between the dipole moment and the radius to the observer increases from zero to $\pi/2$ radians, when the distance to the observer is constant.

1.49. Three point charges are located as follows: $q_1 = +2 \times 10^{-10}$ coulomb at the origin; $q_2 = -1 \times 10^{-10}$ coulomb at $(1,0,0)$ cm; $q_3 = +3 \times 10^{-10}$ coulomb at $(1,2,0)$ cm.

    a. Find the electric dipole moment vector of the system.

    b. Find, to the dipole approximation, the electrostatic potential at the point $(30,0,0)$ cm.

    c. By what percentage does this result differ from the true potential at that point?

1.50. Given a straight line charge extending along the x axis from $x = -b/2$ to $x = +b/2$, with a variable linear density $\lambda = kx$, where k is a constant.

    a. Find the vector dipole moment of the line charge.

    b. Find the electrostatic potential and field of the line charge at the point $(0,y,z)$, if $\sqrt{y^2 + z^2} \gg a$.

Note: The answer may be checked as a limiting case of Prob. 1.27.

1.51. Show that a necessary and sufficient condition that the vector dipole moment of a system of electric charges be independent of a shift of the origin of coordinates is that the total charge of the system be zero.

1.52. Carry the expansion in the text, for the potential of a system of charges whose size is small compared with the observer's distance, to the next degree (second), and thus find the cartesian expression for an electric quadrupole field.

CHAPTER 2

THE ELECTROSTATIC FIELD OF FREE CHARGES

2.1. Introduction. The problem of ascertaining the electric field at every point of a system of charges is straightforward and elementary in principle so long as all the charges in the system are given. If the system is finite, the potential may be evaluated by performing the scalar integration

$$U = \frac{1}{4\pi\epsilon_0} \int_{\text{all charges}} \frac{dq}{r} \tag{2.1}$$

where r is the distance from the charge element dq to the point of observation. From U the field is obtained immediately. Even if the system is infinite, the process is only slightly more difficult, and the field may be found from the vector integral

$$\mathbf{E} = \frac{1}{4\pi\epsilon_0} \int_{\text{all charges}} \frac{\mathbf{r}^0 \, dq}{r^2} \tag{2.2}$$

The problem encountered in practice is usually much more subtle. There will often be conductors in the system, and either the total charge or the potential of each conductor will be specified; and in addition, there may be known fixed charges. One of the unknowns of such a system is the surface density of charge for each conductor, which may be determined after we know the solution for the electric field. Thus the integrals of the preceding paragraph are useless for determining the electric field. A further degree of complication is introduced when dielectric material is present in the system, for then bound charges are induced which also are not given at the outset, but which may be determined from the solution for the electric field. This complication we reserve until the next chapter. In this chapter we shall limit ourselves to systems involving conductors and possibly also fixed electric charges, that is, systems involving only free charge.

The mathematical process making possible a solution for an electrostatic system where the charge distribution is not entirely known at the outset is the solving of a partial differential equation in such a way as to satisfy certain known conditions of the problem. These conditions are called boundary conditions, because they literally specify certain relationships obtaining at boundary surfaces, such as conductor-space boundaries. We shall concern ourselves in this chapter with obtaining the differential equation which is satisfied by the electrostatic potential function in any system not containing bound charges, with specifying the nature of the boundary conditions, and developing a particular method of solution of certain simple systems. The solution of a problem by direct use of the differential equation and the boundary conditions often leads to considerable complexity of mathematics, involving generalized coordinate systems and expansion of functions in various kinds of infinite series. Such methods are for the most part beyond the scope of this book. The particular method of electrostatic images, which we shall consider, involves less advanced mathematics, but logically rests upon the theory of the solutions of the differential equation with boundary conditions; so we must start with an outline of this general theory.

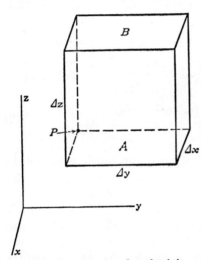

FIG. 2.1. Construction for obtaining Poisson's equation.

2.2. Poisson's Equation in Space. Laplace's Equation.

The electric field in a system containing no bound charge satisfies a differential form of Gauss' law. To obtain this equation, consider a small rectangular box whose edges are parallel to the coordinate axes and whose dimensions are Δx, Δy, and Δz. This box, pictured in Fig. 2.1 is to be only a mathematical construction made at some arbitrary point of our system $P(x,y,z)$, which we may take as a corner point of the box; and for convenience, let P be that corner point having lowest algebraic values of x, y, and z. Consider the electric flux out from the box through the two opposite faces A and B which are parallel to the xy plane. Only the z component of the electric field will contribute to this flux; a positive z component of field gives an inward flux through A and an outward flux through B. Let a general point on face A have coordinates $(x + \alpha\,\Delta x, y + \beta\,\Delta y, z)$, and let a corresponding point on B have coordinates $(x + \alpha\,\Delta x, y + \beta\,\Delta y, z + \Delta z)$. Here α and β are variable positive fractions running between zero and unity, and they will serve as the variables in the computation of the electric flux from the two faces A and B of the box. The values of (x,y,z), and of $(\Delta x, \Delta y, \Delta z)$ will be considered fixed during the computations.

We shall now specify that the box we are discussing shall be small, so that the electric field over the faces A and B may be expressed by a Taylor's expansion in the variables α and β. This expansion is, for the z component of the field, as follows. On A,

$$(E_z)_A = E_z(x,y,z) + \left(\frac{\partial E_z}{\partial x}\right)_{x,y,z} a\, \Delta x + \left(\frac{\partial E_z}{\partial y}\right)_{x,y,z} \beta\, \Delta y$$
$$+ \text{ quadratic and higher-order terms in } (a\,\Delta x) \text{ and } (\beta\,\Delta y) \quad (2.3)$$

$$(E_z)_B = E_z(x,y,z) + \left(\frac{\partial E_z}{\partial x}\right)_{x,y,z} a\, \Delta x + \left(\frac{\partial E_z}{\partial y}\right)_{x,y,z} \beta\, \Delta y + \left(\frac{\partial E_z}{\partial z}\right)_{x,y,z} \Delta z$$
$$+ \text{ quadratic and higher-order terms in } (a\,\Delta x), (\beta\,\Delta y), \text{ and } \Delta z \quad (2.4)$$

We have been obliged to use the first-order terms of the expansion, that is, to remember that the electric field is a function of position, in order to get a nonzero answer for the net electric flux from our box; but we shall neglect quadratic and higher-order terms, assuming that Δx, Δy, and Δz are to be considered as small as necessary so that the remainder of the series expansion becomes as small as we please relative to the first-order terms. Let us now use these expansions to compute the electric flux through faces A and B:

$$\Phi_B = \int_B (E_z)_B\, dS \qquad \Phi_A = \int_A (E_z)_A\, dS \qquad (2.5)$$

Now the element of area on the faces A and B has the form

$$dS = d(\alpha\, \Delta x)\, d(\beta\, \Delta y) = \Delta x\, \Delta y\, d\alpha\, d\beta \qquad (2.6)$$

Therefore

$$\Phi_B = E_z(x,y,z)\, \Delta x\, \Delta y \int_0^1 \int_0^1 d\alpha\, d\beta + \left(\frac{\partial E_z}{\partial x}\right)_{x,y,z} (\Delta x)^2\, \Delta y \int_0^1 \int_0^1 \alpha\, d\alpha\, d\beta$$
$$+ \left(\frac{\partial E_z}{\partial y}\right)_{x,y,z} \Delta x (\Delta y)^2 \int_0^1 \int_0^1 \beta\, d\alpha\, d\beta$$
$$+ \left(\frac{\partial E_z}{\partial z}\right)_{x,y,z} \Delta x\, \Delta y\, \Delta z \int_0^1 \int_0^1 d\alpha\, d\beta \qquad (2.7)$$

where all factors which are constant during the integration have been taken outside the integral signs. These integrals are elementary, and have the values 1, ½, ½, and 1, respectively. Thus the flux out through B is

$$\Phi_B = E_z\, \Delta x\, \Delta y + \frac{1}{2}\left(\frac{\partial E_z}{\partial x}\right)(\Delta x)^2\, \Delta y + \frac{1}{2}\left(\frac{\partial E_z}{\partial y}\right)\Delta x (\Delta y)^2$$
$$+ \left(\frac{\partial E_z}{\partial z}\right)\Delta x\, \Delta y\, \Delta z \qquad (2.8)$$

in which expression we have simplified the highly explicit notation we have been using. By an exactly similar process we evaluate the flux into the box through face A:

$$\Phi_A = E_z \, \Delta x \, \Delta y + \frac{1}{2}\left(\frac{\partial E_z}{\partial x}\right)(\Delta x)^2 \, \Delta y + \frac{1}{2}\left(\frac{\partial E_z}{\partial y}\right)\Delta x (\Delta y)^2 \qquad (2.9)$$

which is the same as Φ_B except that it lacks the last term. Thus the net flux out from the box through the pair of faces A and B is

$$\Phi_{AB} = \Phi_B - \Phi_A = \left(\frac{\partial E_z}{\partial z}\right)\Delta x \, \Delta y \, \Delta z \qquad (2.10)$$

By a similar procedure we may obtain the net flux out from the box through the other two pairs of parallel faces. The symmetry of expression (2.10) shows at once that the results will be

$$\left(\frac{\partial E_x}{\partial x}\right)\Delta x \, \Delta y \, \Delta z \qquad \left(\frac{\partial E_y}{\partial y}\right)\Delta x \, \Delta y \, \Delta z \qquad (2.11)$$

The entire outward flux is therefore

$$\Phi = \left(\frac{\partial E_x}{\partial x} + \frac{\partial E_y}{\partial y} + \frac{\partial E_z}{\partial z}\right)\Delta x \, \Delta y \, \Delta z \qquad (2.12)$$

Now if there is a volume density of free charge, $\rho(x,y,z)$ in the system, the net charge enclosed by the box may be found by a volume integration over the volume ΔV of the box:

$$q = \int_{\Delta V} \rho \, dV \qquad (2.13)$$

This integration can be performed by making a Taylor's expansion of the ρ function, much as we did with the electric field to find the electric flux. The labor involved is superfluous, here, because the limiting value of the integral as Δx, Δy, Δz approach zero is simply that due to the zero-order term in the Taylor's expansion, and may be written down at once:

$$q = \rho(x,y,z) \, \Delta V = \rho(x,y,z) \, \Delta x \, \Delta y \, \Delta z \qquad (2.14)$$

Now we substitute Eqs. (2.12) and (2.14) into Gauss' law for a system containing no bound charge:

$$\epsilon_0 \Phi_E = q \qquad (2.15)$$

The result is

$$\epsilon_0 \left(\frac{\partial E_x}{\partial x} + \frac{\partial E_y}{\partial y} + \frac{\partial E_z}{\partial z}\right)\Delta x \, \Delta y \, \Delta z = \rho(x,y,z) \, \Delta x \, \Delta y \, \Delta z \qquad (2.16)$$

Therefore

$$\frac{\partial E_x}{\partial x} + \frac{\partial E_y}{\partial y} + \frac{\partial E_z}{\partial z} = \frac{1}{\epsilon_0}\rho \qquad (2.17)$$

which is the differential equation we have been seeking. It is understood that both sides of the equation are to be evaluated at the same point of space, and further that the equation is true for all points of space in a system containing no bound charge. The left-hand member of the equation is called in vector analysis the divergence of the electric field vector, and written div **E**. Thus Eq. (2.17) may be abbreviated to read

$$\text{div } \mathbf{E} = \frac{1}{\epsilon_0} \rho \tag{2.18}$$

Corresponding to Eq. (2.17) there is a differential equation satisfied by the electrostatic potential function U. From Eqs. (1.33), we know that

$$E_x = -\frac{\partial U}{\partial x} \qquad E_y = -\frac{\partial U}{\partial y} \qquad E_z = -\frac{\partial U}{\partial z} \tag{2.19}$$

Substitution of these expressions yields a second-order differential equation called Poisson's equation:

$$\frac{\partial^2 U}{\partial x^2} + \frac{\partial^2 U}{\partial y^2} + \frac{\partial^2 U}{\partial z^2} = -\frac{1}{\epsilon_0} \rho \tag{2.20}$$

This equation, like (2.17), applies in this form only in absence of bound charge density. Its form in regions where there is no free charge density either is important enough to be exhibited:

$$\frac{\partial^2 U}{\partial x^2} + \frac{\partial^2 U}{\partial y^2} + \frac{\partial^2 U}{\partial z^2} = 0 \tag{2.21}$$

This is called Laplace's equation. Equation (2.20), with its counterpart for the more general case including dielectric materials, and Eq. (2.21) form the basis for the theoretical development of the problem of determining the electric field in a given electrostatic system. They are particularly suitable for analysis because the dependent variable is a scalar function rather than a vector function.

2.3. Boundary Conditions. Electrostatic systems without bound charge can consist only of conductors, free charge, and space. The conductor boundaries form boundaries of the entire space where the electric field exists and where the potential function is required, for the field is zero and the potential constant within conductor material. From this point of view, the body of conducting material appears as a "hole" in the electrostatic system, a region void of field and of interest. Conductor boundaries may or may not completely enclose the system; for if the space of the system extends to infinity, we may imagine it to be enclosed only if we include in our list of its boundaries an infinite closed surface. Conditions on the conductor surfaces, and if necessary the infinite surface, are called boundary conditions of the system.

The free charge of the electrostatic system may be on conductors, in which case it will appear as a surface density, or in very limited regions of space as point charges, or in space as a volume density of charge, or occasionally in space as filaments or sheets where a linear or surface density would be specified. The charge in space will usually be among the known sources of the electric field, while the surface density of charge on conductors is an unknown to be determined after the solution for the potential function has been obtained. The total charge on a conductor may be given, however, as a source of the field; or the potential of a conductor may be known, as, for example, when it is at zero potential when it is said to be "grounded." These last data are properly termed boundary conditions; for the potential of a conductor is the potential of an equipotential boundary surface of the system, while the total charge of the conductor is expressible as a surface integral over the conductor boundary. This integral for the ith conductor, whose surface is S_i, is

$$q_i = \int_{S_i} \sigma \, dS \tag{2.22}$$

and the surface density of charge σ is given by Eq. (1.78):

$$\sigma = \epsilon_0 E \tag{2.23}$$

Furthermore, the electric field intensity E at the conductor surface is given by

$$E = -\frac{\partial U}{\partial n} \tag{2.24}$$

Therefore

$$\sigma = -\epsilon_0 \frac{\partial U}{\partial n} \tag{2.25}$$

where n is a length coordinate in the outward normal direction to the conductor surface and U is the value of the potential function in the region outside the conductor surface. Thus the charge on the ith conductor is expressible in terms of an integral over the boundary S_i involving the potential function:

$$q_i = -\epsilon_0 \int_{S_i} \frac{\partial U}{\partial n} \, dS \tag{2.26}$$

The question now is what boundary conditions are sufficient to lead to a unique solution of Poisson's equation for the system. A straightforward mathematical process, beyond the scope of this book, gives the answer for systems such that the potential function U if properly chosen approaches zero on the infinite, closed, boundary surface (if the system extends to infinity at all) at least as fast as the reciprocal first power of the distance from the origin of coordinates. This will in fact always be the case when the charges which act as sources of the field are confined to a finite region including the origin. The answer for such systems is that for each conductor in the system it is sufficient to specify, besides its size and shape, either its total electric charge or its potential. The other quantity, for each conductor, may be determined by use of the solutions for the potential function, directly if it is the potential which is to be found, or by use of Eq. (2.26) if it is the charge. It is to be understood, however, that unless the value of the potential is given on at least one conductor, or at some reference point of the system, then the solution for the potential function will always be arbitrary to the extent of an undetermined additive constant.

2.4. Poisson's Equation in Less than Three Cartesian Coordinates. If we write Poisson's or Laplace's equation in one or two cartesian coordinates, we imply that the potential does not vary at all with the omitted coordinates. This might conceivably be strictly true in a limited region of an electrostatic system under very special conditions; but we could hardly be sure of it a priori unless the system had an infinite translational symmetry along the omitted coordinates. This in turn means that in a system for which only two cartesian coordinates were used, all boundaries would be infinite cylinders (of course, not necessarily circular); while in a system for which only one cartesian coordinate was used, all boundaries would be infinite planes. In both systems, all charge densities would extend infinitely far from the origin. Now obviously such systems are ideal and not real. Furthermore, the uniqueness theorems of the preceding section do not apply to such systems, since the potential does not approach zero on an infinitely distant closed surface about the observer.

Nevertheless, Poisson's equation or Laplace's equation is simpler when one or two of the cartesian coordinates are omitted; and solutions may be determined, possibly within an additive constant, when appropriate boundary conditions are given. The solutions, once obtained, are then useful because they give approximations to the actual solutions for real systems in regions where the potential function is nearly independent of one or two of the cartesian coordinates. Such cases are quite frequently encountered in practice. For example, the electrostatic potential of a d-c transmission cable or line is approximately independent of the coordinate parallel to the line; while the potential in a parallel-plate condenser may be made, by guard rings, to depend almost wholly upon the single coordinate normal to the plates. It is appropriate to note here some general characteristics of solutions and of boundary conditions in the ideal systems of one or two cartesian coordinates.

One Cartesian Coordinate. In this case, Poisson's and Laplace's equations are merely second-order ordinary differential equations. Their solutions may be written precisely in terms of integrals, with two constants of integration which are to be determined from the boundary conditions. One of the constants is always the additive constant peculiar to the potential function; it is determined only whenever the value of the potential is specified at some point of the system. In our one-coordinate systems, this specification will usually be for some conductor surface. Only two independent conditions will completely determine the potential in a region between two conductor boundaries. Besides the potential of a boundary we may be given its surface density of charge. Total charge on a conductor will not have any meaning, since the conductor surfaces are infinite. The most concentrated form of free charge in a system depending only on one cartesian coordinate is the thin, infinite, plane sheet of charge having uniform density. This is what corresponds to the point charge in systems involving all the coordinates.

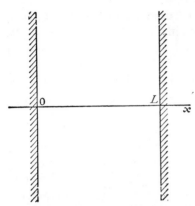

FIG. 2.2. Problem for Laplace's equation in one dimension.

As the simplest example of an ideal system involving only one cartesian coordinate, consider the region between two infinite plane conductor surfaces, with no volume charge density in the region. Let the coordinate x have its origin at the left-hand surface (see Fig. 2.2). The potential V in the region satisfies Laplace's equation in one coordinate:

$$\frac{d^2 U}{dx^2} = 0 \tag{2.27}$$

This may immediately be integrated to yield

$$U = ax + b \tag{2.28}$$

where a and b are the constants of integration.

To apply the boundary conditions, let us substitute this general solution into Eq. (2.25) of the preceding section. Since x is the outward normal coordinate to the surface of the left-hand conductor, the surface charge density there is

$$\sigma_0 = -\epsilon_0 a \tag{2.29}$$

Likewise, the surface charge density on the right-hand plate, where the outward normal coordinate is $-x$, is

$$\sigma_L = +\epsilon_0 a \tag{2.30}$$

We notice from Eqs. (2.29) and (2.30) that the surface charge densities on the two surfaces are always equal, but of opposite sign. If either charge density is given as a boundary condition, the constant a is immediately determined by one of these equations. If in addition the potential is given at either surface, then the constant b may be found by using Eq. (2.28). Or, if the potential is given on both surfaces, Eq. (2.28) can be used to find both the constants; the charge densities can then be deduced from (2.29) and (2.30).

Two Cartesian Coordinates. A very powerful and general method of obtaining solutions of Laplace's equation in two cartesian coordinates is provided by the theory of functions of a complex variable, but the method is beyond the scope of this book. Solutions are frequently written in terms of polar coordinates, r and θ, in which they often take one of the following forms, or a sum of such forms:

$$\ln r$$
$$r^m \cos m\theta \qquad r^{-m} \cos m\theta$$
$$r^m \sin m\theta \qquad r^{-m} \sin m\theta$$

where m is any integer.

Boundary conditions are, as usual, of two principal types: either the value of the potential is specified on a conductor, or else charge is given per unit length of the conductor along the cartesian coordinate omitted from Poisson's or Laplace's equation. The total charge of conductors cannot be given, since in these ideal systems the conductors are infinitely long and hence have infinite surface area.

If the trace of a conductor surface in the plane of x and y, the coordinates on which the potential depends, is a curve L, and if differential length of this curve be called dl, then the charge of the conductor per unit length along the z axis is

$$\lambda = \int_L \sigma \, dl \tag{2.31}$$

where σ is the surface charge density of the conductor. If n represents a coordinate always normal to the conductor surface and out from it, then as usual we may write

$$\sigma = -\epsilon_0 \frac{\partial U}{\partial n} \tag{2.32}$$

so that

$$\lambda = -\epsilon_0 \int_L \frac{\partial U}{\partial n} \, dl \tag{2.33}$$

The concentration of free charge which appears in systems involving two cartesian coordinates is the line charge: an infinite, straight filament of uniform linear charge density. It is this which corresponds in these systems to the point charge in systems involving all the coordinates.

2.5. Electrostatic Images. The theory of electrostatic images is a method of obtaining solutions of Poisson's equation or Laplace's equation without going through the mathematical details of solving a partial differential equation. Its usefulness is limited to a relatively small number of cases, but these are interesting and important.

Let us suppose that a distribution of fixed free charges, represented by the volume density ρ_f, is specified in a region V of an electrostatic system. The boundaries of V are to consist of conductor surfaces, with perhaps an infinite surface about the observer. Sufficient boundary conditions are to be given to ensure a unique solution for the electrostatic potential function in the region, although the additive constant may be left unspecified.

Now we may consider that the potential U in the region is the sum of two terms. The given fixed charges, taken by themselves as if isolated in space, contribute to the potential a term

$$U_1 = \frac{1}{4\pi\epsilon_0} \int_V \frac{\rho_f}{r} \, dV \tag{2.34}$$

The rest of the potential function is due to the distribution σ of surface charge density over the conducting boundaries of the region V. Let these conducting boundaries be S_j. Then the second term of the potential is

$$U_2 = \frac{1}{4\pi\epsilon_0} \int_{\text{all } S_j} \frac{\sigma}{r} \, dS \tag{2.35}$$

The total potential in the region is now

$$U = U_1 + U_2 \tag{2.36}$$

The equations we have written are correct, but do not yet constitute a solution of the problem, since the surface density function σ is not known. It may happen, however, and this is the foundation of the method of images, that the conducting boundary surfaces of V are so simple in form that it is known how to create equipotential surfaces of this same shape by distributions of fixed free charge. Specifically, it may be known from work with fixed charges that if we imagine the conductors of our given electrostatic system to be removed and the region V' of space which is separated from V by the boundaries of the system to contain a fictitious distribution of fixed charge represented by a volume density ρ_i, then the potential U_i due to the ρ_i will, when added to the potential U_1, yield equipotential surfaces coinciding with the S_j boundaries. The charges ρ_i are called image charges. It may further be possible so to specify the charge distribution ρ_i that not only are the S_j surfaces equipotential, but also the potentials are those given as boundary conditions. On the other hand, on some particular conductor surface S_k, the total charge q_k may be given instead of the potential. Suppose this surface S_k completely encloses a part V'_k of the space V' cut off from the region V under consideration by the boundaries of the system. Then, by Gauss' law, if we are to represent correctly the contribution of the charge q_k to the field of the system, we must make the total image charge within S_k equal to q_k, that is,

$$q_k = \int_{V_k} \rho_i \, dV \tag{2.37}$$

Finally, if we have in this way determined an image distribution of charge, ρ_i, such that the surfaces coinciding with conducting boundaries

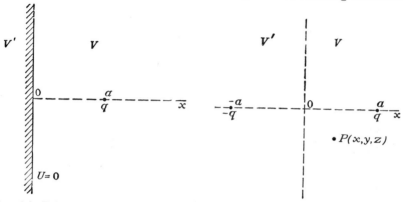

FIG. 2.3. Point charge and infinite conducting plane.

FIG. 2.4. Substitution of an image charge for the infinite conducting plane.

are equipotential, and such that specified boundary conditions of potential or of total charge are likewise fulfilled, then we know from the uniqueness theorems that the resulting potential

$$U_1 + U_i = U \tag{2.38}$$

is the solution of the problem not only on the boundaries, but throughout the region V. The potential U_i due to the image charges is then identical with the unknown potential U_2 due to the unknown distribution σ on the conductors. The analytical form of U_i is given by the integral

$$U_i = \int_{V'} \frac{\rho_i}{r} \, dV \tag{2.39}$$

A simple example will help to illustrate this theory of images. Consider the system shown in Fig. 2.3, consisting of a fixed point charge q at distance a from an infinite, plane, conducting surface which is maintained at ground potential. It is required to find the potential U in the region V on the side of q. For analysis, let the conducting surface be the plane $x = 0$, and let q be located at $x = a$. Now it takes only a little experience with electrostatics to know that an infinite, plane, zero-potential surface results from a pair of equal and opposite point charges

$+q$ and $-q$, and that it is the surface perpendicular to the line joining the charges at the point midway between them.   Therefore, the appropriate image charge for this problem is a point charge $-q$ located at $x = -a$. The conclusion reached by image theory is now that at all points of the region V of the system of Fig. 2.3, the potential is identical with that in the same region of the system shown in Fig. 2.4, in which the conductor has been substituted by the image charge $-q$.   In particular, at the point $P(x,y,z)$, the potential directly due to the original fixed charge is

$$U_1 = \frac{1}{4\pi\epsilon_0} \frac{q}{\sqrt{(x-a)^2 + y^2 + z^2}} \tag{2.40}$$

while the potential due to the image charge, and hence also that due to the induced surface density on the conducting plane, is

$$U_i = U_2 = \frac{1}{4\pi\epsilon_0} \frac{-q}{\sqrt{(x+a)^2 + y^2 + z^2}} \tag{2.41}$$

The solution for the actual potential everywhere in the region $x > 0$ is therefore

$$U = \frac{q}{4\pi\epsilon_0} \left(\frac{1}{\sqrt{(x-a)^2 + y^2 + z^2}} - \frac{1}{\sqrt{(x+a)^2 + y^2 + z^2}} \right) \tag{2.42}$$

We may solve for the unknown surface density of charge induced on the conductor by using (2.25).   Here the outward coordinate normal to the conductor surface is $+x$; thus

$$\sigma = -\epsilon_0 \left(\frac{\partial U}{\partial x} \right)_{x=0} \tag{2.43}$$

If we substitute Eq. (2.42) into (2.43), we have for the induced surface density the explicit formula

$$\sigma = - \frac{qa}{2\pi(a^2 + y^2 + z^2)^{3/2}} \tag{2.44}$$

Thus the given problem has been completely solved by electrostatic image theory.

2.6. Image Problems Involving a Spherical Conductor.   To solve problems involving a spherical conductor by image theory, we must know how to produce a spherical equipotential surface by simple charge distributions.   Such distributions are easily found.   First, a spherically symmetrical distribution of charge will produce spherical equipotentials concentric with the distribution.   In particular, this is true also of any charge so concentrated as to be called a point charge.   A more complex charge distribution consisting of a pair of point charges of opposite signs has a single spherical equipotential surface, the zero-potential surface. An elementary computation, starting from the potential function for the pair of point charges, shows that this zero-potential sphere may be described as follows in terms of the two charges q_1 and q_2 and their separation a. Its radius is

$$R = \left| \frac{q_1 q_2}{q_1{}^2 - q_2{}^2} \right| a \qquad (2.45)$$

Its center is located on the straight line containing the pair of charges, at a distance x_0 from charge q_1:

$$x_0 = \frac{q_1{}^2}{q_1{}^2 - q_2{}^2} a \qquad (2.46)$$

in which expression a positive result for x_0 means that the center is located on the side of q_1 on which q_2 lies, while a negative result means that the center lies on the opposite side of q_1. Notice that if $x_0 > 0$, then $x_0 \geqq a$, so that the center of the sphere cannot lie between the two charges. Furthermore, just one of the two intersections of the sphere with the line of the charges always falls between the charges: for a moment's consideration of the potential function shows that it changes monotonically from $-\infty$ to $+\infty$ in the segment of the line between the two charges.

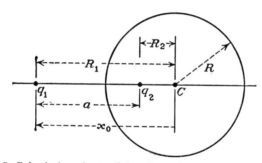

FIG. 2.5. Spherical equipotential surface of a pair of point charges.

For application of this spherical equipotential to image problems, it is convenient to have expressions in which the radius R of the sphere is a given datum, together with the specification of one of the charges, say q_1, at a distance $R_1 = |x_0|$ from the center of the sphere. The second charge q_2 is then located on the same radius line as q_1 at a position

$$R_2 = \frac{R^2}{R_1} \qquad (2.47)$$

The value of q_2 is

$$q_2 = -\frac{R}{R_1} q_1 \qquad (2.48)$$

These relations follow from (2.45) and (2.46), and should be checked by the reader.

The various quantities in the above equations are shown in Fig. 2.5, which is drawn to represent the case $q_2 = -\frac{1}{2}q_1$.

Now suppose we have to solve an electrostatic system such as shown in Fig. 2.6, in which a point charge q_1 is located at a distance R_1 from a conducting sphere of radius R and center C. The given data must also include, in order to specify the problem, either the potential or the total charge of the sphere. Suppose $R_1 > R$. It is required to find the potential function at all points of the region V outside of the sphere. Now, from the foregoing discussion, we know that to cause the spherical surface of radius R about C to be equipotential in the presence of the point charge q_1, we may suppose the conductor to be replaced by an image charge q_2 in space at the position R_2 (see Fig. 2.7). R_2 and q_2 are determined by Eqs. (2.47) and (2.48). Furthermore, we know that the

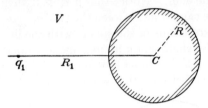
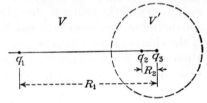

FIG. 2.6. Point charge and conducting sphere.

FIG. 2.7. Conducting sphere replaced by image charges.

addition of another point charge q_3 at C will still leave the spherical surface equipotential. This follows from the scalar nature of the potential functions, according to which the total potential at a point is the sum of the separate potentials due to all charges (cf. Sec. 1.7). For, since the part of the potential due to q_1 and q_2 together is constant over the spherical surface, and also the part due to q_3 is constant over the surface, the total potential must be constant over the surface. In particular, the potential of the surface is now

$$U_s = \frac{q_3}{4\pi\epsilon_0 R} \qquad (2.49)$$

since that part of the potential due to q_1 and q_2 is zero on the surface; and the total charge enclosed by the surface is

$$q = q_2 + q_3 \qquad (2.50)$$

The given problem is now essentially solved. By image theory, the quantities U_s and q of Eqs. (2.49) and (2.50) are to be the potential and charge of the conducting sphere which charges q_2 and q_3 are to replace. Now since either U_s or q is given, and since q_2 and R_2 are already determined by Eqs. (2.47) and (2.48), it is possible to find q_3 by use of either (2.49) or (2.50); and the other equation of the pair (2.49) and (2.50) then gives the unknown quantity of the pair U_s and q. Finally, with q_2, R_2, and q_3 all determined, we may now say that the potential in the region V

outside the sphere is that due to the set of charges q_1, q_2, and q_3 in empty space. If the distances from these charges to an observation point P in V are, respectively, r_1, r_2, and r_3, then our solution may be written in abbreviated form:

$$U = \frac{1}{4\pi\epsilon_0}\left(\frac{q_1}{r_1} + \frac{q_2}{r_2} + \frac{q_3}{r_3}\right) \tag{2.51}$$

which may easily be expressed in terms of the coordinates of P by writing out the distances r_1, r_2, r_3.

We shall sketch rapidly the problem in which the system to be solved is a spherical cavity within a conductor containing the inducing charge q_1, which is located at $R_1 < R$ (see Fig. 2.8). In this problem the total charge on the conductor is on an outer surface which does not bound our region V at all, and whose shape is not given in the problem. Hence neither this total charge nor the absolute potential of the

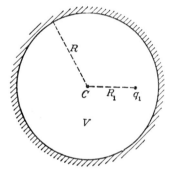

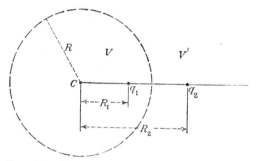

FIG. 2.8. Point charge within a spherical cavity of a conductor.

FIG. 2.9. Conducting walls of spherical cavity replaced by an image charge.

conductor can be of importance to the problem; yet for completeness we shall call the potential of the conductor U_c and consider it to be known.

To make the surface equipotential in the presence of q_1, with the conductor removed, we must introduce an image charge q_2 at position R_2, as specified in Eqs. (2.47) and (2.48). This time $R_2 > R$, as shown in Fig. 2.9. Now q_1 and q_2 alone would give the spherical surface a zero potential. To obtain the potential U_c by charges placed outside the region V where the solution is required, we could introduce a thin layer of uniform surface charge density σ_0 just around the spherical surface. This still leaves the surface equipotential, and raises its potential to

$$U_c = \frac{1}{4\pi\epsilon_0 R} 4\pi R^2 \sigma_0 = \frac{R\sigma_0}{\epsilon_0} \tag{2.52}$$

which determines σ_0, since U_c is given. This equation follows from Eq. (1.68). It should be noted that σ_0 has nothing to do with the surface charge density σ actually induced on the walls of the cavity. This charge is, by Eq. (2.25), $\sigma = -\epsilon_0(\partial U/\partial n)$, where n is a coordinate normal to the surface of the cavity, directed inward.

Our solution is now complete. We may state that the potential in the region V of the given system is identical with that which would be produced in that same region by the system of charges q_1, q_2, and σ_0 all located in empty space. Therefore, if

r_1 and r_2 are the distances from an observation point P to the charges q_1 and q_2, the potential at P is

$$U = \frac{1}{4\pi\epsilon_0}\left(\frac{q_1}{r_1} + \frac{q_2}{r_2}\right) + U_c \tag{2.53}$$

The last part of the potential is that due to σ_0. The charge σ_0 alone, in empty space, would produce a constant potential U_c at all points inside it, since we saw in Sec. 1.10 that the region wholly inside a spherically symmetrical isolated charge distribution is field-free.

2.7. Equipotential Surfaces in the Form of Circular Cylinders.

A cylindrical surface is defined in analytic geometry as one whose equation can be written in terms of only two cartesian coordinates. Thus an electrostatic problem involving cylindrical equipotentials is a problem in two cartesian coordinates, as discussed in Sec. 2.4. All charge distributions are independent of the third cartesian coordinate, and hence are infinitely long. We shall here apply image theory to cylindrical problems in which the cross sections of the conductor surfaces are circular.

The simplest charge configuration producing equipotentials which are circular cylinders is one in which the charge density function has rotational symmetry about an axis. In particular, this is true of a line charge. We found in Sec. 1.10, that a line charge has a potential function

$$U = -\frac{\lambda}{2\pi\epsilon_0}\ln\frac{r}{b} \tag{2.54}$$

where r is the cylindrical radius or distance from the line charge to the observer, λ is the charge per unit length, or strength, of the line charge, and b is an arbitrary constant. We also obtain circular cylinders for all the equipotential surfaces due to a pair of parallel line charges of equal strength but opposite sign. If r_+ and r_- are the distances from a point of observation to the two line charges of strengths $+\lambda$ and $-\lambda$, as in Fig. 2.10, then by addition the potential at the point of observation is

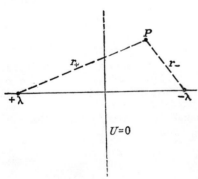

FIG. 2.10. Parallel line charges and zero-potential plane.

$$U = \frac{-\lambda}{2\pi\epsilon_0}\ln\frac{r_+}{b_+} + \frac{\lambda}{2\pi\epsilon_0}\ln\frac{r_-}{b_-}$$

Combining the two logarithms, and choosing the arbitrary constants as equal, we obtain

$$U = \frac{\lambda}{2\pi\epsilon_0}\ln\frac{r_-}{r_+} \tag{2.55}$$

The choice of constants has amounted to letting the potential at a point infinitely distant from the pair of charges be zero. It implies also that the plane which perpendicularly bisects the strip of plane surface between the two line charges is a zero-potential plane. To derive the equations of the equipotential surfaces, consider their traces in the plane perpendicular to the line charges. Locate the charges at $x = -a/2$, and $x = +a/2$, as in Fig. 2.11. Then

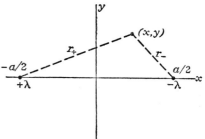

$$r_+ = \sqrt{\left(x + \frac{a}{2}\right)^2 + y^2}$$

$$r_- = \sqrt{\left(x - \frac{a}{2}\right)^2 + y^2}$$

(25.6)

FIG. 2.11. Coordinates in which equipotential surfaces are derived for parallel line charges.

The curve whose potential is a constant U_1 is given from Eq. (2.55) as

$$U_1 = \frac{\lambda}{2\pi\epsilon_0} \ln \frac{r_-}{r_+} \tag{2.57}$$

whence

$$\frac{r_+}{r_-} = K_1 \tag{2.58}$$

a constant which is related to U_1 by

$$U_1 = \frac{-\lambda}{2\pi\epsilon_0} \ln K_1 \tag{2.59}$$

Now the equipotential curve U_1 has the equation

$$\frac{\sqrt{\left(x + \frac{a}{2}\right)^2 + y^2}}{\sqrt{\left(x - \frac{a}{2}\right)^2 + y^2}} = K_1 \tag{2.60}$$

This equation, as a little algebra shows, represents a circle whose center is located at

$$x_1 = \left(\frac{K_1^2 + 1}{K_1^2 - 1}\right)\frac{a}{2} \tag{2.61}$$

and whose radius R is given by

$$R = \left|\frac{K_1}{K_1^2 - 1}\right| a \tag{2.62}$$

We have now shown that every equipotential curve is a circle, so that the equipotential surfaces of our system form a family of circular cylinders whose positions and radii are given by Eqs. (2.61) and (2.62) in terms of the parameter K_1, which is in turn related by (2.59) to the value of the potential. If desired, we may substitute (2.59) into (2.61) and (2.62) and thus obtain the elegant forms

$$x_1 = \frac{a}{2} \coth \left(\frac{2\pi\epsilon_0}{-\lambda} U_1 \right) \tag{2.63}$$

$$R = \frac{a}{2} \left| \operatorname{cosech} \left(\frac{2\pi\epsilon_0}{-\lambda} U_1 \right) \right| \tag{2.64}$$

in terms of hyperbolic functions. Figure 2.12 shows a few of the equipotential curves, together with corresponding values of the parameter K_1.

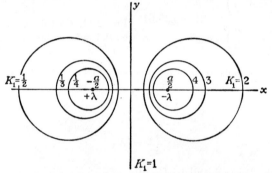

Fig. 2.12. Equipotential surfaces of parallel line charges.

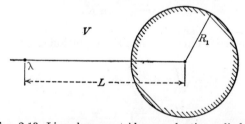

Fig. 2.13. Line charge outside a conducting cylinder.

2.8. Line Charge and Conducting Circular Cylinder. The results of the preceding section may be used to solve the problem of Fig. 2.13 by image theory. Given a line charge of strength λ at distance L from the center of a circular conducting cylinder of radius R_1 bearing a charge λ_1 per unit length: to find the potential, within an arbitrary constant, everywhere outside the cylinder. It will be possible to make the cylindrical surface equipotential in the presence of the given line charge by introducing an image charge $-\lambda$ at the appropriate distance a from the given charge; and further it will be possible to make the charge per unit length enclosed by the cylinder agree with the given quantity λ_1 by an additional image charge λ' located on the axis of the cylinder, and such that

$$\lambda' = \lambda + \lambda_1 \qquad (2.65)$$

The additional line charge, λ', will still leave the cylinder equipotential, as required. Thus, if we can locate the position of the required charge $-\lambda$, the problem is essentially solved. Let the distance of this line charge from the axis of the cylinder be called b (see Fig. 2.14). Then, in

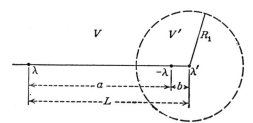

FIG. 2.14. Conducting cylinder replaced by image charges.

terms of the quantities used in the last section,

$$b = \left| x_1 - \frac{a}{2} \right| = \left| \frac{a}{K_1{}^2 - 1} \right| \qquad (2.66)$$

by Eq. (2.61). But

$$a = \frac{R_1 |K_1{}^2 - 1|}{K_1} \qquad (2.67)$$

by Eq. (2.62). Therefore

$$b = \frac{R_1}{K_1} \qquad (2.68)$$

This still does not determine b, since the parameter K_1 is not known. To complete our analysis, we may express the given distance L in terms of the quantities of the preceding section:

$$L = \left| x_1 + \frac{a}{2} \right| = \left| \frac{aK_1{}^2}{K_1{}^2 - 1} \right| \qquad (2.69)$$

Again introducing the value of a, we obtain

$$L = R_1 K_1 \qquad (2.70)$$

Equation (2.70) gives us the parameter K_1, in terms of given quantities; therefore we may substitute from it into (2.68) to find the required distance b:

$$b = \frac{R_1{}^2}{L} \qquad (2.71)$$

Our problem is now completed, in principle. The potential at any point outside the cylinder of Fig. 2.13 is the sum of the potentials due to the pair of line charges $+\lambda$ and $-\lambda$, and the line charge λ', all in empty space at known positions relative to the axis of the cylinder. If the distances from the observer to these charges are, respectively, r_+, r_-, and r', then the potential at the observer is

$$U = \frac{\lambda}{2\pi\epsilon_0} \ln \frac{r_-}{r_+} - \frac{\lambda'}{2\pi\epsilon_0} \ln \frac{r'}{b'} \qquad (2.72)$$

Here the arbitrary constant of the potential function is b'.

The corresponding problem is that of the field inside a cylindrical cavity in a conductor when a line charge of strength λ is placed in the cavity, parallel to the axis of the cavity and at distance L from it. In this problem, the potential of the conductor will be assumed to be known, and its total charge is irrelevant. Details of the solution will be left as an exercise for the reader.

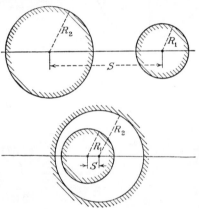

2.9. Two Conducting Circular Cylinders. Another problem which we are now in position to solve, and one of some practical interest, is that of the determination of the potential at every point in the region between two conducting surfaces in the form of circular cylinders of radii R_1 and R_2, with their axes parallel and separated by a distance S. There are two cases to be considered: the case in which one surface is enclosed by the other, and the case in which the two surfaces are external to one another. These two cases are sketched in Fig. 2.15.

FIG. 2.15. External and internal cases of parallel, conducting cylinders.

In the external case, we wish to determine the field in the region bounded by the two cylinders and an infinite cylindrical surface. Our work on the field of a pair of parallel, equal, and opposite line charges will be applicable here if the two cylinders have equal and opposite charges $\pm\lambda$ per unit length, which means that the potential at infinite distance is finite relative to the cylinders. If we can find a pair of line charges, one within each cylinder and of the specified strength, so located that two of their equipotential surfaces coincide with the given cylinders, then the field of the line charges is identical with that of the cylinders in the region in question. The potential difference between the cylinders may be given in the problem instead of the charge per unit length; and in the solution these quantities will appear as proportional to each other.

For the internal case, the total charge on the outer conductor is irrelevant to the determination of the field within it, and thus its potential will be taken as a known but arbitrary constant of the problem. Then either the potential or the charge per unit length of the inner cylinder, together with the geometry of the problem, will determine the field in the region between conductors. The problem is solved by finding a pair of equal line charges of opposite sign, one properly located within the inner cylinder and the other properly located outside the outer cylindrical surface. These line charges are given a strength numerically equal to the charge per unit length of the inner cylinder, or such as will give a specified potential difference between cylinders. The potential of the outer cylinder is made to fit the arbitrary given value simply by adding the proper constant to the potential due to the pair of line charges.

Let us refer to the results of Sec. 2.7 to complete the details of the problem. Let the potential of the two cylinders be, respectively, U_1 and U_2. Suppose we replace the two cylinders by a pair of line charges of strength $+\lambda$ and $-\lambda$ located at positions $-a/2$ and $+a/2$, as in Sec. 2.7. We shall also use the constants K_1 and K_2 which specify the two cylinders, and which are related to the potentials as before:

$$U_1 = \frac{-\lambda}{2\pi\epsilon_0} \ln K_1 \tag{2.73}$$

$$U_2 = \frac{-\lambda}{2\pi\epsilon_0} \ln K_2 \tag{2.74}$$

We shall adopt sign conventions in which R_1, R_2, S, and a are all positive; and K_1 and K_2 are positive by their definition. The linear charge density λ may be allowed to represent either a positive or a negative quantity. Let us also adopt the convention that in the internal case the radius R_2 is the larger: $R_2 > R_1$.

Now the radii of the two cylinders are related to the quantities K_1, K_2, and a by Eq. (2.62):

$$R_1 = \pm \left(\frac{K_1}{K_1{}^2 - 1}\right) a \tag{2.75}$$

$$R_2 = \pm \left(\frac{K_2}{K_2{}^2 - 1}\right) a \tag{2.76}$$

The distance S between axes of the cylinders is written in terms of the same quantities by use of Eq. (2.61):

$$S = |x_2 - x_1| = \pm \left(\frac{K_2{}^2 + 1}{K_2{}^2 - 1} - \frac{K_1{}^2 + 1}{K_1{}^2 - 1}\right) \frac{a}{2} \tag{2.77}$$

In our present problem, the quantities R_1, R_2, and S are known; they determine the quantities K_1, K_2, and a through Eqs. (2.75) to (2.77), when due regard is paid to signs. The solutions for K_1 and K_2 are

$$K_2 = g_2 \pm \sqrt{g_2{}^2 - 1} \tag{2.78}$$

$$K_1 = g_1 \pm \sqrt{g_1{}^2 - 1} \tag{2.79}$$

Here the symbols g_2 and g_1 stand for the following quantities:

$$g_2 \equiv \frac{S^2 + R_2{}^2 - R_1{}^2}{2SR_2} \tag{2.80}$$

which is good for both the external and internal cases; and

$$g_1 \equiv \pm \frac{S^2 + R_1{}^2 - R_2{}^2}{2SR_1} \tag{2.81}$$

where the positive sign is for the external case, the negative sign for the internal case. Equations (2.80) and (2.81) will be seen to give values for g_1 and g_2 which are always positive. This must be so since the signs of K_1 and K_2 are the same as those of g_1 and g_2 in Eqs. (2.78) and (2.79), and the K_1 and K_2 are intrinsically positive.

The ambiguities of sign in Eqs. (2.78) and (2.79) have a simple interpretation which is made clear by reference to Fig. 2.12. Notice first that $g_1 > 1$ and $g_2 > 1$ to yield real solutions. The positive signs on the radicals then give $K_1 > 1$ and $K_2 > 1$, while the negative signs give $K_1 < 1$ and $K_2 < 1$. Thus the positive signs refer to cylinders on the right in that figure, while the negative signs refer to cylinders on the left. Also, the two solutions for the K_1 are reciprocals of each other, and similarly for the K_2; and this means that the two solutions yield cylinders of the same size. It is clear now that for the external case we must take opposite signs in the two equations (2.78) and (2.79), while for the internal case we must take similar signs. The remaining choice is concerned with whether the axis of cylinder 2 lies to the right or the left of the axis of cylinder 1. For the external case, this means choosing $K > 1$ for the cylinder on the right. For the internal case, the axis of the cylinder with the smaller value of K lies to the right.

It is now easy to locate the two image line charges required to duplicate the field of the conducting cylinders. The distance a between the line charges is derived immediately from Eq. (2.75) or Eq. (2.76) by using the value of either K_1 or K_2. The origin of coordinates of Sec. 2.7, which is located midway between the line charges, is determined by using Eq. (2.61), which gives the algebraic position of the axis of either cylinder relative to this origin as

$$x_i = \left(\frac{K_i^2 + 1}{K_i^2 - 1}\right) \frac{a}{2}$$
$$i = 1 \text{ or } 2 \tag{2.82}$$

The strength $\pm\lambda$ of the image line charges which is the same as the charge per unit length of the cylinders may be given in the problem, as discussed earlier in this section; and if so, the image charges are now completely specified. The potential in the region of interest is given then by Eq. (2.55):

$$U = \frac{\lambda}{2\pi\epsilon_0} \ln \frac{r_-}{r_+} \tag{2.83}$$

where r_- and r_+ are the distances from the observer to the image line charges at $+a/2$ and at $-a/2$, respectively. An arbitrary constant may be added, of course, if desired.

It frequently happens that λ is not given, but instead the difference of potential, $(U_2 - U_1)$, between the cylinders is specified; or if λ is given, $(U_2 - U_1)$ may be required. We shall conclude our study of the problem by showing how λ and $(U_2 - U_1)$ are related to one another. From Eqs. (2.73) and (2.74),

$$U_2 - U_1 = \frac{-\lambda}{2\pi\epsilon_0} \ln \frac{K_2}{K_1} \tag{2.84}$$

Since K_2 and K_1 are now known, this equation suffices in principle to relate λ and $(U_2 - U_1)$. For practical use it is well to rewrite Eq. (2.84) in terms of the geometry of the problem. We start by substituting Eqs. (2.78) and (2.79) into (2.73) and (2.74), and using the relation

$$\pm \cosh^{-1} u = \ln (u \pm \sqrt{u^2 - 1}) \tag{2.85}$$

Therefore

$$U_1 = \pm \frac{\lambda}{2\pi\epsilon_0} \cosh^{-1} g_1 \tag{2.86}$$

$$U_2 = \pm \frac{\lambda}{2\pi\epsilon_0} \cosh^{-1} g_2 \tag{2.87}$$

The negative signs in Eqs. (2.78) and (2.79) correspond to the positive value of the double-valued function $\cosh^{-1} u$ here, and the positive signs correspond to the negative value. For clarity we have written the signs explicitly, and chosen the positive value for the symbol $\cosh^{-1} u$. If the cylinders are external, one potential is positive and the other is negative so that

$$U_2 - U_1 = \pm \frac{\lambda}{2\pi\epsilon_0} (\cosh^{-1} g_2 + \cosh^{-1} g_1) \tag{2.88}$$

which by an identity for inverse hyperbolic functions is

$$U_2 - U_1 = \pm \frac{\lambda}{2\pi\epsilon_0} \cosh^{-1}[g_1 g_2 + \sqrt{(g_1^2 - 1)(g_2^2 - 1)}] \qquad (2.89)$$

Putting in the expressions (2.80) and (2.81) appropriate to the external case gives, finally,

$$U_2 - U_1 = \pm \frac{\lambda}{2\pi\epsilon_0} \cosh^{-1} \frac{S^2 - R_2^2 - R_1^2}{2R_1 R_2} \qquad (2.90)$$

A similar process yields for the internal case

$$U_2 - U_1 = \pm \frac{\lambda}{2\pi\epsilon_0} (\cosh^{-1} g_2 - \cosh^{-1} g_1)$$

$$= \pm \frac{\lambda}{2\pi\epsilon_0} \cosh^{-1}[g_1 g_2 - \sqrt{(g_1^2 - 1)(g_2^2 - 1)}] \qquad (2.91)$$

Therefore

$$U_2 - U_1 = \pm \frac{\lambda}{2\pi\epsilon_0} \cosh^{-1} \frac{R_2^2 + R_1^2 - S^2}{2R_1 R_2} \qquad (2.92)$$

PROBLEMS

2.1. Show directly by differentiation in cartesian coordinates that the electrostatic potential of a point charge in space satisfies Laplace's equation everywhere except at the location of the charge.

2.2. Use the integral form of Gauss' law to find the electric field within a spherical ball of uniform charge density ρ. Express this field in cartesian coordinates and components. Now check the differential form of Gauss' law by substituting this field to find the charge density function again.

2.3. Show that for a spherically symmetrical charge density distribution $\rho(r)$, for which the electrostatic potential function also has the spherically symmetrical form $U(r)$, Poisson's equation takes the form

$$\frac{1}{r^2} \frac{d}{dr} \left(r^2 \frac{dU(r)}{dr} \right) = -\frac{1}{\epsilon_0} \rho(r)$$

Use $r = \sqrt{x^2 + y^2 + z^2}$.

2.4. By the result of Prob. 2.3, derive the most general spherically symmetrical potential function which can exist within the spherically symmetrical charge distribution

$$\rho = kr$$

where k is a constant. Interpret any constants of integration in the answer.

2.5. An arbitrary system of electric charge in space has rotational symmetry around the x axis. Let x_0 be a point on the x axis where the electric field vanishes and in the neighborhood of which no charge density exists. Show by Laplace's equation that if the potential is expanded in a three-dimensional Taylor's series about the point x_0, the result to the second-degree terms is

$$U = a(2x^2 - y^2 - z^2) + b$$

where a and b are constants.

2.6. Substitute into Laplace's equation a general function $U(r)$ of only

$$r = \sqrt{x^2 + y^2 + z^2}$$

Show then by integration that the most general potential which is a function of r only and which satisfies Laplace's equation is

$$U(r) = \frac{A}{r} + B$$

where A and B are constants.

2.7. Use the results of Prob. 2.6 together with the material of Sec. 2.3 on boundary conditions to solve the problem of the potential between concentric, conducting, spherical surfaces *in vacuo*. The inner surface of radius a bears a total charge q, while the outer is grounded *i.e.*, at zero potential, and has radius b.

2.8. Solve the problem of an ideal parallel-plate condenser by use of Laplace's equation and boundary conditions. Let the potential be a function of x only, the coordinate normal to the plates. Let the two plates have area 100 cm² each, separation 0.1 cm, and potentials, respectively, zero and 1,000 volts. Find the potential function and electric field in the empty space between plates, and find the surface charge densities and the total charges on the inner surfaces of the plates.

2.9. In an electron tube in which electrons are emitted from a heated, plane, metal surface and collected by a parallel metal plate, the potential function may have the form $U = Kx^{4/3}$, where x is the coordinate normal to the electrode surfaces and K is constant under given operating conditions.

a. Find the charge density function in the space between electrodes.

b. Assuming the electrode separation to be L, find the total space charge between electrodes for a plate area A.

c. Find the surface charge density on the emitter at $x = 0$ and on the plate at $x = L$.

d. Why must the total charge for area A of the tube vanish?

2.10. For the image problem of the point charge and conducting plane, check Eq. (2.37) by integrating Eq. (2.44) to find the total charge induced on the plane.

2.11. Use the example of the point charge and infinite conducting plane to set up a theorem for the field of a general distribution of fixed charge in the vicinity of an infinite conducting plane.

2.12. Two semi-infinite conducting planes meet in a right dihedral angle; and inside the corner which they form is a point charge q at distances a and b, respectively, from the two planes. Show how the field in the region containing the point charge can be specified in terms of image charges if the conducting planes are at zero potential. Write the resulting potential function in a cartesian coordinate system.

2.13. Using the answer of the preceding problem, find the surface charge density induced on perpendicular, semi-infinite, grounded conducting planes by a point charge q inside the corner. In particular, what must the total induced charge be? What is the value of the charge density right at the corner?

2.14. Given two semi-infinite, zero-potential, conducting planes meeting in a right dihedral angle, the region V outside the corner being empty except for a set of real point charges. What must this set of charges be in order that the charge induced on the conducting planes should be represented by a single point-image charge q located inside the corner at distances, respectively, a and b from the planes?

2.15. Prove Eqs. (2.45) and (2.46), for the radius and center location of the spherical equipotential surface of a pair of point charges of opposite sign.

2.16. Assuming the truth of Eqs. (2.45) and (2.46), deduce Eqs. (2.47) and (2.48) for the location and magnitude of the image of a point charge in a spherical conductor.

2.17. A point charge q_1 in space is at a distance R_1 from the center of a conducting sphere of outer radius $R < R_1$. The sphere is insulated and has no net charge.

a. Letting q_1 be on the polar axis of a spherical coordinate system with origin at the center of the sphere, express the potential at an arbitrary point outside the sphere in terms of spherical coordinates.

b. Use this potential function to derive an explicit expression for the induced charge density on the spherical surface.

2.18. A point charge of 2×10^{-10} coulomb is located in space at a distance of 4 cm from the center of a conducting sphere whose radius is 3 cm. Find the resulting electrostatic force on the point charge (*a*) if the sphere is insulated and has no net charge; (*b*) if the sphere is grounded, so as to be at zero potential.

2.19. A point charge q is located within an otherwise empty spherical cavity of radius R in a conductor. Find the electrostatic force on q when it is displaced a distance r from the center of the cavity. Show that for $r \ll R$, this force is proportional to r. Is the equilibrium at the center stable or unstable?

2.20. Justify the natural assumption that the electric dipole moment of a charge distribution induced in a spherical conductor by an external point charge is equal to that of the image charges.

2.21. Find the electric dipole moment of the charges induced in a conducting sphere by an external point charge q_1 at distance R_1 from the center of the sphere. Express the result in terms of the electric field which q_1 would produce at the distance R_1 *in vacuo.* As a special case of this result, find the dipole moment induced in a conducting sphere when it is placed in an originally uniform electric field due to fixed charges.

2.22. For Sec. 2.7, prove (*a*) Eqs. (2.61) and (2.62), starting with (2.60); (*b*) Eqs. (2.63) and (2.64), starting with (2.59), (2.61), and (2.62).

2.23. An infinite, straight line charge of uniform strength 10^{-9} coulomb/m is located in empty space parallel to an infinite plane conducting boundary which is grounded.

a. Find the potential function in the space containing the line charge.

b. Find the charge density at a general point on the conductor surface.

2.24. An infinite line charge whose strength is 10^{-8} coulomb/m is located in space parallel to the axis of a conducting circular cylinder of outside radius 2 cm, at a distance of 3 cm from the axis. The cylinder is held at ground potential.

a. Find the potential function in the space exterior to the cylinder, and express it in polar coordinates with origin at the axis.

b. Find the surface density of charge at a general point on the cylinder.

c. Find the induced charge per unit length on the cylinder.

2.25. An infinite, straight line charge of uniform linear density λ is located in an otherwise empty cavity of a conductor. The walls of the cavity form a circular cylinder of radius R, parallel to whose axis and at distance r is the line charge. Find the electrostatic potential function at a general point within the cavity.

2.26. Suppose an isolated, bare d-c power line has a radius R of $\frac{1}{4}$ cm and is stretched at a constant height $h = 10$ m above conducting earth. The power line has a potential relative to ground of $U = -30,000$ volts. Find the charge per meter length on the power line, first in symbols and then for the given data.

2.27. Given two parallel, conducting circular cylinders whose axis separation is 10 cm and whose radii are, respectively, 2 and 3 cm. Let a potential difference of 4,000 volts be applied between the cylinders, which are at finite potential relative to an infinitely remote point.

a. Sketch the problem as you wish to arrange it.

b. For this arrangement, find the algebraic values of the constants K_1 and K_2 characterizing the two cylinders.

c. Find by use of these constants the charge per unit length on the cylinders.

d. Check the result by direct use of the appropriate final formula (2.90) or (2.92).

2.28. An infinitely long, circular, conducting cylinder of 2 cm outer radius is placed in a circularly cylindrical cavity of radius 3 cm in a grounded conductor. The axes are parallel and ½ cm apart. The inner cylinder is given a charge of 10^{-7} coulomb/m.

a. Find the location of the image line charges.

b. Find the potential at a general point in the space for which the line charges are useful.

c. Find the potential difference between the cylinders.

d. At what place is the electric field most intense? Find its maximum value.

CHAPTER 3

DIELECTRIC THEORY

3.1. Introduction. The importance of the electrical properties of uncharged, insulating material is readily shown by a simple demonstration experiment. Let an insulated metal plate be mounted parallel to a grounded plate and be connected to an electroscope for indicating its potential. Charge the insulated plate until the leaves of the electroscope show an appreciable potential, and then pass a plate of glass between the two metal plates. The electroscope leaves will fall, showing a drop in the potential of the insulated plate.

It will be our purpose in this chapter to give an account of the electrical behavior of insulating materials. These materials are called dielectrics when reference is made to their contribution to the electric field. We shall survey the subject from two points of view, the microscopic and the macroscopic. The microscopic viewpoint will give the physical picture of the mechanism by which dielectrics affect the electric field, and will consider the atomic or molecular structure of the material. The macroscopic viewpoint will describe the effect of dielectrics in experiments where the macroscopic electric field, *i.e.*, the field averaged over a space large compared with atomic dimensions, is all that can be observed.

It should be remarked that the results we obtain by consideration of ideal insulating materials will still be useful in treating actual materials, which always have some conducting ability, however small. The conductivity is simply an additional, independent property of the material which we are leaving out of consideration in this chapter. All substances possess both dielectric and conducting properties; in some the conduction is predominant, in others it is secondary.

3.2. Electric Polarization. A body of dielectric matter may contribute in either or both of two ways to the macroscopic field of an electrostatic system. It may bear free charge, that which is produced by macroscopic migration of elementary charges. More interesting is the ability of a dielectric having no free charge to produce an electric field. It may do so because the elementary systems of which it is composed, whether atoms, molecules, or units of crystal structure, consist of charged particles even though they have no net charge. The dipole moments characterizing these elementary systems entirely account for the macroscopic electric field due to neutral dielectric matter. It is not surprising

63

that this should be true for the external field of a dielectric body, for the dipole moment of a neutral, electrostatic system has been shown in Sec. 1.14 to determine its distant field, so long as this moment is non-vanishing. We shall show that the molecular dipole moments determine the macroscopic field produced by the dielectric even within its own volume.

The dipole moment of a system A of charges has been defined in Sec. 1.14 by an integral over charge elements dq:

$$\mathbf{p} = \int_A \mathbf{r} \, dq \tag{3.1}$$

where $\mathbf{r}$ is the position vector of the element dq relative to an arbitrary origin. This quantity has two properties of especial importance to our present work. The dipole moment is invariant to a shift of the origin point, so long as the total charge of the system A is zero. The reader was asked to demonstrate this invariance in Prob. 1.51. Furthermore, suppose the system A to be subdivided into n parts A_j, each having its dipole moment $\mathbf{p}_j$:

$$\mathbf{p}_j = \int_{A_j} \mathbf{r} \, dq \tag{3.2}$$

Since an integral is a sum, it is evident that (3.1) can be broken down into partial sums over the subsystems A_j:

$$\int_A \mathbf{r} \, dq = \sum_{j=1}^{n} \int_{A_j} \mathbf{r} \, dq$$

Hence the dipole moment of any system is the vector sum of the moments of its parts:

$$\mathbf{p} = \sum_{j=1}^{n} \mathbf{p}_j \tag{3.3}$$

Consider the application of these statements to a volume ΔV of neutral dielectric material, so chosen as never to cut across a molecular system of charges. If each molecular system in ΔV is electrically neutral, its dipole moment $\mathbf{p}_j$ is characteristic of that molecule and its orientation, but is independent of the location of the molecule. If there are m molecules in ΔV, the total dipole moment $\Delta \mathbf{p}$ of the dielectric matter in ΔV is thus the sum

$$\Delta \mathbf{p} = \sum_{j=1}^{m} \mathbf{p}_j \tag{3.4}$$

The quotient of $\Delta \mathbf{p}$ by ΔV is the average volume density of electric dipole moment, or the average dipole moment per unit volume, of the matter in

ΔV. This quantity may be assumed to approach a limiting value as ΔV shrinks about a point within the dielectric so as to become macroscopically infinitesimal but not zero. Because of the large numbers of molecules per unit volume in matter of ordinary density, it is possible to suppose that ΔV always contains a large number m of molecules even in the limit, so that statistical fluctuations in the macroscopic limit of $\Delta \mathbf{p}/\Delta V$ are negligible. The statement that such a limit exists and constitutes a vector point function, continuous except on boundaries, will be considered a definition of macroscopic continuity in the dielectric properties of the matter. We shall assume such continuity. The limit of $\Delta \mathbf{p}/\Delta V$ will be designated by $\mathbf{P}$, called the electric polarization of the dielectric:

$$\mathbf{P} \equiv \lim \frac{\Delta \mathbf{p}}{\Delta V} \qquad \Delta V \text{ becoming small} \qquad (3.5)$$

Having explained the nature of the limiting process in this definition, we shall feel free to denote it by the usual notation of the differential calculus even though the latter implies perfect continuity:

$$\mathbf{P} = \frac{d\mathbf{p}}{dV} \qquad (3.6)$$

The differential dipole moment associated with the differential volume element dV in a dielectric, which from the macroscopic viewpoint is now a continuous medium, is therefore

$$d\mathbf{p} = \mathbf{P} \, dV \qquad (3.7)$$

The polarization vector $\mathbf{P}$ forms the link between the microscopic and macroscopic models of neutral dielectric matter. Together with any free charge densities that may exist, the polarization completely characterizes the macroscopic state of dielectric matter in an electrostatic system.

According to the pattern of Eq. (1.102), the electrostatic potential of the neutral but polarized dielectric matter in a volume element $d\mathbf{V}$ is now

$$dU = \frac{\mathbf{P} \cdot \mathbf{r}^0 \, dV}{4\pi\epsilon_0 r^2} \qquad (3.8)$$

provided the observer is at such a distance from dV that higher-order multipole moments are to be neglected. Here r is the distance to the observer from an arbitrary origin within dV; but since dV is infinitesimal in size, we may speak of r simply as the distance from dV to the observer. As usual, $\mathbf{r}^0$ is the unit vector directed from dV toward the observer. The permittivity ϵ_0 of space is used in Eq. (3.8) since the elementary charges which compose the dielectric are situated in otherwise empty space. To put it differently, the dielectric matter is here represented by the dipole moment **P**, and must not be put in twice by using a permittivity other than ϵ_0. When Eq. (3.8) is integrated over the volume V of a dielectric body, it yields the fundamental expression

$$U = \frac{1}{4\pi\epsilon_0} \int_V \frac{\mathbf{P} \cdot \mathbf{r}^0}{r^2} \, dV \qquad (3.9)$$

This integral gives the contribution of the dielectric body, resulting from its polarization, to the potential at a point of observation external to the body. It is understood that if the dielectric is not electrically neutral, but carries a distribution of free electric charge, such free charge contributes independently to the potential. This is a consequence of the independent interaction of all electrostatic charges as stated in Sec. 1.2 and applied to the electrostatic potential in Eq. (1.44).

It is sometimes helpful to consider an oversimplified model of dielectric matter, in which the actual molecular dipoles with their statistical distribution of moments are replaced by average molecules all alike in any infinitesimal region. The average dipole moment $\bar{\mathbf{p}}$ assigned to each molecule is then prescribed so that the polarization **P** in the neighborhood has its actual value. If the local volume density of molecules is N_1, which means that there are $N_1 \, dV$ molecules in a macroscopically infinitesimal volume element dV at a certain point, the total dipole moment of the matter in dV is then

$$d\mathbf{p} = \bar{\mathbf{p}} N_1 \, dV \qquad (3.10)$$

The value of the average molecular dipole moment $\bar{\mathbf{p}}$ at this point is obtained at once by comparison with Eq. (3.7):

$$\bar{\mathbf{p}} = \frac{1}{N_1} \mathbf{P} \qquad (3.11)$$

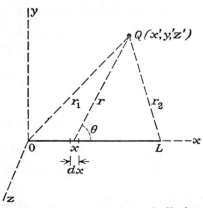

Fig. 3.1. Linear chain of electric dipoles.

3.3. A One-dimensional Model, and a Mathematical Transformation.

A simplified one-dimensional model of a dielectric may be helpful in understanding an important transformation of Eq. (3.9). Consider a chain of microscopic electric dipoles along the x axis between $x = 0$ and $x = L$, all having their dipole moments in the x-direction. Figure 3.1 represents such a chain, with an observation point Q at (x',y',z'). Suppose the algebraic sum of the dipole moments in the interval dx is dp, and that we define

$$\frac{dp}{dx} \equiv A(x) \qquad (3.12)$$

the dipole moment per unit length of the chain. We shall postulate that $A(x)$ is a continuous function of x. The dipole moment in an interval dx will be

$$dp = A(x) \, dx \tag{3.13}$$

Now the contribution to the potential at Q due to the dipoles in an element dx at a position x is

$$dU = \frac{dp \, \cos \theta}{4\pi\epsilon_0 r^2} \tag{3.14}$$

where r is the distance from dx to Q, that is,

$$r = \sqrt{(x' - x)^2 + y'^2 + z'^2}$$

and θ is the angle between r and the positive x axis. We can write

$$\cos \theta = \frac{x' - x}{r} = -\frac{dr}{dx} \tag{3.15}$$

By substitution of Eqs. (3.13) and (3.15), (3.14) becomes

$$dU = -\frac{1}{4\pi\epsilon_0} \frac{A(x)}{r^2} \frac{dr}{dx} \, dx$$

Therefore

$$dU = -\frac{1}{4\pi\epsilon_0} \frac{A(x)}{r^2} \, dr \tag{3.16}$$

If the values of r corresponding to the end points $x = 0$ and $x = L$ are r_1 and r_2, respectively, then the total potential at Q due to the chain is

$$U = -\frac{1}{4\pi\epsilon_0} \int_1^{r_2} \frac{A(x)}{r^2} \, dr \tag{3.17}$$

This integral may be transformed into an interesting form by integration by parts; for

$$-\frac{dr}{r^2} = d\left(\frac{1}{r}\right) \tag{3.18}$$

Thus

$$U = \frac{1}{4\pi\epsilon_0} \int_{r=r_1}^{r_2} A(x) \, d\left(\frac{1}{r}\right) = \frac{1}{4\pi\epsilon_0} \frac{A(x)}{r} \Big|_{r=r_1}^{r_2} - \frac{1}{4\pi\epsilon_0} \int_{r=r_1}^{r_2} \frac{dA(x)}{r} \tag{3.19}$$

Now $dA(x)$ may be written $dA(x)/dx \, dx$; thus, finally, we obtain

$$U = \frac{1}{4\pi\epsilon_0} \left[\frac{A(L)}{r_2} - \frac{A(0)}{r_1} \right] - \frac{1}{4\pi\epsilon_0} \int_{x=0}^{L} \frac{1}{r} \frac{dA(x)}{dx} \, dx \tag{3.20}$$

This form has an interesting interpretation if we compare the potential due to a point charge, $U_1 = q/4\pi\epsilon_0 r$. It will be seen that the potential of the chain may be considered due to a point charge of $+A(L)$ at the end $x = L$, a point charge of $-A(0)$ at the end $x = 0$, and a linear density of charge $-dA(x)/dx$ distributed along the chain. These charges are not readily identifiable with microscopic features of the system of charges making up the chain. They are fictitious charges which enter into a macroscopic analysis, and which may be considered to replace the dielectric chain completely so far as the potential at an outside point is concerned. When these charges are used to compute the potential, they are considered to be located in space devoid of the dielectric material they replace. Such charges are called bound, since they represent the effect of charges in the constitution of matter which are not free to migrate, but which may undergo only the microscopic displacements involved in formation or orientation of molecular dipoles.

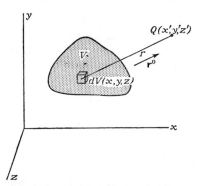

3.4. Bound Charge. From the simplified case of the preceding section, we may expect that the potential produced at an outside point by a polarized dielectric in three dimensions can be accounted for by a bound charge produced within the dielectric material and hence expressible as a volume density, together with a bound charge at the boundaries of the material which would appear as a surface density. To show that such is indeed the case, we shall perform a mathematical transformation of Eq. (3.9),

FIG. 3.2. Dielectric body with external point of observation.

which we developed in Sec. 3.2 for the potential due to a dielectric body occupying volume V as observed outside V:

$$U(x',y',z') = \frac{1}{4\pi\epsilon_0} \int_V \frac{\mathbf{P}(x,y,z) \cdot \mathbf{r}^0}{r^2} \, dV \tag{3.9}$$

Reference will be made to a body of simple shape such as shown in Fig. 3.2, although the result will be true regardless of the complexity of V. Let the volume element dV be located at (x,y,z), and the observer Q at (x',y',z'). The distance r is then

$$r = \sqrt{(x' - x)^2 + (y' - y)^2 + (z' - z)^2}$$

The unit vector $\mathbf{r}^0$ is directed from dV toward Q.

We begin the transformation by expressing in analytical form the scalar product in the numerator of the integrand. The unit vector $\mathbf{r}^0$ is expressible as $\mathbf{r}/r$, where $\mathbf{r}$ is the vector distance from dV to Q. Thus, in terms of the unit vectors $\mathbf{i}$, $\mathbf{j}$, and $\mathbf{k}$ along the coordinate axes

$$\mathbf{r}^0 = \frac{(x' - x)\mathbf{i} + (y' - y)\mathbf{j} + (z' - z)\mathbf{k}}{\sqrt{(x' - x)^2 + (y' - y)^2 + (z' - z)^2}} \tag{3.21}$$

By a trick similar to that used in Sec. 3.3 we may rewrite this as

$$\mathbf{r}^0 = -\left[\mathbf{i} \frac{\partial r}{\partial x} + \mathbf{j} \frac{\partial r}{\partial y} + \mathbf{k} \frac{\partial r}{\partial z} \right] \tag{3.22}$$

Now we separate $\mathbf{P}$ into its components:

$$\mathbf{P}(x,y,z) = \mathbf{i}P_x(x,y,z) + \mathbf{j}P_y(x,y,z) + \mathbf{k}P_z(x,y,z) \tag{3.23}$$

Substitution of Eqs. (3.22) and (3.23) into (3.9) yields

$$U = -\frac{1}{4\pi\epsilon_0} \left\{ \int_V \frac{P_x}{r^2} \frac{\partial r}{\partial x} \, dV + \int_V \frac{P_y}{r^2} \frac{\partial r}{\partial y} \, dV + \int_V \frac{P_z}{r^2} \frac{\partial r}{\partial z} \, dV \right\} \tag{3.24}$$

It will be convenient to consider these integrals separately, so let us abbreviate by writing

$$U = U_1 + U_2 + U_3 \tag{3.25}$$

Now, still following the procedure of the preceding section, consider the term U_1, and write

$$-\frac{1}{r^2} \frac{\partial r}{\partial x} = \frac{\partial}{\partial x} \left(\frac{1}{r} \right) \tag{3.26}$$

Also, let us write $dV = dx \, dy \, dz$ and use an iterated integral. Thus

$$U_1 = \frac{1}{4\pi\epsilon_0} \iiint P_x \frac{\partial}{\partial x} \left(\frac{1}{r} \right) dx \, dy \, dz \tag{3.27}$$

Imagine the x integration to be performed first, so that this x integral represents the contribution of a straight rod of material of infinitesimal cross section $dy \, dz$ (see Fig. 3.3). Suppose the body to have a shape so simple that the rod cuts its surface at only two places whose x

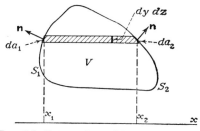

FIG. 3.3. Integration with respect to x.

coordinates are x_1 and x_2. Then the x integral of (3.27) is

$$\int_{x_1}^{x_2} P_x \frac{\partial}{\partial x} \left(\frac{1}{r} \right) dx$$

This may be integrated by parts:

$$\int_{x_1}^{x_2} P_x \frac{\partial}{\partial x} \left(\frac{1}{r} \right) dx = \left[\frac{P_x(x,y,z)}{r} \right]_{x=x_2} - \left[\frac{P_x(x,y,z)}{r} \right]_{x=x_1}$$
$$- \int_{x_1}^{x_2} \frac{1}{r} \frac{\partial P_x}{\partial x} \, dx \tag{3.28}$$

Substituting back into (3.27), we have

$$U_1 = \frac{1}{4\pi\epsilon_0} \left\{ \iint \left[\frac{P_x}{r}\right]_{x=x_2} dy\, dz - \iint \left[\frac{P_x}{r}\right]_{x=x_1} dy\, dz \right.$$
$$\left. - \iiint \frac{1}{r} \frac{\partial P_x}{\partial x} dx\, dy\, dz \right\} \quad (3.29)$$

The limits of integration of Eq. (3.29) now require discussion. In the y and z integrations, the values of x_2 vary over the part S_2 of the surface of the body whose unit outward normal $\mathbf{n}$ has a positive x component, while x_1 is on the part S_1 where $\mathbf{n}$ has a negative x component. Furthermore, the area da_2 cut out by the cross section $dy\, dz$ on S_2 has $dy\, dz$ for its projection on the yz plane, so that if $\mathbf{n}$ is the unit outward normal at da, then

$$dy\, dz = \mathbf{n} \cdot \mathbf{i}\, da_2 = n_x\, da_2$$

where we have used the symbol n_x for the x component of $\mathbf{n}$. Similarly, at the other end of the rod we may write

$$dy\, dz = -n_x\, da_1$$

The double integrals may then be written simply as surface integrals. One other change which we shall make in the form of Eq. (3.29) is to turn the last term back into the simpler form of a volume integral. With all of these substitutions, (3.29) becomes

$$U_1 = \frac{1}{4\pi\epsilon_0} \left\{ \int_{S_2} \frac{P_x n_x}{r} da_2 + \int_{S_1} \frac{P_x n_x}{r} da_1 - \int_V \frac{1}{r} \frac{\partial P_x}{\partial x} dV \right\} \quad (3.30)$$

This may be compressed, since the two surface integrals together cover the entire boundary S:

$$U_1 = \frac{1}{4\pi\epsilon_0} \int_S \frac{P_x n_x}{r} da - \frac{1}{4\pi\epsilon_0} \int_V \frac{1}{r} \frac{\partial P_x}{\partial x} dV \quad (3.31)$$

Finally, we can write similar expressions for U_2 and U_3 by symmetry, and add them to obtain the required transformation of Eq. (3.9):

$$U = \frac{1}{4\pi\epsilon_0} \left\{ \int_S \frac{P_x n_x + P_y n_y + P_z n_z}{r} da \right.$$
$$\left. - \int_V \frac{1}{r} \left(\frac{\partial P_x}{\partial x} + \frac{\partial P_y}{\partial y} + \frac{\partial P_z}{\partial z} \right) dV \right\} \quad (3.32)$$

Here the surface integral may be rewritten in terms of the scalar product of two vectors to give

$$U = \frac{1}{4\pi\epsilon_0} \int_S \frac{\mathbf{P} \cdot \mathbf{n}}{r} da - \frac{1}{4\pi\epsilon_0} \int_V \frac{1}{r} \left(\frac{\partial P_x}{\partial x} + \frac{\partial P_y}{\partial y} + \frac{\partial P_z}{\partial z} \right) dV \quad (3.33)$$

It is at once clear from this form that the potential at Q due to the entire dielectric body is the same as if it were replaced by a system of bound charges in empty space. A part of these bound charges appears on the surface of the dielectric as a surface density σ' whose value is

$$\sigma' \equiv \mathbf{P} \cdot \mathbf{n} \tag{3.34}$$

The remaining bound charge appears throughout the volume V as a volume density ρ':

$$\rho' \equiv -\left(\frac{\partial P_x}{\partial x} + \frac{\partial P_y}{\partial y} + \frac{\partial P_z}{\partial z}\right) \tag{3.35}$$

The scalar function in the brackets is called the divergence of the vector point function $\mathbf{P}$, and is sometimes written in the abbreviated form div $\mathbf{P}$. Thus

$$\rho' = -\,\text{div}\,\mathbf{P} \tag{3.36}$$

It is not difficult to show that these bound charge densities are consistent with an artificial macroscopic picture of the dielectric in which positive and negative elementary particles in the material are considered to form separate volume densities ρ_+ and ρ_- occupying the same space within the dielectric. When the dielectric is unpolarized, ρ_+ and ρ_- are everywhere equal in magnitude, and so cancel each other. Polarization involves a relative displacement of the positive and negative densities. This has the effect of producing a thin region at the boundaries of the dielectric where only one of the volume densities exists, and which is describable as a surface density. Furthermore, if the displacement of the volume densities within the material is nonuniform, the effect is to distort the charge density distributions so that the resultant volume charge density no longer vanishes. We shall not look further into this representation of the polarization process. It is simple in appearance but raises several questions when carefully examined, particularly the question of just why it gives the electric field correctly.

The bound charge in a region of a polarized dielectric will be defined naturally as a volume integral of ρ' or a surface integral of σ' or their sum, as required by the region considered. It is interesting to note that the total bound charge of a dielectric body of volume V and complete boundary surface S is zero. For, by the definition above, this total charge is

$$q_{\text{total}} = \oint_S \sigma'\,da + \int_V \rho'\,dV \tag{3.37}$$

After substitution for the bound densities, we obtain

$$q_{\text{total}} = \oint_S \mathbf{P} \cdot \mathbf{n}\,da - \int_V \text{div}\,\mathbf{P}\,dV \tag{3.38}$$

where **n** is unit normal to S outward from V. Now a fundamental theorem of vector calculus states that for any vector point function **P**, continuous with its first derivatives within a volume V bounded completely by a surface S,

$$\oint_S \mathbf{P} \cdot \mathbf{n} \, da \equiv \int_V \operatorname{div} \mathbf{P} \, dV \tag{3.39}$$

This is sometimes known as the divergence theorem. By its use in Eq. (3.38), one obtains immediately that

$$q'_{\text{total}} = 0 \qquad \text{Q.E.D.} \tag{3.40}$$

A proof of the divergence theorem was given in essence in Sec. 2.2, in terms of the electric field vector **E**. This vector obeys Gauss' law for a system of electric charges in free space, which, when the charges are described by the volume density ρ, takes the form

$$\epsilon_0 \oint_S \mathbf{E} \cdot \mathbf{n} \, da = \int_V \rho \, dV \tag{3.41}$$

where V, S, and **n** are related as above. In Sec. 2.2 it was shown that (3.41) implies that

$$\epsilon_0 \operatorname{div} \mathbf{E} = \rho \tag{3.42}$$

Substitution of (3.42) into (3.41) now yields the divergence theorem, which has the nature of a mathematical identity.

3.5. Electric Field within a Dielectric. The analysis of Sec. 3.4 is limited to points of observation far enough from the molecules of the dielectric that their electric field is of the dipole form. We shall now inquire as to the macroscopic electric field at points within the dielectric material. As a matter of definition, we mean by the macroscopic electric field the time and space average of the microscopic field, that is, force per unit test charge, over a region macroscopically infinitesimal. The time average must usually be taken because the period of electronic motions, and even of thermal motions, is very short compared to ordinary times of observation; and anyway, since we are at present discussing electrostatics, we imply the time average. Taking the time average of electronic motion, if done explicitly with reference to specific molecules, involves quantum mechanics. For our purposes, however, we shall not specialize sufficiently in this field to require more than the general picture that the time averaging smears out the point charges making up the molecule into an effective charge density distribution. For investigation of the behavior of dielectric materials under electromagnetic fields of high frequency, the time average may be discarded, at least in part; but these considerations belong to the specialized field of dispersion theory. As to the space average, we shall understand it to include space interior as well as exterior to the molecules of the dielectric.

Consider a point of observation $Q(x_0, y_0, z_0)$ in the dielectric from a microscopic viewpoint. There will be a distance b from Q at or beyond which the molecular systems in the dielectric may be considered to be electric dipoles with a local, average dipole moment $\bar{\mathbf{p}}$. Although b is many molecular diameters, it may still be treated as macroscopically infinitesimal since simple molecules have dimensions of the order of only 10^{-8} cm. Let us circumscribe Q by a spherical surface S_0 of radius b with Q at its center (see Fig. 3.4). The theory of the preceding section gives us a way of computing the field $\mathbf{E}'$ at Q due to all the dielectric external to S_0. In addition we must now find the average contribution $\mathbf{E}_0$ to the field at Q by all the molecules which are contained in the volume V_0 enclosed by S_0. This average will be computed by considering Q to move about in a random way within a macroscopically small region, carrying S_0 with it. Put in another way, the averaging will be taken to mean that Q is randomly located relative to the molecules of the dielectric. The macroscopic electric field is then the sum of $\mathbf{E}'$ and $\mathbf{E}_0$:

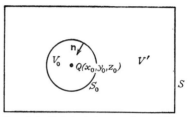

FIG. 3.4. Point of observation within dielectric material.

$$\mathbf{E} = \mathbf{E}' + \mathbf{E}_0 \tag{3.43}$$

The computation of $\mathbf{E}'$ is quite straightforward, for Q is a point outside the dielectric material so far as molecules external to S_0 are concerned. It is as though we were computing the field in a cavity of the dielectric bounded by S_0 except for the important difference that the presence of a cavity would alter the field and hence the polarization of the dielectric. Our problem involves the actual polarization $\mathbf{P}$ in the dielectric, with no cavity present; yet the separate consideration of the material outside S_0 involves treating S_0 as one of the boundary surfaces for this material. Let V' stand for the volume occupied by the dielectric outside S_0, and let S stand for all other boundaries of V' besides S_0, that is, for all the actual boundaries of the dielectric body. Now from the analysis of Sec. 3.4 we may consider that the partial electric field $\mathbf{E}'$ at Q due to dielectric material in V' is such as would be produced by a volume distribution of charge in V':

$$\rho' = -\left(\frac{\partial P_x}{\partial x} + \frac{\partial P_y}{\partial y} + \frac{\partial P_z}{\partial z} \right) \tag{3.44}$$

together with a surface distribution of charge on S and on S_0:

$$\sigma' = \mathbf{P} \cdot \mathbf{n} \tag{3.45}$$

where **n** is unit normal vector always outward to V'. These fields may be written as integrals, using the symbol r for the distance from an element of integration to the observer at point Q and $\mathbf{r}^0$ for the corresponding unit vector:

$$\mathbf{E}' = \frac{1}{4\pi\epsilon_0} \int_{V'} \frac{\mathbf{r}^0 \rho' \, dV}{r^2} + \frac{1}{4\pi\epsilon_0} \int_S \frac{\mathbf{r}^0 \sigma' \, da}{r^2} + \frac{1}{4\pi\epsilon_0} \int_{S_0} \frac{\mathbf{r}^0 \sigma' \, da}{b^2} \qquad (3.46)$$

These terms we shall abbreviate by writing

$$\mathbf{E}' = \mathbf{E}'_v + \mathbf{E}_s + \mathbf{E}_s{}^0 \qquad (3.47)$$

Consider first the value of the partial field $\mathbf{E}_s{}^0$, which results from bound charge on the artificially introduced boundary S_0. The value of σ' may be obtained from Eq. (3.45), and the unit vector $\mathbf{r}^0$ from the element of integration toward the observer may be identified with **n**. Thus

$$\mathbf{E}_s{}^0 = \frac{1}{4\pi\epsilon_0} \int_{S_0} \frac{(\mathbf{P} \cdot \mathbf{n})\mathbf{n}}{b^2} \, da \qquad (3.48)$$

This field may be evaluated readily. S_0 was assumed to be infinitesimal on a macroscopic scale, and consequently the polarization **P** may be taken as constant at all points of S_0, with the magnitude and direction which this vector function has at the point Q. The result of an elementary integration is found, after some algebraic work, to be

$$\mathbf{E}_s{}^0 = \frac{1}{3\epsilon_0} \mathbf{P} \qquad (3.49)$$

We shall not stop to prove Eq. (3.49) here, for this result will not be needed in the subsequent analysis.

The next task is to evaluate the average field $\mathbf{E}_0$ due to the dielectric material within S_0. We have said that the average here means that point Q at the center of S_0 is to occupy a random position in a macroscopically small region of dielectric, carrying the surface S_0 with it. This implies that if we divide S_0 into equal microscopic volume elements dV, each of these elements has an equal probability of containing the center of a molecule. If there are N_1 molecules per unit volume in V_0, the region enclosed by S_0, then the probability of the center of one molecule being in dV is $N_1 \, dV$. In the process of averaging, we shall treat all the molecules of the dielectric as alike, at least by classes; and to simplify the discussion we shall consider just one class. Suppose the electric field due to a single molecule is a function $\mathbf{f}(\xi,\eta,\zeta)$ of coordinates ξ, η, ζ relative to the center of the molecule and parallel respectively to x, y, z. The field at Q due to a molecule at a position x, y, z relative to Q is then $\mathbf{f}(-x,-y,-z)$: for the position of Q in the coordinate system of the molecule is $\xi = -x$, $\eta = -y$, $\zeta = -z$. The total field $\mathbf{E}_0$ at Q due to molecules in V_0 is then the sum of elements

$$dE_0 = \mathbf{f}(-x,-y,-z)N_1\,dV \qquad (3.50)$$

so that

$$\mathbf{E}_0 = N_1 \int_{V_0} \mathbf{f}(-x,-y,-z)\,dV \qquad (3.51)$$

Since V_0 is taken as spherical, there is a symmetrical element of volume at $-x$, $-y$, $-z$ to every element at x, y, z; thus this integral has the same value if we remove the negative signs and write more simply

$$\mathbf{E}_0 = N_1 \int_{V_0} \mathbf{f}(x,y,z)\,dV \qquad (3.52)$$

Now the integrand $\mathbf{f}(x,y,z)$ represents just the field of a molecule located at Q. The components of this field may be expressed in terms of a potential function U_M for one molecule:

$$f_x = -\frac{\partial U_M}{\partial x} \qquad f_y = -\frac{\partial U_M}{\partial y} \qquad f_z = -\frac{\partial U_M}{\partial z} \qquad (3.53)$$

In these terms the x-component of the field $\mathbf{E}_0$ is

$$E_{0x} = -N_1 \int_{V_0} \frac{\partial U_M}{\partial x}\,dV$$

which we can write out in cartesian coordinates as

$$E_{0x} = -N_1 \iiint_{V_0} \frac{\partial U_M}{\partial x}\,dx\,dy\,dz \qquad (3.54)$$

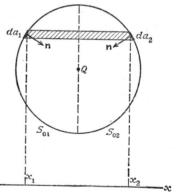

FIG. 3.5. Integration with respect to x within the sphere S_0.

For given values of y and z, let the limits of integration of x be x_1 and x_2, as in Fig. 3.5. Then the x integral becomes

$$\int_{x_1}^{x_2} \frac{\partial U_M}{\partial x}\,dx = U_M(x_2,y,z) - U_M(x_1,y,z) \qquad (3.55)$$

Now divide the surface S_0 into two parts as shown, so that the column-shaped volume element produced by the x integration cuts the part S_{01} of the surface in da_1, while it cuts the other part S_{02} in da_2. The two parts of S_0 are then the hemispheres separated by the plane $x = 0$. We may now write

$$dy\,dz = -n_x\,da_2 = +n_x\,da_1 \qquad (3.56)$$

where n_x is here the x component of the inward unit normal vector to S_0 at the positions of the da elements. Now putting Eq. (3.55) into (3.54) and using (3.56), we have

$$E_{0x} = +N_1 \int_{S_{02}} U_M n_x \, da_2 + N_1 \int_{S_{01}} U_M n_x \, da_1 \qquad (3.57)$$

These integrals may be combined into a single surface integral covering the whole of S_0:

$$E_{0x} = N_1 \int_{S_0} U_M n_x \, da \qquad (3.58a)$$

The same sort of process may be gone through to obtain similar expressions for the y and z components of $\mathbf{E}_0$:

$$E_{0y} = N_1 \int_{S_0} U_M n_y \, da \qquad (3.58b)$$

$$E_{0z} = N_1 \int_{S_0} U_M n_z \, da \qquad (3.58c)$$

Equations (3.58) are equivalent to the single vector equation

$$\mathbf{E}_0 = N_1 \int_{S_0} U_M \mathbf{n} \, da \qquad (3.59)$$

where $\mathbf{n}$ as always is the unit vector inward to S_0.

Equation (3.59) allows a computation of $\mathbf{E}_0$ without a detailed knowledge of the charge distribution in a molecule; for it involves the value of the molecular potential only at a distance b from the center of the molecule, where b is the radius of S_0. We have already assumed that b is sufficiently large that at this distance from a molecule its potential is essentially that of a dipole, if it has a dipole moment at all. Thus, if the average dipole moment of a molecule is $\bar{\mathbf{p}}$, we may immediately write down the function U_M on S_0:

$$U_M = -\frac{\bar{\mathbf{p}} \cdot \mathbf{n}}{4\pi\epsilon_0 b^2} \qquad (3.60)$$

Here the inward unit normal $\mathbf{n}$ to S_0 is opposite to a unit vector directed from the dipole to the element da, for the dipole we are now considering is located at the center of the sphere S_0.

From Eq. (3.11), we have $\bar{\mathbf{p}} = 1/N_1 \mathbf{P}$, so (3.60) becomes

$$U_M = -\frac{\mathbf{P} \cdot \mathbf{n}}{4\pi\epsilon_0 b^2 N_1} \qquad (3.61)$$

Substitution of Eq. (3.61) into (3.59) yields

$$\mathbf{E}_0 = -\frac{1}{4\pi\epsilon_0 b^2} \int_{S_0} (\mathbf{P} \cdot \mathbf{n})\mathbf{n} \, da \qquad (3.62)$$

This is just the negative of the partial field $\mathbf{E}_s^0$ as given in Eq. (3.48). Hence the two fields $\mathbf{E}_0$ and $\mathbf{E}_s^0$ cancel one another. By combination of

Eqs. (3.43), (3.47), (3.48), and (3.62) we now obtain the result we are seeking, the macroscopic electric field in the dielectric:

$$\mathbf{E} = \mathbf{E}_v' + \mathbf{E}_s \tag{3.63}$$

The notation $\mathbf{E}_v'$ is more complex than necessary. It was defined as the integral

$$\mathbf{E}_v' = \frac{1}{4\pi\epsilon_0} \int_{V'} \frac{\mathbf{r}^0 \rho' \, dV}{r^2} \tag{3.64}$$

over the volume of the dielectric but excluding an infinitesimal sphere of radius b about the observation point where $r = 0$. Since b is infinitesimal from the macroscopic viewpoint, this integral approaches as near as we please to, and in fact defines the value of, the improper integral over the whole volume V of the dielectric,

$$\mathbf{E}_v = \frac{1}{4\pi\epsilon_0} \int_{V} \frac{\mathbf{r}^0 \rho' \, dV}{r^2} \tag{3.65}$$

provided this latter integral converges. In Sec. 1.8 we established this convergence. The integral $\mathbf{E}_v$ is simpler in form than $\mathbf{E}_v'$ since its field of integration V is simpler. Thus we may write our result for the field within the dielectric as

$$\mathbf{E} = \mathbf{E}_v + \mathbf{E}_s = \frac{1}{4\pi\epsilon_0} \int_{V} \frac{\mathbf{r}^0 \rho' \, dV}{r^2} + \frac{1}{4\pi\epsilon_0} \int_{S} \frac{\mathbf{r}^0 \sigma' \, da}{r^2} \tag{3.66}$$

In words, this expression means that the average field inside the dielectric may be computed by considering the entire effect of the dielectric material to be the contribution of the bound charge densities ρ' and σ' to the electrostatic system. Note carefully in Eq. (3.66) that the dielectric constant is ϵ_0, that of empty space, in which the bound charge densities must be considered to reside. This is the same statement that was made in Sec. 3.5 for the field at an exterior point. In all cases, then, the entire effect of the dielectric on the electric field is accounted for by bound charge distributions, of surface and volume types, considered to be located in empty space.

3.6. Electric Displacement. We have found in the preceding sections that at all points of an electrostatic system, whether in dielectric material or not, the macroscopic electric field may be deduced by adding appropriate bound charge densities to the free charge densities and considering all these charges to reside in free space. It follows immediately that Gauss' law in a general system can be written

$$\epsilon_0 \Phi_E = \epsilon_0 \oint_{S} \mathbf{E} \cdot \mathbf{n} \, da = (q + q')_{\text{inside } S} \tag{3.67}$$

where q and q' are, respectively, the net algebraic free and bound charges enclosed by the surface S. The differential form of this equation at a point where the volume densities ρ and ρ' of free and bound charge are finite is like Eq. (2.17) with the addition of the ρ':

$$\epsilon_0 \left(\frac{\partial E_x}{\partial x} + \frac{\partial E_y}{\partial y} + \frac{\partial E_z}{\partial z} \right) = \rho + \rho' \qquad (3.68)$$

See Sec. 2.2 for the mathematical process involved here.

Equation (3.68) may be rewritten by substitution for ρ' [from Eq. (3.35)]:

$$\frac{\partial}{\partial x} (\epsilon_0 E_x + P_x) + \frac{\partial}{\partial y} (\epsilon_0 E_y + P_y) + \frac{\partial}{\partial z} (\epsilon_0 E_z + P_z) = \rho \qquad (3.69)$$

Equation (3.69) leads us to define a new macroscopic field vector $\mathbf{D}$, called the electric displacement:

$$\mathbf{D} \equiv \epsilon_0 \mathbf{E} + \mathbf{P} \qquad (3.70)$$

Equation (3.69) then states that a fundamental property of electric displacement is its connection at each point of space, whether in dielectric or outside, with the free charge density ρ:

$$\frac{\partial D_x}{\partial x} + \frac{\partial D_y}{\partial y} + \frac{\partial D_z}{\partial z} = \rho \qquad (3.71)$$

The importance of electric displacement results from its simple relationship to free charge; for free charge is usually the primary source of an electrostatic field. We shall find further use for the electric displacement in the study of electromagnetic waves. Notice that dimensionally $\mathbf{D}$ is the same as $\mathbf{P}$, and has units of coulombs/meter^2 in the mks system.

The differential relation (3.71) implies the existence of a Gauss law for the flux of the $\mathbf{D}$ vector. From comparison of Eqs. (3.67), (3.68), and (3.71) it appears at once that Gauss' law for the electric displacement is

$$\Phi_D \equiv \oint_S \mathbf{D} \cdot \mathbf{n}\, da = q_{\text{inside } S} \qquad (3.72)$$

Here q is net algebraic free charge in S. The equivalence of Eqs. (3.72) and (3.71) is seen to be another example of the divergence theorem which was applied in Sec. 3.4 to the polarization vector, if q is written as $\int_V \rho\, dV$. Equation (3.72) remains valid, however, even when the surface S encloses boundaries containing surface densities of charge.

It should be understood that the $\mathbf{D}$ and $\mathbf{E}$ vectors differ fundamentally in that the macroscopic $\mathbf{E}$ vector is the average of the microscopic electric field, while the $\mathbf{D}$ vector is defined entirely on a macroscopic basis. To a microscopic observer, there would be no bound charge nor polarization, and no occasion would arise for defining electric displacement.

3.7. Electric Susceptibility and Dielectric Constant. The electric polarization vector **P**, as introduced in Sec. 3.2, involves the position in the molecules of the dielectric of the ultimate charged particles composing them. The presence of an electric field in the dielectric must affect **P** in general, since by definition the electric field results in force on electric charge. In a rough way, we shall expect the effect of **E** on **P** to be such as to increase a component of **P** in the direction of **E**; for the relative displacement of the positive to the negative particles of a molecule will be correlated with the directions of the electric force on these particles, which is in the same sense as **E** for positive charge and in the opposite sense for negative charge. In this section we shall make some generalizations on the experimental connection of **P** and **E**, together with a number of definitions. Equations relating **P** or **D** to **E** are given the general name of constitutive equations.

The usual behavior of dielectrics is that **P** vanishes when **E** vanishes. This is not universally true, however. It was found by Eguchi[1] that a mixture of beeswax and resin exhibits a permanent polarization if it is subjected to an electric field in the molten state and then hardened in the field. Specimens of material exhibiting this phenomenon are called electrets.[2] Electrets are rare enough that we shall neglect permanent polarization in the following discussion. Another phenomenon to be neglected for the present is dielectric absorption, which refers to the apparent absorption and subsequent release of free charge by a dielectric. This will be mentioned in Sec. 11.12 in connection with condensers.

A large class of dielectrics, including fluids, amorphous solids, and some crystals, is electrically isotropic. This means that the electric properties of such materials are the same in all directions. If the material has no directional characteristics, the electric polarization **P** resulting from an electric field **E** must be parallel to the field; and **P** and **E** will have the same sense, as may be seen from the argument of the first paragraph. It follows now from the definition of electric displacement that **D** has the same direction as **E**. For isotropic materials, we may write functional relationships between **P** and **E** and **D** and **E** at a given point of the material as follows:

$$\mathbf{P} = \chi(E)\mathbf{E} \tag{3.73}$$

$$\mathbf{D} = \epsilon(E)\mathbf{E} \tag{3.74}$$

where the scalar quantity $\chi(E)$ is called the *electric susceptibility* of the material, and the scalar quantity $\epsilon(E)$ is the *electric inductive capacity*, or more briefly, its *dielectric constant*, or *permittivity*. In general, as the notation indicates, these quantities are functions of the magnitude of the

---

[1] M. Eguchi, *Proc. Phys.-Math. Soc. Japan*, **1**, 326–331 (1919).

[2] For a brief discussion of electrets, see A. Gemant, *Physics Today*, **2**, 8 (1949).

electric field, but not functions of its direction. It is conceivable that $\chi(E)$ and $\epsilon(E)$ might be multiple-valued functions of E, depending partly on the history of the specimen, as is indeed the case for the corresponding property of ferromagnetic materials. In electrostatics, however, $\chi(E)$ and $\epsilon(E)$ may almost always be considered as single-valued functions. Furthermore, $\chi(E)$ and $\epsilon(E)$ are usually constant, except perhaps for very intense fields. When these quantities are constant, that is independent of field strength, they will simply be written χ and ϵ so that instead of Eqs. (3.73) and (3.74) we have

$$\mathbf{P} = \chi\mathbf{E} \tag{3.75}$$
$$\mathbf{D} = \epsilon\mathbf{E} \tag{3.76}$$

We shall use the term linear dielectric to mean one in which χ and ϵ are independent of the field strength.

It should be pointed out that $\chi(E)$, χ, $\epsilon(E)$, and ϵ are not necessarily constant with respect to variation of position in the dielectric. If they vary with the space coordinates of the point of observation for a given field strength, then the dielectric material is said to be inhomogeneous; but in the important special case where these quantities are the same for all points of the dielectric at a given field strength, the dielectric is said to be homogeneous. Notice that whenever the material is nonlinear, the quantities $\chi(E)$ and $\epsilon(E)$ will be implicitly functions of the space coordinates, since E will in general vary with the coordinates, even though the material is homogeneous.

The definition of electric displacement gives a simple relationship between the susceptibility and the dielectric constant for all isotropic dielectrics:

$$\epsilon(E) = \epsilon_0 + \chi(E) \tag{3.77}$$

or, for linear materials,

$$\epsilon = \epsilon_0 + \chi \tag{3.78}$$

Notice that in empty space, where $\mathbf{P}$ is always zero and hence χ is zero, the constant ϵ_0 becomes the dielectric constant. Hence the name "dielectric constant of free space" for ϵ_0. It is convenient to introduce here a dimensionless ratio of the dielectric constant in a dielectric to that of free space:

$$K_\epsilon \equiv \frac{\epsilon}{\epsilon_0} \tag{3.79}$$

The corresponding form of Eq. (3.79) for a nonlinear dielectric is

$$K_\epsilon(E) \equiv \frac{\epsilon(E)}{\epsilon_0} \tag{3.80}$$

The ratio K_e or $K_e(E)$ so defined is called the specific electric inductive capacity of the material, or, more briefly, we shall call it the specific dielectric constant or specific permittivity. We may express K_e in terms of χ as follows:

$$K_e = 1 + \frac{\chi}{\epsilon_0} \tag{3.81}$$

with a corresponding equation for nonlinear media.

The case of anisotropic materials is much more complex mathematically, and we shall have no occasion to use it in a treatment of this scope. Anisotropic materials are those for which the electrical characteristics depend on direction. The relation between **P** and **E** or between **D** and **E** is expressible not by a single quantity, but by a set of six independent quantities called a symmetric tensor of second rank. What this amounts to is that each component of **P** or **D** depends on all three of the components of **E**. Anisotropic materials fall into the same categories as isotropic materials: linear and nonlinear, homogeneous and inhomogeneous.

3.8. Electrostatic Potential in a Dielectric System. It has been shown in Chap. 1 that the electrostatic field of a system of free charges in empty space can be expressed in terms of a single-valued scalar potential function U which is uniquely defined except for an additive constant. The demonstration of this theorem rested upon the inverse-square relationship between the field and the charges which are its sources. In the present chapter we have shown that the macroscopic electric field in or near dielectric material may also be expressed in terms of the inverse-square law, except that now bound charges are to be added to the free charges. It follows that the macroscopic, electrostatic field may always be expressed by a single-valued potential function. The same symbol U employed in Chap. 1 will be used, and it will be related to the macroscopic field always by the formulas

$$\mathbf{E} = -\,\mathbf{grad}\ U \tag{3.82}$$

or

$$E_x = -\frac{\partial U}{\partial x} \qquad E_y = -\frac{\partial U}{\partial y} \qquad E_z = -\frac{\partial U}{\partial z} \tag{3.83}$$

It follows also that the relationship between the macroscopic potential function U and its sources, consisting of both free and bound charges, is the same as that between the free-space potential function and its sources. We may therefore write for the macroscopic potential, following Eq. (1.45),

$$U = \frac{1}{4\pi\epsilon_0} \int_{\substack{\text{all free}\\\text{charge}}} \frac{dq}{r} + \frac{1}{4\pi\epsilon_0} \int_{\substack{\text{all dielectric}\\\text{volume}}} \frac{\rho'\,dV}{r} + \frac{1}{4\pi\epsilon_0} \int_{\substack{\text{all dielectric}\\\text{surfaces}}} \frac{\sigma'\,da}{r} \tag{3.84}$$

Here dq stands for any element of free charge, whether resulting from volume, surface, or line density, or from point charges, while the bound charges appear only as volume and surface densities ρ' and σ' given by Eqs. (3.34) and (3.35). As usual, r stands for the distance from the charge element to the observer.

The differential equation relating the macroscopic potential to its sources may be written down at once as an extension of Poisson's equation for empty space (Eq. 2.20), by the addition of the bound to the free charge density:

$$\left(\frac{\partial^2 U}{\partial x^2} + \frac{\partial^2 U}{\partial y^2} + \frac{\partial^2 U}{\partial z^2}\right) = -\frac{1}{\epsilon_0}\,(\rho + \rho') \qquad (3.85)$$

Equation (3.85) is also an immediate deduction from Eq. (3.68), when combined with Eqs. (3.83).

Equations (3.84) and (3.85) are important not as a means of computing the potential, but simply as a statement of the fact that the entire contribution of dielectrics to an electrostatic field is expressible in terms of bound charge densities. In an actual problem, both the U function and the bound charge densities are generally unknown at the outset. We shall develop methods for the solution of electrostatic problems involving dielectric material in following sections.

3.9. Boundary Conditions on the Field Vectors. We have frequently found it convenient to introduce surface discontinuities into the analysis of electrostatic systems. These may be infinitesimally thin surface layers of charge, or they may be surfaces where the nature of the medium changes discontinuously. It is important now to establish the behavior of the three electrostatic vector functions **E**, **D**, and **P** at such surfaces. In this discussion, the macroscopic electric field will be treated, for on a microscopic scale surface densities of charge are seen to have finite thickness because they must have finite volume density of charge; and surfaces of discontinuity of material no longer appear mathematically sharp because of the molecular structure of matter.

Consider first the electric field vector at a boundary S between materials numbered 1 and 2. Let S be a surface which has a tangent plane at every point, so that an infinitesimal piece of it will be plane. The trace of this plane is shown in Fig. 3.6. Draw a rectangular loop $abcd$ with sides ab and cd parallel to S, one side being in each material. If we form the negative line integral of the **E** vector about this closed loop, we obtain zero as the result. This was shown in Sec. 1.5 to be a statement of the conservative nature of the electric field, and we have shown in Sec. 3.8 that the macroscopic electric field has the same character. Let the sides ab and cd have length l, and let the ends of the rectangle have length w. Take a unit vector **p** tangent to the surface S and parallel to the sides ab and cd. The line integral of the field taken clockwise around the loop is

$$0 = \oint \mathbf{E} \cdot d\mathbf{l} = \int_a^b \mathbf{E} \cdot d\mathbf{l} + \int_b^c \mathbf{E} \cdot d\mathbf{l} + \int_c^d \mathbf{E} \cdot d\mathbf{l} + \int_d^a \mathbf{E} \cdot d\mathbf{l} \quad (3.86)$$

Now suppose that l and w are both infinitesimals. Let $w \to 0$ first, so that the loop shrinks indefinitely near to S on both sides of it. $\mathbf{E}$ will remain finite, for a surface density of charge does not produce an infinite field strength. Thus as $w \to 0$ the integrals over bc and da become as small as we please, and may be neglected. Furthermore, since l is to be infinitesimal, the value of $\mathbf{E}$ can be considered constant in the intervals ab and cd. Let the values of $\mathbf{E}$ right at the boundary be $\mathbf{E}_1$ and $\mathbf{E}_2$,

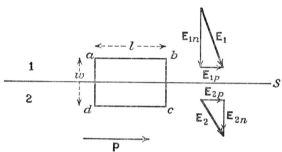

FIG. 3.6. Rectangular path for the line integral of the electric field at a boundary.

respectively, on the two sides of S and at the location of the loop $abcd$. Then

$$\int_a^b \mathbf{E} \cdot d\mathbf{l} = \mathbf{E}_1 \cdot \mathbf{p}l \quad (3.87a)$$

and

$$\int_c^d \mathbf{E} \cdot d\mathbf{l} = -\mathbf{E}_2 \cdot \mathbf{p}l \quad (3.87b)$$

Then Eq. (3.86) becomes

$$0 = (\mathbf{E}_1 - \mathbf{E}_2) \cdot \mathbf{p}l$$

so that

$$(\mathbf{E}_1 - \mathbf{E}_2) \cdot \mathbf{p} = 0 \quad (3.88)$$

The force of Eq. (3.88) is not apparent until it is stated that $\mathbf{p}$ is any tangent unit vector whatever and that the equation holds for all such vectors. This is only true if the part of $\mathbf{E}$ which is tangential to the surface is the same on the two sides of S. Let us therefore resolve $\mathbf{E}$, on each side of S, into a normal component $\mathbf{E}_n$ and a tangential component $\mathbf{E}_p$, so that as a vector equation

$$\begin{aligned}\mathbf{E}_1 &= \mathbf{E}_{1n} + \mathbf{E}_{1p} \\ \mathbf{E}_2 &= \mathbf{E}_{2n} + \mathbf{E}_{2p}\end{aligned} \quad (3.89)$$

In these terms, the content of Eq. (3.88) may be expressed thus

$$\mathbf{E}_{1p} = \mathbf{E}_{2p} \qquad\qquad (3.90)$$

In words, this is briefly stated as follows: the tangential component of the electric field is continuous across any boundary.

Next construct a closed mathematical surface G having two equal faces A_1 and A_2 parallel to the boundary and on opposite sides of it (see Fig. 3.7). Let A_3 stand for the remaining part of G, which joins the two

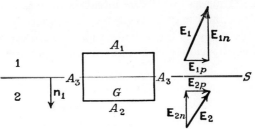

FIG. 3.7. Gaussian surface enclosing a boundary.

faces and is entirely perpendicular to S. Let $\mathbf{n}_1$ be a unit vector outward from medium 1. According to Gauss' law,

$$\oint_G \mathbf{E} \cdot \mathbf{n} \, dS = \int_{A_1} \mathbf{E} \cdot \mathbf{n} \, dS + \int_{A_2} \mathbf{E} \cdot \mathbf{n} \, dS + \int_{A_3} \mathbf{E} \cdot \mathbf{n} \, dS$$
$$= \frac{1}{\epsilon_0} (q + q') \quad (3.91)$$

where $\mathbf{n}$ is to be taken as a unit vector always outward from G, and q and q' are the free and bound charges enclosed by G. Consider all the surfaces as infinitesimal, but let A_3 approach zero while the faces A_1 and A_2 approach infinitely near to S. The integral over A_3 then becomes zero, since the $\mathbf{E}$ vector is finite. Furthermore, let A be the value of the infinitesimal area of A_1 and A_2, and let $\mathbf{E}_1$ and $\mathbf{E}_2$ be the values of the field, considered constant, over these two infinitesimal faces. Equation (3.91) may now be written

$$-\mathbf{E}_1 \cdot \mathbf{n}_1 A + \mathbf{E}_2 \cdot \mathbf{n}_1 A = \frac{1}{\epsilon_0} (q + q') \qquad (3.92)$$

Now the charge enclosed by G is entirely due to free and bound surface charge density on S. The volume enclosed by G approaches zero as we let A_3 approach zero, so that the contribution to $q + q'$ of any finite volume density of charge in G becomes negligibly small. The contribution of the surface densities σ and σ' to $q + q'$ is $A(\sigma + \sigma')$, which is unaffected by the process of letting A_3 approach zero, since the surface charge densities are considered to be in an infinitely thin layer, all of which is contained between A_1 and A_2. Making this substitution for

$q + q'$ in Eq. (3.92), we obtain

$$(\mathbf{E}_2 - \mathbf{E}_1) \cdot \mathbf{n}_1 A = \frac{1}{\epsilon_0} (\sigma + \sigma')A$$

Therefore

$$(\mathbf{E}_2 - \mathbf{E}_1) \cdot \mathbf{n}_1 = \frac{1}{\epsilon_0} (\sigma + \sigma') \qquad (3.93)$$

In terms of the magnitudes of the normal field components,

$$E_{2n} - E_{1n} = \frac{1}{\epsilon_0} (\sigma + \sigma') \qquad (3.94)$$

Equation (3.93) or (3.94) is the boundary condition for the normal component of the electric field. Evidently this component is not in general continuous across the boundary, but has a discontinuous change of $1/\epsilon_0(\sigma + \sigma')$.

For the electric displacement vector, we find a boundary condition only on the normal component. The analysis is just the same as for the normal component of the electric field: it begins with Gauss' law for the electric displacement:

$$\oint_G \mathbf{D} \cdot \mathbf{n} \, dS = q \qquad (3.95)$$

The result is the boundary condition

$$(\mathbf{D}_2 - \mathbf{D}_1) \cdot \mathbf{n}_1 = \sigma \qquad (3.96)$$

The magnitudes of the normal components of displacement are thus related by

$$D_{2n} - D_{1n} = \sigma \qquad (3.97)$$

Finally, the behavior of the electric polarization vector at a boundary may be expressed as a boundary condition on $\mathbf{P}$ in terms of σ'. In view of the analysis of earlier sections, it seems odd to call this a condition on $\mathbf{P}$, since σ' itself was derived from $\mathbf{P}$; but the equation is of the same form as the normal boundary conditions of this section. From Eq. (3.34) we see that the polarization vector in material 1 contributes a bound surface density of charge of $\mathbf{P}_1 \cdot \mathbf{n}_1$, while the vector in material 2 contributes $-\mathbf{P}_2 \cdot \mathbf{n}_1$. Thus the total bound surface density is

$$\sigma' = \mathbf{P}_1 \cdot \mathbf{n}_1 - \mathbf{P}_2 \cdot \mathbf{n}_1$$

Therefore

$$(\mathbf{P}_2 - \mathbf{P}_1) \cdot \mathbf{n}_1 = -\sigma' \qquad (3.98)$$

This may be written in terms of the normal, scalar components as

$$P_{2n} - P_{1n} = -\sigma' \qquad (3.99)$$

It will be noted that Eqs. (3.93), (3.96), and (3.98) are consistent with the definition of electric displacement, $\mathbf{D} = \epsilon_0\mathbf{E} + \mathbf{P}$.

By use of the constitutive equations of Sec. 3.7, both normal and tangential boundary conditions may be found for all three of the vectors

D, E, and **P** without reference to the bound surface charge. These conditions are easily written out in case the materials at an interface are isotropic [see, for example, Eq. (3.103), Sec. 3.10].

3.10. Boundary Conditions for the Macroscopic Electrostatic Potential. The electrostatic potential function is a useful tool for analysis of systems with dielectrics, just as it was found to be in Chap. 2 for systems without dielectrics. It is important therefore to know the behavior of the macroscopic potential function at boundaries or surface layers of charge.

As in the preceding section, let S be a boundary separating two regions which are in general occupied by different materials. The potential functions on the two sides of S may be called U_1 and U_2. These functions may be entirely different in form in the regions separated by S.

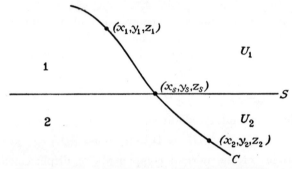

FIG. 3.8. Path of line integration crossing a boundary.

Each function is only determined within an arbitrary additive constant, by its definition; but it will be useful and sensible to make these constants agree with one another. By this we shall mean that if the negative line integral of the electric field, which represents by definition a change of potential, is taken from any point (x_1,y_1,z_1) on the side of material 1 to any point (x_2,y_2,z_2) on the side of material 2, its value is to be equal to $U_2(x_2,y_2,z_2) - U_1(x_1,y_1,z_1)$. That this is possible is guaranteed by the conservative character of the electrostatic field. If this agreement is made concerning the additive constants, the first boundary condition on the potential functions is extremely simple: $U_1 = U_2$ on the boundary. A proof of this may be made as follows. So far as the macroscopic electric field is concerned, we have seen before that a boundary may be considered to consist of a surface density of real and bound charge. Let a line C cross the boundary S in a general point of the boundary (x_s,y_s,z_s). Let (x_1,y_1,z_1) and (x_2,y_2,z_2) be points on C in media 1 and 2, respectively (see Fig. 3.8). We have agreed that

$$-\int_{x_1,y_1,z_1}^{x_2,y_2,z_2} \mathbf{E} \cdot d\mathbf{l} = U_2(x_2,y_2,z_2) - U_1(x_1,y_1,z_1) \qquad (3.100)$$

Now E remains finite at a surface layer of charge, and hence the integral approaches zero if its two limit points approach one another by approaching the point (x_s,y_s,z_s) on S. Because of the infinite thinness postulated for a surface layer of charge, the points on the two sides of S can both approach infinitely close to (x_s,y_s,z_s). Hence in the limit,

$$U_2(x_s,y_s,z_s) - U_1(x_s,y_s,z_s) = 0 \qquad (3.101)$$

which was to be proved.

It is interesting to notice that this boundary condition is equivalent to the tangential boundary condition of the electric field vector, except for an additional condition on the additive constants. Thus Eq. (3.88)

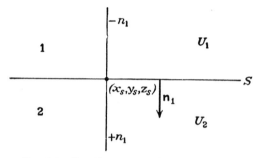

FIG. 3.9. Coordinate normal to a boundary.

or (3.90) may be deduced immediately from Eq. (3.101); for from the latter it follows that the negative space derivative of the potential function in any direction tangent to the boundary is the same on the two sides of the boundary.

Another boundary condition on the electrostatic potential function is simply a restatement of the condition on the normal component of the electric field. Let the scalar n_1 be a coordinate measured along a straight line intersecting the boundary S at the general point (x_s,y_s,z_s). Let the coordinate n_1 increase positively in the sense of the unit normal $\mathbf{n}_1$ external to medium 1 (see Fig. 3.9). The statement of Eq. (3.93) or (3.94) in terms of the potential functions U_1 and U_2 is now

$$-\left(\frac{\partial U_2}{\partial n_1}\right)_{x_s,y_s,z_s} + \left(\frac{\partial U_1}{\partial n_1}\right)_{x_s,y_s,z_s} = \frac{1}{\epsilon_0}(\sigma + \sigma') \qquad (3.102)$$

A more special but more useful equation may be written for the case in which both materials separated by S are isotropic. Let ϵ_1 and ϵ_2 be the respective values of the dielectric constant of these materials at the place (x_s,y_s,z_s) on the boundary. Then the boundary condition on electric displacement, Eq. (3.96) of the preceding section, may be written

$$(\epsilon_2 \mathbf{E}_2 - \epsilon_1 \mathbf{E}_1) \cdot \mathbf{n}_1 = \sigma \qquad (3.103)$$

This now becomes, in terms of the potential functions:

$$-\epsilon_2 \left(\frac{\partial U_2}{\partial n_1}\right)_{x_s,y_s,z_s} + \epsilon_1 \left(\frac{\partial U_1}{\partial n_1}\right)_{x_s,y_s,z_s} = \sigma \tag{3.104}$$

It may be well to include with the foregoing boundary conditions the statement that on a conductor boundary S_c the potential function is constant:

$$U(S_c) = \text{constant} \tag{3.105}$$

See Sec. 1.12 for discussion of conductors. At a conductor boundary, we may also write a special form of Eq. (3.104). Let the conductor be material 1; then $\partial U_1/\partial n_1 = 0$, since the potential is constant within the metal. Equation (3.104) then reads

$$-\epsilon_2 \left(\frac{\partial U_2}{\partial n_1}\right)_{x_s,y_s,z_s} = \sigma$$

Dropping the unnecessary subscripts, we may write

$$-\epsilon \left(\frac{\partial U}{\partial n}\right)_{x_c,y_c,z_c} = \sigma \tag{3.106}$$

Here it is understood that ϵ and U refer to the region just outside the conductor, while n is a coordinate perpendicular to the conductor surface with its positive sense outward. Instead of (x_s,y_s,z_s) we have written (x_c,y_c,z_c) to remind the reader that Eq. (3.106) refers to points on a conductor boundary.

3.11. The Poisson Equation. In systems containing conductors in empty space, we saw in Chap. 2 that the solution for the electric field or potential was not to be obtained from the charge distribution by integration, since the charge distribution on conductor surfaces is generally an unknown in the problem. When dielectrics are present, the solution is still more difficult because of the presence of bound charge densities which are also unknowns. We proceed, then, as in Chap. 2, to show what differential equation the electrostatic potential must satisfy, at least in the more usual case of linear isotropic dielectrics. The potential function for a given system may in principle be found by solving the differential equation subject to the boundary conditions specified in the problem.

It is necessary to use a constitutive equation relating $\mathbf{D}$ or $\mathbf{P}$ to $\mathbf{E}$ in order to solve a system containing dielectrics, for otherwise there are too many unknowns. We shall consider only the case of the isotropic linear dielectric for which

$$\mathbf{D} = \epsilon \mathbf{E} \tag{3.107}$$

Here the dielectric constant ϵ is to be considered a given function of the space coordinates. ϵ may be constant in given regions, if the material is homogeneous, piece by piece; or the dielectric may be inhomogeneous throughout. Now the electric displacement was shown in Sec. 3.6, to satisfy the differential equation

$$\frac{\partial D_x}{\partial x} + \frac{\partial D_y}{\partial y} + \frac{\partial D_z}{\partial z} = \rho \tag{3.71}$$

Combining Eqs. (3.107) and (3.71), we obtain

$$\frac{\partial(\epsilon E_x)}{\partial x} + \frac{\partial(\epsilon E_y)}{\partial y} + \frac{\partial(\epsilon E_z)}{\partial z} = \rho \tag{3.108}$$

Next, we may express the components of electric field in terms of the electrostatic potential. Let U stand for the potential function in all regions of the system. Then

$$E_x = -\frac{\partial U}{\partial x} \qquad E_y = -\frac{\partial U}{\partial y} \qquad E_z = -\frac{\partial U}{\partial z} \tag{3.109}$$

therefore Eq. (3.108) may be written as

$$\frac{\partial}{\partial x}\left(\epsilon \frac{\partial U}{\partial x}\right) + \frac{\partial}{\partial y}\left(\epsilon \frac{\partial U}{\partial y}\right) + \frac{\partial}{\partial z}\left(\epsilon \frac{\partial U}{\partial z}\right) = -\rho \tag{3.110}$$

This is a generalized Poisson equation.

Equation (3.110) may be made the basis of a uniqueness theorem, whose details are beyond the scope of this volume, but whose results we may quote. The solution of (3.110) is uniquely determined, at least within an additive constant, if the geometry of the system is given, including the functions ϵ and ρ at all points, together with the following conditions:

1. Either the potential or the total charge of each conductor in the system is specified. If the potential of one conductor is specified, then the additive constant of the potential is determined.

2. The free surface charge density, if any, is a known function of position at all points of all nonconducting boundaries.

3. If the system extends to infinity, certain conditions must be met to ensure proper behavior of the potential there. The reader is referred to Chap. 2 for discussion of this point, and for treatment of systems in which the potential is independent of one or two of the cartesian coordinates.

In connection with these boundary conditions, it is well to state explicitly the connection between the potential function and charge on conductors.   From the boundary condition (3.106) of Sec. 3.10,

$$\sigma = -\epsilon \left(\frac{\partial U}{\partial n}\right)_{x_c, y_c, z_c} \tag{3.106}$$

where n is a coordinate perpendicular and outward to the conductor surface at the point where σ and ϵ are evaluated.   Thus the total charge on the conductor whose surface is S_i is given by

$$q_i = \int_{S_i} \sigma \, da = -\int_{S_i} \epsilon \frac{\partial U}{\partial n} \, da \tag{3.111}$$

In case the dielectric is homogeneous around the surface S_i, ϵ is a constant and may be taken outside the integral:

$$q_i = -\epsilon \int_{S_i} \frac{\partial U}{\partial n} \, da \tag{3.112}$$

Equation (3.110) simplifies if ϵ is a constant, at least in each region of space comprising the system.   It then takes on the form usually called the Poisson equation:

$$\frac{\partial^2 U}{\partial x^2} + \frac{\partial^2 U}{\partial y^2} + \frac{\partial^2 U}{\partial z^2} = -\frac{1}{\epsilon}\rho \tag{3.113}$$

Notice carefully that in all of the equations of this section we have used the dielectric constant of the material but have never had to consider bound charges.   On the other hand, none of the formulas of recent sections in which bound charges do appear contain ϵ, although some involve ϵ_0.   Thus the presence of dielectrics may be accounted for either by bound charges in empty space or, for isotropic media, by the dielectric constant.   The latter procedure is the one which leads to solution of actual problems, but the former provides an illuminating concept.

3.12. The Special Case.   There is one class of electrostatic systems in which the dielectric adds no complication to the solution.   These are systems whose entire volume is filled with a single isotropic linear homogeneous dielectric.   If the system under consideration extends to infinity, then the dielectric must be infinite in extent, or at least its outer boundaries must be so far away from the observer that their surface bound charge produces a negligible field.   If the system is finite in extent, and completely bounded by conductor walls, then the dielectric need only fill this enclosed space.

Under these conditions, the dielectric constant ϵ is everywhere the same, and the Poisson equation (3.113) becomes identical to that which would apply to a similar system whose space is empty of dielectric but whose volume charge density is decreased in the ratio ϵ_0/ϵ.   Furthermore, the boundary condition (3.106) becomes identical to the condition for the similar system devoid of dielectric with the surface charge density decreased in the same ratio ϵ_0/ϵ. Boundary condition (3.101) is independent of the dielectric. Line or point charges in a system can be treated as limiting cases of surface densities or of volume densities. It follows now from consideration of uniqueness that the solution of any electrostatic system all of whose space is filled with a single linear homogeneous dielectric is identical with that in a system of the same geometry but devoid of dielectric, in which all free charges are reduced in the ratio ϵ_0/ϵ. Another way of stating this is that for a given set of free charges in the given system, the potential and hence the electric field are reduced in the ratio ϵ_0/ϵ by the presence of the all-pervading linear dielectric ϵ.

As a simple example of the application of this theorem, the electrostatic potential of a point charge q embedded in an infinite, isotropic, linear, homogeneous dielectric is

$$U = \frac{q}{4\pi\epsilon r} \tag{3.114}$$

The electric field of the point charge is

$$E = \frac{q\mathbf{r}}{4\pi\epsilon r^3} \tag{3.115}$$

Equations (3.114) and (3.115) may be generalized by summation or integration for a system of charges or charge densities. Likewise we obtain a simple formula for the electric displacement due to this point charge, by using $\mathbf{D} = \epsilon\mathbf{E}$,

$$D = \frac{q\mathbf{r}}{4\pi r^3} \tag{3.116}$$

These equations are so frequently encountered in elementary treatments of electrostatics that their highly special character is often lost sight of. We shall remind ourselves of this special character by using the term "special case" to refer to an infinite, isotropic, linear, homogeneous dielectric.

The reader should perhaps be warned against a "derivation" of Eq. (3.116), and thence Eq. (3.115), which seems to imply almost universal validity for these equations. Equation (3.116) does not follow from the law for electric displacement,

$$\oint_S \mathbf{D} \cdot \mathbf{n}\, da = q_{\text{inside } S}$$

except for that spherical symmetry about the point charge which is implied by the "special case" conditions. This integral equation is indeed perfectly general in its application; but infinitely many expressions for the field of a point charge could be constructed which would satisfy it.

3.13. Dielectric Image Theory. Image theory can be applied to problems involving two or more homogeneous dielectric materials occupying different regions of space. The electric field in a given region V_i where the permittivity is ϵ_i may be considered to be made up of several fields superposed, each one represented by a term in the potential function. One term will be such as would arise from all the free charges in V_i if they were located in a boundless region occupied by the dielectric ϵ_i. This term, if substituted into the Poisson equation, will yield the function $-\rho/\epsilon_i$ in the region V_i. The actual potential in this region is obtainable by adding to this particular solution of Poisson's equation a solution of the corresponding homogeneous equation, which is Laplace's equation. We may consider this additional part of the potential as being that due to all charges, free or bound, on the boundary of V_i or outside V_i. It may be possible to express this part of the potential as the potential which would be produced by an imaginary set of charges called image charges, located outside V_i; for such a potential satisfies Laplace's equation in V_i. The image charges may be treated as though they were located in a boundless space filled with the dielectric material ϵ_i.

According to the uniqueness theorem, we have the solution for a system if it satisfies the Poisson equation for the system together with the boundary conditions at all surfaces in the system. In the procedure outlined in the preceding paragraph, the choice of image charges is irrelevant to the satisfaction of the Poisson equation; and hence they must be chosen simply to fulfill all the boundary conditions. It must be noted, however, that the conditions at a dielectric interface, Eqs. (3.101) and (3.104), involve the potential function on both sides of the boundary. Hence a solution cannot be obtained for a single region V_i, by the method of images, without simultaneously solving the problem for all adjoining regions. Thus the whole system must in general be solved simultaneously.

To illustrate dielectric image theory, we shall solve the problem of a point charge q at distance L from an infinite, plane interface between two semi-infinite dielectrics (see Fig. 3.10). Call the two regions of the

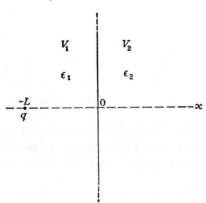

FIG. 3.10. Point charge and infinite, plane dielectric interface.

system V_1 and V_2, having permittivities ϵ_1 and ϵ_2, and separated by the yz plane. The charge is at $x = -L$, in region V_1. Because of the symmetry of the problem, we shall suppose that all image charges lie on the

x axis. For the field in region V_1, let an image charge be q_1 at $x = L_1$, where $L_1 > 0$; for the image charges are outside of the region to which they apply. Likewise, for region V_2 let an image charge be q_2 at $x = -L_2$. The potential in V_1 will now be expressed as

$$U_1 = \frac{1}{4\pi\epsilon_1} \frac{q}{\sqrt{(x + L)^2 + y^2 + z^2}} + \frac{1}{4\pi\epsilon_1} \frac{q_1}{\sqrt{(x - L_1)^2 + y^2 + z^2}} \quad (3.117)$$

Here the first term is the appropriate one for a point charge q at $x = -L$ in an infinite medium ϵ_1. It is the term which would satisfy the Poisson equation if there were a finite volume charge distribution. In this problem, the charge density is zero everywhere except at $x = -L$ where it is artificially made infinite, by the concept of point charge: and it may be readily verified that the first term of (1) yields a zero charge density except at $(-L,0,0)$ when substituted into the Poisson equation, and also behaves properly at points near to the charge discontinuity. The second term is due to the image charge; and we shall see whether we can determine its unknown constants L_1 and q_1 so as to satisfy the boundary conditions. The potential in region V_2 will be expressible as due solely to its image charge, since there are no free charges in V_2:

$$U_2 = \frac{1}{4\pi\epsilon_2} \frac{q_2}{\sqrt{(x + L_2)^2 + y^2 + z^2}} \quad (3.118)$$

Here are two more constants, q_2 and L_2, which we may use to fulfill boundary conditions. We are treating the image charge q_2 as if it were embedded in an infinite region filled with the material ϵ_2.

The boundary in this problem is the plane $x = 0$, at every point of which we must have

$$U_1 = U_2 \quad (3.119)$$

and

$$\epsilon_1 \frac{\partial U_1}{\partial x} = \epsilon_2 \frac{\partial U_2}{\partial x} \quad (3.120)$$

The remainder of the problem involves substituting Eqs. (3.117) and (3.118) into (3.119) and (3.120), and then putting $x = 0$. The resulting equations are identities in y and z when we assign the following values to the undetermined constants:

$$L_1 = L \qquad q_1 = \frac{\epsilon_1 - \epsilon_2}{\epsilon_1 + \epsilon_2} q$$

$$L_2 = L \qquad q_2 = \frac{2\epsilon_2}{\epsilon_1 + \epsilon_2} q \qquad (3.121)$$

Thus the postulated image charges do yield the solution of the problem, for they allow the boundary conditions to be satisfied; and the values and positions of these charges have been determined. Substitution of these constants back into Eqs. (3.117) and (3.118) gives the solution of the problem, for we have evaluated the potential function throughout the system.

3.14. Local Field. Permanent and Induced Dipole Moments. The foregoing development and elaboration of dielectric theory has rested on the postulates that the dielectric is composed of electric dipoles of molecular size, situated in otherwise empty space, and that the fields of these dipoles superpose to produce the large-scale effects of dielectric matter. Nothing has been said about the nature of the dipoles themselves, nor of the deductions which may be made about the molecular structure of matter from observation of dielectric constants. These important questions involve the subjects of kinetic theory, quantum mechanics, and physical chemistry, and therefore they properly lie outside the scope of this book. The student of electromagnetism is entitled nevertheless to some statement concerning the structure of dielectrics, so that he can see the application of his work to other fields, and so that he may have an accurate even if undetailed picture of causes of dielectric properties.

The idea underlying the theory of dielectric structure, due to P. Debye, is that the electric dipole moments of the molecules constituting the material are in some cases produced by the electric field to which they are subjected, while in other cases these moments exist even in the absence of a field. The molecules in these two cases are called, respectively, nonpolar and polar. In the nonpolar case, it is easy to see that when subjected to an electric field, a molecule in which the centers of positive and negative charge are originally coincident will develop a dipole moment in the direction of that field: for the positive charge experiences a force in the field direction, and the negative charge a force in the opposite direction. The result must then be a straining of the molecule, the separation of the two centers of charge, in order that a balancing force may be produced by the agent which holds the molecule together. In the case of polar molecules, such a strain takes place also, but here there is an entirely different process to be considered as well. Because of the thermal agitation of the molecules in any dielectric material, kinetic theory predicts that the permanent dipole moments of polar molecules have random orientations in space unless there is an orienting couple applied to them. An applied electric field provides such an orienting couple. Thus in the absence of an orienting field, the dipole moments of a group of many molecules tend to cancel one another, leaving on the average no net dipole moment per unit volume. An applied field causes partial lining up of the dipoles, thereby producing an average dipole moment different from zero and so polarizing the dielectric. The higher the temperature, the greater is the thermal agitation and hence the less complete is the lining up of polar molecules. Thus materials composed of polar molecules will be expected to show a temperature dependence of their dielectric constant even for constant density, while no such temperature effect occurs for purely nonpolar materials.

In relating the dielectric constant of a material to the properties of its constituent molecules, it is necessary to know the average electric field to which any particular molecule is subjected when the dielectric is polarized. This is often called the local field $\mathbf{F}$. $\mathbf{F}$ differs from the macroscopic field $\mathbf{E}$, which is the average field in a macroscopically small region; for the center of a given molecule does not occupy a random position in the dielectric, but is always at least twice the molecular radius from the center of another molecule. Lorentz carried through a calculation of the local field following earlier work by Mossotti[1] and Clausius. The result for the case of materials of random structure such as gases, as well as for cubic crystals, is called the Clausius-Mossotti formula.

The calculation can be carried through in more than one way. The usual procedure considers any given molecule to be situated at the center of a spherical cavity in the dielectric, the cavity having the volume $1/N_1$ proper to each molecule. The polarization of the dielectric in the vicinity of the cavity is considered to be uniform with its average value $\mathbf{P}$ in the macroscopic neighborhood of the given molecule. Note that this would not be the case for an empty cavity, since an empty cavity deforms the field; but here the cavity is not empty, as it contains the number of molecules (one) appropriate to its volume. The field contributed by the presence of the cavity at its center, where the given molecule is considered to be, is then just the field $\mathbf{E}_s{}^0$ of Eqs. (3.46) to (3.48) in the development of Sec. 3.5. Thus the field at the molecule is the average field outside the cavity, which is $\mathbf{E}$, plus $\mathbf{E}_s{}^0$:

$$\mathbf{F} = \mathbf{E} + \mathbf{E}_s{}^0 \tag{3.122}$$

According to Eq. (3.49), the local field is therefore

$$\mathbf{F} = \mathbf{E} + \frac{\mathbf{P}}{3\epsilon_0} \tag{3.123}$$

Equation (3.123) is one of several relations frequently called the Clausius-Mossotti equation. Since $\mathbf{P} = (\epsilon - \epsilon_0)\mathbf{E} = \epsilon_0(K_e - 1)\mathbf{E}$, where K_e is the specific permittivity of the dielectric, Eq. (3.123) can be rewritten in the form

$$\mathbf{F} = \frac{K_e + 2}{3} \mathbf{E} \tag{3.124}$$

[1] This name is frequently found misspelled with only one s.

On the basis of Eq. (3.124), Debye built up a widely accepted theory relating the dielectric constant to molecular structure. The polarizability α of a molecule is defined by a relation postulating the dependence of the average vector dipole moment $\bar{p}$ upon the local field $\mathbf{F}$:

$$\bar{p} = \alpha \mathbf{F} \qquad (3.125)$$

By Eq. (3.11), the polarization $\mathbf{P}$ is proportional to $\bar{p}$:

$$\mathbf{P} = N_1 \bar{p} \qquad (3.126)$$

Combination of Eqs. (3.123) to (3.126) yields for the molecular polarizability

$$\alpha = \frac{3\epsilon_0}{N_1} \frac{K_e - 1}{K_e + 2} \qquad (3.127)$$

This equation, like (3.123), is often called the Clausius-Mossotti equation. Now the Debye theory gives for the molecular polarizability an expression involving a constant term α_0 expressing the induced dipole moment per unit field, and a term from kinetic theory involving a permanent dipole moment p_0 if the molecule is polar:

$$\alpha = \alpha_0 + \frac{p_0^2}{3kT} \qquad (3.128)$$

Here T is the absolute or Kelvin temperature, and $k = 1.38 \times 10^{-23}$ joule/deg is the Boltzmann constant. Substitution of Eq. (3.128) into (3.127) results in the Langevin-Debye formula

$$\frac{1}{N_1} \frac{K_e - 1}{K_e + 2} = \frac{1}{3\epsilon_0} \left(\alpha_0 + \frac{p_0^2}{3kT} \right) \qquad (3.129)$$

This equation is so called because Debye's treatment of polar molecules was similar to previous work of Langevin in analysis of magnetic matter.

It is to be observed that according to the Langevin-Debye formula, the quantity

$$\frac{1}{N_1} \frac{K_e - 1}{K_e + 2}$$

should be constant for a given pure material at a given temperature. Experimentally, N_1 is altered by a change of density, perhaps accompanied by change of state. The relation between N_1 and the mass density d is $N_1 = N_A d / W$, where N_A is Avogadro's number and W the molecular weight of the material; so that in turn the quantity

$$\frac{1}{d} \frac{K_e - 1}{K_e + 2}$$

should be constant at a given temperature. This prediction is well verified for gases, although it should be noted that the experimental test is not critical when K_e differs but little from unity as in gases. In this case, the denominator $(K_e + 2)$ is hardly distinguishable from 3, the value which it would take if the macroscopic field $\mathbf{E}$ were used in place of the local field. The agreement with experiment is not so satisfactory for the liquid state of pure substances, and is still worse for solutions. These difficulties have led to criticism of the logic underlying the Clausius-Mossotti and Langevin-Debye equations. In particular, a distinction is made between the orienting and the polarizing parts of the local field; and greater care is exercised in examining the interactions between neighboring molecules. More complicated equations than (3.127) and (3.129) result from these newer theories, and show better agreement with experiment. The interested reader is referred to the literature.[1]

PROBLEMS

3.1. Suppose the electric polarization in a piece of sulfur has a magnitude of 10^{-5} coulomb/m^2. Given that Avogadro's number times the quotient of the density by the atomic weight is the number of atoms per unit volume and that the charge of each sign in an atom is the atomic number times the magnitude of the electronic charge. Look up necessary data in physical or chemical tables.

  a. Find the mean dipole moment of a sulfur atom.

  b. How far must the centers of charge of positive and negative sign in the sulfur atom be separated to produce this moment?

3.2. Given a thin, circular disk of dielectric material having uniform polarization $\mathbf{P}$ parallel to its axis. Find by direct integration over the volume of the disk the electrostatic potential at a point of observation on the axis of the disk, whose distance x from the disk is very large compared with the thickness t of the disk. Deduce from this the electric field on the axis.

3.3. Show that a pair of equal and opposite point charges $\pm q$ with vector separation $\mathbf{l}$ can be represented, so far as concerns the electric field not at a point on the line segment $\mathbf{l}$, by a line of suitable linear polarization and vector length with ideally small dipole elements.

3.4. Given the following charge distribution along the x axis: five charges of -10^{-9} coulomb each at 0, 1, 2, 3, and 4 cm, respectively, and five charges of $+10^{-9}$ coulomb each at 0.1, 1.1, 2.1, 3.1, and 4.1 cm, respectively.

  a. What is the dipole moment per unit length or linear polarization of the system?

  b. What "bound" charges can represent this system, and in what regions of observation is the representation valid?

  c. Find the linear densities λ_+ and λ_- for charges of each sign.

  d. What separation δx of two such linear densities would produce the correct bound charges at the ends of the system?

[1] F. G. Keyes and J. G. Kirkwood, *Phys. Rev.*, **37**, 202 (1931).

J. G. Kirkwood, *J. Chem. Phys.*, **4**, 592 (1936).

L. Onsager, *J. Am. Chem. Soc.*, **58**, 1486 (1936).

M. C. J. F. Bottcher, *Physica*, **9**, 937, 945 (1942).

M. C. J. F. Bottcher, *Colloques internationaux du Centre de la Recherche Scientifique*, **XVII**, 69, 73 (1949). (Note the scrambled page order.)

3.5. Given 50 charges of $+10^{-10}$ coulomb each, and 50 charges of -10^{-10} coulomb each, distributed alternately and evenly along a line 20 cm long. Let the line coincide with the x axis and have its center at the origin.

a. Find the dipole moment per unit length (linear polarization) of the charge distribution.

b. Use this quantity with the theorem of Sec. 3.3 to find the potential at (10,10,0) cm.

c. Would this computation have been valid for the point (0.1,0,0) cm?

d. Compare the result of (*b*) with the potential at the given point of only the two end charges of the distribution.

3.6. Given a long, thin rod of dielectric with cross section A, having uniform polarization **P** parallel to its length L. Find the electrostatic potential due to the rod at a general point far from the rod in comparison with its cross-sectional dimensions, but not necessarily far in comparison with its length.

3.7. Show by a mathematical transformation that for a piece of dielectric with volume V and complete surface S

$$\int_V \mathbf{P}\, dv \equiv \int_V \rho' \mathbf{r}\, dV + \int_S \sigma' \mathbf{r}\, da$$

where **P** is the electric polarization, ρ' and σ' are the bound charge densities, and **r** is the position vector of the point of integration relative to any origin. What does this equation mean? *Hint:* Separate into cartesian components to carry out the proof.

3.8. *a.* Given a right circular cylinder of dielectric material, of length L and radius R, with uniform electric polarization **P** parallel to its axis. For an observer in otherwise empty space on the axis at distance $|x| > L/2$ from the center of the cylinder, find the resulting electrostatic potential and electric field (1) by use of bound charge density and (2) by a volume integration.

b. Repeat (1) for a point on the axis within the cylinder, at $|x| < L/2$.

3.9. A sphere of dielectric material has radius R and uniform electric polarization vector **P** directed along the polar axis of spherical coordinates. Show by the concept of densities ρ_+ and ρ_- of positive and negative charge with a relative displacement $\delta\mathbf{r}$ that the external field of this sphere is simply that of an electric dipole, and find the moment of this equivalent dipole. Use $\rho_+ \, \delta\mathbf{r} = \mathbf{P}$.

3.10. A bar of dielectric material with uniform cross section A and length L has a polarization vector parallel to its length of magnitude $ax + b$, where x is a coordinate parallel to the length of the bar with zero at one face and a and b are constants. Find the electrostatic potential due to the bar at distances large compared with its dimensions.

3.11. A sphere of dielectric material in space has radius R and uniform electric polarization vector **P** along the polar axis. For a point on this axis at distance $x > R$ from the center of the sphere, find the electrostatic potential by integration over the bound charge density. Do the same for an interior point on the axis, at $x < R$.

3.12. Given a sphere of dielectric material of radius R and uniform polarization **P**. Find the macroscopic electrostatic potential function within the sphere, replacing it first by densities ρ_+ and ρ_- of positive and negative charge with a proper relative displacement, and using the potential function within spheres of uniform charge density. Show that the resulting field is uniform and give its magnitude and direction. Use $\rho_+ \, \delta\mathbf{r} = \mathbf{P}$.

3.13. Given a sphere of dielectric material of radius R with radial polarization proportional to the distance from the center.

a. Find all bound charge densities.

b. Show directly that in this case the sum of all the bound charges is zero.

c. What is the macroscopic electric field due to this polarized material, at general points both inside and outside the sphere?

3.14. *a.* Given an isolated sphere of isotropic homogeneous dielectric, with no other free charge than a point charge q located at its center. What may be determined about the electric displacement vector at interior and exterior points with the help of Gauss' law?

b. Answer the same question for an isolated cube of isotropic homogeneous dielectric carrying no other free charge than a point charge q located at its center.

3.15. A metal sphere of 2 cm radius carries a charge of 3×10^{-9} coulomb. It is encased in a spherical shell of isotropic, homogeneous, and linear dielectric material with inner radius 2 cm and outer radius 4 cm, which carries no free charge. Find (*a*) the electric displacement in each region of space; (*b*) the electric field in each region of space; (*c*) the electric polarization in the dielectric; (*d*) the bound charge densities; (*e*) the total bound charges on inner and outer surfaces, respectively, of the shell.

3.16. Show that for the existence of the volume density of bound charge at a point in an isotropic dielectric, it is necessary that either (*a*) the volume density of free charge exist at that point or (*b*) the space derivative of the dielectric constant in some direction at that point be nonvanishing. Discuss sufficient conditions.

3.17. At a point within a certain isotropic dielectric, the specific dielectric constant is 3 and the electric field intensity is 10^5 volts/m. For this dielectric at this point, find (*a*) the electric susceptibility; (*b*) the magnitude of the electric polarization; (*c*) the magnitude of the electric displacement; (*d*) the permittivity.

3.18. Show that within an isotropic, homogeneous, and linear dielectric the volume density ρ' of bound charge is

$$\rho' = -\rho \left(1 - \frac{1}{K_e}\right)$$

where ρ is the volume density of free charge at that same point and K_e is the specific dielectric constant.

3.19. A pair of parallel metal plates whose inner surfaces are $\frac{1}{2}$ mm apart is connected across a 1,000-volt battery. The space between them is filled with an isotropic, homogeneous, and linear dielectric whose specific dielectric constant is 4. For a region far from the edges where the plates appear essentially infinite, find (*a*) the electric field; (*b*) the electric displacement; (*c*) the polarization; (*d*) the free charge densities, which are only on the metal plates; (*e*) the bound charge densities. In working the problem, or else as a check, use two different integral forms of Gauss' law.

3.20. Given a concentric cable of circular cross section, with compound dielectric. The inner conductor has an outside radius a; this is surrounded by a sheath of dielectric with specific dielectric constant K_1 and outer radius b; next comes another sheath of dielectric with constant K_2 and outer radius c; and finally the outer conductor has inside radius c. There is a potential difference U_0 between conductors, and only the conductors bear free charge. Use Gauss' law, and find all free and bound charge densities.

3.21. Given a dielectric sphere of radius R and constant permittivity ϵ, in which a uniform density ρ of free charge exists. Find the electrostatic potential at the center (*a*) by integration over the free and bound charge densities and (*b*) by line integration of the electric field.

3.22. For the case of isotropic materials, find at a dielectric interface (*a*) tangential boundary conditions on **D** and (*b*) both tangential and normal conditions on **P** which do not explicitly involve bound charge density.

3.23. Two isotropic dielectrics, of specific inductive capacities 2 and 3, respectively, meet at an interface. In the first dielectric, the electric field at a point of the interface has a magnitude of 1,000 volts/cm and a direction whose angle to the normal of the interface is $\theta_1 = 45°$.

  a. Find the normal and tangential components of the electric field and displacement at this point of the boundary in the second medium.

  b. Find the direction of the field in the second medium, at this point of the boundary.

3.24. Given an infinite, circular cylinder of isotropic dielectric material, with radius R and constant permittivity ϵ, located in empty space. Suppose a uniform electric field E to exist within the cylinder, in a direction perpendicular to its axis. Find (*a*) the electrostatic potential function at a general point on the boundary but outside the cylinder and (*b*) the electric field at a general point on the boundary but outside the cylinder.

3.25. Two semi-infinite dielectric bodies, having constant permittivities ϵ_1 and ϵ_2, respectively, meet in an infinite plane boundary and carry no free charge. A conducting sphere of radius R is embedded in the dielectrics with its center in the boundary plane, and the sphere carries a free charge q. Find a radial inverse-square field satisfying all boundary conditions for the region outside the sphere, and find the corresponding free and bound charge densities. Make a general argument to show that this field

is the actual one. $\qquad\qquad Ans.\ E = \dfrac{q}{2\pi r^2(\epsilon_1 + \epsilon_2)}.$

3.26. Given a pair of infinite parallel conducting plates separated by an isotropic homogeneous dielectric. The potential difference ΔU between plates, their separation L, and the permittivity ϵ are known.

  a. Set up and solve the differential equation for the electrostatic potential in the region between plates.

  b. Apply boundary conditions to find as many constants as possible.

  c. Deduce from the potential function the field and the free and bound charge densities.

3.27. Repeat the preceding problem for the potential between parallel plates, using the boundary-value method, for the case in which the dielectric is divided by a plane interface parallel to the plates into two regions with different dielectric constants ϵ_1 and ϵ_2.

3.28. Show that if an isotropic homogeneous dielectric sphere, of permittivity ϵ and radius R, is placed in a fixed, uniform, external electric field $\mathbf{E}_0$ in space, the boundary conditions for the electrostatic potential at its surface are satisfied by supposing (*a*) a uniform electric field $\mathbf{E}_1$ within the sphere and (*b*) that the contribution of the sphere to the external field is that of an electric dipole of moment **p** in space. Find $\mathbf{E}_1$ and **p**.

3.29. Show in detail how the use of boundary conditions (3.119) and (3.120) of Sec. 3.13 leads to Eqs. (3.121).

3.30. A point charge of 10^{-10} coulomb is located in empty space at a distance of 2 cm from an infinite, plane surface of a dielectric body whose other boundaries are infinitely remote. The dielectric is isotropic, homogeneous, and linear with a specific dielectric constant of 3. What is the electrostatic force on the charge?

3.31. Given a dielectric body in space having an infinite plane surface, and with its other boundaries infinitely remote from the observer. Suppose it to be isotropic, homogeneous, and linear with permittivity ϵ. Show that an arbitrary charge distribution in the space outside the dielectric produces a polarization whose effects outside and inside the dielectric are representable by certain image distributions, respectively, and specify these distributions. Carry through the argument carefully.

3.32. A thin ring of electric charge with uniform linear density λ is located in space parallel to the infinite, plane boundary of a piece of dielectric material whose other boundaries are infinitely remote, and which is isotropic, homogeneous, and linear with permittivity ϵ. The radius of the ring is R_1 and the distance from its center to the boundary is L. At the place where the axis of the ring cuts the boundary, find (a) the electric field and displacement inside the dielectric and outside and (b) the polarization of the dielectric. See the theorem of the preceding problem.

3.33. a. Given a pair of semi-infinite isotropic dielectric bodies with constant permittivities ϵ_1 and ϵ_2, respectively, meeting in an infinite plane boundary. In each dielectric there is a point charge q, and these two equal charges lie along a common straight line normal to the boundary, at equal distances L from the boundary. Find the electric field and displacement at each charge due to the other.

b. Give the answers also for the similar problem in which the charges are of opposite sign, $+q$ being in ϵ_1 and $-q$ in ϵ_2.

3.34. Given that a certain kind of glass can withstand a field of 100 kv/mm, while its specific dielectric constant is 7.00. At this field strength, find the polarizing field using the Clausius-Mossotti formula. Compare the result with the field of one electronic charge, 1.60×10^{-19} coulomb, at a distance of 10^{-8} cm *in vacuo*.

3.35. Show that the average over all space of the electric field vector in any isolated electrostatic system of finite extent is zero.

3.36. Determine the consistency of

a. The Clausius-Mossotti formula

b. The corresponding equation in which the macroscopic electric field is used for the local field, with the following data for nitrogen:

Density, units	Specific dielectric constant
80	1.04750
130	1.07828
180	1.10953
195	1.11867

3.37. Given the following data for gaseous CO, it is required to obtain the permittivity ϵ at 0°C by use of the Langevin-Debye formula:

Permanent dipole moment: 4.0×10^{-31} coulomb-m

Molecular polarizability for the induced dipole moment only: 2.22×10^{-40} coulomb^2 m/newton

Density: 1.250 g/liter

Molecular weight: 28

3.38. Given that the polarizability of the NH_3 molecule is found by application of the Clausius-Mossotti formula to experimental data to be

$$\alpha = 2.42 \times 10^{-39} \text{ coulomb}^2 \text{ m/newton at 309°K}$$

and

$$\alpha = 1.74 \times 10^{-39} \text{ coulomb}^2 \text{ m/newton at 448°K}.$$

For each temperature, find the part of the polarizability due to the permanent dipole moment and the part due to deformation of the molecule, using the Langevin-Debye formula.

3.39. Given that for HCl gas at 100°C and atmospheric pressure the specific dielectric constant is 1.00258 and the density is 1.200 g/liter. The permanent dipole moment is found by use of the Langevin-Debye formula to be 3.43×10^{-30} coulomb-meter. Assuming the perfect gas law, what is the prediction of the Langevin-Debye formula for the specific dielectric constant at 0°C and 1 atm?

CHAPTER 4

ELECTROSTATIC ENERGY, FORCE, AND CAPACITANCE

4.1. Meaning of Energy. Energy is an enormously useful concept in all fields of physics, including the study of electromagnetism. It is not always easy to understand just what is meant by energy, however, for the term is used differently in different contexts. We shall try to be quite specific in defining energy wherever it is introduced.

It is necessary first to borrow some ideas from thermodynamics. It is possible for energy to be transferred as heat in electromagnetic systems as well as in other systems. In electrostatics, we shall consider the work put into a system or taken out of it in a process where exchange of heat with the surroundings occurs only while the system and the surroundings remain at a constant temperature. Under these conditions the appropriate quantity to be called the energy of the system is what is known in thermodynamics as free energy.[1]

Another important concept is that of reversibility. For our purposes we may say that if a system is reversible, and if a certain amount of work is performed upon it by an external agent while the system undergoes a process, then in the reverse process the system yields the same amount of external work. There are three sources of irreversibility in electromagnetic processes. The one most often encountered is the production of heat in a conductor when charges are transported by the conductor. This may be made as small as we please for a given conductor and given total charge to be passed, if we make the rate of transfer of charge small. A second irreversibility is the radiation of energy in electromagnetic waves. This becomes negligible if all motion of net charge takes place with only small accelerations. We shall assume, in the discussion of electrostatic energy, that it is possible to move free electric charge reversibly and that in such motion the system may be considered to pass through a succession of electrostatic states.

The third source of irreversibility is the production of heat in a dielectric or magnetic medium when its polarization or magnetization changes. We cannot prescribe any method of reducing this energy loss; and it does

---

[1] See, for example, E. Fermi, "Thermodynamics," pp. 77*ff.*, Prentice-Hall, Inc., New York, 1937.

occur in practical dielectrics. Its magnitude for dielectrics is fairly small, however, compared to the corresponding energy loss often encountered in magnetic materials. We shall neglect this irreversibility in this chapter, although it has important practical implications in alternating current apparatus.

Subject to the above considerations, we shall now define the energy of an electrostatic system in some configuration B as the work which must be done by an external agent to bring the system into this configuration starting from a reference configuration A. For the ideal dielectrics with which we are dealing, this work will all be available again in the reverse process. Furthermore in a reversible system the work involved in a given change of configuration is independent of the process by which the system passes from one configuration to the other. It will often be convenient to specify a particular process for purposes of calculation; but in a reversible system the result is perfectly general.

It is important to notice that any assignment of an energy to a system involves an agreement as to what state will be said to have zero energy. Usually, we shall take the zero of energy as corresponding to a state where macroscopic electric fields vanish throughout the system. This will imply that macroscopic charge densities, both free and bound, are likewise zero everywhere in and near the system. Evidently such a definition of zero energy means that we are not considering the intrinsic self-energy of the ultimate particles of matter, nor are we considering the energy involved in their aggregation into uncharged and unpolarized matter. A process by which energy is put into the system will then involve production of macroscopic charge densities (free or bound or both) in the system by relative displacement of some of the positive and negative particles composing the matter in the system. There may be times when it will be convenient to let the system be considered as indefinitely large, so that a given charge configuration may be supposed to be caused by bringing charges up from a very large piece of matter at a very great distance into a region under consideration. In this way, no appreciable charge densities and no appreciable fields are produced at the piece of matter which is the source of the charges. Sometimes one finds energy formulas written in terms of aggregations of charge considered as point charges, in which the energy does not include the energy of aggregation of each point charge but only the energy due to the proximity of the point charges to each other. In such a case, the zero-energy state would be one in which the point aggregations of charge were infinitely removed from one another.

It might be well in this opening section to remark on the units of energy. These are by definition the same as those of work, which in turn are the units of force times distance. We are using mks mechanical units, so that the unit of work is prescribed as the newton meter, which is called the joule.

4.2. A Fundamental Expression for Energy. Let us consider an electrostatic system of finite extent consisting of a certain geometry of conductors, dielectrics, and possibly empty space, and containing finite volume and surface densities of free electric charge. We shall ask what the energy of this system is, that is, the work required to bring it from a condition where the charge densities are all zero to its actual condition. In the discussion we shall assume what is actually the case when charge densities are useful, that vast numbers of elementary charges are involved. This will mean that we may build up the charge densities by such small steps that their increments may be considered continuous.

First of all, consider a system whose total electric charge is zero. The actual process by which the charge densities would ordinarily be produced in such a case is simply transportation of the elementary charges in the materials of the system from one place to another. It will be simpler for analysis to consider a rather artificial process by which all the charges are produced by carrying charge to or from a reservoir of charge at a very great distance from the system. Let us perform this operation in such a way that all the charge densities of the system are built up together, so that at a given point of the process they all have the same fraction α of their final value. In this way the charge of the distant reservoir remains unchanged, and we may take the electrostatic potential of that reservoir as a constant, and in particular as zero, throughout the process. Now the method by which the system is brought from its initial uncharged configuration A to its final charged condition B does not influence the work done during the process, so long as the process has made no alterations in other systems such as the reservoir we have introduced. Thus our artificial method of producing the charges in the system may be used to compute the energy of the system.

Let the macroscopic potential function in the system be $U(x,y,z)$ when the system is charged to its final configuration. When the charge densities all have a fraction α of their final value, the potential function will in general be different, and its form will depend on the value of α, and thus we may write for the potential during the building up of charge a function $U'(\alpha;x,y,z)$ with a parameter α. Let $\rho(x,y,z)$ and $\sigma(x,y,z)$ be the final charge density functions. During the building up of charge, the momentary charge densities are $\alpha\rho(x,y,z)$ and $\alpha\sigma(x,y,z)$. An infinitesimal increment of these charge densities is then $\rho\,d\alpha$ and $\sigma\,d\alpha$. The increment of charge brought to a particular volume element dV of the system is $\rho\,d\alpha\,dV$. By the definition of electrostatic potential in Sec. 1.5, the work done in bringing this charge up from the reservoir is $U'\rho\,d\alpha\,dV$. Similarly, the work done in producing an increment of surface charge in area da is $U'\sigma\, d\alpha\, da$. The work for the whole system during the increment $d\alpha$ is therefore

$$dW = \int_V U'\rho\, d\alpha\, dV + \int_S U'\sigma\, d\alpha\, da \tag{4.1}$$

where V and S, respectively, represent the volume and the surface of the system. The final energy of the system now is found by integration with respect to α over the range zero to one:

$$W = \int_V \rho \int_{\alpha=0}^1 U'\, d\alpha\, dV + \int_S \sigma \int_{\alpha=0}^1 U'\, d\alpha\, da \tag{4.2}$$

The integrals in Eq. (4.2) have been written in this form to remind us that the functions ρ and σ do not involve α, but only (x,y,z).

Equation (4.2) is rather complicated in form, but it is general in the sense that it makes no specification of linearity of the dielectrics of the system. It may be considerably simplified for a system whose dielectrics are all linear, and in which there are no fields due to charges external to the system. In such a system we can write

$$U'(\alpha;x,y,z) = \alpha U(x,y,z) \tag{4.3}$$

A formal proof of this statement may be constructed from the uniqueness theorem for electrostatic systems (Sec. 3.11), using the fact that for linear dielectrics all boundary conditions are linear equations, and the Poisson equation (or its complicated equivalents for nonhomogeneous or anisotropic dielectrics) is a linear equation. In this case, which is the usual one, we can immediately perform the α integration:

$$W = \int_V \rho U \int_{\alpha=0}^1 \alpha\, d\alpha\, dV + \int_S \sigma U \int_{\alpha=0}^1 \alpha\, d\alpha\, da$$

Therefore

$$W = \tfrac{1}{2} \int_V \rho U\, dV + \tfrac{1}{2} \int_S \sigma U\, da \tag{4.4}$$

This equation will be the foundation of our further work with electrostatic energy.

We must now inquire about the energy of a system which is not neutral as a whole but has a net positive or negative charge. The process of bringing the system from a condition in which all charge densities vanish into its final configuration of charge densities then must involve carrying net positive or negative charge to or from some reservoir of charge. This reservoir is likely to be the earth, in practice. However, if the body which acts as a reservoir is small, the process of charging the given system may involve creating appreciable charge densities in the reservoir. This would invalidate the foregoing demonstration, for then the potential of the reservoir is no longer constant during the process.

From a different point of view, we may then consider the system plus the reservoir as a larger system which does remain electrically neutral, so that Eq. (4.2) or (4.4) then applies to the larger system. Thus the work done to charge the original system depends in general on conditions at the reservoir, if the latter is small. Under these conditions, there would be no definite meaning attachable to the energy of our given system. We may hope, however, that if the reservoir is sufficiently large, its effect on the work done in charging our system is negligible. This we shall show only for the specific case in which the reservoir is a large conducting sphere, which will be an approximate electrostatic model of the earth.

Consider, then, a system A whose volume and surfaces are, respectively, V and S, and as reservoir a large conducting sphere G of radius R, outside of which A is located. Let S' be the surface of G. All charge on G will be in the form of a surface density on S' (see Sec. 1.12). Suppose at the start both A and G are uncharged and have zero potential. Let us build up the charge densities in A according to the method used to derive Eqs. (4.2) and (4.4), only now a total net charge q is to be transported to the system from G, leaving G with a total charge $-q$ at the end of the process. Now let the system A be small in dimensions compared to its distance h from the surface of the sphere. A then appears to the sphere to be a point charge at distance h from its surface. The potential of the sphere is now

$$U_G = \frac{1}{4\pi\epsilon_0 R}\left(-q + \frac{qR}{R+h}\right)$$

by the electrostatic image theory of Sec. 2.6. This reduces to

$$U_G = -\frac{qh}{4\pi\epsilon_0 R(R+h)} \tag{4.5}$$

All we require of Eq. (4.5) is to show that $U_G \to 0$ as $R \to \infty$, which holds regardless of the value of h. Therefore as the reservoir G increases in size, its potential remains more nearly zero as we charge our system A. In the limit then, the expressions (4.2) and (4.4) remain valid for systems having a net charge, provided this is derived from a large enough reservoir; for then the assumptions behind these equations are still valid.

The same conclusion is reached by applying Eq. (4.2) or (4.4) to the larger neutral system $A + G$, for then the integral over G approaches zero as the size of the reservoir increases. To show this, we may take the potential on G out from the surface integral, since G is a conductor; and this potential as we have seen, approaches zero as $R \to \infty$.

We conclude that Eqs. (4.2) and (4.4) are valid not only for neutral systems but for charged systems, provided the charge is derived from a large reservoir such as the earth. The proof was only given for a spherical, conducting reservoir at a distance from the system large compared to the system's dimensions, but may be made more general. In particular, the restriction on the relative size of h and the system A may be dropped. Of course, if h is of the same order of magnitude as the dimensions of the system, the proximity of the reservoir G may have an important influence on the values of the potential in the system A and hence on the energy of A; but the formulas (4.2) and (4.4) remain valid.

One reservation should perhaps be made that has not been mentioned. Equations (4.2) and (4.4) do not explicitly involve bound charges, though these charges contribute to the potential and hence are implicit in the U functions. This is because the creation of bound charge is usually spontaneous, and it is the transfer of free charge which we supposed to be responsible for storing energy in a system. There may be systems for which bound charges appear not as induced by free charge, but caused by piezoelectric or pyroelectric effects, that is, by mechanical or thermal strain of the dielectric. Also, there might be permanent polarizations in the system. In such cases Eq. (4.4) is evidently not valid, because the polarization is not then proportional to the electric field. Also, we must expect to have to generalize Eq. (4.2). It might be, for example, that no free charge would exist in a system at all, and yet there would be energy storage because of the bound charges.

4.3. Energy of a System Containing Macroscopic Point Charges. The reader has doubtless noticed in the examples given so far in this book that point charges frequently form part of an electrostatic system. If these charges are to be of a size detectable in ordinary experiments, they are probably not single elementary charges, but assemblages of great numbers of elementary charges. In a practical case, the point charges of a system may be charged conducting or insulating particles whose dimensions are small compared with the other dimensions of the problem. While specifying that these bodies be small enough, the name point charge leaves their size and shape undetermined and implies that these characteristics are immaterial in the problem. Evidently, however, the size and shape of the bodies is of great importance to their energy, since it affects the potential in them. For example, the part of the potential on a small sphere of radius r due to its own charge q is $q/4\pi\epsilon_0 r$, which increases without limit as r approaches zero. It appears therefore that the total energy of a system in which macroscopic point charges appear is not usually of interest, since additional data to that involved in the rest of the problem is required before this energy is determined. We may define the self-energy of a macroscopic particle or point charge as the energy required to charge it when it is very distant from other systems, including the reservoir used to charge it. The process of constructing an electrostatic system containing point charges may then be considered to occur in three steps. First the point charges may be charged in an isolated position. If the self-energy of the ith particle is W_i, then this first step takes an amount of work

$$W_s = \sum_i W_i \qquad (4.6)$$

Next, fixed volume or surface charge densities of the system may be brought in from the reservoir, at the expense of some amount of work W_D. Lastly, the point charges may be assembled into the system, at the expense of work W_A. The total energy of the system is

$$W = W_s + W_D + W_A \qquad (4.7)$$

From what we have said, it appears that only the part

$$W' = W_D + W_A \qquad (4.8)$$

is calculable when the constitution of the point charges is unknown. For lack of a better term, W' may be called the apparent energy of the system.

Care must be taken in the calculation of the work of assemblage W_A. For example, suppose a single point charge q_1 is to be moved up from a great distance to its final position. Let the electric field at the position of q_1 during the process of moving it up be $\mathbf{E}_1(x,y,z)$. This field is to represent the effect of all other charges of the system, including those induced by q_1, but it cannot of course include the field of q_1 directly. Then, according to the definition of $\mathbf{E}_1$ (Sec. 1.4), the force of the field on q_1 at any position is given by

$$\mathbf{F}_1 = q_1\mathbf{E}_1$$

The work done by an external agent to move the charge up to its final position $P_1(x,y,z)$ is now

$$W_{A1} = -q_1 \int_\infty^{P_1} \mathbf{E}_1 \cdot d\mathbf{l} \qquad (4.9)$$

where the path of integration can be chosen at will. The total work of assemblage of any number of charges can be found by bringing them up one after the other and applying (4.9) each time, remembering to include the field of all those charges previously brought up. There is a temptation to avoid the labor involved in this integration by using the potential U_1' at the final position P_1 of the point charge, computed from all charges already in the system exclusive of q_1 itself, but including charges induced by q_1. Here there is a pitfall to be avoided. The work of bringing up q_1 is not in general equal to $q_1 U_1'$. This is because U_1' is defined with reference to a test charge of infinitesimal magnitude. Bringing up an infinitesimal charge leaves the field produced by the system constant, whereas bringing up a finite charge does not, if there are conductors or dielectrics in the system.

This matter is important enough to be illustrated by an example. Suppose we wish to find the work required to bring a point charge q up to a distance l from an infinite, plane, grounded conductor surface. Set up the problem as in Fig. 4.1 with the yz plane as the conductor surface. The field $\mathbf{E_1}$ of Eq. (4.9), when the charge q_1 has been brought to a position x, is that of an image charge $-q_1$ located at $-x$. Thus $\mathbf{E_1}$ is in the x direction, and has the value $q_1/4\pi\epsilon_0(2x)^2$. The integrand of (4.9) is

$$\mathbf{E_1} \cdot d\mathbf{l} = \frac{q_1\,dx}{4\pi\epsilon_0(2x)^2}$$

Therefore

$$W_{A1} = -\frac{q_1^2}{16\pi\epsilon_0} \int_{-\infty}^{-l} \frac{dx}{x^2} = -\frac{q_1^2}{16\pi\epsilon_0 l}$$
$$(4.10)$$

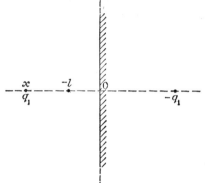

FIG. 4.1. Point charge approaching an infinite, plane conducting boundary.

This is the correct energy of assembly of the system. Now when q_1 is at its final position $x = -l$, the potential at this point exclusive of the direct contribution of q_1 itself is that produced by the image charge:

$$U_1' = -\frac{q_1}{4\pi\epsilon_0(2l)} = -\frac{q_1}{8\pi\epsilon_0 l} \qquad (4.11)$$

Evidently $q_1 U_1'$ gives twice the value of the actual energy; or in this case

$$W_{A1} = \tfrac{1}{2} q_1 U_1' \qquad (4.12)$$

We shall now derive a general formula for the apparent energy of a linear system containing point charges, from which Eq. (4.12) could have been deduced immediately. Suppose first that point charges of the system are composed of rigidly fixed distributions of free charge, and that no induced charges will occur in these point charges. Apply Eq. (4.4) to the completed system containing these point charges, together with an arbitrary arrangement of conductors, dielectrics, and fixed charge densities. Let V_i and S_i stand for the volume and surfaces of the point charge q_i of the system, while V' and S' stand for the volume and the surfaces of the system exclusive of point charges. Then

$$W = \tfrac{1}{2} \int_{V'} \rho U\,dV + \tfrac{1}{2} \int_{S'} \sigma U\,da + \tfrac{1}{2} \sum_i \int_{V_i} \rho U\,dV$$
$$+ \tfrac{1}{2} \sum_i \int_{S_i} \sigma U\,da \qquad (4.13)$$

Now suppose the potential at a general point within the point charge q_i to be written as in Sec. 3.8:

$$U_i = \frac{1}{4\pi\epsilon_0} \int \frac{dq}{r} \tag{4.14}$$
$$\text{all charges} \atop \text{free + bound}$$

Split this potential into two parts: U_i'' involving the fixed, free charges composing the charge q_i, and U_i' involving all the other charges of the system. Thus in each charge q_i we split the potential function U_i into parts such that

$$U_i = U_i' + U_i'' \tag{4.15}$$

Expression (4.13) now becomes:

$$W = \tfrac{1}{2}\int_{V'}\rho U\, dV + \tfrac{1}{2}\int_{S'}\sigma U\, da + \tfrac{1}{2}\sum_i\int_{V_i}\rho U_i'\, dV + \tfrac{1}{2}\sum_i\int_{S_i}\sigma U_i'\, da$$
$$+ \tfrac{1}{2}\sum_i\int_{V_i}\rho U_i''\, dV + \tfrac{1}{2}\sum_i\int_{S_i}\sigma U_i''\, da \tag{4.16}$$

The reason for this complicated form is that we can identify the sum of the last two terms as the self-energy of the point charges:

$$W_s = \sum_i\left(\tfrac{1}{2}\int_{V_i}\rho U_i''\, dV + \tfrac{1}{2}\int_{S_i}\sigma U_i''\, da\right) \tag{4.17}$$

Because of the supposition of fixed charge distributions within each point charge, and by the definition of the U_i'', these integrals yield the same values of energy when the system is assembled as when the point charges are all isolated. Therefore these energies are the same as those in Eq. (4.6) of this section. By comparing Eqs. (4.7) and (4.8) we note that the apparent energy of the system is then the remainder of (4.16):

$$W' = \tfrac{1}{2}\int_{V'}\rho U\, dV + \tfrac{1}{2}\int_{S'}\sigma U\, da + \tfrac{1}{2}\sum_i\int_{V_i}\rho U_i'\, dV$$
$$+ \tfrac{1}{2}\sum_i\int_{S_i}\sigma U_i'\, da \tag{4.18}$$

The two last terms can be written in a more compact form. Since the charges q_i were assumed to be as small as we please compared with the whole system, the variation of the partial potential U_i', due to everything outside q_i, is negligible within q_i. Thus the last two integrals become simply

$$\tfrac{1}{2}\sum_i U_i'\left(\int_{V_i}\rho\, dV + \int_{S_i}\sigma\, da\right) = \tfrac{1}{2}\sum_i U_i' q_i$$

Our result is now that the apparent energy of the whole system is given by

$$W' = \tfrac{1}{2} \int_{V'} \rho U \, dV + \tfrac{1}{2} \int_{S'} \sigma U \, da + \tfrac{1}{2} \sum_i q_i U_i' \qquad (4.19)$$

It is well to repeat that here the integrations are over just those parts of the system where there are continuous charge distributions and that bound charge distributions do not appear explicitly. Induced charges on conductors are included since they are free charge. It should be noticed that since the surface of a conductor is an equipotential, and since all the charge of a conductor is on its surface, the presence of a conductor whose charge is q_c and whose potential is U_c contributes a term $\tfrac{1}{2} q_c U_c$ to the apparent energy of the system. Thus if S'' stands for any nonconducting surfaces which may have fixed surface density of charge, we may again rewrite our formula for apparent energy:

$$W' = \tfrac{1}{2} \int_{V'} \rho U \, dV + \tfrac{1}{2} \int_{S''} \sigma U \, da + \tfrac{1}{2} \sum_{\substack{c \\ \text{all} \\ \text{conductors}}} q_c U_c + \tfrac{1}{2} \sum_{\substack{i \\ \text{all} \\ \text{point charges}}} q_i U_i' \qquad (4.20)$$

Quite frequently, as in the example given earlier in this section, a system will contain no fixed, free densities of charge except for point charges or charges on conductors. In this case Eq. (4.20) gives the apparent energy without integrations. Notice that conductors on which either the potential or the total charge vanish have no explicit contribution to this calculation of the energy.

It remains only to justify the use of Eqs. (4.19) and (4.20) regardless of the internal constitution of the point charges. It is true that if there are conductors and dielectrics in the constitution of a point charge, the distribution of charge density and also the partial potential U_i'' will change somewhat as the point charge is brought up from an isolated position to its place in the system. The question is whether this will appreciably affect the self-energy of the point charge as computed from Eq. (4.17), for our derivation assumed that the integrals (4.17) had the same value when the point charges were assembled into the system as when isolated. The simplest answer is that if the charges act as points, the work of assembling them into a system must be independent of their internal changes, which occur spontaneously. The apparent energy W' must therefore be independent of the internal constitution of the point charges. Hence our results (4.19) and (4.20) must still be correct, even though the assumption that the point charges consist of rigidly distributed fixed charges is violated.

4.4. Energy of Elementary Particles. It is frequently necessary in atomic physics to consider from a microscopic viewpoint systems composed of elementary charged particles. These particles may then appear individually in the analysis, rather than being accounted for by a macroscopic charge density. Usually, the elementary particles are treated as point charges, whose structure is on a much smaller scale than the other distances of the problem and is totally unknown. The analysis of the preceding section is appropriate for treating the external energy of such systems, since the structure of the point charges does not enter into the final equations. The potentials and fields involved then will be microscopic rather than macroscopic.

If we inquire about the self-energy of an elementary particle, such as the electron, from an electrostatic viewpoint, we are really only playing a game with our formulas. There is in the first place no knowledge of the internal structure of the electron, nor even of its exact size. Besides this, the energy of a system is defined by the work required to assemble it starting from one specified configuration. The electron cannot be considered capable of assembly by bringing up smaller charges to form a submicroscopic charge density; for no smaller quantities of charge are known experimentally than the total charge of the electron. Therefore, if we apply such a formula as Eq. (4.4) to a supposed structure for the electron, there is serious question whether the result means anything at all.

In spite of this, it is amusing to try applying our energy formulas to a simple model of the electron and to equate the electrostatic self-energy to the Einstein self-energy m_0c^2. Here m_0 is the rest mass of the electron and c the velocity of light *in vacuo*. If, for instance, we suppose the charge e of the electron to be distributed uniformly over the surface of a sphere of radius r, the potential at all points of this surface would be

$$U = \frac{e}{4\pi\epsilon_0 r}$$

and the formal value for the electrostatic self-energy would be, from Eq. (4.4),

$$W = \frac{e^2}{8\pi\epsilon_0 r} \tag{4.21}$$

Equating this to m_0c^2 we obtain

$$r = \frac{e^2}{8\pi\epsilon_0 m_0 c^2} \tag{4.22}$$

The only remarkable thing about this formula is that it does give a sensible answer; that is, the value is not inconsistent with other knowledge. If we substitute the values into Eq. (4.22), we obtain 1.41×10^{-15} m.

4.5. Electrostatic Energy in Terms of Field Vectors. The electrostatic energy of a system containing macroscopic charge densities ρ and σ, relative to a state where all charge densities and fields are zero, is given by Eqs. (4.2) and (4.4) in terms of these densities and the macroscopic potential function U. Now ρ and σ are related to the electric displacement vector **D**, while U is related to the electric field vector **E**. The energy equations may be transformed mathematically so as to involve only these vectors **D** and **E**, provided the distribution of charge densities is finite in extent. We shall show this transformation for a linear dielectric and for a simple system in which the only boundaries are the surfaces of a conductor. Generalization of the proof involves only some complexities which we wish to omit.

Consider then an isolated conductor C whose surface S_c bears a charge density σ, embedded in an infinite linear dielectric which need not be isotropic or homogeneous (see Fig. 4.2). In the space outside the conductor there may be an arbitrary volume charge density function ρ, provided this function vanishes within a finite distance from the conductor, but we suppose there is no cavity containing free charge within C. The energy of the system is given by Eq. (4.4):

$$W = \tfrac{1}{2} \int_V \rho U \, dV + \tfrac{1}{2} \int_{S_c} \sigma U \, da \quad (4.4)$$

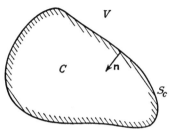

Here the volume V is all space outside the conductor. Let us "enclose" the volume V by describing an infinite spherical surface S_∞ about an origin in the conductor. Thus S_c and S_∞ are the two boundaries of V. Denote an outward unit normal from V on either boundary by $\mathbf{n}$.

FIG. 4.2. Isolated conductor.

This means that $\mathbf{n}$ is inward to the conductor C. We may now write

$$\sigma = -\mathbf{D} \cdot \mathbf{n} \quad\quad\quad (4.23)$$

by Eq. (3.96). Also, from Eq. (3.71),

$$\rho = \frac{\partial D_x}{\partial x} + \frac{\partial D_y}{\partial y} + \frac{\partial D_z}{\partial z} \quad\quad (3.71)$$

Making these substitutions in Eq. (4.4), we obtain

$$W = \tfrac{1}{2} \int_V \left(U \frac{\partial D_x}{\partial x} + U \frac{\partial D_y}{\partial y} + U \frac{\partial D_z}{\partial z} \right) dV - \tfrac{1}{2} \int_{S_c} U\mathbf{D} \cdot \mathbf{n} \, da \quad (4.24)$$

It will now be necessary to add the integral $-\tfrac{1}{2} \int_{S_\infty} U\mathbf{D} \cdot \mathbf{n} \, da$, in order to perform formally the desired transformation. This integral is actually zero under the specified conditions; for the functions U and $\mathbf{D}$ will fall off rapidly with increasing distance from the whole system. If the system has a net charge, these functions fall off as $1/R$ and $1/R^2$, respectively, at great distances R from the system, provided the dielectric is homogeneous. If the net charge of the system is zero, the decrease of these functions with distance is even more rapid. Inhomogeneities of the dielectric may have, in practice, only a minor effect on the behavior of these functions. Since the surface S_∞ increases only as R^2, we are assured that in the limit as R increases

$$-\tfrac{1}{2} \int_{S_\infty} U\mathbf{D} \cdot \mathbf{n} \, da = 0 \quad\quad\quad (4.25)$$

Therefore we may add this integral to Eq. (4.24), to obtain

$$W = \tfrac{1}{2} \int_V \left(U \frac{\partial D_x}{\partial x} + U \frac{\partial D_y}{\partial y} + U \frac{\partial D_z}{\partial z} \right) dV - \tfrac{1}{2} \int_{S_c + S_\infty} U \mathbf{D} \cdot \mathbf{n} \, da \tag{4.26}$$

where the surface integral now completely encloses V. The advantage of this is that the surface integral may be transformed into a volume integral by use of the divergence theorem. See Sec. 3.4 where this identity is given in terms of the $\mathbf{P}$ vector, as Eq. (3.39),

$$\oint_S \mathbf{P} \cdot \mathbf{n} \, da = \int_V \operatorname{div} \mathbf{P} \, dV \tag{3.39}$$

Here S is the complete boundary surface enclosing V. Let us apply this theorem to the surface integral in Eq. (4.26), which involves the vector $(U\mathbf{D})$ in place of $\mathbf{P}$:

$$\int_{S_c + S_\infty} (U\mathbf{D}) \cdot \mathbf{n} \, da = \int_V \left[\frac{\partial}{\partial x} (UD_x) + \frac{\partial}{\partial y} (UD_y) + \frac{\partial}{\partial z} (UD_z) \right] dV \tag{4.27}$$

We may split this volume integral into two by using the product rule of differential calculus:

$$\oint_{S_c + S_\infty} (U\mathbf{D}) \cdot \mathbf{n} \, da = \int_V \left(U \frac{\partial D_x}{\partial x} + U \frac{\partial D_y}{\partial y} + U \frac{\partial D_z}{\partial z} \right) dV$$
$$+ \int_V \left(D_x \frac{\partial U}{\partial x} + D_y \frac{\partial U}{\partial y} + D_z \frac{\partial U}{\partial z} \right) dV \tag{4.28}$$

Substitution of Eq. (4.28) into (4.26) cancels the first integral of (4.26) and leaves:

$$W = \tfrac{1}{2} \int_V - \left(D_x \frac{\partial U}{\partial x} + D_y \frac{\partial U}{\partial y} + D_z \frac{\partial U}{\partial z} \right) dV \tag{4.29}$$

Finally, Eq. (4.29) may be rewritten by noting that the integrand is just $\mathbf{D} \cdot \mathbf{E}$, since $E_x = -(\partial U/\partial x)$, etc. Thus we obtain the desired formulation of the electrostatic energy of a system in terms of $\mathbf{D}$ and $\mathbf{E}$:

$$W = \tfrac{1}{2} \int_V \mathbf{D} \cdot \mathbf{E} \, dV \tag{4.30}$$

To generalize this equation, notice that V is all space except for the volume of the conducting body C; while under our assumption, there was no free charge and hence zero field everywhere inside C. We may therefore obtain the energy of the system equally well by indicating that the volume integral shall be taken over all space:

$$W = \tfrac{1}{2} \int_{\text{all space}} \mathbf{D} \cdot \mathbf{E} \, dV \tag{4.31}$$

It should be mentioned that in practice, the integral need only be evaluated over a large enough volume to approach its limit to the desired accuracy. This means that the volume of integration must include all regions where the fields produced by the system are appreciable. The convergence of the integral as V expands without limit is seen to be a consequence of Eq. (4.25), if we retrace our steps; and (4.25) in turn is a consequence of our assuming a system in which all free charge was confined in a finite space. Because of the convergence of Eq. (4.31), we need not be troubled by philosophical questions of whether there can be any other systems in the universe if (4.31) is to apply. Other systems, including the reservoir from which our given system was originally charged, need only be far enough away.

We must make two more comments on the result of this section. Notice first that Eq. (4.31) does not depend on any assumption of isotropy or homogeneity of the dielectric. Even sharp dielectric interfaces may readily be included in the proof by using the boundary conditions of Secs. 3.9 and 3.10. If the dielectric is isotropic, then $\mathbf{E}$ and $\mathbf{D}$ have the same direction and are related by $\mathbf{D} = \epsilon\mathbf{E}$, where ϵ is in general a function of the coordinates. Equation (4.31) becomes for this case

$$W = \tfrac{1}{2} \int_{\text{all space}} \epsilon E^2 \, dV \qquad (4.32)$$

The second comment concerns the meaning of the transformation from Eq. (4.4) to (4.31). Equation (4.4) seems to imply that the energy is distributed only where there is charge density, while Eq. (4.31) seems to imply that the energy resides wherever there is an electric field. Actually, neither equation implies anything, mathematically, about a space distribution of energy in the system. Each equation is simply a method of computing the total energy of the system with reference to the state of no charge densities or fields. It is doubtful whether the concept of a space distribution of electrostatic energy, which would be expressed as an energy density function, has any experimental significance. Yet the quantity

$$w \equiv \tfrac{1}{2}\mathbf{D} \cdot \mathbf{E} \qquad (4.33)$$

is sometimes called the energy density of the electrostatic field. From our present viewpoint, we must think of this as purely a definition. An additional physical postulate is needed when we apply Eq. (4.33) to an electromagnetic wave, as we shall do later on, and relate this expression to an observable quantity.

4.6. Linear Systems of Conductors. Consider an electrostatic system composed of linear dielectric material and conductors, and suppose that the conductors bear all the free charge of the system. The potential function in the system then satisfies Laplace's equation, derived from (3.113) by setting $\rho = 0$ if the dielectric is homogeneous:

$$\frac{\partial^2 U}{\partial x^2} + \frac{\partial^2 U}{\partial y^2} + \frac{\partial U^2}{\partial z^2} = 0 \qquad (4.34)$$

In the nonhomogeneous case, a somewhat more complex differential equation results from (3.110). Now these equations are *linear* in the function $U(x,y,z)$; that is, if $U^{(a)}$ and $U^{(b)}$ are two solutions, then $aU^{(a)} + bU^{(b)}$ is likewise a solution for any pair of constants a, b. The same property of linearity characterizes all the boundary conditions of the problem. At a dielectric interface, where according to the postulates of this section there must be no free surface charge σ, if $U^{(a)}$ and $U^{(b)}$ satisfy Eqs. (3.101) and (3.104), so does $aU^{(a)} + bU^{(b)}$. At a conductor surface, if $U^{(a)}$ and $U^{(b)}$ satisfy Eq. (3.105) with constant values $V^{(a)}$ and $V^{(b)}$, then $aU^{(a)} + bU^{(b)}$ satisfies this equation with a constant value $aV^{(a)} + bV^{(b)}$. Finally, if the solutions $U^{(a)}$ and $U^{(b)}$ correspond to charges $q^{(a)}$ and $q^{(b)}$ on a conductor, the solution $aU^{(a)} + bU^{(b)}$ corresponds to a charge $aq^{(a)} + bq^{(b)}$.

A simple relation between the charges and potentials of the conductors of such a linear system results from these linearity properties. Suppose the jth conductor has a potential V_j when only the kth conductor has a charge and this charge is q_k. If q_k is multiplied by a factor a, so is V_j; thus $V_j \propto q_k$, or

$$V_j = p_{jk}q_k \qquad (4.35)$$

where the constant of proportionality is labeled p_{jk}. This constant is evidently a characteristic of the geometry and the dielectric constants of the system. Next suppose only the lth conductor is charged. By the same reasoning,

$$V_j = p_{jl}q_l \qquad (4.36)$$

where p_{jl} is another constant. If now both the k and l conductors are charged simultaneously, linearity tells us that

$$V_j = p_{jk}q_k + p_{jl}q_l \qquad (4.37)$$

The generalization of Eq. (4.37) for a system with N conductors is

$$V_j = \sum_{n=1}^{N} p_{jn}q_n \qquad (4.38)$$

These constants p_{jn} are called *coefficients of potential*.

Just as the conductor potentials in a given geometry are determined when the charges of all conductors are given, so are the charges determined when the potentials of all conductors are given. We may therefore solve Eqs. (4.38) for the charges in terms of the potentials. The solutions of this set of linear equations form another set of linear equations

$$q_n = \sum_{j=1}^{N} c_{nj} V_j \qquad (4.39)$$

The new constants c_{nj} are called coefficients of capacitance when the two indices are alike, or coefficients of induction when the indices are unlike. They are expressible in terms of the p_{jn} by relations which are conveniently written with determinants.

4.7. Energy of a Linear System of Conductors. We already have developed formulas which will give the energy of a system of conductors and linear dielectrics in which all free charge is that of the conductors. To adapt Eq. (4.4), we must simply put $\rho = 0$ and remember that U is a constant V_j over a given conductor surface and that the integral $\int_{S_j} \sigma \, da$ over a conductor surface is the charge q_j of that conductor. Summing over all the N conductor surfaces, we then obtain

$$W = \frac{1}{2} \sum_{j=1}^{N} V_j q_j \qquad (4.40)$$

This may be rewritten now in terms of the coefficients of potential by using Eq. (4.38):

$$W = \frac{1}{2} \sum_{j=1}^{N} \sum_{n=1}^{N} p_{jn} q_j q_n \qquad (4.41)$$

Likewise, using Eq. (4.39) with appropriate indices,

$$W = \frac{1}{2} \sum_{j=1}^{N} \sum_{n=1}^{N} c_{jn} V_j V_n \qquad (4.42)$$

Suppose now that we apply Eq. (4.41) to a system in which only two conductors are charged, the others all being insulated and having a zero charge. Call the charged conductors r and s. The energy of the system when these conductors have respective charges q_r and q_s is

$$W = \frac{1}{2}(p_{rr} q_r^2 + p_{rs} q_r q_s + p_{sr} q_s q_r + p_{ss} q_s^2) \qquad (4.43)$$

It is very instructive to compute this energy for the pair of conductors in a different manner from that used in the derivation of Eq. (4.4). There we thought of the charges in the system as being built up simultaneously in all parts of the system by the transfer of charge from a large reservoir. We have stated that the work done in assembling a conservative linear system is the same for any process, and depends only on the initial and final configurations of the system. Let us now suppose our charges q_r and q_s to be brought up not simultaneously, but q_r first; and then q_s is brought up, while q_r is held constant. Equation (4.41) gives the work to charge conductor r when $q_s = 0$ (and all other charges are zero):

$$W_1 = \tfrac{1}{2}p_{rr}q_r^2 \tag{4.44}$$

We next proceed to charge conductor s. At a stage in this process, let the momentary charge q_s' on s be a fraction α of its final value q_s, so that $q_s' = \alpha q_s$. Then from Eq. (4.38), the momentary potential V_s' on s is

$$V_s' = p_{sr}q_r + p_{ss}(\alpha q_s) \tag{4.45}$$

The element of work required to bring up an infinitesimal charge from the reservoir is then, by the nature of electrostatic potential,

$$dW_2 = V_s' \, dq_s' = V_s' q_s \, d\alpha \tag{4.46}$$

Therefore

$$dW_2 = p_{sr}q_r q_s \, d\alpha + p_{ss}q_s^2 \alpha \, d\alpha \tag{4.47}$$

The entire work required in charging s is found from Eq. (4.47) by integration with respect to α between the limits zero and one. Remembering that all other quantities in Eq. (4.47) are constant during this integration, we obtain immediately

$$W_2 = p_{sr}q_r q_s + \tfrac{1}{2}p_{ss}q_s^2 \tag{4.48}$$

The work done in charging our two conductors by this process is now:

$$W = W_1 + W_2 = \tfrac{1}{2}p_{rr}q_r^2 + p_{sr}q_r q_s + \tfrac{1}{2}p_{ss}q_s^2 \tag{4.49}$$

Comparison of this equation with (4.43) yields:

$$\tfrac{1}{2}(p_{rs} + p_{sr}) = p_{sr}$$

Therefore

$$p_{rs} = p_{sr} \tag{4.50}$$

Equation (4.50) is a fundamental relationship between any pair of the coefficients of potential for a linear system of conductors and dielectrics. In words, this relation says that the potential to which conductor r is brought by unit charge on s is the same as the potential produced on s by unit charge on r. Notice how the power of the energy concept is demonstrated by our derivation.

The algebraic connection between the coefficients p_{rs} and c_{mn} can be used to show that symmetry like that of Eq. (4.50) holds also for the coefficients of induction:

$$c_{mn} = c_{nm} \tag{4.51}$$

The reader may construct this proof with the help of an algebra text which gives the application of determinants to solutions of sets of linear equations. It is much more profitable, for acquisition of skill in analyzing electrostatic problems, to prove Eq. (4.51) directly by an argument from the energy of the system. This may be done by considering a case in which all conductor potentials in the system except two are zero. The energy of the system may be written out from Eq. (4.42). A separate computation of the energy may then be made by supposing first one conductor to be charged to its final potential, say V_m, all other conductors having their potential maintained at zero during the process. The maintenance of a conductor at zero potential during the building up of charge in a system requires no work, since transfer of infinitesimal charges from the zero-potential reservoir to a zero-potential conductor requires no work. Next another conductor is charged from zero to its final potential V_n, while V_m is held constant and all other conductors are kept grounded. In this process, it is essential to note that work is done not only to charge the nth conductor, but also to maintain the nonzero potential V_m of the mth conductor, since the charge of the mth conductor is affected. Finally, equating the total work done in this two-stage process to that obtained for the system from Eq. (4.42) yields the desired relation (4.51). The details are left to the reader as a problem.

We may make some further deductions about the coefficients of potential, capacitance, and induction by energy considerations. The energy of an electrostatic system is always positive in relation to the state where no fields are present. This is shown, at least for isotropic systems, by the form of Eq. (4.32). From Eqs. (4.41) and (4.42) it is seen immediately that all coefficients p_{jj} and c_{kk} are positive, if we consider the energy of systems where only one conductor at a time is charged, or where only one conductor at a time has a potential other than zero.

Next suppose that only two conductors of a system are charged, their charges being q_r and q_s. Their energy is given by Eq. (4.49). The condition that this energy be always positive is

$$p_{rr}q_r^2 + 2p_{sr}q_rq_s + p_{ss}q_s^2 > 0 \qquad (4.52)$$

Let us write

$$q_r = \beta q_s \qquad (4.53)$$

Then Eq. (4.52) becomes

$$q_s^2(p_{rr}\beta^2 + 2p_{sr}\beta + p_{ss}) > 0 \qquad (4.54)$$

This inequality must hold for all values of β. A necessary and sufficient condition that this be so is that

$$p_{ss} > 0 \qquad (4.55)$$

(as we have already remarked), and that there be no value of β for which

$$p_{rr}\beta^2 + 2p_{sr}\beta + p_{ss} = 0 \qquad (4.56)$$

For if $p_{ss} > 0$, the inequality (4.54) holds when $\beta = 0$; and if and only if the expression on the left of (4.54), as a function of β, never reaches zero, then it remains positive as the inequality requires. The quadratic formula for the solution of Eq. (4.56) is

$$\beta = \frac{-2p_{sr} \pm \sqrt{4p_{sr}^2 - 4p_{rr}p_{ss}}}{2p_{rr}} \qquad (4.57)$$

This has no real solution as required, if and only if

$$p_{sr}^2 < p_{rr}p_{ss} \qquad (4.58)$$

since $p_{rr}p_{ss}$ is positive. The inequality (4.58) is thus always true, and represents a general relation between the coefficients of potential. The same argument applied to the coefficients of capacitance and induction yields the same relations:

$$c_{sr}^2 < c_{rr}c_{ss} \qquad (4.59)$$
$$c_{ss} > 0 \qquad (4.60)$$

4.8. Further Properties of the Coefficients of Potential, Induction, and Capacitance. Other general statements may be made concerning the coefficients of potential, capacitance, and induction of a linear system. These we shall state without formal proof. The proofs are simple and rest upon Gauss' law, but they will be omitted for brevity. The coefficients of potential satisfy the inequalities

$$p_{jj} \geqq p_{ij} \qquad (4.61)$$
$$p_{ij} > 0 \qquad i \neq j \qquad (4.62)$$

These inequalities state that if only one conductor of the system is charged, the jth, say, positively, then its own potential is at least as great as that anywhere in the system and that the resulting potential is positive for all other conductors of the system. The coefficients of induction are all negative or zero:

$$c_{ij} \leqq 0 \qquad i \neq j \qquad (4.63)$$

This means that if only one conductor is at a potential above zero, while all other conductors are at zero potential, the charges on the zero-potential conductors are all either negative or zero. When the induced charges are trapped by subsequent insulation of the conductors bearing them, these conductors are said to be charged by induction.

When a conductor 1 is completely enclosed by a conductor 2, 1 is said to be electrostatically shielded by 2 from any parts of the system outside

2.   Supposing a conductor 3 to lie outside 2, the reader may show that

$$c_{13} = 0 \qquad (4.64)$$
$$c_{12} = -c_{11} \qquad (4.65)$$
$$p_{12} = p_{22} \qquad (4.66)$$
$$p_{13} = p_{23} \qquad (4.67)$$

4.9. Condensers.   In the broadest sense of the word, a condenser, or capacitor, is simply a pair of conductors insulated from one another. The system of which they form a part may contain other conductors; and some of these may be grounded while some may be insulated so as to have fixed charges.   We shall continue to suppose all dielectrics to be linear.   Let our pair of conductors be called 1 and 2, and let them originally have any common potential V_0, as we may ensure by momentarily connecting them together with a wire.   Now let an electric charge q be added to that which may already be on 1, raising its potential to V_1; and a charge $-q$ be added to 2, lowering its potential to V_2.   We shall call q the charge of the condenser.   The difference of the potentials so created we shall call $V \equiv V_1 - V_2$.   Because of the linear nature of the equations relating charges to potentials in the system, it will follow that $q \propto V$.   We shall define the capacitance of the condenser C by the relation

$$q = CV \qquad (4.68)$$

This quantity C is of such great practical use that its units have been given a special name.   If q is in coulombs and V in volts, then the units of C are coulombs per volt.   This unit is called the farad, in honor of Michael Faraday.[1]   It will also apply to the coefficients of capacitance and induction c_{jj} and c_{ij}.   Coefficients of potential may be expressed in farads^{-1}.

Consider the foregoing process next from the viewpoint of energy storage.   No work is required to maintain other neighboring conductors at ground potential or at fixed charges.   The total work done in the process is therefore that required to transport charge q from conductor 2 to conductor 1; for the addition of $-q$ to 2 is equivalent to the subtraction of $+q$ from it.   At a stage of this process the potential difference may have a fraction α of its final value; and then the charge transported has the same fraction α of its final value.   An element of charge is therefore $q\,d\alpha$, and the work done to transport this element is

$$dW_c = (\alpha V)q\,d\alpha = qV\alpha\,d\alpha \qquad (4.69)$$

Integration from the beginning of the process, $\alpha = 0$, to its conclusion, $\alpha = 1$, gives the total energy stored in the process

$$W_c = \tfrac{1}{2}qV \qquad (4.70)$$

[1] 1791–1867.

Alternative forms of this expression are obtained by use of Eq. (4.68):

$$W_c = \tfrac{1}{2}CV^2 = \frac{q^2}{2C} \tag{4.71}$$

It is often convenient to restrict the word condenser to rather special systems of two conductors in close proximity, for which the coefficients of capacitance and induction are related approximately by $c_{11} = c_{22} = -c_{12}$ and $c_{1j} = c_{2j} = 0$ for $j > 2$. The capacitance is then $C = c_{11}$, and the charges q_1 and q_2 are just $\pm q$. Such a system we shall call an ideal condenser. Note that the sum of the charges on the two conductors of an ideal condenser is always zero. Ideal condensers of this sort may be connected together into systems of condensers by wires. An equivalent capacitance exists between any two terminals of such a network. In the next section we shall consider basic laws of such networks.

The measurement of the capacitance of a condenser is a means of determining specific inductive capacities. If the region occupied by the field of a condenser is completely filled with a homogeneous isotropic dielectric, the charge on the condenser for a given potential difference is directly proportional to the permittivity ϵ of the dielectric. See Sec. 3.12 for the detailed proof of this statement. It follows now that the capacitance C of the condenser is proportional to ϵ. If the capacitance of a given pair of conductors is C_0 when the space occupied by their field is evacuated and is C when this space is filled with a dielectric of permittivity ϵ, then

$$\frac{C}{C_0} = \frac{\epsilon}{\epsilon_0} = K_e \tag{4.72}$$

Thus the ratio C/C_0 is the same as K_e, the specific inductive capacity of the dielectric.

Certain simple geometries are frequently used in constructing a condenser whose capacitance may be computed readily. The most usual examples are the parallel-plate condenser, the cylindrical condenser, and the spherical condenser. In the two former cases, the field near the edges is nonuniform and difficult to compute unless guard sections are employed. These are continuations of the condenser plates, isolated from the central portion by a small gap, and maintained at the same potential as the plates. If the fields in the condensers are thus made uniform, it is easy to compute the capacitances. The reader may work out for himself that for a parallel-plate condenser in which the inner surface of each plate has an area A, and the separation between the surfaces is s, the capacitance is

$$C_{pl} = \frac{A\epsilon}{s} \tag{4.73}$$

For the cylindrical condenser with inner and outer radii a and b, respectively, and length L,

$$C_{\text{cyl}} = \frac{2\pi \epsilon L}{\ln (b/a)} \tag{4.74}$$

Finally, for the spherical condenser with inner and outer radii a and b,

$$C_{\text{sph}} = \frac{4\pi \epsilon}{(1/a) - (1/b)} \tag{4.75}$$

4.10. Networks of Condensers.   Consider first a parallel connection of two ideal condensers C_1 and C_2, each designated by the symbol —⊣⊢—, as shown in Fig. 4.3.   Let a total charge $+q$ be placed on the connected terminals at A, and a total charge $-q$ at B.   This charge q we shall call the charge of the combination. The resulting potential difference V between A and B is the potential difference of the combination.   The parallel connection has the effect of causing the potential difference on each of the component condensers to be equal to V; thus we may write

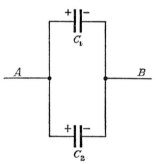

Fig. 4.3. Condensers in parallel.

$$V_1 = V_2 = V \tag{4.76}$$

The charge q has been divided between the component condensers.   If q_1 and q_2 are the charges of the two components, respectively, then

$$q = q_1 + q_2 \tag{4.77}$$

Application of Eq. (4.68) to each condenser yields the relations

$$q_1 = C_1 V_1 \qquad q_2 = C_2 V_2 \tag{4.78}$$

Combining Eqs. (4.76) to (4.78), we have

$$q = (C_1 + C_2)V \tag{4.79}$$

Now the equivalent capacitance C of the combination will be defined as the ratio of the total charge to the total potential difference:

$$C \equiv \frac{q}{V} \tag{4.80}$$

Evidently for the parallel connection we have

$$C = C_1 + C_2 \tag{4.81}$$

Let us analyze a series combination as shown in Fig. 4.4. Since the net charge on the pair of conductors connected together at the center of the diagram is zero when the condensers are uncharged, and since these terminals are insulated from the rest of the system, it follows that the two charges q_1 and q_2 are equal in magnitude and have a polarity as indicated in the figure when the combination as a whole is charged by impressing a potential difference across the terminals A and B. The charge q of a combination is defined in general as the total charge on the conductor(s) connected to an external terminal of the combination. Thus in the series connection,

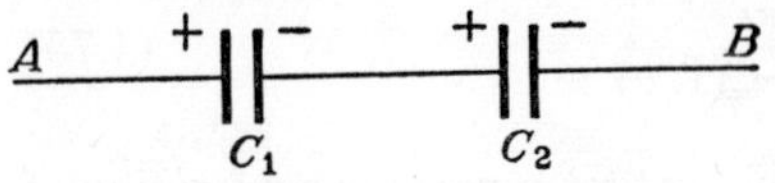

$$q = q_1 = q_2 \tag{4.82}$$

FIG. 4.4. Condensers in series.

The potential difference of the combination, considering the polarity of the condensers, is

$$V = V_1 + V_2 \tag{4.83}$$

since potential differences add algebraically. Using Eqs. (4.78), (4.82), and (4.83), we obtain

$$V = q\left(\frac{1}{C_1} + \frac{1}{C_2}\right) \tag{4.84}$$

whence, by comparing Eq. (4.80),

$$\frac{1}{C} = \frac{1}{C_1} + \frac{1}{C_2} \tag{4.85}$$

which is the law for series combinations of capacitors. Both this and the law for parallel capacitors (4.81) may be extended immediately to include any number of components.

More complex networks of condensers may easily be imagined. In general, there will always be a pair of wires called terminals on which the charge q is supplied to the network and between which the potential difference of the network exists.

The basic equations (4.38) and (4.39), Sec. 4.6, are linear relations between charges and potentials; thus for any network of ideal condensers subject to the conditions of Sec. 4.6 (linear dielectrics, and all free charge to be on conductors) we are assured of the linear relation (4.80) between q and V. The equivalent capacitance C is therefore defined by (4.80) for any two-terminal network of ideal condensers, and is constant.

Some networks may be broken down into series and parallel combinations of condensers or sets of condensers; and then Eqs. (4.81) and (4.85) are sufficient tools for determining the equivalent capacitance. Other networks, such as the one shown in Fig. 4.5, cannot be resolved into series and parallel combinations. These may be solved by a set of simultaneous equations based on the following principles:

1. The algebraic sum of charges on conductors connected to a terminal is $\pm q$, where q is the charge of the network.

2. The algebraic sum of charges on a set of insulated conductors all connected together at a junction, but not forming a terminal, remains constant, and is zero if the component condensers were uncharged when connected together.

3. The potential difference between any two points of the network is the algebraic sum of the potential differences across the condensers forming any path between the two points of the network. By the general conservative nature of electrostatic fields, this potential difference is the same for any path chosen (see Sec. 1.5). The potential difference V of the network is that which exists between the terminals.

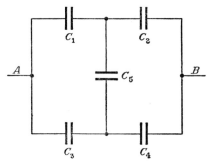

4. For each condenser separately, the condenser relation $q_i = C_i V_i$ holds.

5. The equivalent capacitance of the network is given by Eq. (4.80).

FIG. 4.5. A complex network of condensers.

4.11. Forces on Electrostatic Charge Distributions. The concept of electric field was introduced in Sec. 1.4 by considering the force on a point charge. If we let the electric field at the location of a charge q be $\mathbf{E}'$, and consider that $\mathbf{E}'$ excludes the direct field of q itself but includes the field of all charges which may be induced elsewhere in the system by q, then we have for the total electrostatic force on q

$$\mathbf{F} = q\mathbf{E}' \tag{4.86}$$

We should like to extend our ideas to the analysis of electrostatic force on volume and surface densities of electric charge.

First, let us consider why the field $\mathbf{E}'$ was used in Eq. (4.86). The point charge is a discontinuity deliberately put into the macroscopic picture of an electrostatic system. Formally, it has an infinite volume density of charge occupying a zero volume of space. The result of this is an electric field $\mathbf{E}_s$ of the charge itself, which is exactly

$$\mathbf{E}_s = \frac{q\mathbf{r}}{4\pi\epsilon_0 r^3} \tag{4.87}$$

Evidently E_s becomes infinite at the position of the charge, $r = 0$. Not only so, but E_s also becomes indeterminate in direction at the charge, for there $\mathbf{r} = 0$. Thus the price of the concept of point charge is that we forego any possibility of analyzing conditions within the charge, such as the field there or the force on only one part of the charge. This is why we had to exclude the self-field (4.87) in writing Eq. (4.86) for a point charge. It was correct to make this omission because the self-field within any system of charges makes no contribution to the total resultant force on the system. Electrostatic forces obey the third law of Newton, that equal and opposite reaction always accompanies action. This is evident from the Coulomb law as stated in Eq. (1.1). The sum of all internal forces between parts of an electrostatic system must therefore be zero, that is, the system cannot produce a net force on itself, or "lift itself by its bootstraps." The internal electrostatic forces merely produce internal stresses, which in turn may be balanced by mechanical or other forces. In terms of electric field, the third law of Newton therefore means that the direct electric fields produced by charges of an electrostatic system may result in internal stresses but will always yield a zero total force on the system as a whole. We may then omit these self-fields produced by the charges of a given system, and consider only the field $\mathbf{E}'$ of charges outside the system in determining the total force on a system. This was done of necessity for a small system treated as a point charge.

When the volume density of charge ρ remains finite, the self-field of the charge dq contained within an infinitesimal volume dV is infinitesimal. The reader may quickly convince himself of this by considering as an example a spherical volume containing uniform charge density. The field of such a sphere is readily computed by Gauss' law, and for an interior point or on the surface it is found to be proportional to the distance of the point from the center. Hence the field of the sphere approaches zero as its radius approaches zero. Now because of the infinitesimal nature of the self-field of the charge $dq = \rho\, dV$, this charge is subjected just to the macroscopic field $\mathbf{E}$ at dV. We shall therefore write, for the force on dq,

$$dF = \mathbf{E}\rho\, dV \qquad (4.88)$$

The total electrostatic force on a system whose volume densities of charge are finite is therefore given by the vector integral

$$\mathbf{F} = \int_{\text{whole system}} \mathbf{E}\rho\, dV \qquad (4.89)$$

It is also valid to apply Eq. (4.88) to parts of a system if it is desired to find local stresses.

We must next consider forces on a surface density of charge. These are especially important since the charge on conductors is all in the form of surface density. We shall treat the case of systems not containing dielectrics. Now a true surface density is another artificial discontinuity which is introduced for convenience into macroscopic analysis, for it involves an infinite volume density just as the point charge does. The electric field of a surface layer of charge is simpler than that of the point charge, however, in that only its component normal to the layer is discontinuous, and even this component remains finite. At points indefinitely near to a surface layer of free charge σ, the layer in the immediate vicinity looks plane. Gauss' law, or a direct integration, shows that there is produced a field

$$E_{s\perp} = \frac{\sigma}{2\epsilon_0} \qquad (4.90)$$

on both sides of the layer, the field on each side being outward from the layer if σ is positive. This field is produced by just the element $\sigma\, da$ of the charge layer which lies in the vicinity of the point where the field is observed, as the direct integration shows. To be more detailed in this statement, we may place the point of observation infinitely near to the layer, since the layer is pictured as infinitely thin. Then a macroscopically infinitesimal area element da can still subtend a solid angle of essentially 2π steradians at the point of observation, and in this way only the charge in da is needed to yield the field (4.90). Note that we have not assumed that σ is constant over the layer, but only that it is a continuous function so that in an infinitesimal area da its value is essentially constant. The field (4.90) at a given point near the layer is computed just from the value of σ near that point. Notice also that the field (4.90) is not the total field of a whole layer of charge, for more distant parts of the layer may make important contributions at the observation point. For example, in the case of a conducting surface, the remoter parts of the surface charge just balance the field (4.90) at any point just inside the conductor surface, where the field must vanish.

Now consider how to find the force on an element $\sigma\, da$ of a surface layer of charge. By the boundary conditions of Sec. 3.9, the field at $\sigma\, da$ is uncertain only because of the discontinuity σ in the normal component of the electric displacement. This means that the discontinuity of the electric field is σ/ϵ_0 in the normal direction. This discontinuity of the field is due to the charge of the element $\sigma\, da$ itself, for it is just accounted for by Eq. (4.90). Appealing again to Newton's third law, we may subtract vectorially the self-field $\mathbf{E}_{s\perp}$ of Eq. (4.90) from the total field $\mathbf{E}$ in the vicinity of $\sigma\, da$, in order to find the total electric force on $\sigma\, da$. The resulting field

$$\mathbf{E}' = \mathbf{E} - \mathbf{E}_{s\perp} \qquad (4.91)$$

is now continuous at the surface layer, and from it we obtain the force on $\sigma\, da$:

$$dF = E'\sigma\, da \qquad (4.92)$$

Finally, we may integrate Eq. (4.92) over a part of a surface distribution, or even a whole surface distribution, to find a finite partial or total force.

As an example of the foregoing discussion, consider the electrostatic stress, that is, force per unit area, on the surface of a charged conductor. In the conductor material, the total field E is zero; and the field $E_{s\perp}$ just inside the conductor is $\sigma/2\epsilon_0$ directed into the conductor. Therefore the field E' is $\sigma/2\epsilon_0$ directed outward from the conductor material as appears from Eq. (4.91). The same answer is reached by using Eq. (4.91) for an observer just outside the conductor surface. Now the force on the charge in an area element da of the conductor surface is, from Eq. (4.92),

$$dF = \frac{\sigma^2}{2\epsilon_0}\, da \qquad (4.93)$$

The direction of dF is always out from the conductor surface, since E' is outward when σ is positive, and E' is inward when σ is negative. This is indicated in Eq. (4.93) by the appearance of σ to an even power.

4.12. Total Electrostatic Force on a System in Vacuo. The general problem of electrostatic force in systems including dielectric material may be formulated by a stress analysis which becomes too involved for the purposes of this book. There are, however, some general statements which can be made from energy considerations, and these will be the subject of the next section. In the present section we shall treat the special case of a system which contains dielectrics or conductors in its composition, and which is located in empty space. The electric field of the system at external points can always be represented as due to a set of charges *in vacuo*. These may be just the free and bound charges of the system; but some of the bound charge or some of the induced charge may be represented by image charges.

Let the symbol R stand for the system in question, and let R' be any system of charges *in vacuo* yielding the same field as R at all external points. Let all charge and matter external to R be considered as another system, which will be called S. The total electrostatic force on R is thus the force F exerted on R by S. Since electrostatic forces obey Newton's third law, R exerts an electrostatic force $-F$ on S. In order to keep the systems static, there must be also some force or forces of nonelectrostatic nature applied; but how this is done is not pertinent to the present investigation. Now if R is replaced by the equivalent system R', the system S perceives no change, the external fields of R and R' being by hypothesis identical. The force exerted by R' on S is therefore the same as $-\mathbf{F}$, the force exerted by R on S. Then by Newton's third law, the force which S exerts on R' is $\mathbf{F}$, and this is the same as that exerted by S on R.

We have thus demonstrated that bound charges and image charges may be used for computing the total electrostatic force on a system *in vacuo*. It appears from a similar argument that these charges may be used also for computing torques. It must be noted, however, that bound or image charges have nothing to do with actual stress distributions. The reason for limiting the theorem of this section to systems *in vacuo* is to exclude the mechanical stresses which can be transmitted to the system by a fluid or solid dielectric.

4.13. Electrostatic Force and Torque Derived by Energy Considerations. Let us denote by the symbol A a body which forms part of an electrostatic system S. We shall make no particular restrictions about the nature of S; it may, for instance, contain dielectrics. The body A may be immersed in a fluid dielectric, which is a part of the system S. Let a cartesian coordinate describing the position of A be x, and let an angle describing rotation of A about a particular axis Z be θ. Let the electrostatic energy W of the system S be expressed explicitly as a function of x or θ, and of any other independent variables and parameters. If the electric charges of the system S produce a total force component F on the body A in the direction of positive x, then a small displacement dx of the body A results in a mechanical work output from the system:

$$dW_m = F \, dx \tag{4.94}$$

Similarly, if the body A is rotated about the axis Z through a small angle $d\theta$, the existence of a torque L of electrostatic origin about Z will result in a work output:

$$dW_m = L \, d\theta \tag{4.95}$$

Now let us limit the discussion to reversible systems at constant temperature such as were discussed in Sec. 4.1 in which no sources of energy other than electrostatic and thermal are available. The work dW_m done in the motion of A is then at the expense of the electrostatic energy W of the system S of which A is a part; so that

$$dW_m = -dW \tag{4.96}$$

Combining Eq. (4.96) with (4.94) and (4.95), we have at once two very useful relations:

$$F = -\frac{\partial W}{\partial x} \tag{4.97}$$

$$L = -\frac{\partial W}{\partial \theta} \tag{4.98}$$

It should be remarked that F and L include the effect of mechanical pressure of any fluid dielectric which may surround A, in so far as this pressure is a result of the electric fields of the system.

As an elementary application of Eq. (4.97), consider the problem of an ideal parallel-plate condenser with a fluid dielectric. The ideal case of a uniform field between the plates can actually be achieved to a good approximation by the use of guard rings. If the plate area (the inner face of each plate) is a, the separation of the inner faces of the plates is s, and the charge of the condenser is q, then the electric displacement inside is

$$D = \frac{q}{a} \tag{4.99}$$

Thus the electric field is

$$E = \frac{q}{\epsilon a} \tag{4.100}$$

where ϵ is the permittivity of the dielectric. The electrostatic energy is

$$W = \tfrac{1}{2} \int_{\text{condenser}} \mathbf{D} \cdot \mathbf{E} \, dV + W_0 = \frac{ax}{2}\frac{q}{a}\frac{q}{\epsilon a} + W_0 = \frac{q^2 x}{2\epsilon a} + W_0 \tag{4.101}$$

to which, for rigor, there has been added a constant W_0 representing the integration of $\tfrac{1}{2}\mathbf{D} \cdot \mathbf{E}$ over all space exterior to the condenser including the guard ring system. The force on one condenser plate is now given immediately by substituting Eq. (4.101) into (4.97):

$$F = -\frac{q^2}{2\epsilon a} \tag{4.102}$$

The negative sign here shows that the force on either plate is toward the other, that is, in such a sense as to decrease the separation x.

It may be noted that in principle Eq. (4.102) gives an experimental method of measuring ϵ, if the unit of charge is already specified. Also, we may rewrite Eq. (4.102) in terms of the potential difference between condenser plates, which is

$$V = Ex = \frac{qx}{\epsilon a} \tag{4.103}$$

Therefore

$$F = -\frac{\epsilon a V^2}{2x^2} \tag{4.104}$$

Now if ϵ is known, the measurement of the force between condenser plates becomes an absolute indication of the applied potential V. An instrument for determining potentials in this way is called a Kelvin absolute electrometer.

There is an important class of problems in which the free charges of a system are all upon conductors and the potentials of all conductors are maintained constant during any mechanical motions occurring in the system. To maintain the potentials, there must be energy sources such as batteries in the system. Let us inquire again as to the force component F in the direction of the cartesian coordinate x describing the position of a body A of the system. Let the electrostatic potential energy function be called W. Let the mechanical work output during a small displacement dx be dW_m, and let dW_b represent the work put into the system by the batteries during this displacement. The energy balance sheet now reads

$$F \, dx = dW_m = -(dW)_V + dW_b \tag{4.105}$$

The subscript on the symbol $(dW)_V$ reminds us that all conductor potentials are to be held fixed during the supposed motion of A. This will mean in general that the charges on all conductors will be variable. This is just the opposite situation to that considered earlier in this section, where the hypothesis was made that there were no batteries; for if there are no batteries, the conductors must be insulated except those which may be grounded, and the charges on ungrounded conductors remain constant during a supposed motion. In such a case, it is the potentials which vary during the motion. It is absolutely essential to bear this distinction in mind. On this account, it is wise to express the electrostatic energy function W in terms of the charges and not the potentials of the conductors in the system before substitution into Eqs. (4.96) to (4.98); for there the potentials involve the coordinates x and θ implicitly. Likewise, for Eq. (4.105) and the equations we are about to write down for the constant-potential case, W should be expressed in terms of the potentials and not in terms of the charges of the conductors.

Let us now limit our considerations to systems where the dielectric material is linear in character, and where all the free charges q_i are on conductors whose potentials are, respectively, V_i. The electrostatic energy function for such a system is to be found from Eq. (4.4) or (4.20):

$$W = \tfrac{1}{2} \sum_i q_i V_i \tag{4.106}$$

Therefore

$$dW = \tfrac{1}{2} \sum_i q_i \, dV_i + \tfrac{1}{2} \sum_i V_i \, dq_i \tag{4.107}$$

Now when all conductor potentials are held constant by batteries, all the dV_i are zero. Therefore

$$(dW)_V = \tfrac{1}{2} \sum_i V_i \, dq_i \tag{4.108}$$

By the definition of potential, the batteries must do work

$$dW_b = \sum_i V_i \, dq_i \qquad (4.109)$$

Thus it appears that

$$dW_b = 2(dW)_V \qquad (4.110)$$

Comparison of Eq. (4.105) now shows that

$$F \, dx = dW_m = +(dW)_V \qquad (4.111)$$

We conclude from Eq. (4.111) that the force F is now to be obtained by the equation

$$F = + \left(\frac{\partial W}{\partial x} \right)_V \qquad (4.112)$$

The change in sign of Eq. (4.112) relative to (4.97) results from the fact which is evident from (4.110) and (4.111) that now when the system does mechanical work its own potential energy increases by the same amount, while the batteries supply the double energy. For this case of constant conductor potentials we may write for the torque on the body A

$$L = + \left(\frac{\partial W}{\partial \theta} \right)_V \qquad (4.113)$$

PROBLEMS

4.1. Given the following system of three point charges *in vacuo*: $q_1 = +10^{-10}$ coulomb at the origin; $q_2 = -8 \times 10^{-10}$ coulomb at $(3,0,0)$ cm; $q_3 = -2 \times 10^{-10}$ coulomb at $(0,4,0)$ cm. Find the work of assembling the system, assuming only the electrostatic forces to act, from an initial state in which all three point charges are infinitely separated from each other. Demonstrate that this work is independent of the order in which the charges are brought into position.

4.2. Given two thin spherical shells S_1 and S_2 of electric charge *in vacuo*, with radii R_1 and R_2 and total charges q_1 and q_2 distributed uniformly over each shell. Let $R_1 > R_2$, and let shell S_2 lie wholly within S_1. Under this condition, find the total electrostatic energy of the system, and show that it is independent of the location of S_2 in S_1.

4.3. Given three point charges, q_1 and q_2 of $+2 \times 10^{-3}$ microcoulomb each and q_3 of -2×10^{-3} microcoulomb, in space at the corners of an equilateral triangle whose side is $a = 10$ cm.

a. Find the electrostatic energy of the system, using an appropriate general formula.

b. Suppose the triangle is made smaller until its side length is $a' = 5$ cm. Find the work required, both (1) by use of the electrostatic energy for the system and (2) by direct integration of force into distance over some particular process.

4.4. A point charge q is located at the center of a spherical shell of dielectric material with permittivity ϵ, inner radius a, and outer radius b. Elsewhere there is empty space. Find the apparent electrostatic energy of the system.

4.5. A point charge of 2×10^{-10} coulomb is located 15 cm outside of the surface of a conducting sphere *in vacuo* whose radius is 50 cm. Find the apparent electrostatic energy of the system (a) if the sphere is grounded and (b) if the sphere is insulated and uncharged.

4.6. A point charge of 3×10^{-10} coulomb is within a spherical cavity of 2 cm radius in a conductor. The cavity is filled with a fluid dielectric of permittivity $4\epsilon_0$. How much work is required to move the charge from the center of the cavity to a point $\frac{1}{2}$ cm from the center? $Ans.$ -3.37×10^{-10} joule.

4.7. Find the electrostatic energy of a sphere of radius R containing a uniform volume density ρ of charge and existing in otherwise empty space. If an electron is assumed to be constructed according to this model, obtain an expression for its radius by equating the electrostatic to the self-energy, and compare Eq. (4.22), Sec. 4.4.

4.8. A conducting sphere of radius R_1 is enclosed by a spherical shell of isotropic, linear, and homogeneous dielectric, with inner and outer radii, respectively, R_1 and R_2 and having permittivity ϵ. The conductor is given a charge q and the system is isolated and in $vacuo$. What is the electrostatic energy?

4.9. Find the electrostatic energy of the ideal parallel-plate condenser described below (a) by integration over the field in the condenser and (b) by integration over the charge density. The condenser consists of two conductors having parallel inner surfaces of area 40 cm² separated by 1 mm. The space between plates is occupied by two slabs of homogeneous isotropic dielectric of permittivities $3\epsilon_0$ and $6\epsilon_0$, respectively, each of uniform width $\frac{1}{2}$ mm. Edge effects are to be neglected, so that the field is assumed uniform in each dielectric and is confined within the condenser. One plate is grounded, the other is at +300 volts, and the dielectrics carry no free charge.

4.10. Given a conducting sphere in $vacuo$ having radius R and carrying charge q_1, find its electrostatic energy by integrating over the field, and check the result against the value obtained by integration over the charge density.

4.11. Given two similar spherical conductors in $vacuo$, each of radius R and with a distance L between their centers. If $L \gg R$, so that each sphere appears to the other as indefinitely small, find the coefficients of induction and of capacitance. Carry the approximation to neglect of second and higher-order terms in the ratio R/L.

$$Ans. \quad p_{11} = p_{22} = \frac{1}{4\pi\epsilon_0 R} \qquad p_{12} = p_{21} = \frac{1}{4\pi\epsilon_0 L}$$

$$c_{11} = c_{22} = 4\pi\epsilon_0 R \qquad c_{12} = c_{21} = -\frac{4\pi\epsilon_0 R^2}{L}$$

4.12. Given the following system of conductors in $vacuo$: A is a sphere of outer radius a located concentrically in the cavity of a spherical shell B whose inner and outer radii are, respectively, b_1 and b_2. C is a third sphere of outer radius c, whose center is at a large distance L from the center of B. Neglecting second and higher-degree terms in the ratios b_2/L and c/L, find all coefficients of induction and capacitance.

4.13. Use coefficients of potential to demonstrate that the potential of an uncharged and insulated conducting sphere in $vacuo$ due to the presence of a point charge q at distance r from its center is $q/4\pi\epsilon_0 r$.

4.14. Carry through the proof of Eq. (4.51), Sec. 4.7, as suggested in the text by considering the work required to raise the potentials of two conductors of a linear system in sequence, all other conductors being at ground potential.

4.15. Prove Eqs. (4.64) to (4.67), Sec. 4.8.

4.16. Given three very thin, concentric spherical shells of conducting material, having radii, respectively, $R_1 < R_2 < R_3$. The spaces between spheres are filled with isotropic, linear, and homogeneous dielectric materials, the permittivities of which are ϵ_{12} between R_1 and R_2, and ϵ_{23} between R_2 and R_3. Outside is empty space. Find all coefficients of induction and of capacitance.

4.17. Given a spherical conducting shell A with internal and external radii, respectively, a_1 and a_2 in empty space and a concentric sphere B of outer radius b inside it.

The space between spheres is filled with isotropic, linear, and homogeneous dielectric material of permittivity ϵ.

a. Find all coefficients of induction and of capacitance.

b. Check all the general relations, as given in Secs. 4.7 and 4.8, which should hold between these coefficients.

4.18. An isolated conducting sphere *in vacuo* has an outer radius of 50 cm, and it is to be charged by induction using a point charge of 10^{-9} coulomb at a distance of 10 cm outside of its surface. Find the induced charge.

4.19. Given a conducting sphere of outer radius 10 cm located concentrically within a conducting spherical shell whose inner and outer radii are, respectively, 10.1 cm and 10.5 cm. The system is in empty space, and the region between spheres is empty. Find the coefficients of capacitance and use them to find the charges and the electrostatic energy if the potentials of the inner and outer conductors relative to ground are, respectively, (*a*) -400 and $+600$ volts; (*b*) $+400$ and $+600$ volts; (*c*) $-1,000$ and 0 volts. Relate the answers to the discussion of condensers in the text.

4.20. An experimenter builds a condenser of two pieces of brass tubing each 2 cm long, one having an outer radius of 2 mm, the other having an inner radius of 3 mm. He separates them by a glass tube of specific dielectric constant 6 filling the space between tubes. Neglecting edge effects, find the maximum capacitance of the condenser when assembled.

4.21. It is required to design an air condenser of interleaved parallel plates to have a capacitance of 0.0005 μf. If there are to be 10 plates meshed with 11 plates, all plates having the same size and shape, and if the space between neighboring surfaces is to be 1 mm, find the area of each plate.

4.22. Develop a formula for the capacitance, neglecting edge effects, of a parallel-plate condenser of area A and plate separation l, when a dielectric slab of permittivity ϵ and thickness t partially fills the space between the plates. The slab is to be as large as the plates, and is parallel to them.

4.23. Find the capacitance between points A and B of the network of Fig. 4.5, Sec. 4.10.

4.24. Suppose that a condenser box is made with three capacitors whose values are, respectively, 1, 2, and 4 μf. These are connected to conducting bars as shown; and by use of plugs, adjacent bars may be connected at will. What values of capacitance are available between terminals?

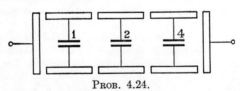

PROB. 4.24.

4.25. *a.* A condenser of 4 μf capacitance is charged to a potential of 400 volts. Find the charge and the stored energy.

b. When charged but disconnected from the battery, this condenser is connected across another of 2 μf, initially uncharged. What are the final potential across it, and the final energy?

4.26. *a.* Two condensers of 2 and 5 μf, respectively, are connected in series across a 1,000-volt battery. What are the charges and potential differences?

b. The condensers are then disconnected from the battery and connected across each other. For both polarities of the final connection, find the resulting potential difference.

4.27. Given a linear system containing two conductors, either isolated or in the vicinity of ground (equals a large, zero-potential reservoir). Show that the charge vs. voltage characteristics of the system can always be represented by a network of three ideal condensers as shown, one between the two conductors and the other between each conductor and ground. Express the coefficients of capacitance in terms of the capacitances of these condensers, and conversely.

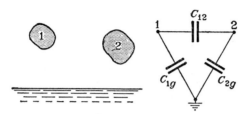

PROB. 4.27.

4.28. Generalize the preceding problem to a linear system with any number of conductors, either isolated or near ground, expressing all coefficients of capacitance in terms of ideal capacitors between pairs of conductors and between conductors and ground. The capacitances of the ideal condensers in this representation between pairs of conductors are called *direct capacitances*.

4.29. Prove directly by integration, and without recourse to the law of action and reaction, that the force on a spherical shell of charge of infinitesimal thickness and uniform surface density, in the field of a point charge, is (a) the same as if the charge of the shell were concentrated at its center, if the point charge is outside the shell; (b) zero, if the point charge is inside the shell.

4.30. A spherical conductor of radius R carrying charge q is located *in vacuo*. If the sphere is made up of two separable hemispheres, what force is required to hold its two halves together?   *Ans.* $+\dfrac{q^2}{32\pi\epsilon_0 R^2}$.

4.31. Two thin, rectangular plates of metal, each measuring 10×20 cm, are hinged together along one of their long sides like the covers of a book, and they carry an electric charge of $+10^{-9}$ coulomb each. When they lie flat together, find the force which, if exerted on the edges opposite the hinges, is required to hold them together. Assume the charge is uniformly distributed over one surface (which?) of each sheet, and so neglect edge effects.

4.32. Given an ideal parallel-plate condenser whose plates have area A and separation D. A slab of isotropic, homogeneous, and linear dielectric of permittivity ϵ and thickness D can be inserted to fill the space in the condenser, yet without quite touching the plates. Find the force between the plates in the following cases, neglecting edge effects.

a. Without dielectric, the potential difference between plates being V.

b. The condenser is initially charged to potential difference V without the dielectric, after which the plates are insulated and the slab inserted.

c. The potential difference V is maintained across the condenser when the slab is inserted.

4.33. Check the equation for electrostatic force on an elementary area of charged conductor surface, with vacuum outside, from a semimicroscopic point of view in which the surface charge has finite thickness. Let the volume charge density be finite and depend in an arbitrary manner on a coordinate normal to the conductor surface. The conductor surface is to have a radius of curvature very much larger than the total thickness of the charge layer, so the surface may be treated as plane. Gauss' law may be used to find the electric field within the layer.

4.34. Given two infinitely long, parallel conducting cylinders with circular cross section, having equal outer radii R and a distance $L > 2R$ between their axes. The two cylinders have charges $+\lambda$ and $-\lambda$ per unit length, respectively. Find the force per unit length between them *in vacuo* (cf Secs. 2.7 and 2.9).

$$Ans. \ \frac{\lambda^2}{2\pi\epsilon_0 L \ \sqrt{1 - 4R^2/L^2}}.$$

4.35. Two bare copper tubes of circular cross section with parallel axes form a d-c transmission line. The outer radius of each tube is 5 mm and their axes are 5 cm apart. When one is grounded and the other is at a potential of 10,000 volts, find the force per unit length between them. See the preceding problem.

4.36. Suppose that the capacitance of a variable air condenser changes linearly from 50 to 350 $\mu\mu f$ during a rotation from 0 to 180°. When set at 60°, a potential difference of 500 volts is applied across the condenser. What electrostatic torque does it experience and in what direction? (Electrostatic voltmeters are constructed on this principle, with a spring to provide restoring torque.)

4.37. The variable air condenser of the preceding problem is charged to a potential difference of 500 volts when at its maximum capacitance (at 0° setting), and is then disconnected. Supposing it to be well enough insulated to hold its charge, what is the electrostatic torque when it is subsequently rotated to an angle of 60°?

4.38. Given two coaxial metal tubes of circular section *in vacuo*, one having an outer radius of 20 mm, the other an inner radius of 21 mm. The tubes are of considerable length compared to their separation, and they overlap for only part of the length of each so that edge effects change but little as the inner tube slides axially. When connected across a 400-volt battery, what is the electrostatic force between them?

4.39. What is the force between two parallel, circular plates provided with guard sections, under the following conditions: plate radius 10 cm; plate separation 3 mm; dielectric air (vacuum); potential difference 1,000 volts?

4.40. A parallel-plate condenser has plate area A and separation D. An isotropic, homogeneous, and linear dielectric slab of permittivity ϵ and thickness D is inserted to fill the space, but may be withdrawn without friction. With the slab in place, the condenser is charged to a potential difference V. Find the work required to withdraw the slab and the accompanying change of the electrostatic energy of the system (*a*) when the potential difference V is maintained by a battery through the process; (*b*) when the condenser plates, having been charged, are insulated during the process.

4.41. Given a cylindrical condenser of length L, the gap between its electrodes being a circular shell of inner radius a and outer radius b. A cylindrical tube of isotropic homogeneous dielectric with permittivity ϵ has just these radii, and the same length L which is much larger than a and b. When the dielectric tube is about half inserted and a potential difference V is applied to the condenser, find the electrostatic force between it and the condenser. Show why edge effects are small for the problem as stated.

CHAPTER 5

ELECTRIC CURRENT

5.1. Electric Current and Density. The study of steady electric currents began with Luigi Galvani (1737–1798), who observed their stimulating effect upon muscular tissue. Some of the striking effects of current flow are luminosity of electric discharges, heating, power transmission, electrolysis, and magnetic forces. We may identify electric current as a flow of electric charge. It is easily demonstrated in the laboratory that the leakage of electrostatic charges is a current, and conversely that the flow of a current can cause concentrations of electric charge.

Electric current may ordinarily be considered continuous from the macroscopic viewpoint, just as a flow of liquid is treated as continuous in hydraulics. From the microscopic viewpoint, however, a current is usually a drift or flow of elementary charged particles. There may also be a flow of electric charge in the structure of a single elementary particle, such as the electron, and this flow would be continuous even in a microscopic picture.

Let us first introduce a precise definition of the magnitude of an electric current. This must be stated with reference to a particular surface S in space, which may have a finite or an infinite area. The electric current across S is now defined as the rate at which electric charge moves across S:

$$I \equiv \frac{dq}{dt} \tag{5.1}$$

Here the symbol I stands for the electric current, while dq is the infinitesimal amount of electric charge that has crossed S in the infinitesimal time interval dt. In this definition we have pictured dq/dt as the limit $\lim_{\Delta t \to 0} \Delta q/\Delta t$, where Δq is the finite increment of charge crossing S in time Δt. One may equally well consider the form dq/dt as the derivative of a function $q(t)$ expressing the total algebraic quantity of charge which has crossed S in time t. The definition (5.1) is strictly speaking that of instantaneous current, although this adjective is usually omitted except in description of a-c circuits where special terms are to be defined anyway. An average current across S would be simply

$$I_{\text{AV}} \equiv \frac{\Delta q}{\Delta t} \tag{5.2}$$

for the finite interval of time Δt.

We shall take as the unit of electric current the ampere, which may be established absolutely in terms of the mks mechanical system of units by means of the magnetic effects of electric current. The definition of the ampere is discussed in Sec. 7.3. Given the time unit, the second, our definition of current now determines the charge unit, called the coulomb, as the ampere-second. In words, the coulomb is the charge transported in one second by a steady current of one ampere. The reader should note that in analysis we have been treating electric charge as the basic quantity characteristic of electromagnetism, but that the current unit is the one to be established directly by experiment.

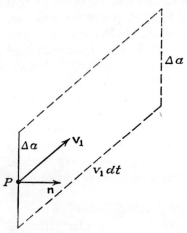

FIG. 5.1. Flow of charge carriers past a small area.

It is convenient to define a vector point function called current density which expresses the rate and direction of transportation of electric charge at every point of space. For this purpose, let us consider the current across a small plane surface S whose area is Δa, and whose unit normal is $\mathbf{n}$ in the sense in which current flow across S is to be called positive (see Fig. 5.1). We now make the physical hypothesis that there is a velocity $\mathbf{v}_1$ which is common to all charges of a certain kind in the near vicinity of S when Δa becomes sufficiently small in all its dimensions, i.e., shrinks about a point P in Δa. This velocity may be only a small drift superposed upon very much larger random velocities, as is the case for electrons in a metal. It is not strictly necessary to suppose that each charge has the same velocity as every other charge near P, or even that the velocity of a given charge is constant in time. The symbol $\mathbf{v}_1$ in general may mean an average over all charges in a neighborhood of P at a given time. The physical assumption in this general case is that $\mathbf{v}_1$ is a continuous function of time and space except for possible space discontinuity at a boundary. The net charge crossing S in an infinitesimal time interval dt, due to the motion of carriers whose charge is q_1 and whose number per unit volume is n_1, is the total charge of the carriers contained in the prism or cylinder of slant height $v_1 \, dt$ and face area Δa. The volume dV of this figure is $(v_1 \, dt) \, \Delta a \cos \alpha$, where α is the angle between v_1 and n, or more briefly in vector notation

$$dV = \mathbf{v}_1 \cdot \mathbf{n} \, dt \, \Delta a \qquad (5.3)$$

The infinitesimal charge crossing the surface is

$$dq = n_1 q_1 \, dV \qquad (5.4)$$

The current across S is therefore

$$\Delta I = n_1 q_1 \mathbf{v}_1 \cdot \mathbf{n} \, \Delta a \tag{5.5}$$

where the symbol ΔI is used since the current is that which crosses Δa. This equation becomes exact when Δa approaches zero by shrinking about the point P. To indicate this in our final result, we shall rewrite it in differential form:

$$dI = n_1 q_1 \mathbf{v}_1 \cdot \mathbf{n} \, da \tag{5.6}$$

The product

$$\mathbf{J} = n_1 q_1 \mathbf{v}_1 \tag{5.7}$$

which appears in Eq. (5.6) is the vector which we shall call the current density. Substitution of (5.7) in (5.6) gives

$$dI = \mathbf{J} \cdot \mathbf{n} \, da \tag{5.8}$$

Equation (5.8) is much more general than (5.6). For example, we may find more than one type of charged particle participating in the current flow, as is the case with electrolytic solutions. Equation (5.7) must then be generalized to

$$\mathbf{J} = \sum_i n_i q_i \mathbf{v}_i \tag{5.9}$$

where the summation is over all types of carriers of charge. Equation (5.8) still remains valid with this value for $\mathbf{J}$. Likewise we may obtain Eq. (5.8) from a picture in which no discrete charges appear at all, but instead a charge density ρ is conceived to move with a velocity $\mathbf{v}$, both ρ and $\mathbf{v}$ being functions of the coordinates and perhaps of the time. Since the product $n_1 q_1$ of Eq. (5.7) is a charge density when viewed macroscopically, it is easy to see that in terms of moving charge density ρ_1 we may write in place of Eq. (5.7)

$$\mathbf{J} = \rho_1 \mathbf{v}_1 \tag{5.10}$$

The general validity of Eq. (5.8) results from the fact that basically it rests upon the conservation of electric charge and upon the physical postulate that the velocity function $\mathbf{v}_i$ may be considered continuous either for particles or for charge density. From these postulates, it follows that the current across an arbitrary infinitesimal surface depends upon the orientation of the surface in the manner expressed by Eq. (5.8). Since we know the form of this equation to be physically correct, we may now consider it to be the defining equation for the current density vector. Equation (5.9), of which (5.7) is a special case, and Eq. (5.10) are then simply relations between $\mathbf{J}$ and the velocities that produce it. Equation (5.8) may be integrated to yield the total current across a finite surface S:

$$I = \int_S \mathbf{J} \cdot \mathbf{n} \, da \tag{5.11}$$

It should be noted carefully that current density can perfectly well exist in the absence of any net macroscopic charge density. There may be both positive and negative elementary particles present in a conductor, in such numbers that the resulting net charge in every macroscopic element of volume vanishes. If charges of both signs are free to migrate simultaneously, they make contributions of the same sign to the current density, since the sense of v_i reverses with the sign of q_i.

5.2. Surface Current Density. It is occasionally convenient to consider a current flow confined to a surface, that is, to a region whose thickness is vanishingly small from a macroscopic viewpoint. This concept is employed in the theory of magnetic materials. We may analyze surface currents by considering them to flow in a region V of finite thickness b one of whose boundary surfaces

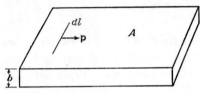

FIG. 5.2. Current flow past a line on the surface of a slab.

is S; and then b can be allowed to become indefinitely small. Suppose that a small enough region A of S about any point on S can be considered plane. Let us examine the current flow parallel to this plane in the slab one of whose surfaces is A and whose thickness is b, as shown in Fig. 5.2. Let dl be an infinitesimal straight line segment in A, and let p be a unit vector in A perpendicular to dl. Consider the current flow in the slab past the line segment dl, that is, the current which crosses a plane surface R cutting perpendicularly across the slab and intersecting A in dl. R is then a cross section of the slab having area

$$da = b \, dl \qquad (5.12)$$

and having unit normal p.

Now suppose that a current density vector $\mathbf{J}$ exists within the region V. Let $\mathbf{J}$ be a continuous function only of position on S, so that $\mathbf{J}$ is considered to be either constant across the thickness b of V, or else to represent an average over b. We are not concerned here with current flow across S; therefore the vector $\mathbf{J}$ will be supposed to be everywhere tangent to S. The current dI through the cross section R of the slab of Fig. 5.2 is now

$$dI = \mathbf{J} \cdot \mathbf{p}b \, dl \qquad (5.13)$$

If we introduce the surface current density $\mathbf{K}$ as the vector

$$\mathbf{K} = b\mathbf{J} \qquad (5.14)$$

then the current crossing R and passing dl becomes

$$dI = \mathbf{K} \cdot \mathbf{p} \, dl \qquad (5.15)$$

Equation (5.15) will be taken rather than (5.14) as defining the surface current density $\mathbf{K}$, for the thickness b of the surface is irrelevant to the concept of surface current. The foregoing "derivation" of Eq. (5.15) from consideration of the current density $\mathbf{J}$ within the region V serves two purposes. First, it shows that this definition has a form which is physically correct, that is, consistent with the concept of current as transportation of electric charge. Second, it shows by Eq. (5.14) that a finite surface current $\mathbf{K}$ implies the existence of an infinite current density $\mathbf{J}$, if the thickness b of the surface region V approaches zero. This discontinuity of $\mathbf{J}$ is entirely analogous to the discontinuity of charge density ρ which is introduced into macroscopic analysis by the concept of surface charge density.

Equation (5.15) can be integrated to yield the total current passing a curve $\mathcal{L}$ in the surface S. The segment dl now represents an infinitesimal part of the curve $\mathcal{L}$, and the unit normal $\mathbf{p}$ is now a variable with position along $\mathcal{L}$. The total current I across $\mathcal{L}$ is then

$$I = \int_{\mathcal{L}} \mathbf{K} \cdot \mathbf{p}\, dl \tag{5.16}$$

5.3. Continuity. The conservation of electric charge requires that the charge density and current density functions be related. We have stated that either may exist without the other, or that both may exist together, but this does not mean that they are quite independent of one another. Let us derive the relation between them for a system where the volume density of charge ρ and the current density $\mathbf{J}$ are finite and together completely describe the charge and current of the system. We shall consider these functions to be continuous, so that any macroscopic discontinuities are to be treated simply as regions of rapid change.

Consider a volume V enclosed by a fixed surface S. Let $\mathbf{n}$ be the unit normal to S everywhere out from V. If currents are flowing, there may in general be a net rate of change of charge within V, for in general the net current in or out from V will not vanish. An expression for this net current is obtained at once from Eq. (5.11). Considering the current positive if outward from V, we have

$$I = \oint_S \mathbf{J} \cdot \mathbf{n}\, da \tag{5.17}$$

From the definition of current, I is the rate at which charge flows out from V across S; and by conservation of charge, I is the rate at which the net charge q in V is decreasing. Thus

$$I = -\frac{dq}{dt} \tag{5.18}$$

so that

$$\oint_S \mathbf{J} \cdot \mathbf{n} \, da + \frac{dq}{dt} = 0 \tag{5.19}$$

Now q may be expressed in terms of charge density ρ:

$$q = \int_V \rho \, dv \tag{5.20}$$

In this way we are led to an integral equation connecting J and ρ:

$$\oint_S \mathbf{J} \cdot \mathbf{n} \, da + \int_V \frac{\partial \rho}{\partial t} \, dv = 0 \tag{5.21}$$

The integral equation (5.21) holds for any arbitrary volume V with its enclosing surface S, and requires the existence of a differential relation between $\mathbf{J}$ and ρ which holds at every point of space. We have gone through the mathematical argument for this derivation in Sec. 2.2; only there we worked with Gauss' law of Sec. 1.9 [Eq. (1.67)]. The reader can apply that discussion to the present case by simply putting the function $\mathbf{J}$ in place of the function $\epsilon_0 \mathbf{E}$ and $-\partial \rho / \partial t$ for ρ. See also the discussion of the divergence theorem in Sec. 3.4. The resulting differential equation in $\mathbf{J}$ and ρ is

$$\left(\frac{\partial J_x}{\partial x} + \frac{\partial J_y}{\partial y} + \frac{\partial J_z}{\partial z} \right) + \frac{\partial \rho}{\partial t} = 0 \tag{5.22}$$

This is called the equation of continuity. In the abbreviated notation of vector calculus, it is written

$$\operatorname{div} \mathbf{J} + \frac{\partial \rho}{\partial t} = 0 \tag{5.23}$$

5.4. Conductivity. Let us inquire what makes currents flow and what stops them once started. If all moving charge is called current, there are some cases where the current is self-maintaining. The motion of charges within atoms and molecules is ceaseless; and the motion of charged particles in interstellar space is practically unhindered by collisions. Likewise currents in some materials at temperatures close to absolute zero may persist of themselves. Ordinarily however, we are concerned with currents involving motion of charged particles within solid, liquid, or gaseous materials at ordinary temperatures. These currents are observed to involve an expenditure of energy which appears as heat and sometimes as radiation. It is therefore necessary for power to be supplied to the moving charges in order to keep them flowing. From a mechanical point of view, we may think of a force applied to the moving charges as the cause of their motion. The mechanism by which currents produce heat may also be considered as a force, this time opposed to the direction of motion of the charges and having the nature of a viscous force depending on velocity. It is not our purpose at the moment to make these ideas more precise by presenting a theory of conduction. We shall, however, consider the relationship between current density and electric field; for evidently one of the most important ways of exerting a force on a charge to keep it in motion is to establish an electric field in the space where it moves.

Whatever the exact conditions of conduction, it is evident that the velocity of the elementary carriers of charge will be dependent on the force these carriers experience in the direction of their motion. Thus the current density will depend on the electric field.

It is possible that the electric field will affect not only the velocities of the charged carriers but also their number. This occurs in gases as well as in many solid materials.

We may use the macroscopic electric field for our discussion, for it is the average field and we are interested in motions of macroscopic magnitude. For the present, let us consider currents whose sole cause is an electric field. J should therefore vanish with E. In isotropic materials, J should have the direction of E, since E is force per unit positive charge. In equation form, what we have said amounts to

$$J = f(E) \tag{5.24}$$

with $f(0) = 0$; and in isotropic material,

$$J = gE \tag{5.25}$$

This equation serves to define a scalar quantity g called the conductivity of the material, in addition to indicating the common direction and simultaneous vanishing of J and E. It implies some functional relation between the magnitudes J and E, but does not specify this relation. We may not assume in general that g is independent of E; but since the material is isotropic, g does not depend on the direction of E. Experimentally, however, there are many materials for which g is independent of E over an extremely large range of field strength. Such materials are said to be linear conductors, or to obey Ohm's law. In words, the current density in a linear conductor is directly proportional to the electric field in the conductor. The most important class of linear conductors is the metals. Although electrolytic conductors may also be linear, their linearity is generally masked by other effects.

The conductivity g may of course depend on the space coordinates within a conductor. If, however, g is independent of the space coordinates, at least for a constant value of electric field, the conducting material is said to be homogeneous.   It is possible also that g may vary with time, although we shall not usually consider this to be the case.   Besides depending on these variables, g may show important dependence upon the physical conditions prevailing in a given material, in particular the temperature.   The conductivity may depend markedly on the presence of small amounts of impurities, and on the previous thermal or mechanical treatment of the material.   An important study is the effect of a magnetic field on the direction or magnitude of the current in a conductor, although such effects are usually small.   It is not impossible that for very large, steady current densities the magnetic field of the current itself may affect the current distribution.

It is sometimes convenient to work with the reciprocal of the conductivity; this is called the resistivity of the material:

$$r_1 \equiv \frac{1}{g} \tag{5.26}$$

In problems involving changing currents, the ratio of a change in $\mathbf{J}$ to the corresponding change in $\mathbf{E}$ may be of greater importance than the ratio of the total values of these quantities.   Using the scalar magnitudes J and E, we may define the differential conductivity

$$g' \equiv \frac{dJ}{dE} \tag{5.27}$$

g' will be identical with g in general only for linear materials.   While g is always positive, g' may be negative; and in fact, negative differential conductivity is very important in practical applications.

The mks unit of conductivity is, from the definition of Eq. (5.25),

$$\frac{\text{amperes/meter}^2}{\text{newtons/coulomb}}$$

This may be rewritten as

$$\frac{\text{amperes}}{(\text{joule/coulomb}) \text{ meter}} = \frac{\text{amperes}}{\text{volt-meter}}$$

In terms of quantities soon to be introduced, the most usual names for this unit are

$$\frac{1}{\text{ohm-meter}} = \frac{\text{mho}}{\text{meter}}$$

Materials are broadly classified in terms of their conductivity as conductors and insulators.   The range of conductivity observed between good conductors and good solid insulators is enormous, being of the order of twenty-four powers of ten.   One of the best conductors is pure annealed copper, whose conductivity at 20°C is 5.800×10^7 mho/m.

5.5. Joule Heat. We have indicated in the preceding section that the forces which an electric field produces on the moving charges of a conductor are balanced by a resistive force like that of viscosity. The motion of the charges therefore implies an energy transformation in which heat appears at the expense of the electric field or of whatever mechanism maintains the electric field. If F_i is the force exerted by the field on a type of carrier whose average velocity is v_i, then the average power which the field puts into one such carrier is $F_i \cdot v_i$, and this is also the average power which is transformed into heat per carrier. If there are n_i carriers per unit volume, the heat produced per unit volume of conductor per unit time is, in mechanical units, $n_i F_i \cdot v_i$. If there are several types of carriers of charge in the conductor, each designated by a value of the index i, then the total power appearing as heat per unit volume of the conductor is the sum

$$P_1 = \sum_i n_i F_i \cdot v_i \tag{5.28}$$

The force F_i may be written in terms of the charge q_i per carrier and the electric field E at a particular place in the conductor:

$$F_i = q_i E$$

Substitution of this into Eq. (5.28) gives

$$P_1 = \left(\sum_i n_i q_i v_i \right) \cdot E \tag{5.29}$$

which has been written in such a form as to facilitate comparison with the expression (5.9) for current density:

$$J = \sum_i n_i q_i v_i \tag{5.9}$$

We obtain therefore

$$P_1 = J \cdot E \tag{5.30}$$

as the basic equation for the heating caused by flow of current in a conductor when the current is produced by an electric field. This equation remains correct even when a magnetic field is present, but its meaning needs to be reexamined if still other types of forces act on the carriers of charge. Although we shall see that a magnetic field in general produces a force on a moving charge in addition to any force due to an electric field, the magnetic force does no work on the charge.

If we now specialize our considerations to the case of an isotropic conductor for which, according to Eq. (5.25),

$$J = gE \tag{5.25}$$

we may write for the power dissipated as heat per unit volume

$$P_1 = gE^2 \tag{5.31}$$

It will be noted here that the heat developed per unit volume per unit time depends on the square of the electric field, and is always positive since g is essentially positive. Thermodynamically speaking, the process is said to be irreversible. This is equally true in anisotropic conductors for which a more complex expression than Eq. (5.31) is necessary.

The irreversible transformation of electrical energy into heat when current flows in a conductor is called Joule heating.[1] The units of P_1 in these equations are simply mks units of power per unit volume, namely,

$$\frac{\text{joule}}{\text{sec meter}^3} = \frac{\text{watt}}{\text{meter}^3}$$

5.6. The Electric Field in a System Containing Electric Current. There are only two known sources for a macroscopic electric field. One is net electric charge, either free or bound, and this has been treated in detail in earlier chapters under the heading of electrostatics. The other is a changing magnetic field, as we shall discuss later under electromagnetic induction. Steady electric currents do not of themselves directly produce or modify electric fields, since the magnetic fields of such currents are steady.

The role of conductors in affecting the electric field of a system in which currents are flowing is very different from their role in an electrostatic system, for if currents flow there is no longer the condition that the electric field in conductors be zero. We may easily find a general boundary condition which applies when the charge densities of the system are constant. Suppose the current density is finite but in general discontinuous just at the boundary between two media, with values $\mathbf{J}_1$ and $\mathbf{J}_2$, in medium 1 and medium 2, respectively (see Fig. 5.3). Consider a small volume V bounded by two equal, plane surfaces A, one in each medium, parallel to the boundary and separated by an infinitesimal distance t. The volume V also has a bounding surface of width t connecting the two faces at their edges like the sides of a pillbox, in the form of a cylinder normal to the boundary. As t approaches zero, the area of these sides likewise approaches zero, and the total charge entering or leaving V passes across the faces A. If $\mathbf{n}$ is the unit normal to the boundary outward to medium 1, the net rate at which charge enters V is

$$\frac{dq}{dt} = \mathbf{J}_1 \cdot \mathbf{n} - \mathbf{J}_2 \cdot \mathbf{n} \tag{5.32}$$

Let us now require that a steady state has been reached in which

[1] In honor of James Prescott Joule (1818–1889).

$dq/dt = 0.$ Then

$$\mathbf{J}_1 \cdot \mathbf{n} = \mathbf{J}_2 \cdot \mathbf{n} \tag{5.33}$$

Supposing the two media to be isotropic and to have conductivities g_1 and g_2, respectively, we may write Eq. (5.33) in the form

$$g_1\mathbf{E}_1 \cdot \mathbf{n} = g_2\mathbf{E}_2 \cdot \mathbf{n} \tag{5.34}$$

which is a condition on the normal components of the electric field at a boundary.

A particular case of this boundary condition is especially important, the case where one of the materials separated by the boundary is a good

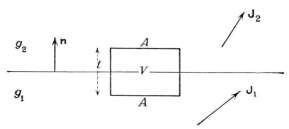

FIG. 5.3. A boundary between conducting media.

insulator. Let $g_2 = 0$, so that $\mathbf{J}_2 = 0$. Then we obtain from Eq. (5.34), if g_1 remains nonvanishing,

$$\mathbf{E}_1 \cdot \mathbf{n} = 0 \tag{5.35}$$

This means that at a conductor-insulator boundary and during steady state when no charges are being built up, the lines of electric force on the conducting side are parallel to the boundary. The existence of a parallel component of electric field on the conductor side of a boundary means that there is an equal component just outside the conductor in the insulator. The reader may compare Sec. 3.9 for a proof that the parallel component of electrostatic field is continuous across a boundary; and it turns out, as we shall show in Sec. 12.9, that this is true in general. Therefore in a system where currents are flowing, the field just outside a conductor surface in an insulator is not in general entirely normal to the surface as was the case in electrostatics.

5.7. Potential Difference in a Nonstatic System. We have noted in the preceding section that in general an electric field may have as its sources either net electric charge or a changing magnetic field or both. Let us consider a system in which changes of net charges occur not too rapidly if at all. To be somewhat definite, we may require that if τ is a time interval in which light can traverse the system, the changes in positions and magnitudes of charges in this interval are negligible. In such a case, we may define within the system an instantaneous field of electrostatic type $\mathbf{E}_s$. This field is not static, for it may change with time; but it is to be related at any instant to the distribution of electric charge at that instant in the same way as the electrostatic field is to static charge. For example, if the charges are specified by a volume distribution ρ, which is now a function of time as well as of position,

$$\mathbf{E}_s = \frac{1}{4\pi\epsilon_0} \int_{\text{all space}} \frac{\mathbf{r}\rho \, dV}{r^3} \tag{5.36}$$

It will turn out in a more general analysis than we can undertake here (cf. Sec. 12.12) that the actual field in such a system as we are considering may be written as a sum of this quasi-electrostatic field $\mathbf{E}_s$ plus another partial field $\mathbf{E}_m$ which may be thought of as due to changing magnetic fields:

$$\mathbf{E} = \mathbf{E}_s + \mathbf{E}_m \tag{5.37}$$

The two partial fields of Eq. (5.37) have very different properties. The line integral of $\mathbf{E}_s$ around any closed loop is zero, since $\mathbf{E}_s$ at a given instant is just like an electrostatic field (see Sec. 1.5). This means that $\mathbf{E}_s$ may be derived from a scalar potential function U exactly like the electrostatic potential function except that it is in general a function of time as well as space. This function has for its differential corresponding to a vector displacement $d\mathbf{l}$ in space

$$dU = -\mathbf{E}_s \cdot d\mathbf{l} \tag{5.38}$$

Furthermore, the function U has the property that the difference between its values at any two points 1 and 2 of a given system at a given time is unique; that is, that

$$\Delta U \equiv U_2 - U_1 = -\int_1^2 \mathbf{E}_s \cdot d\mathbf{l} \tag{5.39}$$

is independent of the path of integration. This difference ΔU is called the potential difference between the points. It is often abbreviated PD. The uniqueness of the potential difference for a given pair of points means that if the integral (5.39) is extended around a closed path, its value is always zero; and thus we return to the statement at the beginning of this paragraph.

Now the remainder of the electric field, the term $\mathbf{E}_m$, may not in general be expressed in terms of a scalar potential function at all. Its line integral around a closed loop does not in general vanish. We may summarize by saying that if a system has a quasi-static term $\mathbf{E}_s$ as part of its electric field, then for this part only we may define a quasi-static potential function with the properties of the electrostatic potential. It may happen that a system has no such field as $\mathbf{E}_s$ at all; or it may have a field which is constant in time and is entirely of the type $\mathbf{E}_s$.   Different regions of a single system sometimes have different types of field.

The reader should bear in mind that electric potential difference is dimensionally and by physical interpretation the work per unit test charge which is required of an external agent to move the charge from the point 1 to the point 2, considering only the force due to the partial field $\mathbf{E}_s$. This may be stated more usefully for present purposes as the negative of the work done by the field $\mathbf{E}_s$ on the unit test charge during the motion of the charge from 1 to 2.   The test charge is considered so small as not to affect the field $\mathbf{E}_s$ in which it finds itself.

5.8. Electromotive Force.   Let us consider a system in which the electric field has been written as the sum of a quasi-static field $\mathbf{E}_s$ and another field $\mathbf{E}_m$ as discussed in the preceding section.   We shall examine the energy balance for the motion of a charged particle q which moves as a carrier of electric charge.   From the definition of electric field as force per unit charge, the force on q due to the total electric field is

$$\mathbf{F}_e = (\mathbf{E}_s + \mathbf{E}_m)q \qquad (5.40)$$

Now there may be other forces on q.   There is a magnetic force in general if a magnetic field exists, but this force, although it may perform an essential function in a generator or motor, does no work, for it acts at right angles to the motion of q; therefore it will be omitted from present consideration.   There are other forces, however, which may do work on q. One such force may be described as mechanical, if the material containing q is moved mechanically, as for example in a generator.   There are other forces which may be described as quantum-mechanical in nature, and occur for example in electrolytic cells or in thermocouples.   All such forces, and in fact all forces except $\mathbf{F}_e$ and the dissipative force to be mentioned next, will be lumped under the symbol $\mathbf{F}'$.   Lastly, if the charged particle moves in a conduction process through conducting material, there is a dissipative force $\mathbf{F}_j$ which may be conceived to produce the Joule heating attending the conduction as discussed in Sec. 5.5.   This force differs from $\mathbf{F}_e$ and $\mathbf{F}'$ in that its direction depends on the direction of motion of q, so as always to oppose the motion of q; thus producing the loss of energy to heat.   In addition, the magnitude of $\mathbf{F}_j$ depends on the velocity of the charge q, which is not generally the case for the forces $\mathbf{F}_e$ and $\mathbf{F}'$ (cf. Prob. 5.41); and $\mathbf{F}_j$ vanishes at zero velocity.   We have now for the total force on q

$$\mathbf{F} = q\mathbf{E}_s + q\mathbf{E}_m + \mathbf{F}' + \mathbf{F}_j \qquad (5.41)$$

Consider now the energy balance when the charge q moves through the infinitesimal displacement $d\mathbf{l}$.   The total work done on q is $\mathbf{F} \cdot d\mathbf{l}$. This work must either be zero or appear as kinetic energy of the particle q.

We shall limit ourselves here to cases where this kinetic energy is negligibly small. This will certainly be the case in a conduction process, where the drift velocities of the carriers of charge are always very small. Atomic or electronic masses are so small that even the velocities encountered in the moving parts of an electrostatic generator will give the particle negligible kinetic energy. Thus we can write

$$q\mathbf{E}_s \cdot d\mathbf{l} + q\mathbf{E}_m \cdot d\mathbf{l} + \mathbf{F}' \cdot d\mathbf{l} + \mathbf{F}_j \cdot d\mathbf{l} = 0 \qquad (5.42)$$

Note however that Eq. (5.42) will not hold when q moves *in vacuo* in an accelerating machine such as a cyclotron where its kinetic energy may become not merely appreciable but enormous.

We can identify the quantity $\mathbf{E}_s \cdot d\mathbf{l}$ in Eq. (5.42) as $-dU$, the negative differential of the potential function as discussed in the preceding section. Solving for this quantity, we obtain

$$dU = \mathbf{E}_m \cdot d\mathbf{l} + \frac{1}{q}\mathbf{F}' \cdot d\mathbf{l} + \frac{1}{q}\mathbf{F}_j \cdot d\mathbf{l} \qquad (5.43)$$

Notice that Eq. (5.43) has been written for displacements $d\mathbf{l}$ which are in the actual lines of motion of the carrier charges q in the system, and is restricted also to displacements occurring with the actual velocity of the carrier charges at that point in the system. This is the case because the dissipative force $\mathbf{F}_j$, as well as the magnetic force excluded from consideration, depends on the vector velocity of the carriers.

Let us next integrate Eq. (5.43) over a conducting path along which a carrier would actually flow in the system. Call the path $\mathcal{L}$, and let the integration run from a point 1 to a point 2 in the sense of flow of the charge q. The left-hand side of the equation then becomes the potential difference between the two points, while we retain the integrals on the right:

$$\Delta U = U_2 - U_1 = \int_1^2 \mathbf{E}_m \cdot d\mathbf{l} + \int_1^2 \frac{1}{q}\mathbf{F}' \cdot d\mathbf{l} + \int_1^2 \frac{1}{q}\mathbf{F}_j \cdot d\mathbf{l} \quad (5.44)$$

In case the conditions in the system are changing with time, we shall understand Eq. (5.44) to be evaluated at a particular instant without regard to the actual time a charge would take to complete the path; and this is valid, since (5.43) is good at a given instant for each part of the path separately.

We shall begin discussing the significance of Eq. (5.44) by defining the sum of the first two integrals as the electromotive force $\mathcal{E}$, along the path $\mathcal{L}$ between points 1 and 2:

$$\mathcal{E} \equiv \int_1^2 \mathbf{E}_m \cdot d\mathbf{l} + \int_1^2 \frac{1}{q}\mathbf{F}' \cdot d\mathbf{l} \qquad (5.45)$$

The electromotive force represents the work per unit charge supplied to a charge q as q moves from 1 to 2 along the path $\mathcal{L}$. Work supplied by the quasi-static electric field $\mathbf{E}_s$ is specifically excluded but all other sources of energy are included. The energy supplied by a changing magnetic field is specifically mentioned in the first integral while the second integral stands for the energy from other sources. We shall use the abbreviation emf for electromotive force. Evidently its dimensions are the same as those of potential difference, so that an appropriate unit is the volt = joule/coulomb. To sum up the meaning of the term emf, we may say that it is a measure of the processes which may exist along the path $\mathcal{L}$ by which energy may be transferred from some non-electrostatic type of energy source into energy of an electric current.

It is very important to notice that an emf is, in principle, reversible. This is the case because in the integrals of Eq. (5.45) the integrands do not depend on the direction of motion of the charge. Thus the sign of the integrals reverses when their limits are reversed, which according to our physical interpretation means that the charge passes in the reverse direction. This is not true at all of the last integral of Eq. (5.44), in which the dissipation force $\mathbf{F}_j$ is always opposed to the direction of displacement $d\mathbf{l}$ of the charge; and we have already noticed that Joule heating is irreversible. We should perhaps remark that in some voltaic cells where an emf is created, there is in practice a lack of reversibility because some associated process is irreversible. An example is bubbling off of gas from an electrode of such a cell.

We should like to draw a few general conclusions from Eq. (5.44) regarding the potential difference in a system between two points on a streamline of current flow. There are, according to this equation, two conditions which may imply a potential difference between the points. Either an emf may exist along the conducting path, or a flow of current may exist [guaranteeing that the last integral of Eq. (5.44) exists]. Of course, both may exist together, provided they do not cancel one another. Since the dissipation integral is always negative, while the emf may be either positive or negative, the sign of ΔU in Eq. (5.44) may be either positive or negative. Hence the sign of the potential difference is not determined just by the direction of current flow. Next, notice that if the current ceases to flow,

$$\Delta U = \mathcal{E} \tag{5.46}$$

for then $\mathbf{F}_j$ vanishes. Thus an emf may be measured by determining the potential difference which it creates when no current flows.

Finally, remember that ΔU is produced by the presence of net electric charges. We deduce therefore that an emf may result in the building up of net electric charge. It is helpful to have this definite picture in one's mind of how an emf creates a potential difference, namely, by forcing electric charge to distribute itself so as to produce a quasi-static electric field and hence a potential difference.

We have developed the concept of emf from the point of view of the individual carriers of charge, in order to get a physical picture of its meaning.   In practice it may be confusing to follow through with this picture in detail, for there may be various carriers in different parts or even the same part of a system.   In Sec. 5.10 we shall apply the concepts we have introduced to a system without inquiring about the detailed picture of the conduction processes within the system.

5.9. Two-terminal Passive Systems.   D-C Resistance.   The terminals or electrodes of a conducting system are those regions of contact by which current flows between the system and the outside world.   Ideally, and to a useful approximation in practice, a terminal is composed of material whose conductivity is so high that the electric field and resulting potential difference in the terminal are negligible at the actual current densities.   It is then permissible to treat the terminals as equipotential regions and their boundaries as equipotential surfaces.   In particular, there is then a unique potential difference between any pair of terminals under given conditions in the system.

Conducting systems are to be classified as active or passive according as they do or do not contain any emf.   Equation (5.46) indicates that no potential difference can appear between terminals of a passive system unless current flows in the system.   This current may flow through other terminals than those whose potential difference is observed, as is the case in a precision low resistor with separate current and potential terminals; but it must flow from and to the outside world since a purely internal current would require an internal energy source to provide the Joule heat, and such a source implies an emf in the system.   We shall, however, consider only two-terminal systems for the present, that is systems in which only two terminals are in use.

Let the potential difference across a two-terminal system be designated by V, with the convention that when V is positive terminal 1 is at a higher potential than terminal 2.   Thus $V \equiv U_1 - U_2$.   Let a steady current I flow through the system, I being considered positive when current enters via terminal 1 and leaves at terminal 2.   In general, V is some function of I, vanishing with I as remarked above.   It is useful to define a quantity R called the d-c resistance of the system between the terminals at the given current:

$$R \equiv \frac{V}{I} \qquad\qquad (5.47)$$

It often happens that the resistance so defined is independent of the current flowing, provided the temperature of the system is held constant. In such a case, the system is said to be linear, and the constancy of the ratio (5.47) is called Ohm's law.[1] Definition (5.47) is valid, however, even when the system is nonlinear. The unit of resistance is seen to be

$$\frac{\text{volt}}{\text{ampere}} = \frac{\text{joule/coulomb}}{\text{ampere}} = \frac{\text{joule}}{\text{ampere}^2\ \text{second}} = \frac{\text{watt}}{\text{ampere}^2}$$

This unit is so much used as to have been given its own name, the ohm.

The resistance of a system between two terminals may be related to the Joule heat loss within the system for a given current flow. The power supplied to the system is VI, and if there are no internal emfs this power must all appear as Joule heating P_j. Thus

$$P_j = VI \tag{5.48}$$

Substitution from (5.47) yields two forms of some usefulness:

$$P_j = I^2R \tag{5.49}$$

$$P_j = \frac{V^2}{R} \tag{5.50}$$

Equation (5.49) would be, in fact, as good a definition of resistance as Eq. (5.47), with the added advantage of relating R to the basic process which causes finite resistance, namely, Joule heat dissipation. Notice that R is intrinsically positive for passive systems, since the irreversible power P_j is positive.

When a system is nonlinear, it may be useful to define an incremental resistance

$$R_{inc} \equiv \frac{dV}{dI} \tag{5.51}$$

The right-hand member of Eq. (5.51) may be considered the limit of a ratio of increments, $\lim_{\Delta I \to 0} \Delta V/\Delta I$, or as the derivative of the curve obtained by plotting V as a function of I for the given system. This graph of V against I is very useful for systems having extreme departure from linearity, as is the case in an electric discharge. Incremental resistance can be negative. Such negative resistance has important practical significance, for it may result in oscillation or instability. The reciprocal of resistance is called conductance, and is frequently designated by the letter G:

$$G \equiv \frac{1}{R} \tag{5.52}$$

Its mks unit is called the mho, which seems to demonstrate that scien-

[1] In honor of George Simon Ohm (1787–1854).

tists are not without a sense of humor. The conductance of a two-terminal network is, by Eq. (5.47),

$$G = \frac{I}{V} \tag{5.53}$$

Incremental conductance is likewise useful:

$$G_{inc} \equiv \frac{dI}{dV} \tag{5.54}$$

5.10. Two-terminal Active Systems with Direct Current. It is clear from Eqs. (5.44) and (5.46) that the potential difference between terminals of an active system, *i.e.*, one containing emf, depends in general on the current flowing but does not in general vanish with current. Let us consider the electrical properties of a two-terminal, active conducting system without presuming any knowledge of the internal mechanism of the system. The electrical properties are entirely defined at a given time by the characteristic function relating the potential difference V and the current I. Without knowledge of the energy transformations occurring in the system, we may still write an energy balance equating the net output power to the net power transferred reversibly into the electrical system minus the irreversible Joule heat lost to the system. This balance reads

$$IV = I\varepsilon - I^2R \tag{5.55}$$

Here the reversible power is assigned to a net emf ε, while the Joule heat is accounted for by the effective resistance R. A sign convention has been chosen such that positive current corresponds to current flow from the lower to the higher potential terminal within the system and thus from higher to lower potential in the external circuit. If positive current is that which enters the system by terminal 1 and leaves by terminal 2, as in the preceding section, then the potential difference is $V \equiv U_2 - U_1$, opposite to the convention used for passive systems.

Now from Eq. (5.55), it is evident that the potential difference across the active system is

$$V = \varepsilon - IR \tag{5.56}$$

The next question is how to define ε and R from a knowledge simply of the characteristic function $V(I)$. If ε and R are both allowed to be functions of the current, it is clear that there are infinitely many ways of specifying these two functions so that Eq. (5.56) will yield $V(I)$. Of these specifications some may be much simpler than others. For linear systems, the graph of $V(I)$ is a straight line. In such a case, it is simplest to identify the slope of the $V(I)$ graph as $-R$ and its V intercept V_0 as the emf $\mathcal{E}$, so that both R and $\mathcal{E}$ are defined to be independent of the current. Then

$$\mathcal{E} = V_0 \tag{5.57}$$

$$R = -\frac{dV}{dI} \tag{5.58}$$

If the potential difference observed for current I_1 is V_1, the resistance (5.55) for a linear, active system is given by

$$R = \frac{V_0 - V_1}{I_1} \tag{5.59}$$

If the characteristic function of an active system is not linear, then either $\mathcal{E}$ or R or both must be considered to be dependent on the current. The choice is purely arbitrary, although knowledge of the structure of the system may make a particular choice more natural than any other. For example, a system containing a battery together with a nonohmic resistance like a lamp filament is most reasonably described by a constant emf and variable resistance; while a motor or generator, whose speed and field strength may depend on the current, presumably should be assigned a variable emf and a reasonably constant resistance.

5.11. Charge within a Conductor. It was shown in Sec. 1.12 that in an electrostatic system all net electric charge on a conductor resides on the surface of the conducting material. This statement remains true for a homogeneous, isotropic, linear conducting material even when currents are flowing. Such a material is characterized by the constitutive equations

$$\mathbf{J} = g\mathbf{E} \tag{5.25}$$

and, from Sec. 3.7,

$$\mathbf{D} = \epsilon\mathbf{E} \tag{5.60}$$

where g and ϵ are constants. To prove the theorem, we postulate the general validity of the differential equation for the electric displacement $\mathbf{D}$:

$$\frac{\partial D_x}{\partial x} + \frac{\partial D_y}{\partial y} + \frac{\partial D_z}{\partial z} = \rho \tag{5.61}$$

This equation was set up in Sec. 3.6 for the electrostatic case, and its general character is discussed in Sec. 12.4. It is to be combined with the equation of continuity, as stated in Sec. 5.3,

$$\frac{\partial J_x}{\partial x} + \frac{\partial J_y}{\partial y} + \frac{\partial J_z}{\partial z} + \frac{\partial \rho}{\partial t} = 0 \tag{5.22}$$

Using Eqs. (5.60) and (5.25) in (5.61) and (5.22), respectively, we obtain

$$\rho = \epsilon \left(\frac{\partial E_x}{\partial x} + \frac{\partial E_y}{\partial y} + \frac{\partial E_z}{\partial z} \right) \tag{5.62}$$

and

$$\frac{\partial \rho}{\partial t} = -g \left(\frac{\partial E_x}{\partial x} + \frac{\partial E_y}{\partial y} + \frac{\partial E_z}{\partial z} \right) \tag{5.63}$$

Hence the charge density function ρ satisfies the partial differential equation

$$\frac{\partial \rho}{\partial t} = -\frac{g}{\epsilon} \rho \tag{5.64}$$

The general solution of this equation is

$$\rho = \rho_0(x,y,z)e^{-(g/\epsilon)t} \tag{5.65}$$

where $\rho_0(x,y,z)$ is an arbitrary distribution of charge density supposed to exist in the material at a time $t = 0$. Equation (5.65) shows that such a supposed charge distribution dies out at all points within the conductor at a common rate as t increases, and asymptotically approaches zero. The quantity ϵ/g, called the relaxation time of the material, is the time in which the charge density falls to $1/2.7$ . . . of its initial value. The relaxation time is a convenient measure of the speed with which any charges initially in the material would die out.

Now if charge density within a homogeneous, isotropic, linear conducting material can only decay, it must actually be zero there:

$$\rho \equiv 0 \tag{5.66}$$

Nothing in this theorem forbids the permanent existence of surface density of charge on conductor boundaries or on an interface between two conducting materials; for the equations used in the proof assume continuity of the functions involved, and thus are valid only within the body of the material.

5.12. Steady Current Flow in a Region without EMF. A problem of some practical interest is the determination of the current density function **J** for steady current flow in a conductor. The limitation to steady flow is made so that we may postulate the absence of electromotive force in the region of the problem. In the absence of emf, the total electric field **E** is of the type which was called quasi-electrostatic and designated $\mathbf{E}_s$ in Sec. 5.7. This means that **E** may be expressed in terms of a scalar potential function U:

$$E_x = -\frac{\partial U}{\partial x} \qquad E_y = -\frac{\partial U}{\partial y} \qquad E_z = -\frac{\partial U}{\partial z} \tag{5.67}$$

The current density function **J** in an isotropic medium is obtained from the constitutive equation

$$\mathbf{J} = g\mathbf{E} \tag{5.25}$$

We shall treat only the problem of a linear homogeneous material; thus the conductivity g is to be constant, at least by subregions. For such a material, we may use the theorem of Sec. 5.11 that the charge density throughout is zero; and this being so at all times, the rate of change of charge density also vanishes at all points inside the conducting material:

$$\frac{\partial \rho}{\partial t} = 0 \tag{5.68}$$

The equation of continuity, Eq. (5.22), then shows that the current density function in the region satisfies the differential equation

$$\frac{\partial J_x}{\partial x} + \frac{\partial J_y}{\partial y} + \frac{\partial J_z}{\partial z} = 0 \tag{5.69}$$

Equations (5.67), (5.25), and (5.69) characterize the current flow within a region of a homogeneous, linear, isotropic conductor where there is no emf. When combined, they show at once that the potential function in such a region satisfies Laplace's equation:

$$\frac{\partial^2 U}{\partial x^2} + \frac{\partial^2 U}{\partial y^2} + \frac{\partial^2 U}{\partial z^2} = 0 \tag{5.70}$$

This is the same equation as holds for a region of an electrostatic system where there is no charge density and where the electric inductive capacity ϵ is constant.

Once the potential function U is known for a given system, the problem is evidently solved, for Eqs. (5.67) and (5.25) together then yield the current density function. Equation (5.70) has an infinite number of solutions, however, and in order to pick out the solution of a given problem it is necessary to specify the behavior of the function U at the boundaries of the system. In Chaps. 2 and 3 consideration has been given to the problem of finding solutions of Laplace's equation satisfying given boundary conditions. We shall state here only the nature of the boundary conditions of conduction problems, with an indication of what conditions are sufficient to specify a solution.

There are three types of boundaries which are encountered in problems of steady current flow. In every problem there is at least a pair of electrodes in contact with the conducting material where **J** is to be found. The boundaries between the electrodes and the material are subject to two conditions. According to the definition of Sec. 5.9, electrodes or terminals are conductors which are postulated to be essentially equipotential over their boundary of contact with the system under investigation. Thus on each electrode boundary, the potential function is a constant:

$$U_i = V_i \qquad (5.71)$$

on the ith electrode. Another boundary condition at an electrode surface concerns the current flow between the system and the electrode. Let $\mathbf{n}$ be a unit vector always normal to the electrode boundary and outward from the system to be solved. The current out from the system into the electrode through an element da of the boundary is

$$dI = \mathbf{J} \cdot \mathbf{n}\, da \qquad (5.72)$$

Because of Eq. (5.25),

$$dI = g\mathbf{E} \cdot \mathbf{n}\, da \qquad (5.73)$$

In terms of the potential function, Eq. (5.73) may be written

$$dI = -g\frac{\partial U}{\partial n}\, da \qquad (5.74)$$

where n is a coordinate perpendicular to the boundary with its positive sense out from the system. Equation (5.74) follows formally from (5.73) by use of (5.67); but its correctness is to be seen at once from the fact that $-(\partial U/\partial n)$ is the component of electric field along the coordinate n. It may be noted that actually the total vectors $\mathbf{J}$ and $\mathbf{E}$ are in the normal direction, either inward or outward, at all points of the electrode boundary; for the boundary is an equipotential surface. Integration of Eq. (5.74) is usually necessary for obtaining a useful boundary condition, since the total current to the electrode is either known or is required to be found:

$$I_i = -\int_{S_i} g\frac{\partial U}{\partial n}\, da \qquad (5.75)$$

Here S_i is the boundary surface of the ith electrode. The symbol g has been included under the integral for generality, but it may be withdrawn if the electrode is in contact with only a single, homogeneous conducting material.

A second type of boundary often encountered in a current flow problem is an outer boundary of the conductor, that is, a boundary with an insulating medium into which no current flows. We found in Sec. 5.6 that the electric field at such a boundary on the conducting side is entirely parallel to the boundary:

$$\mathbf{E} \cdot \mathbf{n} = 0 \qquad (5.76)$$

Writing this in terms of the potential function and the coordinate normal to the boundary, we have

$$\frac{\partial U}{\partial n} = 0 \tag{5.77}$$

The third type of boundary, less often found than the other two, is an interface between subregions of different and nonzero conductivities. In this case, a different potential function $U^{(m)}$ is used for each subregion, and these may be related through the use of the boundary conditions of Sec. 5.6, provided the state is steady so that there is no growth or decay of charge on the boundary. The reader may for himself express these boundary conditions in terms of the $U^{(m)}$ functions and the conductivities. See Secs. 3.9 and 3.10 for the corresponding conditions in nonconducting systems.

We give without proof a statement of what constitutes a sufficient set of boundary conditions to specify the solution of a system. It is first supposed that the conductivity is known everywhere in the system. Next, Eq. (5.77) must be employed at all boundaries with insulators, and the condition mentioned in the preceding paragraph must be used at all conductor interfaces (not including electrode boundaries) if the system has subregions. If the conducting material extends to infinity, we shall specify that the electrodes still remain finite in size unless we are treating a special problem involving fewer than three cartesian coordinates. See the outline of such problems in electrostatics in Sec. 2.4. Finally, it is the electrode boundary conditions which are of the greatest interest. We have our choice of specifying the electrode potentials V_i or the electrode currents I_i, for each electrode of the system. The solution then yields the quantity not specified for each electrode. There is still the usual arbitrary, additive constant involved in the potential function, unless one electrode potential is specified absolutely; but this is not usually of interest.

It is now possible to formulate a theorem of great practical importance concerning passive, two-terminal conducting systems whose material is linear. The resistance of such a system can in principle be determined by the boundary-condition method of this section. Given the current I (positive at one electrode and negative at the other), the solution for the potential function U yields the potential difference V between terminals. Conversely, given V we obtain I, for V determines the two electrode potentials except for the additive constant. The interesting thing to notice is that since the conductivity is by hypothesis independent of the current density or the electric field, that is, the conductor material is linear, then all the equations of this section are linear. This means that if I is multiplied by a factor K, V is multiplied by the same factor, and conversely. Consequently the ratio of V to I, which is the resistance of the system, is independent of I or V. The entire system is then a linear system in the sense in which the term is used in Sec. 5.9.

5.13. Current Flow in a Wire. Resistivity. For practical purposes, it is important to analyze the problem of steady current flow in a wire in which all cross sections are alike, and to which terminals are connected at its ends. We shall suppose there is no emf in the wire, so that a quasi-electrostatic field and an electric potential function exist in the wire. By the word wire, we shall imply a conductor whose length is very much greater than its transverse dimensions. This postulate allows us to suppose that for most of the length of the wire, the electrode configuration is irrelevant. Electrode geometry must indeed influence the current flow near the ends of the wire, but its effects should rapidly become negligible as the distance from the end becomes large compared to the transverse dimensions of the wire. Neglecting the end effects then, we shall suppose that over every cross section of a wire whose cross sections are all alike, the magnitude of the current density function varies in the same manner with coordinates in the cross section.

Let us first inquire as to the direction of the current density vector $\mathbf{J}$, and hence the direction of the electric field in the wire. The lines of flow and of electric force must be normal to the cross sections of the wire, if we define the cross sections as planes normal to the outer boundary surface of the wire. For, if these lines all diverged from the axis of the wire or converged toward the axis, there would be concentrations of current density at the axis or at the boundaries, contrary to the supposition made above. If the lines are all inclined in one particular direction, again there would be changes of current distribution from one cross section to another. One might imagine that the lines of flow could be helical, like the cords in a rope. This would preserve the same current distribution in every cross section, but would require a component of electric field everywhere tangent to a circle around the axis of the wire. Around such a circle the line integral for the potential function would be nonvanishing, contrary to the postulate that we have a quasi-static electric field.

Let us now connect like points of every cross section of the wire by a line $\mathfrak{L}$. We shall assume no appreciable torsion of the wire if its cross sections are not circular; thus $\mathfrak{L}$ will run perpendicular to the cross sections. At this point of each cross section let the conductivity be g, which is therefore constant along the given line $\mathfrak{L}$. In the absence of emf and of intense magnetic fields, the current density at points on $\mathfrak{L}$ is

$$\mathbf{J} = g\mathbf{E} \qquad (5.25)$$

where $\mathbf{E}$ is the quasi-static electric field. Now at every point of $\mathfrak{L}$, the magnitude of $\mathbf{J}$ is constant by hypothesis and the direction of $\mathbf{J}$ is along $\mathfrak{L}$

as shown in the preceding paragraph. Hence the electric field **E** is constant in magnitude along $\mathfrak{L}$, and has everywhere the direction of $\mathfrak{L}$. Let two points along $\mathfrak{L}$ be at a distance apart l, as measured along $\mathfrak{L}$. It now follows from the definition of potential that the potential difference V between these points is proportional to l:

$$V = El \tag{5.78}$$

Since the lines of electric force are normal to the cross-section planes of the wire, these planes are equipotential surfaces. Therefore Eq. (5.78) gives the potential difference between a pair of cross sections of the wire whose distance along a flow line is l, the field along $\mathfrak{L}$ being E. A straight wire has all its cross sections parallel, so that l is the same along every flow path between a pair of cross sections. Therefore E must be constant over every part of the cross section of a straight wire. Wires may be considered approximately straight when they are bent only in radii of curvature very large compared to their cross section dimensions. For all ordinary purposes now, we may use Eq. (5.78) to find the (constant) magnitude of the electric field within a wire in which the potential drops by an amount V in a length l:

$$E = \frac{V}{l} \tag{5.79}$$

The total current carried by the wire may be formed by integrating the magnitude of the current density vector over a cross section S, for we have seen that **J** is normal to the cross sections:

$$I = \int_S J \, da \tag{5.80}$$

Substituting for J from Eq. (5.25), and using the constancy of the magnitude of the electric field, we may write

$$I = E \int_S g \, da \tag{5.81}$$

This result takes an especially simple form if the wire is homogeneous, with a cross-sectional area A:

$$I = EgA \tag{5.82}$$

The resistance of length l of the wire is found by combining Eqs. (5.81) and (5.79) with the definition of resistance:

$$R = \frac{l}{\int g \, da} \tag{5.83}$$

In the special case of a homogeneous wire, this reduces to

$$R = \frac{l}{gA} \tag{5.84}$$

Quite frequently, one sees this written in terms of the resistivity r_1 of the material, which is defined to be

$$r_1 \equiv \frac{1}{g} \qquad (5.85)$$

Then,

$$R = \frac{r_1 l}{A} \qquad (5.86)$$

Evidently resistivity has the units of ohm-meters in the mks system. Sometimes, rather confusingly, this unit is stated as ohm per meter cube. This must not be taken to mean ohm per meter^3, which is dimensionally not resistivity at all. It means, rather, that the resistivity is numerically the resistance of a unit-sized cube of material in which the current flow is uniform and normal to a pair of faces of the cube.

One other conventional way of stating resistivity, used frequently enough to require mention, is in ohms per mil-foot. This is the resistance of a piece of homogeneous wire of the material in question whose length is one foot, and whose cross-sectional area is that of a circle of one thousandth of an inch in diameter. This area of a circle of one thousandth of an inch in diameter is called a circular mil. Thus if the cross section A of a wire is given in circular mils, and its length in feet, these units may be used directly in Eq. (5.86) if the resistivity is given in ohms per mil-foot. Notice that the ohm per mil-foot, like the ohm per meter cube, has a name which is not dimensionally correct.

5.14. Temperature Coefficient of Resistivity. The temperature dependence of the resistivity of most conductors is large enough to be of considerable practical importance. We shall define the temperature coefficient of resistivity, a quantity which describes the average fractional rate of change of resistivity over a range of temperature. If the resistivity of a material at temperature t_1 is r_{11} and at temperature $t_1 + \Delta t$ the resistivity is $r_{11} + \Delta r_1$, then the temperature coefficient of resistivity for this interval is

$$\alpha_1 \equiv \frac{\Delta r_1}{r_{11} \, \Delta t} \qquad (5.87)$$

Evidently units of α_1 are reciprocal degrees, usually on the centigrade scale. When the reference temperature is zero centigrade, as is usual in tabulations, the symbol α_0 may be given to the temperature coefficient.

The value of the temperature coefficient will in general depend both on the reference temperature t_1 and on the size of the interval Δt for a given conducting material. For pure metals in the usual range of laboratory temperature, α depends relatively little on the size of the temperature interval, which is equivalent to saying that the resistivity of a pure metal is a fairly linear function of temperature. In fact, as a rough rule, the resistivity of a pure metal increases directly as temperature on the Kelvin scale. For pure metals, then, over a considerable range, or for any material in a sufficiently restricted range, the temperature coefficient may be used to compute to a fair first approximation the resistivity r_1 at a temperature t within the interval Δt. Assuming that α_1 is approximately the same over a part of the interval as over the whole of it,

$$\frac{r_1 - r_{11}}{r_{11}(t - t_1)} \doteq \alpha_1 \tag{5.88}$$

therefore

$$r_1 \doteq r_{11}[1 + \alpha_1(t - t_1)] \tag{5.89}$$

The resistance of a particular conductor is affected by temperature not only through the temperature dependence of its resistivity, but also through the change of its dimensions due to thermal expansion. This effect is very small for pure metals, for which α_0 is of the order of magnitude $\frac{1}{273}$ per °C, while the thermal expansion coefficients are of the order of 10^{-5} per °C. Nevertheless, there are certain alloys especially developed for small temperature coefficient of resistivity for which the thermal expansion may be as important as the change of resistivity. The reader may work out the total effect of temperature on the resistance of a wire by use of Eq. (5.86).

The temperature coefficient of resistivity may have either a positive or a negative sign. It is generally positive for most metals and alloys, and negative for semiconductors, electrolytic conductors, and dielectrics.

PROBLEMS

5.1. The diameter of No. 18 copper wire is 1.024 mm, and when the wire is exposed it can safely carry 5 amp. Likewise No. 6 wire, with a diameter of 4.115 mm can carry 70 amp. Compute and compare the allowed current densities for these two cases.

5.2. In the atmosphere, a downward electric current whose density is about 2.0×10^{-16} amp/cm² is observed in fine weather. This is due chiefly to small ions both positive and negative, of which the density for either sign is about 600 per cm³. Assuming that each ion carries one electronic unit of charge, $e = \pm 1.60 \times 10^{-19}$ coulomb, and that the velocities of ions of both signs are the same in magnitude, find the mean velocity of an ion.

5.3. Supposing that one electron per atom in a copper wire is free to take part in the conduction of electricity, find the average drift velocity of the electrons when a current of 10 amp flows in a No. 16 wire having a cross section of 1.31 mm². Given that the density of copper atoms is DN_A/W, where the mass density $D = 8.93$ g/cm³, atomic weight $W = 63.6$, Avogadro's number $N_A = 6.02 \times 10^{23}$ per g-mole, and the electronic charge is -1.60×10^{-19} coulomb.

5.4. Given a cylindrical conducting shell of axial length L and inner and outer radii a and b, respectively. A current flows around this conductor with density $\mathbf{J} = J_0 \mathbf{\theta}^0/r$, where J_0 is constant, r is the cylindrical radius to the point of observation, and $\mathbf{\theta}^0$ is the tangential unit vector, which is always perpendicular to both the cylindrical radius and axis. Find the total current carried by the shell.

5.5. Show that if a surface bearing a net surface density σ of electric charge moves with a velocity $\mathbf{v}$ everywhere tangent to the surface, the result is a surface current of density $\mathbf{K} = \sigma\mathbf{v}$.

5.6. In a Van de Graaff electrostatic generator, a sheet of electric charge is carried on a paper belt into the high-voltage terminal. When the belt is 47 in. wide and travels at 4,520 ft/mm, and the current carried is 0.8 ma, what is the surface density of charge on the belt?

5.7. *a.* Referring to Prob. 5.5, find the surface current density at a general place on a sphere of radius R bearing a uniform surface density σ of electric charge and rotating about a diameter with an angular speed ω (radians per second).

b. Find the total current flowing on this sphere across a line fixed in space and stretching once from pole to pole on the sphere.

5.8. Consider the leakage current between the inner and outer conductors of a concentric cable of circular cross section, in which the insulating material has cylindrical symmetry but otherwise need not be homogeneous. Show that the radial component of current density at a general point must be proportional, in steady state where no charges are building up, to the inverse first power of the cylindrical radius to that point.

5.9. Suppose that current flows between two concentric spherical surfaces of radii a and b and that the current density in this region is everywhere radially outward with a magnitude $J = J_0 r^3 e^{-kt}$, where t is time, r is the radius to the point of observation, and J_0 and k are constants. Find the charge density function in the region.

Ans. $(5J_0/k)r^2 e^{-kt}$.

5.10. The mobility of a type of carrier of electric current is defined as the average velocity acquired by such a carrier per unit field strength: $u_i \equiv v_i/E$. Write formulas for the resistivity of an isotropic material containing several carriers, as well as for the current density in such a material, in terms of the mobilities of the carriers.

5.11. The conduction of the atmosphere is found to be due to four types of carriers, small and large ions of both signs. For the following densities and mobilities, and for a downward electric field of 200 volts/m, find the atmospheric conductivity and current density:

Small ions, positive: 110/cm³, $1.5 \dfrac{\text{cm/sec}}{\text{volt/cm}}$

Small ions, negative: 130/cm³, $1.5 \dfrac{\text{cm/sec}}{\text{volt/cm}}$

Large ions, positive: 50,000/cm³, $.0004 \dfrac{\text{cm/sec}}{\text{volt/cm}}$

Large ions, negative: Same

(See Prob. 5.10.)

5.12. *a.* The conductivity of copper is 5.8×10^7 mho/m, and steady current densities of 5×10^6 amp/m² are not unusual. Find the corresponding electric field in the copper.

b. The conductivity of sulfur is about 10^{-15} mho/m. Find the current density in sulfur when it is subjected to an electric field of 2,000 volts/cm.

5.13. In an elementary picture of metallic conduction, the carriers are free electrons of charge $-e$ and mass m, which have a high average thermal speed $\bar{c}$ and a mean free path λ between collisions. In the short time between collisions an applied electric field accelerates an electron and produces an average drift velocity opposite to the field direction; but the electron rebounds from the next collision in a perfectly random direction. Show that this picture yields a linear conductor, and find an expression for the conductivity.   *Ans.* $g = \dfrac{ne^2\lambda}{2m\bar{c}}$, where n is the density of electrons.

5.14. Suppose that the heat produced in a wire of circular cross section is dissipated entirely by radiation from its surface and that the maximum heat dissipation per unit surface, as limited by the allowable temperature rise, is W. For a wire of isotropic, linear, and homogeneous material of conductivity g, find the maximum allowed values of current density and of total current. Let the wire have radius a.

$$Ans.\ J_{\max} = \sqrt{\frac{2gW}{a}};\ I_{\max} = \pi\sqrt{2gWa^3}.$$

5.15. A current of 70 amp flows in a No. 6 copper wire whose cross-sectional area is 13.3 mm² and whose conductivity is 5.8×10^7 mho/m. Find the heat developed (*a*) per cubic centimeter and per cubic meter; (*b*) per meter length of wire.

5.16. A bare wire of copper ($g = 5.8 \times 10^7$ mho/m) carries a steady current of 20 amp uniformly distributed over its circular cross section of 1 mm radius. Furthermore, the wire carries a net positive charge of 6×10^{-15} coulomb per meter length, uniformly distributed over its surface. Find the electric field vector at the surface, both inside and outside the wire.

5.17. Consider a boundary between two homogeneous, isotropic, and linear materials characterized, respectively, by dielectric constants ϵ_1 and ϵ_2 and by conductivities g_1 and g_2. Suppose that the current flow is steady and no charge densities are changing with time. If a current I_A crosses unit area of the boundary, at a point, its positive sense being from the second to the first medium, show that there is a surface density of charge

$$\left(\frac{\epsilon_1}{g_1} - \frac{\epsilon_2}{g_2}\right) I_A$$

at this point on the boundary.

5.18. Suppose that a voltaic cell is made by filling with an electrolytic solution the space $a < r < b$ between a spherical metal shell and a smaller, concentric sphere of another metal. The solution is of course conducting, but no other connection is made between the spheres. The inner and outer electrodes have potentials, respectively, V_a and V_b relative to the solution due to an emf existing in a film of thickness t between each electrode and the free solution. Sketch the dependence of the quasi-electrostatic potential function on the radius r. What is the emf of the cell?

5.19. Suppose that a fine conducting wire in the form of a closed circle of 3 cm radius carries a momentarily steady electric current induced in it by a changing magnetic field. The wire is copper, of conductivity 5.8×10^7 mho/m, and has in it a current density which is essentially uniform with a magnitude of 20 amp/m².

a. What is the quasi-electrostatic potential difference between two points diametrically opposite to one another? Explain.

b. What is the emf between these two points, taken in the sense of the current flow?

5.20. Given an aluminum wire whose conductivity is 3.5×10^7 mho/m, carrying a current of uniform density 8×10^5 amp/m².

a. Find the electric field in the wire.

b. Find the potential difference per meter of the wire, if there is no source of emf in the wire.

c. Under what conditions, if at all, could the potential difference vanish?

5.21. In a voltaic cell, the forces producing the emf occur entirely in a thin region between the electrodes and the electrolytic solution. Consider a cell in which the negative electrode is at -0.5 volt relative to a point in the solution near it, and the positive electrode is at $+1.0$ volt relative to the solution in its vicinity, while the cell delivers current to a resistance wire connected across its external terminals. Draw a schematic picture of the variation of the quasi-electrostatic potential with position along a closed conducting path through wire and cell.

5.22. Suppose the wire on the armature of a generator moves in a fixed magnetic field perpendicular to the axis and to the velocity of the wire. From the viewpoint of a fixed observer in space, draw qualitative vector diagrams for the force on and velocity of a carrier electron in the wire, neglecting the field of the wire itself and given that the magnetic force is normal both to the carrier velocity and to the magnetic field. Show that the magnetic force does no work, but that there is a force that does work when and only when current flows. Show also the equilibrant forces, and indicate the sources of all forces.

5.23. The current-voltage relationship for the plate and cathode terminals of a vacuum tube sometimes follows a three-halves power law: $I = kV^{3/2}$ where k is a constant. Suppose that this law holds for a tube whose plate current is 6 ma at 90 volts plate potential. At this operating point, find (a) the (d-c) plate resistance; (b) the incremental plate resistance.

5.24. The power vs. potential difference curve of a lamp near the rated operating point is approximated by

$$P = P_0 \left(\frac{V}{V_0}\right)^k$$

where P_0 is the power at the rated potential difference V_0 and k is a constant exponent. Find expressions for (a) the resistance R in terms of V, V_0, and the resistance R_0 at rated potential difference; (b) R in terms of the current I, the current I_0 at rated potential difference, and R_0; (c) V in terms of I, I_0, and V_0. Show by qualitative sketches the form of these curves for a gas-filled tungsten lamp, $k = 1.5$, and an untreated carbon lamp, $k = 2.3$.

5.25. What is the resistance of a lamp which consumes 60 watts of power at a d-c potential of 115 volts, when operating at the rated voltage?

5.26. A storage battery delivers 5.94 volts to a load which draws a current of 5.00 amp, and 5.92 volts when the load current is increased to 10 amp. Find, assuming the battery to be linear with constant emf, (a) the emf; (b) the potential difference across the battery when it is being charged (i.e., the current is reversed) at a rate of 8 amp; (c) the extra joule heating within the battery caused by the three currents mentioned above. (This is extra since local currents may flow in the battery even on open circuit.)

5.27. A metallic conductor carries a current density due to drift velocity of the electrons. Consider a conductor carrying steady current and moving relative to the laboratory frame of reference, as, for instance, the armature winding of a generator. Show that the current density within the conductor is the same for an observer fixed in the laboratory as for an observer moving with the conductor, to the nonrelativistic approximation in which velocities add vectorially.

5.28. Compute the relaxation times of metallic silver and sulfur, using the following data for permittivity and conductivity:

Silver: $\epsilon = \epsilon_0$ (assumed); $g = 6.1 \times 10^7$ mho/m
Sulfur: $\epsilon = 4\epsilon_0$; $g = 10^{-15}$ mho/m

Check out the units involved.

5.29. Find the two boundary conditions for the potential at an interface between two isotropic media characterized by permittivities ϵ_1 and ϵ_2 and conductivities g_1 and g_2, respectively, in steady state.

5.30. *a.* If the dielectric in a cylindrical condenser is linear, isotropic, and homogeneous in conductivity as well as permittivity and is cut off squarely with the edges of the electrodes at both ends of the condenser in planes normal to the axis, show that the presence of appreciable conductivity makes the electric field within the condenser conform exactly to the ideal field used in computing Eq. (4.74), Sec. 4.9. Use Laplace's equation, boundary conditions, and the uniqueness theorem.

b. Prove a similar theorem for parallel-plate condensers.

5.31. Show that in any two-electrode condenser filled with an isotropic, homogeneous, linear, and conducting medium, the product of the capacitance and resistance between electrodes equals the relaxation time of the medium.

5.32. Use the theorem of the preceding problem to find the leakage resistance per meter length between conductors of a concentric cable of circular cross section with rubber insulation. The insulating layer has the following specifications: inner and outer radii 2 mm and 5 mm; resistivity 6.0×10^{12} ohm-m.

5.33. Suppose current electrodes could be formed on the inner and outer surfaces of a spherical shell of iron whose radii are 2 cm and 4 cm, respectively, and whose conductivity is 1.0×10^7 mho/m. Find the resistance of the system.

5.34. Consider the interior of an isotropic medium characterized by a permittivity ϵ and conductivity g which are in general functions of the space coordinates. Show that the volume density of free electric charge, in the steady state where this density is independent of time, is given by

$$\rho = \mathbf{E} \cdot \left[\left(\frac{\partial \epsilon}{\partial x} \mathbf{i} + \frac{\partial \epsilon}{\partial y} \mathbf{j} + \frac{\partial \epsilon}{\partial z} \mathbf{k} \right) - \frac{\epsilon}{g} \left(\frac{\partial g}{\partial x} \mathbf{i} + \frac{\partial g}{\partial y} \mathbf{j} + \frac{\partial g}{\partial z} \mathbf{k} \right) \right]$$
$$\equiv \mathbf{E} \cdot \left(\operatorname{grad} \epsilon - \frac{\epsilon}{g} \operatorname{grad} g \right)$$

where $\mathbf{E}$ is the electric field vector. Use this to prove again Theorem 5.66, Sec. 5.11, and to show an extension as well as some limitations of the validity of that theorem.

5.35. A piece of wire 200 m long and 0.205 mm² in cross section has a potential difference of 3.00 volts applied across it; and the current in it is then found to be 0.188 amp. Find (*a*) its resistivity and (*b*) the electric field intensity in the wire.

5.36. *a.* Obtain a formula for the resistance of a wire of length l and mass m, of uniform cross section, the material having resistivity r_1 and density D.

b. The so-called mass resistivity of copper is the resistance of a round conductor of 1 gram mass and 1 m length. Find this resistance, given that the conductivity of copper is 5.80×10^7 mho/m and its density 8.89 g/cm³.

c. The legal standard ohm internationally agreed upon in 1908 was the resistance of a mercury column at 0°C, 14.4521 g in mass, of constant cross-sectional area, and length 106.300 cm. On this basis, and given the density of Hg at 0° as 13.596 g/cm³, find the resistivity of Hg.

5.37. Show by use of basic differential equations that if the electric field in a straight conductor of isotropic homogeneous material is to have neither radial components nor components tangential to a circle about the axis, then it necessarily is uniform in magnitude within the wire. Assume no source of emf in the wire.

5.38. *a.* Given the conductivity of copper as 5.80×10^7 mho/m, find the resistance of a copper wire 1 ft long and 1 cir mil in cross section.

b. Write a formula with a numerical coefficient, giving the resistance in ohms of any copper wire of length l in feet and cross sectional area CM in circular mils.

5.39. The American or Brown and Sharpe wire gage provides for a geometric series of diameters from 0.4600 in. to 0.0050 in. numbered 0000, 000, 00, 0, 1, 2, . . . , 36.

  a. Find from this the ratio of diameters of successive members of the series.
  b. Find the percentage error in the following rough rules:
    (1) The resistance per unit length doubles with an increase of three gage numbers.
    (2) The resistance per unit length increases tenfold for an increase of 10 gage numbers.
    (3) No. 10 copper wire has a resistance of 1 ohm per 1,000 ft.

  5.40. A steel wire 100 mils in diameter is made of a material whose resistivity is 60×10^{-8} ohm-m. It is to be coated with copper of resistivity 1.72×10^{-8} ohm-m, in order to double its conductance per unit length. What must be the thickness of the copper sheath?

  5.41. Show that in a linear medium the resistive force $\mathbf{F}_{ji}$ on a carrier of charge q_i is proportional to the drift velocity $\mathbf{v}_i$ and in the opposite direction. Find an expression for the constant of proportionality.

  5.42. Investigate the linearity of dependence of the resistivity of copper on temperature by plotting the ratio $\Delta r_1/\Delta t$ vs. the temperature at the center of the interval, using the following data from the "Handbook of Chemistry and Physics" (29th edition):

Temperature, °C	r_1, ohm-cm
-258.6	0.014
-205.6	0.163
-150	0.567
-100	0.904
$+20$	1.692
$+100$	2.28
$+200$	2.96
$+500$	5.08

  5.43. Given that the temperature coefficient of resistivity of copper is $\alpha_{20} = 0.00393$ per °C, referred to 20°C. If the copper had a linear dependence of resistivity on temperature, at what temperature would the resistivity fall to zero?

  5.44. If carbon has resistivities of 4.60×10^{-5} ohm-m at 20°C and 4.21×10^{-5} ohm-m at 360°C, find its temperature coefficient of resistivity referred to the lower temperature.

  5.45. The coefficient of linear expansion of an isotropic solid in a temperature interval t_1 to $t_1 + \Delta t$ may be defined as

$$\alpha_1' = \frac{\Delta l}{l_1 \, \Delta t}$$

where Δl is the change of any linear dimension whose value at t_1 is l_1.

  a. Derive a formula for the fractional change $\Delta R/R_1$ of resistance of a wire in terms of the temperature change Δt and resistance R_1 at t_1, taking into account both the linear expansion and the temperature coefficient α_1 of resistivity, and keeping only first-order terms in small fractional changes. *Note:* $\Delta R/(R_1 \, \Delta t)$ is the temperature coefficient of resistance of the wire.

  b. Use the result to give a formula for the resistance of iron wire, given the following:

$$r_{20} = 10 \times 10^{-8} \text{ ohm-m}$$
$$\alpha_{20} = 0.0050 \text{ per °C}$$
$$\alpha_{20}' = 0.0000117 \text{ per °C}$$

where the length of wire l_1 is in meters and cross-sectional area A_1 is in square meters, both at 20°C.

CHAPTER 6

DIRECT-CURRENT CIRCUITS

6.1. Components. A circuit is essentially a network of conducting paths. These paths are usually quite well defined, the currents being prevented from leaving the paths by very good insulators. Sometimes however, the paths become diffuse, if the insulation is insufficient; and then we may speak of leakage. Ordinarily and unless otherwise stated, we shall neglect leakage. Physically, a circuit is constructed by placing several conducting systems in contact with each other. We shall examine here the theory of circuits whose components are two-terminal conducting systems.

The part which a two-terminal component plays in a given circuit is completely described by two quantities only: the current I passing through the component and the potential difference V existing between its terminals. We shall assume that the potential difference between terminals has a unique meaning, according to the discussion of Sec. 5.7. Now the particular values of I and V which belong to a given component in a given circuit depend both on the characteristics of the component and on the rest of the circuit. Components may be classified and described by giving the relationship of V to I which is peculiar to them.

There are two broad classifications of components: active and passive (see Secs. 5.9 and 5.10). Passive components are those in which the irreversible Joule heat is the only energy transformation taking place when current flows. The potential drop V in passive components exists only when current flows, and current flows through them only from the higher to the lower potential terminal. For these components, we define as their resistance the ratio

$$R \equiv \frac{V}{I} \tag{6.1}$$

When this ratio is independent of the current flowing, we have the very common case of a linear, passive component. This occurs when the conducting material of the component is linear, which in turn is true of metallic conductors (see Sec. 5.12). For linear components, Eq. (6.1) is known as Ohm's law, and is usually written in the form without fractions

$$V = RI \tag{6.2}$$

which states that the potential difference is directly proportional to the current. The value of R completely describes a linear, passive component so far as circuit analysis is concerned. The corresponding characteristic of a nonlinear, passive component is $R(I)$, which is the functional dependence of the ratio (6.1) upon the current. A passive component is called a resistor, linear or nonlinear as the case may be. Its symbol in a circuit diagram is —WWWW—.

In practical circuit design, account must be taken of the fact that current flow in a resistor produces the irreversible Joule heating. The total electrical power supplied to the resistor is, by the definition of potential difference,

$$P = VI \qquad (6.3)$$

Other forms of Eq. (6.3) are obtained at once by use of Eq. (6.2):

$$P = I^2R = \frac{V^2}{R} \qquad (6.4)$$

All this power appears as heat in the component, by the definition of a passive component. In a state of thermal equilibrium, the resistor must pass this power on to its surroundings by radiation, heat conduction, or convection, and hence its temperature rises above the ambient temperature. The temperature rise must evidently be limited in practice. An excessively high temperature may destroy the resistor, burning it out or damaging it permanently. For precision resistors, the allowable temperature rise is more severely limited by the dependence of resistance upon temperature. Resistors are customarily rated in terms of the allowable power dissipation for their particular application.

Active components are those in which a reversible process occurs when a current flows, by which energy of a nonelectrostatic nature is put into or derived from the electric circuit. When this is the case, there is said to be an electromotive force, abbreviated emf, in the component. By definition of emf as discussed in Sec. 5.8, the measure of the emf is the work transformed reversibly per unit charge that flows. The potential difference V across the component when the current I through it is reduced to zero is usually taken in practice as equal to the emf, unless the value of the emf is known to be dependent upon the current. We shall represent an emf by the symbol for an electric battery, =₁|ı|=±. The positive sign is given to that side of the emf which produces the higher potential, taken algebraically when the current is zero. In our analysis, the script letter $\mathcal{E}$ will denote the emf in volts. An active component always possesses, in addition to its emf, a resistance R. This is a consequence of the irreversible transformation of electrical work into heat which accompanies current flow. If we adopt the conventions that the potential difference V across the active component is positive when it has the same sense as the emf, while the current I is positive when it flows through the emf from the negative to the positive side, then the properties ε and R of the component are related to the observed quantities V and I, by Eq. (5.56),

$$V = \varepsilon - RI \tag{6.5}$$

The two terms of this equation are, respectively, the potential difference which must always exist across an idealized component having an emf ε and zero resistance, and the potential drop across a resistor R carrying the entire current. Thus the general active element may be represented as a combination of an ideal emf and a resistance connected in the manner we shall call series (see Fig. 6.1).

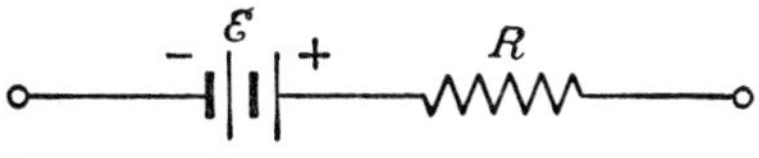

FIG. 6.1. Representation of a two-terminal active component.

Practical considerations limit the current which may safely be passed through an active component. Heat dissipation occurs because of the resistance of the component; thus the consideration of maximum permissible temperature rise enters. The heat dissipation due to the current I is

$$P = I^2 R \tag{6.6}$$

as may be seen by multiplying Eq. (6.5) through by I. The term εI then represents the power produced by the emf, the term VI is the power delivered by the component to the rest of the circuit, and the difference between these quantities is the power lost to heat. If the component is a cell or battery, other considerations may limit the desirable current. In particular, a cell whose emf is used as a standard of comparison must never be allowed to carry much current, the safe limit being on the order of 0.0001 amp. This is the case because too large a current may permanently alter the constitution of the cell.

Two types of circuit components which are often forgotten should be mentioned here. Wires are much used to connect pieces of electrical apparatus. The wire is just as much a component as the bulkier pieces of equipment, for it has a resistance which is never zero except in the superconducting state. A resistance is likewise associated with every contact between wires and other equipment, between wires and wires, or directly between terminals in contact. In practice, connector and contact resistances are usually kept low, and may be quite negligible. In drawing and analyzing circuits, we shall consider connecting wires, symbolized by straight lines, and contacts, symbolized where necessary by dots, to have negligible resistance. In case we wish to include these resistances in a circuit analysis, we shall represent them by resistors inserted into the circuit in the proper places and connected by ideal wires and contacts.

Occasionally it is necessary to treat wires and contacts not merely as passive but rather as active circuit components. For example, if temperature differences exist and dissimilar metals are involved in a circuit, thermal emfs appear which may be very important. Such emfs are to be explicitly drawn in the circuit diagram at the proper places whenever necessary. Unless so indicated, wires and contacts will be assumed to have no emf.

6.2. The Simplest Circuit. Basic Principles. It is instructive to begin the consideration of types of electric circuits with the simplest possible circuit, one composed only of a pair of two-terminal components connected together. This circuit is shown in Fig. 6.2, the components

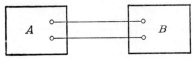

FIG. 6.2. The simplest circuit.

being shown, for generality, simply as boxes each having two terminals.

Now it is no doubt obvious to the reader that if the potential differences across the two components are V_A and V_B, and the currents through them are I_A and I_B, respectively, the relationships which we may write between these quantities are

$$I_A = I_B \tag{6.7}$$

and

$$V_A = V_B \tag{6.8}$$

It is important, however, for later work that we understand how to derive these simple relationships, instead of having merely an intuitive feeling that they are true. Equation (6.7) is a statement of the conservation of electric charge, combined with the postulate that in the type of circuit we are considering there is no time rate of change of net charge density while the currents flow steadily in the circuit. Analytically, it is derivable immediately from the equation of continuity in its integral form, Eq. (5.21). This equation requires that the net current flow into any closed surface be zero when no charge densities are being built up. Thus if we construct a closed surface cutting completely across the circuit at two places, the magnitude of the current must be the same at these two intersections, and the current enters at one intersection and leaves at the other. Hence there is one and only one value of current in this simple circuit, and this is what Eq. (6.7) states. As an alternative, nonmathematical demonstration, we may consider the currents flowing to and from any point of the circuit. If these are unequal, then charge is building up at that point. Since we postulate that no charge is building up, the currents to and from any point of the circuit are equal; and it follows that the current is everywhere the same in our simple circuit.

Consider next the meaning of Eq. (6.8). It states that if we compute the potential difference between the top wire of the diagram of Fig. 6.2 and the bottom wire, according to the definition of this quantity, Eq. (5.39), we get the same answer whether the path of integration passes through component A or component B. This follows from the basic property of the quasi-static potential function, that potential differences are unique for a given pair of points of a given system. Another way of stating this property, which is more useful to circuit theory, is that the algebraic sum of the potential differences encountered as we trace out any closed path is zero; for the potential difference between any point and itself is zero.

The foregoing principles, of which Eqs. (6.7) and (6.8) are the expression for our elementary circuit, may be called the principle of continuity and the principle of uniqueness of potential differences. These principles underlie all our work on d-c circuits. The equations which we may write for any circuit, however complex, are simply applications of these principles. Together with a statement of the electrical characteristics of each component of the system (its resistance and emf), such sets of

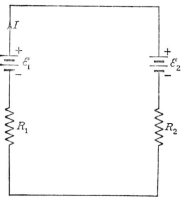

Fig. 6.3. Simple circuit of two active components.

equations are sufficient to solve the circuit. From this point of view, the unknowns of a circuit are the currents flowing in all its branches. Sometimes in practice some of the currents may be given while the characteristics of some of the circuit components may be unknowns. A particular type of problem which often arises is the determination of the resistance between a certain pair of terminals of a passive network. This may be solved by adding a pure emf connected between the given terminals and computing the resulting current I through this emf in the extended network. Since the pure emf maintains a potential difference numerically equal to ε across its terminals, the resistance of the network is then

$$R = \frac{\varepsilon}{I} \tag{6.9}$$

Before leaving this most elementary circuit, we shall write for future reference an expression for the current flow in the general case where both components are active. The components are shown in Fig. 6.3 as having emfs ε_1 and ε_2 and resistances R_1 and R_2. There are evidently two possible ways of connecting the components together: one in which the current flows through both components from the $(-)$ to the $(+)$ terminal of their emfs, and the other in which the current flows in opposite senses through the two emfs. If current I is reckoned positive in the sense from $(-)$ to $(+)$ through $\mathcal{E}_1$, then the solution for the current is

$$I = \frac{\mathcal{E}_1 \pm \mathcal{E}_2}{R_1 + R_2} \tag{6.10}$$

Here the emfs are taken as positive quantities; and the sign in the equation depends on the polarity of the connection.

6.3. Series and Parallel Circuits. A pair of two-terminal circuit components is said to be connected in series when a single connection is made

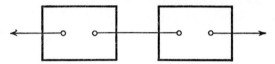

FIG. 6.4. Components in series.

between the components and no other component of the circuit is connected to the two terminals so connected. This is shown diagrammatically in Fig. 6.4, in which the arrows represent connections to the remainder of the circuit. The series connection of two components guarantees, according to the principle of continuity, that the current through the two components is the same. Since potential differences are algebraic scalar quantities, the potential difference across the pair of components is the algebraic sum of the individual potential differences of the components. The definition of series connection may be extended immediately to groups of any number of two-terminal components. The essential condition is that all connections within the series group involve only a pair of terminals of two neighboring components. The current is then common to all the components, and the potential differences across individual components add algebraically to produce the total potential difference. A group of components in series plays the part of a two-terminal component in the network of which it is a part; for by definition, connections to other parts of the network are made only to the two end terminals of the group.

An elementary application of the properties of a series group of components is to resistors. If the resistors have resistances $R_1, R_2, \ldots, R_n$ and the potential drops across them are, respectively, $V_1, V_2, \ldots, V_n$, we have for the total potential drop

$$V = V_1 + V_2 + \cdots + V_n \tag{6.11}$$

But if the current common to the elements is I,

$$I = I_1 = I_2 = \cdots = I_n \qquad (6.12)$$

and then

$$V_1 = IR_1 \qquad V_2 = IR_2 \qquad \cdots \qquad V_n = IR_n \qquad (6.13)$$

Combining Eqs. (6.13) with (6.11), we have

$$V = I(R_1 + R_2 + \cdots + R_n) \qquad (6.14)$$

Evidently the series group of resistors has the same characteristics in a network as a single passive component whose resistance is

$$R = R_1 + R_2 + \cdots + R_n \qquad (6.15)$$

The reader is left to prove for himself that if active elements are connected in series, the combination is identical with a single two-terminal

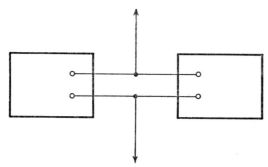

FIG. 6.5. Components in parallel.

component having an emf equal to the algebraic sum of the separate emfs and a resistance equal to the sum of the separate resistances. Such a connection is frequently used for voltaic cells, and the combination is called a battery.

Parallel or shunt connection of a pair of two-terminal components is illustrated in Fig. 6.5. The arrows show where the connections are made to the rest of the network. Any number of two-terminal components is said to be in parallel connection if one terminal of each component is connected to a common junction, while the other terminal of each component is connected to another common junction. The group of components in parallel thus serves in a network as a single element having two terminals, and these terminals are the common junctions. The parallel connection guarantees that all components of the group have the same potential difference across them, for this is an immediate consequence of the principle of uniqueness of potential difference. The principle of continuity says that the total current flowing to and from the parallel group is the algebraic sum of the individual currents in the separate components.

Consider the case when all the components of a parallel group are resistors, R_1, R_2, . . . , R_n. Let their currents be I_1, I_2, . . . , I_n, respectively, when the total current to and from the group is I. Then if V is the common potential difference, we have the following equations for the parallel group:

$$I = I_1 + I_2 + \cdots + I_n \tag{6.16}$$

$$V = V_1 = V_2 = V_n \tag{6.17}$$

$$I_1 = \frac{V}{R_1} \qquad I_2 = \frac{V}{R_2} \qquad \cdots \qquad I_n = \frac{V}{R_n} \tag{6.18}$$

Combining Eqs. (6.16) and (6.18), we obtain

$$I = V\left(\frac{1}{R_1} + \frac{1}{R_2} + \cdots + \frac{1}{R_n}\right) \tag{6.19}$$

From this it is evident that the combined or effective resistance R of the group is given by

$$\frac{1}{R} = \frac{1}{R_1} + \frac{1}{R_2} + \cdots + \frac{1}{R_n} \tag{6.20}$$

It appears from Eq. (6.20) that for parallel resistors the reciprocals of the resistances add together. We may see from this why it is often very convenient in circuit analysis to work with reciprocal resistances. The reciprocal of the resistance of a passive circuit component, called its conductance, was defined in Sec. 5.9:

$$G \equiv \frac{1}{R} \tag{6.21}$$

Equation (6.20) rewritten in terms of the total and individual conductances becomes simply

$$G = G_1 + G_2 + \cdots + G_n \tag{6.22}$$

We shall not give any specific rules here for parallel combinations involving active components. In general such problems may become complex enough to be deserving of more powerful methods of attack than we have so far developed. Parallel combinations of like voltaic cells are a simple example, however; and the reader may be interested in working this case through.

Many networks can in principle be solved by breaking them down into series and parallel groups of components and using the general rules given above for such groups. There are, however, many networks which cannot be analyzed in this way. A simple example is the passive network

shown in Fig. 6.6.   It is therefore necessary to develop general methods
of handling network problems.   These methods are advantageous also
even for solving networks that are composed of series and parallel groups;
for they may reduce the labor to a minimum, as well as systematizing the
procedure.

6.4. Kirchhoff's Laws.   Kirchhoff's laws[1] are a statement of the two
principles mentioned in Sec. 6.2 for
direct current networks, the principle
of continuity and the principle of
uniqueness of potential difference, as
applied to a general network. Let
us introduce them by first defining
some terms relating to all networks
more complex than a simple series
circuit.

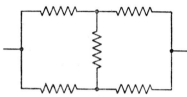

Fig. 6.6. A   complex   network   of
resistors.

Junction.   A point of the circuit where three or more conducting
paths come together.

Branch.   A single conducting path between a pair of junctions, and
on which no other junction is located.

Loop.   A closed conducting path in the network.

Now the first of Kirchhoff's two laws, in accord with the continuity
principle, states that the net charge on any junction is constant:

1. *The algebraic sum of all currents flowing toward any junction is zero.*

To state this in mathematical form, let us call the magnitudes of the
currents meeting at a particular junction I_1, I_2, . . . , I_j, . . . , I_s.
For the present, these symbols all represent positive quantities.   Then
the first law states that

$$\pm I_1 \pm I_2 \cdot \cdot \cdot \pm I_j \cdot \cdot \cdot \pm I_s = 0$$

or more briefly

$$\sum_{j=1}^{s} \pm I_j = 0 \qquad\qquad (6.23)$$

In this equation we may choose the positive sign for currents which flow
toward the junction, the negative for those in the reverse sense.

In formulating Kirchhoff's second law, we shall first suppose that all
components of a network have been represented by their equivalent emf
and effective series resistance, as discussed in Sec. 6.1.   Now the potential
rises by an amount exactly equal to the emf when we trace through a
pure emf from its negative to its positive terminal, that is, in the sense of
current flow which causes energy to pass into the electrical circuit.
Likewise, the potential drops by an amount RI across a pure resistance R

[1] Named for Gustav Robert Kirchhoff (1824–1887).

through which a current I flows, when we trace in the sense of I. Kirchhoff's second law is the statement of the uniqueness of potential difference, according to which the rises of potential must equal the drops of potential as we trace around any closed loop.

2. *When any loop of a network is traced the algebraic sum of the emfs equals the algebraic sum of the RI drops.*

In this statement, the emfs may be considered positive when traced through from negative to positive, and then RI drops are considered positive when the resistance is traversed in the sense of current flow.

Suppose the loop being traced is composed of p branches. Every branch may in general contain several emfs and resistances, with a common current through them. For a typical branch, the jth, let us form the sum of all the resistances and denote it by the symbol R_j; and let the magnitude of the branch current, considered positive for the time being, be I_j. This current is, by nature of a branch, common to all parts of the branch. Suppose also that we denote by the symbol $\mathcal{E}_k$ the typical emf in the loop, without regard to which branch this is located in. Let $\mathcal{E}_k$ also represent a positive quantity, the magnitude of the kth emf; and let there be n emfs in the loop. We may now formulate Kirchhoff's second law for this loop, and for any loop of a d-c network, as follows:

$$\sum_{k=1}^{n} \pm \mathcal{E}_k = \sum_{j=1}^{p} \pm R_j I_j \qquad (6.24)$$

A correct sign convention in this equation is to take the $(+)$ sign for an emf when it is traced through from its $(-)$ to its $(+)$ terminal, and to take the $(+)$ sign for an $R_j I_j$ term when the branch is traced through in the sense of the current I_j. The negative signs are, of course, to correspond to the reverse senses of tracing.

When we speak of the solution of a given network, it is implied that some of the quantities in Eqs. (6.23) and (6.24) are unknown. In practice, the unknowns may be any set of emfs, resistances, and currents, provided enough of the quantities are given to determine the rest. It is customary, however, to give particular attention to the case where all emfs and resistances are given, while the branch currents of the network are the unknowns. This is a naturally important type of problem, since the emfs and resistances are the characteristics of the individual components, remaining constant in the important linear case regardless of the current, while the currents are characteristic of the whole network.

In setting up an actual problem for solution, the question at once arises what sign to attach to the unknown quantities in the Kirchhoff equations. The beginner is frequently puzzled by this. He asks, quite naturally, how he can decide whether to enter a given current I_j as positive or negative, when he does not yet know its actual sense of flow. The difficulty may be met by considering each symbol I_j now to represent an algebraic quantity, and by arbitrarily specifying a positive sense of flow for each I_j. This is conveniently done by marking an arrowhead in each branch. It is agreed that an actual branch current will be considered algebraically positive when it flows in the sense arbitrarily defined as positive, and negative when it flows in the reverse sense. The Kirchhoff equations are now to be set up with the sign for each term to be determined according to rule using the arbitrarily assigned, positive current directions. If the result of the solution is a positive quantity for a given current I_j, this means that the actual branch current is in the assigned positive direction. If, however, the result of the solution is a negative quantity, it simply means that the actual current flows opposite to the assigned arrowhead.

The reader may require to be convinced of the validity of this procedure. The proof is quite simple. If all arrowheads do correspond to the actual current direction, then we are actually setting up the Kirchhoff laws as we originally proposed. But in our formulation of these laws, we stated that all symbols I_j were to be considered as positive quantities. Therefore, in this case, the solution of an actual network must yield positive quantities for all the I_j. Now suppose that any I_j is assigned, instead, a conventional positive sense opposite to its actual sense of flow. Then in all the Kirchhoff equations where this I_j occurs, it occurs with the opposite sign than corresponds to the actual current. No other change is made in our equations; thus their solutions will be as before, except that this current will come out with a negative sign.

In case an emf is unknown, the same procedure as outlined above may be used in setting up the Kirchhoff equations. The unknown emf may be arbitrarily assigned a $(-)$ and a $(+)$ terminal, and the equations set up as if this were its actual polarity. It is now understood that the symbol $\mathcal{E}_k$ for this emf is algebraic: that it may represent a positive quantity, in which case the assigned polarity is the actual polarity; or that it may represent a negative quantity, in which case the actual polarity is opposite to the assigned polarity.

Let us consider next how many independent Kirchhoff equations we may expect to find for a given network. Physically, it is evident that giving all emfs and resistances for a given network is just sufficient to determine all branch currents. Thus if there are b branch currents, there are b unknowns when all emfs and resistances are given. We must therefore have just b independent equations of the network. These will involve some first-law equations and some second-law equations. Consider the first-law equations. A first-law equation states that no charge builds up at the junction for which it is written. Now if this is stated for all junctions but one, it is implied for the remaining junction simply by the assignment of a unique current to each branch of the network, that is, by using the same symbol for the current at the two ends of a branch; for each branch current I_j thus both adds and subtracts charge to the set of junctions at the rate I_j, so leaving the total charge of the junctions constant. We may understand in this way that if a network has j junctions, there are just $(j - 1)$ independent first-law equations to be written.

It follows now that there must be just $[b - (j - 1)]$ independent second-law equations that can be written for a network, *i.e.*, independent both of one another and of the first-law equations. This is called the number of meshes m of the network.

We conclude this section by summarizing the suggested practical directions for solving a network. The crux of the matter is the question of signs.

1. Label all branch currents, marking an arrowhead in the circuit to define an arbitrary positive sense (unless the current is known, in which case its actual sense is to be used).

2. Label all resistances, and determine the sums R_j for each branch.

3. Label all emfs, and mark their actual (or if unknown, their arbitrary) polarities.

4. Write first-law equations for all junctions but one, using the marked arrowheads with the sign rule of the first law. Use the last junction for check, if desired.

5. Choose an arbitrary sense of tracing for each loop used for second-law equations. Write $[b - (j - 1)]$ second-law equations, using the marked arrowheads and polarities with the sign rules of the second law. Examine these to be sure you have a set of independent equations. As a guide, let the loops chosen include every branch at least once.

6. Solve simultaneously for the unknowns.

7. Use the algebraic signs of the quantities solved for, together with your arbitrary conventions of positive sense (and polarity, if any), to determine the actual current sense (or polarity).

8. If desired, other second-law equations may be used to check the solution.

6.5. Loop Currents. The labor of solving a network by Kirchhoff's laws may be somewhat reduced by the method of loop currents. A loop current is one which is considered to flow continuously around a loop of the network, having the same magnitude all the way around. Each branch current is to be expressed as an algebraic sum of the loop currents flowing through that branch, for several currents simultaneously flowing in any conducting path add algebraically.

The utility of the idea of loop currents is due to their fulfilling, by their definition, the principle of conservation of charge, together with the steady-state postulate of d-c networks according to which no net charge densities are being built up anywhere in the network. These concepts are exactly what the first law of Kirchhoff expresses. The use of loop currents to express branch currents therefore ensures that the latter satisfy all the first-law equations for our network. Setting up the network equations in terms of loop currents then involves only the use of Kirchhoff's second law. We noticed in the preceding section that there are $[b - (j - 1)]$ independent second-law equations in a network of j junctions and b branches. If these equations are just to suffice to solve the network, there must be $[b - (j - 1)]$ loop currents. In other words, the number of loop currents required to express all the branch currents of a network is equal to the number of meshes of the network. This is easily seen also from the fact that the first law of Kirchhoff gives $(j - 1)$ independent equations in the b unknowns of the system. It is therefore possible to express these b unknowns in terms of only $[b - (j - 1)]$

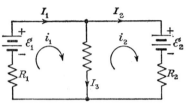

FIG. 6.7. Labeling of currents and loop currents.

variables, a complete set of loop currents. The specification of a complete set of loop currents for a given network is far from unique, for the number of possible loops exceeds the number of meshes of the network. In order that a set of $[b - (j - 1)]$ loop currents be a complete set for a given network, it is evidently necessary that each branch be traversed by at least one loop current. By trial, it will be found that this is also a sufficient condition.

An example may help to clarify the use of loop currents. Figure 6.7 shows a simple circuit having three branches and two junctions, whence $m = 2$. Two loop currents are shown labeled, and in addition the branch currents are labeled. Using the same loops for the second law and arbitrarily tracing clockwise, we obtain the second-law equations in the form

$$\mathcal{E}_1 = i_1 R_1 + i_1 R_3 - i_2 R_3$$
$$-\mathcal{E}_2 = i_2 R_2 + i_2 R_3 - i_1 R_3$$

These may be readily solved for the loop currents:

$$i_1 = \frac{(R_2 + R_3)\mathcal{E}_1 - R_3\mathcal{E}_2}{R_1 R_2 + R_2 R_3 + R_3 R_1} \qquad i_2 = \frac{R_3\mathcal{E}_1 - (R_1 + R_3)\mathcal{E}_2}{R_1 R_2 + R_2 R_3 + R_3 R_1}$$

The branch currents are now

$$I_1 = i_1 \qquad I_2 = i_2 \qquad I_3 = i_1 - i_2$$

To make the example numerical, let $R_1 = R_2 = R_3 = 1$ ohm, $\mathcal{E}_1 = 12$ volts, $\mathcal{E}_2 = 9$ volts. Then

$$i_1 = 5 \text{ amp} = I_1 \qquad i_2 = -2 \text{ amp} = I_2 \qquad I_3 = 7 \text{ amp}$$

The actual branch currents, and a set of actual loop currents, are indicated in Fig. 6.8.

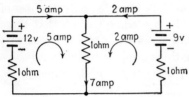

FIG. 6.8. Actual currents and loop currents for particular circuit components.

6.6. Superposition. The example of the preceding section resulted in equations for the branch currents which all had the form

$$I = G_1\mathcal{E}_1 + G_2\mathcal{E}_2 \qquad (6.25)$$

where G_1 and G_2 were coefficients involving only the resistances of the network. It is easy to show that in a general d-c network of linear components, the solution for each branch current is of the form

$$I_j = \sum_{k=1}^{n} {}_jG_k\mathcal{E}_k \qquad (6.26)$$

if there are n emfs $\mathcal{E}_k$ in the network. For given j, the ${}_jG_k$ are n constant coefficients involving only the resistances of the network. The left subscript has been attached to these symbols because their particular value depends on the branch j whose current is being expressed. The right subscript is the index of summation. The ${}_jG_k$ are called transfer conductances of the network. The reason that the branch currents are expressible in form (6.26) is that all the Kirchhoff equations are linear in the branch currents, with coefficients either of unity or resistance sums, while all emfs appear alone and to the first power as separate terms of some of these equations. There are no other kinds of terms. It follows that every branch current is linear in the emfs, with coefficients which involve the resistances and without any additive constant. This may be seen at once by writing the solution for a branch current I_j in determinant form, in which case all emfs appear singly or in sums as elements of one column of the determinant in the numerator, along with zeros from equations with no emf, while the determinant in the denominator of the solution contains no emfs.

The physical interpretation of Eq. (6.26) is that each emf of a linear network produces a current in any given branch quite independently of the action of the other emfs and that the resulting total current in a branch is the algebraic sum of the contributions due to the various emfs of the network. This is called the superposition theorem for d-c networks. Its utility is first as an aid to visualizing the combined effect of several emfs in a network. Second, if a network is already solved, the change in any branch current due to an added emf somewhere in the network may be computed as though the other emfs were all zero.

6.7. Equivalent EMF and Internal Resistance. In this section we shall show that any two terminals of a general network of linear components may be considered the terminals of a single linear component, being equivalent to a pure emf in series with a pure resistance. We shall call the emf the equivalent emf of the network between the given terminals; and the resistance we shall call the internal resistance of the network for the given terminals.

Consider then a linear network N, and two particular terminals 1 and 2. Let us connect an external, pure emf $\mathcal{E}_a$ between terminals 1 and 2. In so doing we add another branch to the network, thus making a new network N'. Let the current in the new branch be called I_a. We shall agree to let the positive sense for this current be that in which it flows when $\mathcal{E}_a = 0$, that is, when the two terminals are short-circuited or connected by a negligible resistance. Now the current I_a for an arbitrary value $\mathcal{E}_a$ can be written in the form of Eq. (6.26), Sec. 6.6,

$$I_a = \sum_{k=1}^{n} {}_aG_k\mathcal{E}_k + {}_aG_a\mathcal{E}_a \qquad (6.27)$$

Here the $\mathcal{E}_k$ are all the emfs of the original network N, but all the transfer conductances ${}_aG_k$ and ${}_aG_a$ are for the extended network N'. We have simply separated the term containing the added emf from the rest of the terms which contain the emfs of N. It is to be noted that the transfer conductances ${}_aG_k$ and ${}_aG_a$ involve only the resistances of the network N'. Furthermore, since the added branch had by hypothesis a zero resistance, the ${}_aG_k$ and ${}_aG_a$ involve only the resistances of the original network N. Since these resistances are by hypothesis all constant (linear components), the transfer conductances are constants of the network which are independent of the emfs of the network.

In interpreting Eq. (6.27), suppose first that $\mathcal{E}_a = 0$. Then by our sign convention, $\sum_{k=1}^{n} {}_aG_k\mathcal{E}_k$ is a positive quantity. This quantity may be called the short-circuit current I_s:

$$I_s \equiv \sum_{k=1}^{n} {}_aG_k\mathcal{E}_k \qquad (6.28)$$

This is a constant for the given network and the pair of terminals, since the ${}_aG_k$ and $\mathcal{E}_k$ are constant. To simplify the appearance of Eq. (6.27), we shall substitute this quantity I_s for the summation; and thus we replace an expression with whose computation we are not here concerned by an important observable characteristic of the two terminals of N. Thus we have

$$I_a = I_s + {}_aG_a\varepsilon_a \qquad (6.29)$$

Before proceeding, we shall adopt a sign convention for the added emf ε_a. Let us take ε_a as a positive quantity when it makes a positive contribution to the branch current I_a. This will mean that we choose signs so that the conductance ${}_aG_a$ is a positive quantity.

We shall next inquire under what conditions the current I_a in the added branch is zero. This may be achieved by giving to the external emf ε_a the particular value

$$(\varepsilon_a)_0 = -\frac{I_s}{{}_aG_a} \qquad (6.30)$$

This quantity is now intrinsically negative, which tells us that the external emf must be connected so as to produce an opposite current from the short-circuit current. The corresponding positive quantity

$$\varepsilon_0 \equiv \frac{I_s}{{}_aG_a} \qquad (6.31)$$

is what we shall call the equivalent emf of the two terminals of the network. Using this quantity, our equation (6.29) now becomes

$$I_a = {}_aG_a(\varepsilon_0 + \varepsilon_a) \qquad (6.32)$$

We make one further alteration of this equation by remembering that the potential difference between terminals of a pure emf is always equal to the value of the emf. Thus the magnitude of the potential difference V between the terminals of our original network N, to which we have supposed the external emf ε_a to be connected, is just that of ε_a. We shall choose the positive sense of V opposite to that of ε_a, and write

$$\varepsilon_a = -V \qquad (6.33)$$

This convention simply calls V a positive quantity for the given pair of terminals when no current I_a passes in the external branch. Substituting into (6),

$$I_a = {}_aG_a(\varepsilon_0 - V) \qquad (6.34)$$

Compare Eq. (6.34) now with Eq. (6.5), Sec. 6.1. According to that equation, the current I through any linear active component having two terminals is related to the potential difference V across its terminals by

$$I = \frac{\varepsilon - V}{R} \qquad (6.35)$$

where $\mathcal{E}$ is its emf and R its resistance. We may therefore identify

$$\frac{1}{{}_aG_a} \equiv R_0 \tag{6.36}$$

as the resistance of the equivalent two-terminal component. Here we have added the subscript to remind us that it is an effective resistance resulting from the whole of a network. This resistance we shall call the internal resistance of the network. Since the ${}_aG_a$ was a constant depending only on the resistances of the original network N, the same is true of R_0. We may also identify $\mathcal{E}_0$ as the quantity which for the given terminals of our entire network corresponds to the emf of a simple two-terminal component.

We have now proved the theorem proposed at the beginning of this section. The use of the pure emf $\mathcal{E}_a$ was only an artifice for bringing out the desired results. The relation (6.34) between V and I_a is characteristic of the network and the pair of terminals chosen, not of the particular nature of the added branch. This relation between V and I_a may be written simply

$$V = \mathcal{E}_0 - I_a R_0 \tag{6.37}$$

where $\mathcal{E}_0$ and R_0 are two constants. Its identity with the relationship characteristic of a linear, two-terminal component shows that any two terminals of any linear network behave like the terminals of a simple linear component. Like a simple component, therefore, the entire network is equivalent, so far as these two terminals alone are concerned, with a series combination of a pure emf $\mathcal{E}_0$ and a pure resistance R_0. It may be of use to express the short-circuit current I_s in terms of these quantities. From Eqs. (6.31) and (6.36), or directly from the foregoing statement, we have

$$I_s = \frac{\mathcal{E}_0}{R_0} \tag{6.38}$$

The values of the characteristic constants $\mathcal{E}_0$ and R_0 are expressed in terms of the emfs $\mathcal{E}_k$ and the transfer constants ${}_aG_k$ and ${}_aG_a$ of the extended network N' by Eq. (6.36), and by the combination of Eqs. (6.31) and (6.28). It is simpler to visualize the problem directly from Eq. (6.37). The equivalent emf is the potential difference appearing across the given terminals when $I_a = 0$, that is, in the original network N. This is simple to compute when the solution of N is known. The internal resistance is the ratio $-V/I_a$ or $+\mathcal{E}_a/I_a$ of the extended network N' when $\mathcal{E}_0 = 0$, that is, if all emfs of the original network N are set to zero, leaving N simply a passive network. This is just the meaning we attached in Sec. 6.2 to the resistance of any passive network between a pair of terminals. Most simply stated, then, to find R_0 consider the network as passive by replacing all emfs with connections. Care must be taken, of course, to retain the resistances characteristic of the active components of the network.

6.8. Thévenin's Theorem. The theorem of the preceding section has a very great utility in circuit analysis. In this connection it is sometimes called Thévenin's theorem. Suppose we desire to find the current in just one branch of a given complex network N. Let the current in this branch be called I_1. The two terminals of the network between which this branch is located may be denoted by A and B. Consider now the reduced network N_0 which remains if branch one is disconnected from A

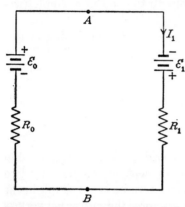

and B. This reduced network has an equivalent emf $\mathcal{E}_0$ and an internal resistance R_0 between A and B, so that it may be replaced by a series combination of a pure emf and a pure resistance. The branch 1 also has an equivalent emf that we may call $\mathcal{E}_1$, which is simply the algebraic sum of the emfs in this branch; and it has an internal resistance R_1 which is the sum of the resistances in the branch. For the purpose of computing I_1 therefore, we have reduced the circuit to the simple connection discussed in Sec. 6.2 (see Fig. 6.9). This figure is drawn for only one of the two possible polarity relations between $\mathcal{E}_0$ and $\mathcal{E}_1$. The current I_1 is, by Eq. (6.10),

Fig. 6.9. Equivalent circuit for finding a branch current by Thévenin's theorem.

$$I_1 = \frac{\mathcal{E}_1 \pm \mathcal{E}_0}{R_1 + R_0} \tag{6.39}$$

the sign depending on the polarity. Our problem is reduced in this way to the determination of $\mathcal{E}_0$ and R_0. This is a simplification over solving the original network N since the reduced network N_0 has less branches. Sometimes we are enabled in this way to use simple series and parallel circuit analysis on a fairly complex network.

An illustration is required to show adequately the usefulness of Thévenin's theorem. Suppose it is required to find the current I_6 of the network of Fig. 6.10. This is a Wheatstone bridge network, much used in the laboratory, with the usually justified assumption of negligible resistance in the battery. It will be noticed that there are six branches, so that the use of Kirchhoff's laws would require the simultaneous solution of six equations. There are three meshes; thus by loop currents we should have to solve three simultaneous equations. To use Thévenin's theorem, we shall remove the branch 6 in which we require to find the current, and thus form the reduced network N_0 of Fig. 6.11. In this network, we may write down immediately the potential difference

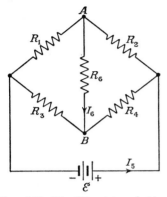

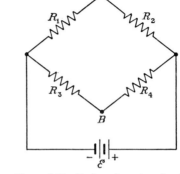

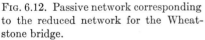

FIG. 6.10. The Wheatstone bridge.

FIG. 6.11. Reduced network for the Wheatstone bridge.

between terminals A and B, which is the equivalent emf $\mathcal{E}_0$ of the network between the two terminals:

$$\mathcal{E}_0 = \frac{R_1}{R_1 + R_2}\, \mathcal{E} - \frac{R_3}{R_3 + R_4}\, \mathcal{E} \qquad (6.40)$$

To find R_0, we draw the corresponding passive network (Fig. 6.12). This

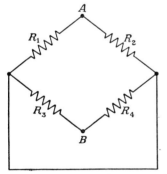

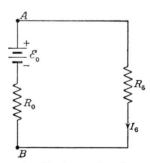

FIG. 6.12. Passive network corresponding to the reduced network for the Wheatstone bridge.

FIG. 6.13. Finalr esult of applying Thévenin's theorem to the Wheatstone bridge.

consists of the series combination of two parallel groups of resistances, R_1 with R_2, and R_3 with R_4, respectively. Thus

$$R_0 = \frac{R_1 R_2}{R_1 + R_2} + \frac{R_3 R_4}{R_3 + R_4} \qquad (6.41)$$

Finally, to find I_6 we connect branch 6 back to the series combination of $\mathcal{E}_0$ and R_0 as in Fig. 6.13. Evidently

$$I_6 = \frac{\mathcal{E}_0}{R_0 + R_6} \tag{6.42}$$

By substitution for $\mathcal{E}_0$ and R_0 we have our answer:

$$I_6 = \frac{\dfrac{R_1}{R_1 + R_2} - \dfrac{R_3}{R_3 + R_4}}{\dfrac{R_1 R_2}{R_1 + R_2} + \dfrac{R_3 R_4}{R_3 + R_4} + R_6} \mathcal{E} \tag{6.43}$$

The Wheatstone bridge is used for comparing resistances. A sensitive galvanometer placed in branch 6 serves as a null indicator. When $I_6 = 0$, the numerator of Eq. (6.43) vanishes, and the result is the well-known relation between the resistances at balance:

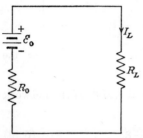

$$R_1 R_4 - R_2 R_3 = 0 \tag{6.44}$$

6.9. Maximum Power Output. The concepts of equivalent emf and internal resistance permit the ready solution of a problem of some practical importance, that of selecting the value of resistance in some branch of a network in order to obtain maximum power dissipation in that resistance. For example, in the Wheatstone bridge circuit of the preceding section, the resistance R_6 is actually a galvanometer; and it is desirable to have as much power as possible to operate the galvanometer.

FIG. 6.14. Equivalent circuit giving power from a network into a load.

Let us call the resistance where maximum power is required the load resistance of the network, R_L. Suppose this resistance simply removed from the network, leaving a reduced network N_0 with two terminals to which R_L is to be connected. Let the equivalent emf and internal resistance of N_0 be $\mathcal{E}_0$ and R_0, respectively. Then the whole network N may be considered to consist simply of R_L connected to $\mathcal{E}_0$ and R_0, as in Fig. 6.14. It must be remembered that this equivalence is good only so far as conditions external to the reduced network N_0 are concerned. Now the current in the load is

$$I_L = \frac{\mathcal{E}_0}{R_0 + R_L} \tag{6.45}$$

The power P_L in the load is $I_L{}^2 R_L$; whence

$$P_L = \mathcal{E}_0{}^2 \frac{R_L}{(R_0 + R_L)^2} \tag{6.46}$$

This power becomes zero when $R_L = 0$, or when $R_L = \infty$; thus we may expect to find a maximum power for some finite R_L. The necessary condition for a maximum or minimum of power as R_L is varied is

$$\frac{dP_L}{dR_L} = 0 \qquad (6.47)$$

Substitution of Eq. (6.46) into (6.47) yields

$$\frac{1}{(R_0 + R_L)^2} - \frac{2R_L}{(R_0 + R_L)^3} = 0 \qquad (6.48)$$

The only finite root of this equation is

$$R_L = R_0 \qquad (6.49)$$

Therefore this is the condition we were seeking, for which the power P_L is maximum.

PROBLEMS

6.1. Four two-terminal components are tested by measuring the potential difference across them when three different currents flow in them. In the data below, positive current I enters terminal 1 and leaves terminal 2, while V has the sign of $V_1 - V_2$, the potential of 1 relative to 2. Characterize each component by two descriptive terms, and by all pertinent constants.

$A: I = -6, -1, +3$ amp; $V = -3, -\frac{1}{2}, +\frac{3}{2}$ volts
$B: I = -5, +5, +10$ amp; $V = +1.990, +2.010, +2.020$ volts
$C: I = -10, 0, +10$ amp; $V = +5.96, +6.00, +6.03$ volts
$D: I = -2, 0, +50$ ma; $V = -50, 0, +75$ volts

6.2. A large 1.5-volt dry cell is commonly tested by observing its short-circuit current, *i.e.*, the current which it can send through an ammeter of negligible resistance. A certain new cell which has a potential difference of 1.54 volts on open circuit (*i.e.*, at zero current), gives a momentary short-circuit current of 35 amp. Find its internal resistance at this current.

6.3. An old and a new dry cell are connected together, positive to positive and negative to negative. The new cell has an emf of 1.55 volts, and an internal resistance of 0.040 ohm; the old has an emf of 1.48 volts and an internal resistance of 0.100 ohm.

a. What current flows?

b. What is the potential difference across the terminals of the cells?

c. What heat dissipation in the two cells results from the connection?

6.4. A nonlinear passive component whose characteristics are given by $I = kV^{3/2}$, with $k = 10^{-2}$ ma/volt$^{3/2}$ is connected to a linear active component whose emf is 100 volts and whose resistance is 5,000 ohms. Find the current and the common potential difference. To avoid solving a cubic equation, the answer may be found with a slide rule using successive approximations. Sketch qualitatively how a graphical solution could be made, or else use a quantitative graphical solution to obtain the answer.

6.5. A precision resistor R_1 may be shunted by a higher resistor R_2 to obtain with precision a value of resistance R slightly less than R_1.

a. Show that the fractional error dR/R of the parallel combination introduced by a fractional error dR_2/R_2 in the shunt is

$$\frac{dR}{R} = \frac{R}{R_2} \frac{dR_2}{R_2}$$

b. Let R_1 = 100.00 ohms, correct to within 0.01 per cent. What precision is required in the shunt resistance R_2 to produce a combined resistance of 99.00 ohms with the addition of only another 0.01 per cent possible error?

6.6. Find the combined parallel resistance of three resistors of 200, 500, and 800 ohms, respectively.

6.7. Find the current in each branch of the network shown. The symbol K stands for 1,000 ohms, V for volts.

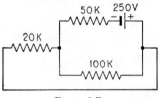

PROB. 6.7.

6.8. Find the resulting emf and resistance of a battery consisting of n identical cells connected (*a*) in series and (*b*) in parallel, the emf of each cell being ε and its resistance R.

6.9. A galvanometer is an instrument for measurement of current. In a d-c circuit it is a linear passive element of resistance R_g. A d-c voltmeter, for measurement of potential difference, usually consists of a galvanometer in series with a resistor M called a multiplier. If the full-scale current of a certain galvanometer is 5 ma and its resistance 40 ohms, find the multiplier resistance which makes it into a voltmeter with a full-scale reading of 10 volts.

6.10. A galvanometer in parallel with a low resistance S, called a shunt, is often used to form a d-c ammeter for current measurement. For the galvanometer of the preceding problem, find the shunt resistance which makes an ammeter whose full-scale reading is 2 amp.

6.11. Develop laws for the combined conductance of (*a*) several conductances in series and (*b*) several conductances in parallel.

6.12. An important theorem of circuit analysis is the complete equivalence of the two passive networks shown, provided the resistances are related as follows:

$$A = \frac{bc}{a+b+c} \qquad B = \frac{ca}{a+b+c} \qquad C = \frac{ab}{a+b+c}$$

$$a = \frac{AB+BC+CA}{A} \qquad b = \frac{AB+BC+CA}{B} \qquad c = \frac{AB+BC+CA}{C}$$

Deduce these relations by requiring that the resistances of the two networks be the same between all corresponding pairs of terminals.

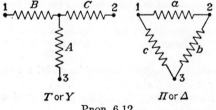

T or Y Π or Δ

PROB. 6.12.

6.13. Further demonstrate the equivalence of the T and Π networks of the preceding problem by showing that when given potentials are applied to any corresponding pairs of terminals in the two networks, the third terminals have the same potential.

6.14. Given the network shown, with values of resistance in ohms. Find the resistance between terminals by using the $\Pi - T$ equivalence theorem (see Probs. 6.12 and 6.13) to replace a Π network, forming part of the given network, with an equivalent T, and thus reducing the problem to one involving only series and parallel combinations. *Ans.* 2.90 ohms.

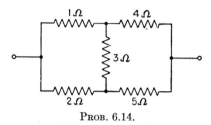

PROB. 6.14.

6.15. Find the resistance between terminals of the network of the preceding problem by using the $T - \Pi$ equivalence theorem the other way, replacing a T section within the given network by an equivalent Π in order to reduce the network to series and parallel combinations of resistors.

6.16. The sensitivity of a galvanometer may be decreased conveniently in known steps by use of an Ayrton shunt. The shunt consists of a resistor R tapped at a

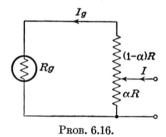

PROB. 6.16.

fraction α of its value, as shown in the diagram, and the galvanometer is represented by its resistance R_g. Show that the galvanometer current I_g is related to the input current by

$$I_g = \alpha \left(\frac{R}{R + R_g} \right) I$$

6.17. Consider the basic circuit of the potentiometer as shown, where R_g is the galvanometer resistance and $\mathcal{E}$ the unknown or standard emf.

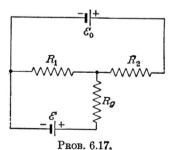

PROB. 6.17.

a. Label all branch currents and set up all possible equations by Kirchhoff's laws.

b. Check the statements of Sec. 6.4 concerning the numbers of independent equations.

c. Obtain the solution for the current in the galvanometer R_g.

6.18. For the given network, find the two battery currents. Suppose the batteries to be without resistance.

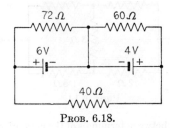

PROB. 6.18.

6.19. Find the minimum number of branches for all numbers of junctions from two to six by trial, drawing a network to illustrate each case. Is there a maximum?

Ans. $b_{min} = \frac{3}{2}j$, j even; $b_{min} = \frac{3}{2}j + \frac{1}{2}$, j odd.

6.20. Show that there are only two distinct networks with four junctions and six branches, provided the constitution of the branches is not considered; and that one of these is essentially equivalent to a network of three junctions and five branches, because of the theorem of Prob. 6.23.

6.21. Show that the potential difference between any pair of junctions of a linear network is unchanged by adding in each branch a pure emf whose potential difference is the same in sign and in magnitude as the total potential difference across the resistances of that branch. What is the effect of the insertion of these emfs upon the branch currents?

6.22. Find the resistance between terminals of the network shown, if all seven of the resistors are identical, each with resistance R.

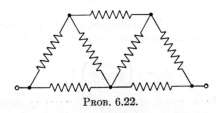

PROB. 6.22.

6.23. Suppose a network is such that its drawing can be cut in two by a line which crosses two and only two branches. What does this statement imply (*a*) about the currents in the two branches; (*b*) about the possibility of rearranging the components in these branches without affecting the currents of the network?

6.24. Given the same network as in Prob. 6.14, find its resistance between terminals by connecting these terminals to a pure emf and computing the current through the emf. Use loop currents for the solution.   *Ans.* 2.90 ohms.

6.25. Find the current (*a*) in the 6-ohm resistor and (*b*) in the 2-ohm resistor of the network shown.

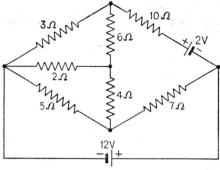

PROB. 6.25.

6.26. Show that if there be added to every branch of a network a pure emf whose potential difference in magnitude and sign is a common constant α times the total potential difference across the resistances of that branch, then the potential difference between any pair of terminals remains unchanged whereas the branch currents are all changed by the common factor $(1 - \alpha)$. *Hint:* First form an extended network by connecting across the given pair of terminals a pure emf $\mathcal{E}_0$ equal to the equivalent emf, so that no current flows in the added branch. Apply superposition theorem to the current in this added branch, and use the theorem of Prob. 6.21.

6.27. Demonstrate that all currents of a network may be written as in Eq. (6.26), Sec. 6.6, considering the solution by determinants of a general set of network equations expressing Kirchhoff's laws.

6.28. Show that a four-terminal network of resistors a and b as shown (an L-type pad), when used to connect two components whose internal resistances are, respec-

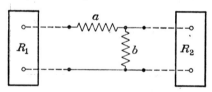

PROB. 6.28.

tively, R_1 and R_2, has the property of presenting to each component an **internal** resistance equal to its own when $R_1 > R_2$, and when

$$a = R_1 \sqrt{1 - \frac{R_2}{R_1}} \qquad b = \frac{R_2}{\sqrt{1 - (R_2/R_1)}}$$

6.29. *a.* Set up equations for the loop currents in the circuit shown, choosing loops such that only one loop current flows through each emf, and using the same loops for setting up the equations by Kirchhoff's second law.

b. From the determinant solution of these equations, pick out the coefficients $_1G_2$ and $_2G_1$, the two transfer conductances between the branches containing the emfs. They should be equal.

c. Consider the symmetry of the coefficients in the set of equations written in *a*, to see why this occurs. Generalize then to an important theorem for networks composed of linear, two-terminal components: the two transfer conductances $_jG_k$ and $_kG_j$ between any given pair of branches are equal. This is called the reciprocity theorem.

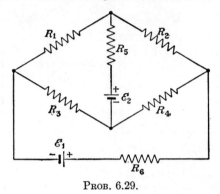

PROB. 6.29.

6.30. Given a Wheatstone bridge with the addition of a 10^{-3} volt thermal emf in one ratio arm as shown in the figure. Find the resulting galvanometer current in the 1,000-ohm resistor which represents the galvanometer. Remember the superposition theorem! The 6-volt battery has negligible resistance.

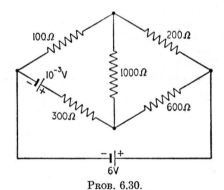

PROB. 6.30.

6.31. Suppose a current I flows through external connections into one terminal and out of another terminal of a linear network N. Show that the changes ΔI_j in the branch currents due to this current I are

$$\Delta I_j = {}_jG_0'R_0I$$

Here R_0 is the internal resistance of the network N between the given pair of terminals. In the extended network N' formed by adding a branch containing only a pure emf between the given terminals of N, $_jG_0'$ is the transfer conductance between the jth branch and the added branch.

6.32. *a.* Check the theorem of the preceding problem by computing the changes in the currents through resistors R_1 and R_2 of the circuit shown, due to a current I, both by Kirchhoff's laws and by the theorem.

b. If $\varepsilon = 60$ volts, $R_1 = 10,000$ ohms, $R_2 = 20,000$ ohms, find the changes in the currents through R_1 and R_2 when a current of $+1$ ma is delivered to the external circuit.

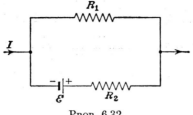

PROB. 6.32.

6.33. An experimenter connects three different storage batteries in parallel, with the same polarity, to a load of 8 ohms. The emfs and internal resistances of the batteries are, respectively, 6.05 volts, 0.02 ohm; 6.00 volts, 0.03 ohm; 5.95 volts, 0.04 ohm.

a. What is the equivalent emf and internal resistance of the set of batteries?

b. When connected to the load, what is the load current?

6.34. Use Thévenin's theorem to compute the current I in the network shown.

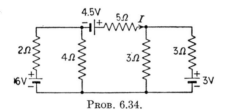

PROB. 6.34.

6.35. Given a pair of batteries, with emfs $\mathcal{E}_1$ and $\mathcal{E}_2$ and resistances R_1 and R_2, connected in parallel and supplying current I to a load.

a. Find a general expression for the current in each battery in terms of the given quantities.

b. Find a general expression for the power dissipated as heat in the batteries.

c. Show that the *increase* of power dissipated in the batteries due to the load current I is just the power dissipated with the same load current in the equivalent battery of emf $\mathcal{E}_0$ in series with internal resistance R_0.

Note. This is in fact a general theorem for linear networks.

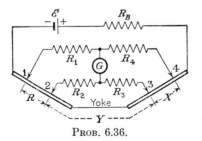

PROB. 6.36.

6.36. The Kelvin bridge shown in the figure is used to compare the low resistance X between points 3 and 4 of a wire or rod with a low variable resistance R between points 1 and 2 on a standard rod. The resistance of the rods, their connecting yoke, and the contacts, between points 2 and 3 is an unknown and possibly variable quantity

Y. The ratio arms R_1, R_2, R_3, and R_4 have large enough values that the contact resistances to the bars at 1, 2, 3, and 4 are negligible. Show that at balance

$$X = R\frac{R_4}{R_1} + \frac{YR_2}{R_2 + R_3 + Y}\left(\frac{R_4}{R_1} - \frac{R_3}{R_2}\right)$$

Thus if fixed ratio arms are used for which $R_4/R_1 = R_3/R_2$, the lead and contact resistances in Y are eliminated.

6.37. Given a slightly unbalanced Wheatstone bridge whose ratio arms are shown in the figure, together with a 6-volt battery of negligible resistance and a 500-ohm galvanometer. Find the galvanometer current and power, and the battery current and power input, when (a) terminals A are connected to the galvanometer and terminals B to the battery and (b) terminals B are connected to the galvanometer and terminals A to the battery.

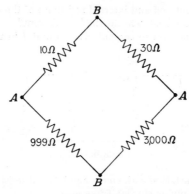

PROB. 6.37.

6.38. A certain linear battery has an open-circuit potential difference of 3.000 volts across its terminals; and when connected to a load of exactly 6 ohms, it delivers a current of 0.490 amp.

    a. What load resistance will draw the maximum power from the battery?

    b. What is this maximum power?

6.39. Given a Wheatstone bridge with a variable standard resistor of 0 to 999.9 ohms, and standard resistors of 1, 10, 100, 1,000, and 10,000 ohms available for fixed ratio arms. The galvanometer, which has a resistance of 1,000 ohms, is connected between the junction of the fixed arms and the junction of the variable arm with an unknown resistance of about 30 ohms.

    a. What ratio arms are selected in order to measure the unknown as accurately as possible?

    b. What maximum power is available to the galvanometer for an unbalance of 0.1 ohm in the variable arm, if the battery is 2 volts of negligible resistance?

6.40. Given a battery of N identical cells, where N is a number with several factors; suppose them to be connected in series parallel with m parallel groups of like polarity each containing n cells in additive series. Show that the maximum power from the battery into a given load resistance is obtained when m and n are so chosen, if possible, as to match the net internal resistance of the battery to the load.

CHAPTER 7

STEADY-STATE MAGNETISM

7.1. Introduction. The study of magnetism is made confusing by the wide difference between the historical approach to the subject and the analytical approach. Historically, permanent magnetism of a natural iron ore called magnetite (Fe_3O_4) was known in ancient times. Forces were observed between specimens of this ore and other specimens, between the ore and metallic iron, and between the ore and the earth. It is clear that these forces are of a different nature from electrostatic forces, for no magnetic interaction is observed between electric charge at rest and magnetized matter. It was not until 1820, by the work of Oersted,[1] that magnetism was found to be connected with current electricity. From the analytical point of view, it now appears reasonable that electric current in the broadest sense, including any moving or spinning charge, is the ultimate source of all magnetic phenomena. We shall see also that changing electric fields have an associated magnetic aspect. There has been a persistent attempt to show the existence of a magnetic particle, a hypothetical elementary particle having a magnetic analogue of the property of electric charge. Despite rather recent efforts in this direction, within the last decade, there is no generally recognized experimental evidence for a particle with such a property. On the other hand, the concept that all magnetism is concerned with moving charge or changing electric fields seems adequate to account for observed facts.

In the present chapter we shall often limit ourselves to steady-state magnetism, although some of our statements will have general validity. Steady-state magnetism is the study of the force interactions in stationary systems involving either permanent magnets or steady electric currents, or both, together with matter. For analytical reasons, we shall require the term "steady state" to imply also that no macroscopic charge density is being built up at any place in the system, as well as that all currents are constant in time. A system so restricted has a simpler electromagnetic field.

It should be admitted at the outset that magnetism is a more complex subject from a mathematical standpoint than electrostatics. The reason for this is that currents rather than charges are the sources of magnetism,

[1] Hans Christian Oersted (1777–1851).

for current density is a vector while charge density is a scalar quantity. Some aspects of magnetic analysis are therefore more appropriate to an advanced treatment employing vector operators.   For this reason, many textbooks develop the subject primarily in a way parallel to that used for electrostatics, with the introduction of a fictitious scalar quantity called magnetic charge.   There is no denying the utility of this concept, which we shall mention in its place; but it seems more suitable for a modern treatment of magnetism to begin rather with the basic study of magnetic effects of electric current.   All our basic definitions in the subject will be made in terms of electric currents.

An important branch of the study of magnetism concerns the magnetic properties of matter.   It is well known that only a few metals, notably iron, nickel, and cobalt, have magnetic characteristics which are strong enough to be observed in crude experiments.   It is not always appreciated that all matter is magnetic.   Although the magnetism of most materials is many orders of magnitude more feeble than that of iron, it is of great interest in the study of the structure of atoms, molecules, and crystals. Such a study lies outside the scope of this book, for the most part, since it entails the use of the quantum mechanics.   We shall, however, be interested in a descriptive treatment of all magnetic materials; and in addition we shall need to examine the macroscopic field in magnetized material.   The cause of all magnetic effects of matter will be taken to be moving or spinning electric charge on an atomic, molecular, or micro-crystalline scale.

7.2. Magnetic Induction.   Our first approach to the study of magnetism will be the consideration of magnetic forces.   Magnetic forces may be defined as those which are exerted on moving charges, and hence on electric currents, because of the velocity of the charge or magnitude of the current.   Such a definition is rigorous if the charge moves without acceleration.   Even for fairly large accelerations, the force on a charge may be considered to be made up of just two parts: one due to the charge alone, which would also be experienced by a charge at rest; and one due to the velocity, the magnetic force.   For violent accelerations, there is a radiation force which we cannot consider now.

It is found possible to describe the magnetic force on a current or moving charge by means of a vector function of position in space.   In steady state, this function does not vary in time, although in a general electromagnetic field it may involve the time.   We shall call this vector point function the magnetic induction.   It is also frequently called magnetic flux density.   The usual symbol for magnetic induction is $\mathbf{B}$.   Being a function describing magnetic force, $\mathbf{B}$ is the analogue of the electric field $\mathbf{E}$, which describes electric force.   In the interest of consistent terminology, $\mathbf{B}$ ought to be called the magnetic field.   The reader should be aware of the danger of confusion in this usage, however, of which we shall say more as we proceed.

In the consideration of magnetic force, we may take for the fundamental problem the determination of the force on an infinitesimal vector length $d\mathbf{l}$ of wire carrying a current I and having negligible transverse dimensions. Experiment shows that this force $d\mathbf{F}$ has the following properties:

1. $d\mathbf{F} \propto I$
2. $d\mathbf{F} \propto dl$
3. $d\mathbf{F}$ depends on the position coordinates (x,y,z) of $d\mathbf{l}$
4. $d\mathbf{F}$ depends on the orientation of $d\mathbf{l}$. We find that
   a. There is always a direction for $d\mathbf{l}$ such that the force $d\mathbf{F}$ vanishes. The flow of the current may have either sense along this direction; if the force vanishes for one sense, it vanishes also for the other.
   b. There is no other orientation of $d\mathbf{l}$ for which $d\mathbf{F}$ vanishes, unless indeed it vanishes for every orientation.
   c. $d\mathbf{F} \propto \sin\theta$, where θ is the angle between the direction of $d\mathbf{l}$ and the direction in which $d\mathbf{F}$ vanishes.
5. The direction of $d\mathbf{F}$ is always perpendicular to $d\mathbf{l}$, and depends on the orientation of $d\mathbf{l}$ in the following manner: $d\mathbf{F}$ is perpendicular to the plane containing $d\mathbf{l}$ and the direction of zero force.
6. The sense of $d\mathbf{F}$ reverses when the current reverses.

It is possible to express all these facts in a single vector equation by use of the vector product, or cross product. Let $d\mathbf{l}$ have the sense in which the current flows. Then

$$d\mathbf{F} \equiv I \, d\mathbf{l} \times \mathbf{B} \qquad (7.1)$$

Here $\mathbf{B}$ is the magnetic induction mentioned above. It is understood that $\mathbf{B}$ is a function of the space coordinates of location of the element $d\mathbf{l}$ and that in general $\mathbf{B}$ may also be a function of time. Equation (7.1) is written as a definition, for it serves to define the function $\mathbf{B}$ as well as to state the experimental facts listed above. Notice that this definition of $\mathbf{B}$ is independent of any properties of the medium in which $d\mathbf{l}$ may be located.

It may be well to review the meaning of the cross product $d\mathbf{l} \times \mathbf{B}$. This product is a vector having a magnitude

$$|d\mathbf{l} \times \mathbf{B}| = dl \, B \sin\theta \qquad (7.2)$$

where θ is the angle (equal to or less than $180°$) between $\mathbf{B}$ and $d\mathbf{l}$. It is evident now that the vector $\mathbf{B}$ has the direction of $d\mathbf{l}$ when the force is zero, or else the opposite direction; so that θ is the same angle denoted by that symbol in paragraph 4c above. Furthermore, the cross product $d\mathbf{l} \times \mathbf{B}$ is understood to mean a vector whose direction is perpendicular both to $d\mathbf{l}$ and to $\mathbf{B}$ and hence to a plane containing the $d\mathbf{l}$ and $\mathbf{B}$ directions. Lastly, $d\mathbf{l} \times \mathbf{B}$ carries the concept of the sense of the cross product. There are two possible senses for a vector perpendicular to the plane of $d\mathbf{l}$ and $\mathbf{B}$, which may be described by the direction of advance of a screw normal to the plane. If we agree that the screw is to turn from the first-named vector to the second through the smaller angle between them, these two senses are the directions of advance of a right-handed or a left-handed screw, respectively. We shall agree to use the right-handed screw rule. In Eq. (7.1), $d\mathbf{F}$ and $d\mathbf{l}$ are physically determined by experiment, as well as by the previous definition of positive electric charge and hence of positive current, so the right-handed screw rule really defines the sense of the magnetic induction vector $\mathbf{B}$.

The relative senses of the three vectors $d\mathbf{F}$, $d\mathbf{l}$, and $\mathbf{B}$ may be illustrated by extending the thumb, forefinger, and middle finger of the right hand so as to be mutually perpendicular. Then the cross product of the thumb into the forefinger has the sense of the middle finger according to the right-handed screw rule. This illustration does not purport to agree with any of the engineers' hand rules, which this author finds extremely awkward to remember. For memory purposes, perhaps the most satisfactory way of describing a cross product is in terms of the screw rule as given above. The agreement to use a given screw rule for the vector cross product should be carried over into the cartesian coordinate system to be employed. If $\mathbf{i}$, $\mathbf{j}$ and $\mathbf{k}$ are the unit vectors along x, y, and z, respectively, then it is usual to let

$$\mathbf{i} \times \mathbf{j} = \mathbf{k} \qquad \mathbf{j} \times \mathbf{k} = \mathbf{i} \qquad \mathbf{k} \times \mathbf{i} = \mathbf{j} \tag{7.3}$$

Now a right-handed system of coordinates is one in which the coordinate senses are related by Eq. (7.3) when the right-handed screw rule is employed, while a left-handed system is described by (7.3) when a left-handed screw rule is employed.

Since electric current is nothing but flowing electric charge, the force on our element of wire carrying a current must be due ultimately to forces on the moving carriers of charge. It is not difficult to deduce from Eq. (7.1) the force on a charge q moving with velocity $\mathbf{v}$. First, however, let us express the current in terms of current density. Supposing a uniform current density $\mathbf{J}$ along the direction of $d\mathbf{l}$ and constant across the cross section A of $d\mathbf{l}$, we have the relation

$$I \, d\mathbf{l} = \mathbf{J}A \, dl \tag{7.4}$$

Since $A \, dl$ is a unit of volume, we may write $dV = A \, dl$, so that (7.4) becomes

$$I \, d\mathbf{l} = \mathbf{J} \, dV \tag{7.5}$$

This little crossover equation between the filamentary and the volume aspects of current flow is worth noting for future analytical use. For the present, we see that we can rewrite Eq. (7.1) in the form

$$d\mathbf{F} = \mathbf{J} \times \mathbf{B}\, dV \tag{7.6}$$

or

$$\frac{d\mathbf{F}}{dV} = \mathbf{J} \times \mathbf{B} \tag{7.7}$$

While this equation has been derived by considering wires in which $\mathbf{J}$ is uniform, it holds quite generally for the magnetic force per unit volume of material in which the current density is distributed in an arbitrary way.

Now to pursue the question of the force per carrier charge, we have only to consider a case in which the current density is the result of motion of carriers of a single type, whose charge is q, whose average velocity is $\mathbf{v}$, and whose number per unit volume is n. According to Eq. (5.7), Sec. 5.1,

$$J = nq\mathbf{v} \tag{7.8}$$

Substitution into Eq. (7.7) yields

$$\frac{d\mathbf{F}}{n\, dV} = q\mathbf{v} \times \mathbf{B} \tag{7.9}$$

But $n\, dV$ is simply the number of charge carriers in the volume dV on which the total magnetic force is $d\mathbf{F}$. Thus $d\mathbf{F}/n\, dV$ is the desired magnetic force per moving charge. Calling this force per moving charge simply $\mathbf{f}_m$, we have now

$$\mathbf{f}_m = q\mathbf{v} \times \mathbf{B} \tag{7.10}$$

It may be well to record here the Lorentz force equation for the total force on an electric charge q. There is an electric force

$$\mathbf{f}_e = q\mathbf{E} \tag{7.11}$$

where $\mathbf{E}$ is the electric field at the location of the charge. This force appears alone when the charge is at rest; but it persists unaltered when the charge is in motion. The total electromagnetic force, exclusive of radiation force, is therefore

$$\mathbf{f} = q(\mathbf{E} + \mathbf{v} \times \mathbf{B}) \tag{7.12}$$

Equation (7.12) is basic for the design of cyclotrons, betatrons, mass spectrographs, and all machines involving ballistics of charged particles.

We have now introduced the concept of the magnetic field as described by the magnetic induction vector. If we are to be very cautious in assigning physical reality to the quantities which we find it useful to define, we may limit ourselves to saying that magnetic forces may be described in terms of the magnetic field. Nevertheless, it is quite proper to consider the field as a property of the space in which it exists. This has the advantage that magnetic forces no longer appear as "action at a distance," but it entails the disadvantage of requiring us to assign properties other than extension to the "nothingness" of empty space.

One further remark is needed concerning the present definition of magnetic induction at a point in space. The symbol $\mathbf{B}$ of Eq. (7.1) is understood to be the induction at the position of $d\mathbf{l}$ exclusive of any direct contribution of the current in $d\mathbf{l}$ to the field. It is necessary to make this statement since we shall see in the following section that there is a magnetic field associated with every current element. For purposes of defining the field at a point of space not actually occupied by a current element in a particular problem, the current element $d\mathbf{l}$ serves just as an idealized test instrument. On the other hand, of course, the element $d\mathbf{l}$ may be part of an actual circuit present in the problem. If $d\mathbf{l}$ is only a test instrument, we need not be concerned about its affecting the system in which we imagine it to be placed, because its length is only infinitesimal, and this means, as will appear in the next section, that the field due to $d\mathbf{l}$ is infinitesimal at any finite distance.

If we use Eq. (7.1) to determine the total force on a complete circuit C carrying current I, we must perform a vector integration over C. Formally, we obtain

$$\mathbf{F} = I \oint_C d\mathbf{l} \times \mathbf{B} \qquad (7.13)$$

The unit for magnetic induction in our mks system is evidently the newton/ampere-meter. It is perhaps more usual to express this unit as the weber/meter², the weber being the mks unit of magnetic flux which will be defined in Sec. 7.6.

7.3. Ampère's Law. It is easily demonstrated that magnetic forces exist in general between a pair of current circuits, and also between different parts of the same circuit. If all magnetic forces are to be described in terms of a magnetic field, the magnetic induction $\mathbf{B}$, we see that steady current must be considered a source of magnetic induction. We shall study in this section the magnetic field of a steady electric current. It will simplify our work to consider the case of a circuit *in vacuo*, so as to avoid speaking of the effect of magnetic matter. This simplification destroys neither the usefulness nor the generality of our remarks. In absence of ironlike (ferromagnetic) matter, any effect of other materials upon the magnetic field is so small as to be negligible for most purposes, so that our results will be immediately applicable to non-ferromagnetic systems. Furthermore, the magnetic effect of the presence of any matter, even ferromagnetic, is simply to superpose a field of its own on the field produced *in vacuo* by the current circuit. What we shall say for a circuit *in vacuo* is therefore in one sense perfectly general, although we must later consider the added field resulting from surrounding matter.

We shall describe the magnetic field of a current circuit as the vector sum of the fields produced by each part of the circuit as if that part were present alone. Experimentally, it is impossible to isolate the field of one part of a circuit, but for analytical purposes it is important to do so. Consider then a basic element of a current circuit composed of a thin wire whose cross-section dimensions are negligible for the problem. Let dl represent an infinitesimal length of wire carrying a current I, and let $d\mathbf{l}$ be a vector having the magnitude and direction of dl, and with the sense of the current flow. Let $\mathbf{r}$ be the displacement vector from dl to a point of observation $P(x',y',z')$. We shall use r to mean the magnitude of $\mathbf{r}$; and we define the unit vector

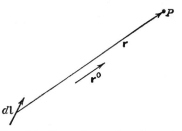

FIG. 7.1. Current-carrying element of wire, and observer.

$$\mathbf{r}^0 \equiv \frac{\mathbf{r}}{r} \tag{7.14}$$

in the direction and sense of $\mathbf{r}$ (see Fig. 7.1).

Now experiment with entire circuits shows that we may consider the element of field $d\mathbf{B}$ at P due to the element $d\mathbf{l}$ of a circuit *in vacuo* to be

$$d\mathbf{B} = C_m \frac{I \, d\mathbf{l} \times \mathbf{r}^0}{r^2} \tag{7.15}$$

where the constant C_m has a universal value once we have fixed the units to be employed. This is frequently known as Ampère's law,[1] in differential form. The cross product shows, according to the discussion of the preceding section, that the field $d\mathbf{B}$ is perpendicular both to $d\mathbf{l}$ and to $\mathbf{r}^0$. The sense of $d\mathbf{B}$ is also properly given by Eq. (7.15), so that when this field is used in Eq. (7.1) of the preceding section, it yields the physically correct sense of the force on another circuit element placed at P.

Let us call a circuit element at P dl', and let $d\mathbf{l}'$ be the vector representing this element and having the sense of the current I' which flows in it. The force on dl' is properly speaking a second-order infinitesimal, since both $d\mathbf{l}'$ and $d\mathbf{B}$ are infinitesimals; therefore we shall remind ourselves of this by writing for it the symbol $d^2\mathbf{F}'$. The prime is essential to specify

[1] In honor of André Marie Ampère (1775–1836).

that this is the force on dl', not that on dl. Now using the definition of magnetic induction, Eq. (7.1), we find that the force between two circuit elements *in vacuo* is

$$d^2\mathbf{F}' = C_m I' I \frac{d\mathbf{l}' \times (d\mathbf{l} \times \mathbf{r}^0)}{r^2} \tag{7.16}$$

Here the numerator contains an expression known as a vector triple product, which can be evaluated in two steps as indicated by the use of parentheses. It may be well to remark that parentheses are essential to keep the expression from being ambiguous. The reader should convince himself that $\mathbf{a} \times (\mathbf{b} \times \mathbf{c})$ is different from $(\mathbf{a} \times \mathbf{b}) \times \mathbf{c}$ by considering the directions of these two expressions. It is interesting to note that the vector triple product $d\mathbf{l}' \times (d\mathbf{l} \times \mathbf{r}^0)$ of Eq. (7.16) does not in general have the direction of $\mathbf{r}^0$, although it may have. Thus Newton's third law does not apply to the interaction of a pair of circuit elements. This need not trouble us, for we have said that it is impossible to isolate the field due to just a part of a circuit. There are, however, other situations which show that Newton's third law does need extension in order to apply to electromagnetic systems.

Now in terms of Eq. (7.16) we are in a position to discuss an important question of units. The length units on the right-hand side of this equation cancel out, provided dl, dl', and r are all expressed in terms of the same length unit. Thus the constant C_m is dimensionally force divided by the square of electric current:

$$[C_m] = \frac{[F]}{[I^2]} \tag{7.17}$$

The particular value of C_m depends on the force and current units employed. Now it turns out in practice that the force between current circuits may be measured in the laboratory with considerable precision; and double integration of Eq. (7.16) over a pair of circuits yields a theoretical expression for this force which may be applied with precision to an instrument of simple geometry. Therefore, given both force and current units, C_m could be accurately determined on the basis of Eq. (7.16). What is actually done in modern practice is rather to use such measurements to standardize a unit of electric current, which is defined by giving C_m an arbitrary value. The absolute ampere (not abampere, which is a cgs unit obtained by taking C_m as unity) is a unit of electric current defined in this way by giving C_m in Eq. (7.16) the arbitrary value of exactly

$$C_m \equiv 10^{-7} \text{ newton/amp}^2 \tag{7.18}$$

Conventional notation for C_m is to write this constant as

$$C_m \equiv \frac{\mu_0}{4\pi} \tag{7.19}$$

Equation (7.19) then defines a new constant μ_0, which is called the permeability of free space. The arbitrary 4π may be considered desirable, even though it complicates the appearance of Eq. (7.16), for it simplifies other equations later. Its inclusion is said to rationalize our magnetic units. Evidently, from Eqs. (7.18) and (7.19),

$$\mu_0 \equiv 4\pi \times 10^{-7} \text{ newton/amp}^2 \tag{7.20}$$

In terms of μ_0, we now rewrite Eqs. (7.15) and (7.16) in their final form:

$$d\mathbf{B} = \frac{\mu_0 I}{4\pi} \frac{d\mathbf{l} \times \mathbf{r}^0}{r^2} \tag{7.21}$$

$$d^2\mathbf{F}' = \frac{\mu_0 I' I}{4\pi} \frac{d\mathbf{l}' \times (d\mathbf{l} \times \mathbf{r}^0)}{r^2} \tag{7.22}$$

In order to find the total magnetic induction at any observation point $P(x',y',z')$, due to a complete circuit, it is necessary to add vectorially all the contributions (7.21) from the parts of the circuit. This may be formally indicated by writing a vector integral to be evaluated by integrating all around the circuit C:

$$\mathbf{B}(x',y',z') = \frac{\mu_0 I}{4\pi} \oint_C \frac{d\mathbf{l} \times \mathbf{r}^0}{r^2} \tag{7.23}$$

Here it is well to use a different notation for the coordinates of $d\mathbf{l}$, say (x,y,z). The distance r is then

$$r = \sqrt{(x'-x)^2 + (y'-y)^2 + (z'-z)^2} \tag{7.24}$$

The sense of $\mathbf{r}^0$ is from (x,y,z) to (x',y',z').

We may also write a formal expression for the total magnetic force between a pair of current circuits C and C' carrying currents I and I', respectively. The force on C' is obtained by a double vector integration of Eq. (7.22):

$$\mathbf{F}' = \frac{\mu_0 I' I}{4\pi} \oint_{C'} \oint_C \frac{d\mathbf{l}' \times (d\mathbf{l} \times \mathbf{r}^0)}{r^2} \tag{7.25}$$

For theoretical purposes, and occasionally for practical purposes, it is valuable to express the magnetic induction in terms of the current densities in the system. This is readily accomplished by applying to Eq. (7.21) the crossover equation (7.5) to which attention was called in the preceding section:

$$I \, d\mathbf{l} = \mathbf{J} \, dV \tag{7.5}$$

The result is that the element of field from the current in the elementary volume dV is

$$d\mathbf{B} = \frac{\mu_0}{4\pi} \frac{\mathbf{J} \times \mathbf{r}^0}{r^2} dV \tag{7.26}$$

Thus the total magnetic induction at an observation point $P(x',y',z')$ is

$$\mathbf{B}(x',y',z') = \frac{\mu_0}{4\pi} \int_{\text{all space}} \frac{\mathbf{J}(x,y,z) \times \mathbf{r}^0}{r^2} dV \tag{7.27}$$

As before, $\mathbf{r}^0$ runs from the element of integration at (x,y,z) toward P.

7.4. Magnetic Field of Wire, Loop, and Solenoid. For future reference and for illustration, we shall use Ampère's law to find the magnetic induction produced by three simple current circuits. The first case is that of the field around a straight portion of wire of negligible cross-section size at a point so near that the wire there subtends an angle of practically 180°. The rest of the circuit containing this portion of wire is to be far enough away to contribute negligible field. This case is often called that of the infinitely long, straight wire, but we have stated it in a realistic way.

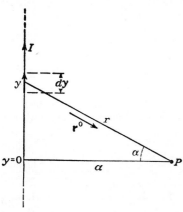

FIG. 7.2. Long, straight wire and observer.

The problem is illustrated in Fig. 7.2. Observation point P is at a perpendicular distance a from the wire. Length along the wire is called y, with y increasing with the sense of the current flow I, and the origin is at the foot of the perpendicular from P to the wire. Distance from a typical element dy of wire to P is called r; and the angle between r and a is called α, with the convention that positive α corresponds to positive y. The unit vector $\mathbf{r}^0$ from dy toward P is shown in the figure, as is the vector element $d\mathbf{l}$ corresponding to dy.

The element of field at P due to the current in dy is given by Ampère's law

$$d\mathbf{B} = \frac{\mu_0 I}{4\pi} \frac{d\mathbf{l} \times \mathbf{r}^0}{r^2} \tag{7.28}$$

Evaluation of the cross product involves the angle θ between $d\mathbf{l}$ and $\mathbf{r}^0$, which is seen from Fig. 7.2 to be

$$\theta = \alpha + \frac{\pi}{2} \tag{7.29}$$

The direction of the cross product at P is perpendicular to the diagram no matter where the element dy is; and its sense is downward into the paper. Thus all elements of the integral have the same direction and their magnitudes add as scalar quantities. Now the magnitude of the element $d\mathbf{B}$ is

$$dB = \frac{\mu_0 I}{4\pi} \frac{\sin \theta \, dy}{r^2} \qquad (7.30)$$

The total magnitude of $\mathbf{B}$ is therefore given by the scalar integral

$$B = \frac{\mu_0 I}{4\pi} \int_{y=-\infty}^{y=+\infty} \frac{\sin \theta}{r^2} \, dy \qquad (7.31)$$

The reader may now follow through for himself the process of expressing

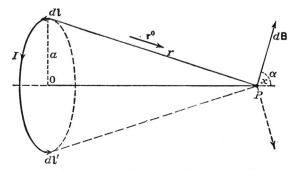

FIG. 7.3. Circular loop with observer on axis.

the integral in terms of only one variable, say y or a. The resulting forms are

$$B = \frac{\mu_0 I}{4\pi} \int_{-\pi/2}^{\pi/2} \frac{\cos a}{a} \, da = \frac{\mu_0 I}{4\pi} \int_{y=-\infty}^{+\infty} \frac{a \, dy}{(a^2 + y^2)^{3/2}} \qquad (7.32)$$

From either of these, our answer is

$$B = \frac{\mu_0 I}{2\pi a} \qquad (7.33)$$

As a vector, $\mathbf{B}$ has the direction and sense of each element (7.28), so that it is perpendicular to the wire and to a, and at P in Fig. 7.2 it is down into the diagram.

The second case to be considered is the field on the axis of a circular loop of radius a carrying current I. Referring to Fig. 7.3, let x be the distance of the observation point P from the plane of the loop. The loop is shown in perspective, and the sample element $d\mathbf{l}$ is taken to lie at the plane of the paper but normal to it, at a distance r from P. $\mathbf{r}^0$ is as always the unit vector from $d\mathbf{l}$ toward P. It will be seen that the cross product $d\mathbf{l} \times \mathbf{r}^0$ yields an element of field $d\mathbf{B}$ in the plane of the paper, normal to the line r, and having the indicated sense when the current I has the sense of the arrowhead. Furthermore, the angle between $d\mathbf{l}$ and $\mathbf{r}^0$ is 90° for all elements of the loop. Thus the magnitude of dB is

$$dB = \frac{\mu_0 I}{4\pi} \frac{dl}{r^2} \qquad (7.34)$$

In the process of integration the elements $d\mathbf{B}$ all have this same magnitude, and lie along a cone of half angle α coaxial with the loop. For every element $d\mathbf{l}$ of the loop there is a symmetrical element $d\mathbf{l}'$, so that the components of induction perpendicular to the axis cancel. The components along the axis all have the same sign, and in the integration they add to yield the total field. Let us therefore write the component of $d\mathbf{B}$ parallel to the axis, and perform a scalar integration:

$$dB_x = \frac{\mu_0 I}{4\pi} \frac{dl}{r^2} \cos \alpha \qquad (7.35)$$

Expressing r and $\cos \alpha$ in terms of the given quantities, we now obtain

$$dB_x = \frac{\mu_0 I}{4\pi} \frac{a}{(a^2 + x^2)^{3/2}} \, dl \qquad (7.36)$$

In the integration x is a constant, so that

$$B_x = \frac{\mu_0 I a}{4\pi (a^2 + x^2)^{3/2}} \int_0^{2\pi a} dl \qquad (7.37)$$

Therefore

$$B_x = \frac{\mu_0 I a^2}{2(a^2 + x^2)^{3/2}} \qquad (7.38)$$

This result may be used to derive an expression for the field on the axis of a solenoid, which is essentially a helical coil with a small pitch angle. The field of such a coil is almost identical with the field of a set of circular loops of the same radius, equally spaced along a common straight axis. The number of loops per unit length of axis is taken equal to N_1, the number of turns per unit length of the solenoid; and each loop is given the current I, the same in magnitude and sense as that which flows in the solenoid. The contributions of all loops to the field at a point of observation O on the axis (see Fig. 7.4) are summed by integration, treating the loops as if they were so densely distributed as to be essentially continuous. Thus the number of loops in an infinitesimal element of length dx of the solenoid is $N_1 \, dx$. We shall not take space to reproduce the details of the problem. It is convenient to use for integration the half angle θ subtended by a loop at the observation point. The result of integration is expressible then in terms of the extreme half angles θ_1 and θ_2 subtended by the ends of the solenoid:

$$B_x = \tfrac{1}{2}\mu_0 N_1 I(\cos \theta_2 - \cos \theta_1) \tag{7.39}$$

If the solenoid becomes very long, $\theta_1 \to 180°$ and $\theta_2 \to 0$ at a point within the solenoid far from either end, so that the field is then

$$B_x = \mu_0 N_1 I \tag{7.40}$$

The reader should examine each of the cases discussed above to determine the relative senses of current and field. For the straight wire, the

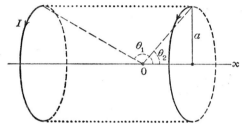

FIG. 7.4. Point of observation on the axis of a solenoid.

field is in the sense of peripheral motion of a right-handed screw of infinitely fine pitch turning so as to advance along the current direction. For the loop and solenoid, the field on axis is in the sense of advance of a right-handed screw which turns in the sense of circulation of the current.

7.5. Vector Potential. We turn our attention in the remainder of this chapter to some very interesting and important properties of the steady magnetic field, all deductions from Eq. (7.27), Sec. 7.3, which may be rewritten in the form

$$\mathbf{B}(x,y,z) = \frac{\mu_0}{4\pi} \int_{\text{all space}} \frac{\mathbf{J}(x',y',z') \times \mathbf{r}}{r^3} \, dV \tag{7.41}$$

Here

$$\mathbf{r} = (x - x')\mathbf{i} + (y - y')\mathbf{j} + (z - z')\mathbf{k} \tag{7.42}$$

and

$$r = [(x - x')^2 + (y - y')^2 + (z - z')^2]^{1/2} \tag{7.43}$$

We may write $\mathbf{J}$ in terms of its components as

$$\mathbf{J}(x',y',z') = J_x\mathbf{i} + J_y\mathbf{j} + J_z\mathbf{k} \tag{7.44}$$

Here the observer's coordinates are (x,y,z), while the element of integration dV, in which the current density is $\mathbf{J}$, is located at x', y', z'. As is customary, the symbols $\mathbf{i}$, $\mathbf{j}$, and $\mathbf{k}$ of Eq. (7.42) are the unit vectors along the cartesian coordinate directions.

The x component of the magnetic induction is found by combination of Eqs. (7.41), (7.42), and (7.44) to be

$$B_x(x,y,z) = \frac{\mu_0}{4\pi} \int_{\text{all space}} \frac{(z - z')J_y - (y - y')J_z}{r^3} \, dV \qquad (7.45)$$

Now the reader may quickly determine from Eq. (7.43) that

$$-\frac{(y - y')}{r^3} = \frac{\partial}{\partial y}\left(\frac{1}{r}\right) \qquad \frac{z - z'}{r^3} = -\frac{\partial}{\partial z}\left(\frac{1}{r}\right) \qquad (7.46)$$

Thus we may write

$$B_x = \frac{\mu_0}{4\pi} \int_{\text{all space}} \left[J_z \frac{\partial}{\partial y}\left(\frac{1}{r}\right) - J_y \frac{\partial}{\partial z}\left(\frac{1}{r}\right) \right] dV \qquad (7.47)$$

Since J_z and J_y are functions of x', y', z' but not of x, y, z,

$$B_x = \frac{\mu_0}{4\pi} \int_{\text{all space}} \left[\frac{\partial}{\partial y}\left(\frac{J_z}{r}\right) - \frac{\partial}{\partial z}\left(\frac{J_y}{r}\right) \right] dV \qquad (7.48)$$

Let us now split this expression into two separate integrals. We may take the derivative signs outside the integral signs, since the limits of integration do not involve the variables of differentiation; and thus we obtain

$$B_x = \frac{\mu_0}{4\pi} \frac{\partial}{\partial y} \int_{\text{all space}} \frac{J_z}{r} \, dV - \frac{\mu_0}{4\pi} \frac{\partial}{\partial z} \int_{\text{all space}} \frac{J_y}{r} \, dV \qquad (7.49)$$

Next define a vector function of the observer's position, $\mathbf{A}(x,y,z)$, called a magnetic vector potential, as follows

$$\mathbf{A}(x,y,z) \equiv \frac{\mu_0}{4\pi} \int_{\text{all space}} \frac{\mathbf{J}(x',y',z')}{r} \, dV \qquad (7.50)$$

In terms of this vector potential, we may rewrite Eq. (7.49):

$$B_x = \frac{\partial A_z}{\partial y} - \frac{\partial A_y}{\partial z} \qquad (7.51)$$

The other components of $\mathbf{B}$ may be written similarly, as will be evident from symmetry:

$$B_y = \frac{\partial A_x}{\partial z} - \frac{\partial A_z}{\partial x} \qquad (7.52)$$

$$B_z = \frac{\partial A_y}{\partial x} - \frac{\partial A_x}{\partial y} \qquad (7.53)$$

Equations (7.51) to (7.53) are abbreviated in vector notation to read

$$\mathbf{B} = \text{curl } \mathbf{A} \qquad (7.54)$$

The magnetic vector potential is frequently used for the computation of magnetic fields, since its mathematical form is simpler than that of Ampère's law. Each cartesian component of $\mathbf{A}$ is simply a scalar potential integral. For application to systems where the current is confined to wires, we may rewrite the integral (7.50) by using the crossover relation $I\,d\mathbf{l} = \mathbf{J}\,dv$. For a single circuit C carrying current I,

$$\mathbf{A} = \frac{\mu_0}{4\pi} I \oint_C \frac{d\mathbf{l}}{r} \qquad (7.55)$$

The reader should be aware that sometimes the integrals (7.50) and (7.55) fail to converge, as, for instance, in the case of an infinitely long, straight wire. It is still true, nevertheless, that a vector potential function can be written for this case such that the magnetic induction is derivable from it by Eq. (7.54). It is a basic characteristic of the magnetic induction vector that in all cases it may be expressed thus by a vector potential function. For a given magnetic field, the vector potential is not unique; but integrals (7.50) and (7.55) give one such function whenever they converge.

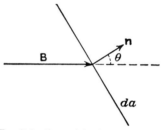

FIG. 7.5. Quantities involved in a computation of magnetic flux.

7.6. Magnetic Flux. For future reference, we shall define the surface integral of the magnetic induction vector, called magnetic flux. Consider an infinitesimal element da of a regular surface S. This element may be made small enough to lie as near as we please to a plane; so we shall consider it to have a definite normal direction with a specified sense. Let unit vector normal to da be represented by the symbol $\mathbf{n}$. We may further suppose da to be small compared to inhomogeneities of the magnetic induction vector $\mathbf{B}(x,y,z)$, so that $\mathbf{B}$ has a specific direction and magnitude at da. The flux of $\mathbf{B}$ across da is then defined as

$$d\Phi \equiv \mathbf{B} \cdot \mathbf{n}\, da = B \cos \theta\, da \qquad (7.56)$$

Here θ is the angle between $\mathbf{B}$ and $\mathbf{n}$ as shown in Fig. 7.5. This quantity $d\Phi$ is analogous to rate of flow of an incompressible fluid across da, the magnetic induction $\mathbf{B}$ taking the place of the point by point velocity of flow of the fluid. The total flux across a finite surface S is now given by the surface integral

$$\Phi = \int_S \mathbf{B} \cdot \mathbf{n}\, da = \int_S B \cos \theta\, da \qquad (7.57)$$

Equations (7.56) and (7.57) have been written both in the elegant notation of vector analysis and in an expanded form to indicate the meaning of that notation.

We are now able to prove a basic property of the magnetic induction, that its net flux (out or in) through any closed surface whatever is always zero. This may be accomplished by considering the quantity

$$\frac{\partial B_x}{\partial x} + \frac{\partial B_y}{\partial y} + \frac{\partial B_z}{\partial z} \equiv \text{div } \mathbf{B} \tag{7.58}$$

known in vector language as the divergence of the vector $\mathbf{B}$. We have shown in Sec. 2.2, in connection with the $\mathbf{E}$ vector, that this quantity represents the flux of the vector outward from an infinitesimal volume dV, divided by the volume dV. Now the total flux out from a finite closed surface S is the sum, that is, the integral, of all the infinitesimal fluxes out from the elements dV of the

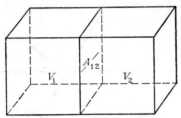

FIG. 7.6. Adjoining volumes.

total volume V enclosed by S. Consider for example the pair of adjoining volumes labeled V_1 and V_2 in Fig. 7.6 and having a common surface A_{12}. The flux Φ_1 out from V_1 includes a contribution Φ_{12} which passes out from V_1 through A_{12}; while this same Φ_{12} passes into volume V_2, and hence contributes an amount $-\Phi_{12}$ to the flux Φ_2 outward from V_2. If now we form the sum

$$\Phi = \Phi_1 + \Phi_2$$

the flux through A_{12} has entered twice with opposite signs, and so cancels out. Thus $\Phi_1 + \Phi_2$ represents the flux only through the outer boundaries of V_1 and V_2, or out of the composite volume $V_1 + V_2 = V$. This reasoning may be continued for any number of adjoining cells which together form a volume V enclosed by an outer surface S. Thus if the magnetic flux outward from the surface of a volume element dV is

$$d\Phi = \left(\frac{\partial B_x}{\partial x} + \frac{\partial B_y}{\partial y} + \frac{\partial B_z}{\partial z}\right) dV \tag{7.59}$$

it follows that from a finite volume V whose surface is S the flux is

$$\Phi = \int_V \left(\frac{\partial B_x}{\partial x} + \frac{\partial B_y}{\partial y} + \frac{\partial B_z}{\partial z}\right) dV \tag{7.60}$$

The identity of expressions (7.57) and (7.60) is in fact well known under the name of the divergence theorem.

In order to prove the proposed theorem that for any closed surface S

$$\Phi = \oint_S \mathbf{B} \cdot \mathbf{n} \, da = 0 \tag{7.61}$$

we need only to show that the integrand of Eq. (7.60) is zero. This may be done at once by expressing **B** in terms of a magnetic vector potential **A**. We have remarked in the preceding section that **B** may always be represented in this way. Substitution of Eqs. (7.51) to (7.53) of the preceding section into the integrand of (7.60) yields zero identically, since order of differentiation is immaterial:

$$\frac{\partial B_x}{\partial x} + \frac{\partial B_y}{\partial y} + \frac{\partial B_z}{\partial z} = 0 \tag{7.62}$$

This equation is characteristic of the magnetic induction vector at all points of space in steady state; and as we shall remark later when we no longer require the magnetic field to be steady, it is valid at all instants of time. Equation (7.62) is known as one of the Maxwell equations of electromagnetism. From it, we immediately deduce the truth of Eq. (7.61) because of (7.60), thus proving the theorem that the net magnetic flux through any closed surface is zero.

It might be helpful for our understanding of the meaning of Eqs. (7.61) and (7.62) to refer to the discussion of electrostatics in Chap. 2. The electrostatic field has the property corresponding to Eq. (7.62) only at points in space where there is no free or bound electric charge density, and the property corresponding to (7.61) only for surfaces enclosing zero net electric charge, free or bound. We may therefore say that the universal validity of Eqs. (7.61) and (7.62) is a statement of the fact that there is no such thing as net magnetic charge. This is the accepted experimental fact. We have not really proved it by our mathematics. These equations are all based on the assumption that all magnetic fields are the result of flowing electric charge, to which later we shall add the possibility of changing electric fields. What we have shown therefore is that this assumption does not lead to anything in magnetism corresponding to net charge. In spite of this, there is a utility for the concept of fictitious bound magnetic charges in magnetic media, which will be mentioned in its place.

For future use, it will be helpful to make a deduction from Eq. (7.61). If C is any closed curve which bounds an open surface S, then for a given C the flux through S is not dependent on the shape of S. For, take two nonintersecting surfaces S' and S'' both bounded by the same curve C. Then Eq. (7.61) yields

$$\int_{S'} \mathbf{B} \cdot \mathbf{n} \, da + \int_{S''} \mathbf{B} \cdot \mathbf{n} \, da = 0 \tag{7.63}$$

if **n** is outward to the closed surface which is formed by S' and S''. But now the relation of **n** to a specified sense around the curve is different depending on whether we are considering S' or S''. We shall define normals **n'** and **n''** related to a positive sense along C as follows: Let a right-handed screw tangent to C turn so as to advance in the positive sense along C. The positive normal $\mathbf{n'}$ to S' or $\mathbf{n''}$ to S'' is in the sense in which the threads of the screw move through the surface in question. With this convention, the reader will be able to see that if $\mathbf{n'} = \mathbf{n}$, then $\mathbf{n''} = -\mathbf{n}$. Eq. (7.63) then becomes

$$\int_{S'} \mathbf{B} \cdot \mathbf{n'} \, da = \int_{S''} \mathbf{B} \cdot \mathbf{n''} \, da \qquad \text{Q.E.D.} \qquad (7.64)$$

The mks unit of magnetic flux is called the weber. Since the unit of magnetic induction is the newton per ampere-meter, that of magnetic flux must be

$$1 \, \frac{\text{newton meter}}{\text{ampere}} = 1 \, \text{weber}$$

This unit is capable of various forms of expression, among which are

$$1 \, \text{weber} = \frac{1 \, \text{joule}}{\text{ampere}} = 1 \, \text{volt-second}$$

The equivalence of these expressions points toward Faraday's law of electromagnetic induction, which is discussed in Chap. 8.

7.7. Ampère's Circuital Law. We come next to the circuital law of Ampère, another highly significant deduction from Ampère's law for steady currents. Here the mathematical process becomes involved; and to avoid overburdening the reader with details we shall state the circuital law without proof. In a later section we shall see that the theorem follows from another which we shall have occasion to develop.

Ampère's law as expressed in Sec. 7.3 is

$$\mathbf{B} = \frac{\mu_0}{4\pi} \int_{\text{all space}} \frac{\mathbf{J} \times \mathbf{r}^0}{r^2} \, dV \qquad (7.27)$$

We shall postulate the steady-state condition as defined in Sec. 7.1. This means that not only the currents but also the electric charges of the system are unvarying. According to the equation of continuity, Eq. (5.23), the steady-state condition that $\partial \rho / \partial t = 0$ is equivalent to

$$\text{div } \mathbf{J} = 0 \qquad (7.65)$$

It is necessary also to postulate that a certain surface integral has a zero limit as the closed surface S' of the integration expands to include all space:

$$\lim_{S' \to \infty} \oint_{S'} \frac{1}{r} \mathbf{J} \cdot \mathbf{n} \, da = 0 \qquad (7.66)$$

Here r is the distance from the element da to the observer. Equation (7.66) is evidently true for any current system which is finite in extent. It holds also for a system of wires carrying finite current, even though these are infinitely long. Now it follows mathematically from Eqs.

(7.27), (7.65), and (7.66) that the line integral of the magnetic induction about any closed curve C is given by

$$\oint_C \mathbf{B} \cdot d\mathbf{l} = \mu_0 \int_S \mathbf{J} \cdot \mathbf{n} \, da \qquad (7.67)$$

The surface integral here is carried out over any surface S bounded by the curve C. The relationship between S and C is the same as that between a butterfly net and the hoop which forms its rim. Positive senses of $d\mathbf{l}$ and of the unit normal $\mathbf{n}$ to the surface element da must be properly related in Eq. (7.67). If a right-handed screw is imagined to advance along C in the positive sense for $d\mathbf{l}$, its rotation carries the screw threads through S from the negative to the positive side for $\mathbf{n}$.

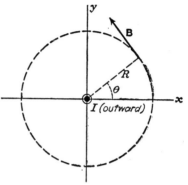

Equation (7.67) is a statement of Ampère's circuital law. We may write it more briefly by identifying the surface integral in Eq. (7.67) with

FIG. 7.7. Application of the circuital law to the field of a long, straight wire.

the current I_C linking C, that is, the current through any surface bounded by C:

$$\oint_C \mathbf{B} \cdot d\mathbf{l} = \mu_0 I_C \qquad (7.68)$$

It is important to understand that the present formulation of the circuital law is restricted in its application to systems of currents *in vacuo*. It will be possible to generalize it later when we study magnetic materials. There will be a still further generalization required before we can state such a law for systems not in steady state, which are at present excluded.

Having stated the circuital law without proof, we ought at least to show a simple case of its application. The magnetic field near a long, thin straight wire *in vacuo* is the simplest one for demonstration of the circuital law. This field was shown in Sec. 7.4 to be

$$B = \frac{\mu_0 I}{2\pi R} \qquad (7.69)$$

at perpendicular distance R from the wire. Its direction is everywhere tangent to a circle of radius R in a plane normal to the wire and having the wire at its center. Furthermore, its sense along this circle is that of rotation of a right-handed screw advancing along the wire in the sense of the current, as shown in Fig. 7.7. Let us perform the integration in cylindrical coordinates R, θ, z, taking z parallel to the wire. A general vector displacement in these coordinates is

$$d\mathbf{l} = \mathbf{R}^0 \, dR + \boldsymbol{\theta}^0 R \, d\theta + \mathbf{k} \, dz \tag{7.70}$$

where $\mathbf{R}^0$ and $\boldsymbol{\theta}^0$ are unit vectors along the radius and normal to it, in the sense of increasing θ, at the location of the element $d\mathbf{l}$, and $\mathbf{k}$ is unit vector along $+z$. The vector form of Eq. (7.69) is

$$\mathbf{B} = \frac{\mu_0 I}{2\pi R} \, \boldsymbol{\theta}^0 \tag{7.71}$$

Therefore

$$\oint_C \mathbf{B} \cdot d\mathbf{l} = \frac{\mu_0 I}{2\pi} \oint_C d\theta \tag{7.72}$$

If the curve C surrounds the wire once, $\oint d\theta$ is $+2\pi$ or -2π according as the sense of integration is counterclockwise or clockwise, while if C does not enclose the wire, θ returns to its initial value at the end of the closed path, giving $\oint d\theta = 0$. Thus Eq. (7.68) is checked for the long, straight wire. The reader should verify the agreement of signs with the convention for the circuital law.

A direct use of the circuital law is in the calculation of the magnetic field in problems of sufficient simplicity and symmetry. As an example, let us show that the field outside a long, solid wire of circular cross section having any finite radius b is still just the same as the field (7.69) for a wire of negligible cross section. For this demonstration, we need first to present a symmetry argument that the magnetic induction at distance R from the wire is the same for any direction of R and has a direction always perpendicular to R. Consider Fig. 7.8, in which a point P of observation is shown at distance R from the axis of the wire. We may suppose the current density to be uniform within the wire (cf. Sec. 5.13); but the result is just as valid if $\mathbf{J}$ is a function only of distance from the axis of the wire. The wire may now be divided into filaments parallel to the axis of the wire and having infinitesimal cross section da, and the magnetic induction at P may thus be considered to be the vector sum of the contributions $d\mathbf{B}$ from these filaments. Figure 7.8 indicates that for any sample filament da' at distance R' from P, there is an equal and symmetrically located filament da'' at an equal distance from P. These filaments are equidistant from the axis of the wire, and hence carry equal currents. Their contributions $d\mathbf{B}'$ and $d\mathbf{B}''$ to the magnetic induction at P are thus equal, and are so oriented by symmetry as to produce a resultant $d\mathbf{B}$ which is perpendicular to R. Integration over the whole wire must therefore produce a field $\mathbf{B}$ which is perpendicular to R, as stated above. Cylindrical symmetry of the wire and the current density guarantees that the magnitude of $\mathbf{B}$ is the same for any point P at the same distance R from the axis. We have now completed the symmetry argument.

Now use the circuital law, choosing as the path of integration a circle C about the axis of the wire, of radius $R > b$, lying in a plane normal to the axis of the wire. At every point of this path $\mathbf{B}$ is tangent to the path by the above proof, and hence parallel to an infinitesimal element $d\mathbf{l}$ of the path. Thus

$$\oint_C \mathbf{B} \cdot d\mathbf{l} = \oint_C BR \, d\theta \qquad (7.73)$$

where $R \, d\theta$ has been written for the magnitude of the element $d\mathbf{l}$, $d\theta$

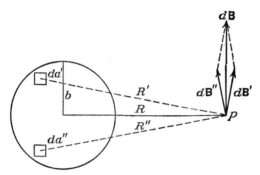

Fig. 7.8. Symmetry of the magnetic field of a wire of circular cross section.

being an element of angle about the center of C. But since C is a circle, R is constant in the integration; and from symmetry again, B is constant. Therefore

$$\oint_C \mathbf{B} \cdot d\mathbf{l} = BR \oint_C d\theta = 2\pi BR \qquad (7.74)$$

Since C surrounds all the current I of the wire, the circuital law (7.68) now gives immediately

$$2\pi BR = \mu_0 I \qquad (7.75)$$

Hence the magnitude of the magnetic induction is

$$B = \frac{\mu_0 I}{2\pi R} \qquad \text{Q.E.D.} \qquad (7.69)$$

7.8. Field of a Distant Circuit. Magnetic Dipole Moment. The magnetic field of a circuit is of very complex form in general, but it becomes simple at a large distance from the circuit. Consider a plane circuit C of rectangular shape lying in the xy plane at the origin, as shown in Fig. 7.9. Let the corners of the circuit be at $(0,0)$, $(a,0)$, (a,b), $(0,b)$, respectively, and let the current I flow in the sense in which the corners are listed. We shall call the coordinates of an element $d\mathbf{l}$ of the circuit (x',y'), and shall let an observation point Q be at (x,y,z) at distance r from the origin. If $r' = \sqrt{(x-x')^2 + (y-y')^2 + z^2}$ is the distance

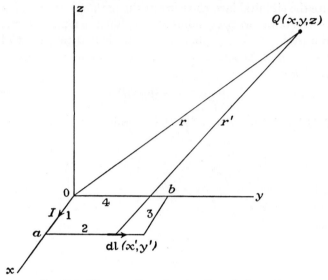

FIG. 7.9. Plane, rectangular circuit, and observer.

from $d\mathbf{l}$ to Q, the magnetic vector potential at Q due to C is

$$\mathbf{A}(x,y,z) = \frac{\mu_0 I}{4\pi} \oint_C \frac{d\mathbf{l}}{r'} \tag{7.76}$$

We shall evaluate $\mathbf{A}$ when the observation point is far enough from C that

$$\frac{a}{r} \ll 1 \qquad \frac{b}{r} \ll 1 \tag{7.77}$$

These inequalities guarantee that at any point (x',y') of the circuit,

$$\frac{x'}{r} \ll 1 \qquad \frac{y'}{r} \ll 1 \tag{7.78}$$

Now let us call the functions r' for the four sides of the circuit r_1, r_2, r_3, and r_4, respectively, beginning at the origin in cyclic order. Equation (7.76) can then be written out as follows:

$$\mathbf{A} = \frac{\mu_0 I}{4\pi} \mathbf{i} \int_0^a \left(\frac{1}{r_1} - \frac{1}{r_3} \right) dx' + \frac{\mu_0 I}{4\pi} \mathbf{j} \int_0^b \left(\frac{1}{r_2} - \frac{1}{r_4} \right) dy' \tag{7.79}$$

where $\mathbf{i}$ and $\mathbf{j}$ are the unit vectors along x and y.

Because of the inequalities (7.78), Eq. (7.79) can readily be evaluated by Maclaurin's expansion of the integrands. The general form is

$$\frac{1}{r'} = \frac{1}{r} + \left[\frac{\partial(1/r')}{\partial x'} \right]_0 x' + \left[\frac{\partial(1/r')}{\partial y'} \right]_0 y'$$

$$+ \text{ quadratic and higher-order terms} \tag{7.80}$$

The derivatives are to be evaluated at $x' = y' = 0$. No terms in z' are needed, for the circuit lies in the plane $z' = 0$. When the coefficients are worked out, (7.80) becomes

$$\frac{1}{r'} = \frac{1}{r} + \frac{x}{r^3} x' + \frac{y}{r^3} y' + \cdots \tag{7.81}$$

Higher terms involve higher powers of x'/r and y'/r, and so in the limit they may be neglected. The first-order terms are necessary, however, for the expression of the integrands of Eq. (7.79). When Eq. (7.81) is used, (7.79) becomes

$$\mathbf{A} \doteq -\frac{\mu_0 I}{4\pi} \mathbf{i} \frac{yb}{r^3} \int_0^a dx' + \frac{\mu_0 I}{4\pi} \mathbf{j} \frac{xa}{r^3} \int_0^b dy' \tag{7.82}$$

The right-hand member of Eq. (7.82) becomes exact in the limit as r increases. We shall call this limiting form the vector potential of a dipole, and denote it by $\mathbf{A}_1$. When the integrals of (7.82) are evaluated we obtain

$$\mathbf{A}_1 = \frac{\mu_0 I ab}{4\pi r^3} (-y\mathbf{i} + x\mathbf{j}) \tag{7.83}$$

It is to be observed that ab is the area of the circuit. The quantity

$$m \equiv Iab \tag{7.84}$$

is the magnitude of the magnetic dipole moment of the circuit C, for we define its magnetic dipole moment as the vector

$$\mathbf{m} \equiv Iab\mathbf{k} \tag{7.85}$$

Here $\mathbf{k}$, the unit vector in the z direction, is the positive normal to the plane of C, related by a right-hand screw rule to the sense of current flow. This is the same rule as that which relates $\mathbf{n}$ to $d\mathbf{l}$ in the Ampère circuital law of Sec. 7.7. In terms of $\mathbf{m}$, we can write the dipole potential (7.83) in the vector form

$$\mathbf{A}_1 = \frac{\mu_0}{4\pi r^3} \mathbf{m} \times \mathbf{r} \tag{7.86}$$

where $\mathbf{r}$ is the vector position of the observer relative to the dipole.

The magnetic induction may be determined by working through Eqs. (7.51) to (7.53) to find $\operatorname{curl} \mathbf{A}_1$. The resulting field of the magnetic dipole whose potential is (7.83) is

$$B_x = \frac{3\mu_0 m}{4\pi} \frac{z}{r^5} x \tag{7.87}$$

$$B_y = \frac{3\mu_0 m}{4\pi} \frac{z}{r^5} y \tag{7.88}$$

$$B_z = \frac{\mu_0 m}{4\pi} \left(-\frac{1}{r^3} + \frac{3z^2}{r^5} \right) \tag{7.89}$$

Simpler expressions for the magnetic field result if we transform to spherical coordinates. If θ is the angle between $\mathbf{r}$ and $\mathbf{m}$, the components of $\mathbf{B}$ in the directions of increasing r and θ are, respectively,

$$B_r = \frac{2\mu_0 m \cos \theta}{4\pi r^3} \tag{7.90}$$

$$B_\theta = \frac{\mu_0 m \sin \theta}{4\pi r^3} \tag{7.91}$$

Compare these forms with the electric field of an electric dipole:

$$E_r = \frac{2p \cos \theta}{4\pi\epsilon_0 r^3} \tag{7.92}$$

$$E_\theta = \frac{p \sin \theta}{4\pi\epsilon_0 r^3} \tag{7.93}$$

It is now evident why the field of the distant circuit is called a dipole field, and why $\mathbf{m}$ is called the magnetic dipole moment of the circuit.

7.9. The Equivalent Network. Dipole Moment of an Arbitrary Circuit. Several important consequences follow from the work of the preceding section. First, the vector potential and hence the magnetic induction of any circuit at any point in empty space or nonmagnetic material outside the wire itself may be found by use of the magnetic dipole moment. This is done by considering the equivalence of a general current loop C to a network of rectangular circuits of infinite fineness whose outer periphery follows C (see Fig. 7.10). Each elementary loop of the net is to carry the same current I as flows in C, and in the same clock sense, so that the currents in the inner conductors of the net will all cancel each other and produce no net magnetic field. The periphery of the network is then entirely responsible for the magnetic field of the network. If the periphery is infinitely fine, it comes as near as we please to C at all points, even though it is jagged in form. The network may be considered to lie in a surface S whose boundary is C, and to be related to C as a butterfly net is to the hoop. The loops of the network are then infinitesimal area elements which together make up S. There is no restriction on the exact form of S or C; in particular C need not be a plane curve.

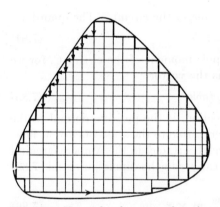

FIG. 7.10. Network of rectangular circuits to replace a given circuit.

It is easy to justify replacing the curve C by the rectangular length elements of the peripheral loops of the network. Figure 7.11 shows an element dl of C, with its neighboring elements dx and dy of the network. Since dl, dx, and dy are all infinitesimal, they lie infinitely near to one another, and hence the distances from each of them to an observer at finite distance are all as nearly alike as we please. The contribution of dl to the vector potential of C at the observer whose distance is r is

$$dA_c = \frac{\mu_0}{4\pi} I \frac{dl}{r} \qquad (7.94)$$

The contribution of the elements dx and dy of the network to its vector potential are

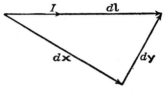

Fig. 7.11. Equivalence of infinitesimal rectangular elements to a circuit element.

$$dA_N = \frac{\mu_0}{4\pi} I \frac{1}{r} (dx + dy) \qquad (7.95)$$

These are equal because of the vector relation between the elements which must hold if the edge of the network is to remain in proximity to C:

$$dl = dx + dy \qquad (7.96)$$

Hence, after integration,

$$A_C = A_N \qquad \text{Q.E.D.} \qquad (7.97)$$

The equivalence of the circuit and the network stated in Eq. (7.97) is only valid at finite distance from the wire C, for this is assumed in the foregoing proof.

In view of the equivalence of the current net to the circuit C, we can set up the vector potential of the circuit as a sum of the elements of potential due to the loops of the net. Each loop, being infinitesimal, produces a pure dipole potential at an observation point at finite distance. Thus if a loop has area dS and its unit positive normal is $\mathbf{n}$, its dipole moment is

$$d\mathbf{m} = I\mathbf{n} \, dS \qquad (7.98)$$

By Eq. (7.86), Sec. 7.8, the vector potential of this elementary loop is

$$dA = \frac{\mu_0}{4\pi} \frac{(d\mathbf{m}) \times \mathbf{r}}{r^3} \qquad (7.99)$$

where $\mathbf{r}$ is vector distance from the elementary loop to the observer.

The vector potential of the entire circuit C is then

$$\mathbf{A} = \frac{\mu_0}{4\pi} \int_S \frac{(d\mathbf{m}) \times \mathbf{r}}{r^3} \qquad (7.100)$$

or

$$\mathbf{A} = \frac{\mu_0 I}{4\pi} \int_S \frac{\mathbf{n} \times \mathbf{r}}{r^3} \, dS \qquad (7.101)$$

This expression although formally correct is not particularly useful in the general case, since it is a more complex integral than Eq. (7.55), Sec. 7.5,

$$\mathbf{A} = \frac{\mu_0 I}{4\pi} \oint_C \frac{d\mathbf{l}}{r} \tag{7.102}$$

The reason for writing Eq. (7.100) is that it has an advantage over (7.102) in yielding a special formula for the limiting case of a circuit whose distance from the observer greatly exceeds its dimensions. If $\mathbf{r}_1$ is the vector distance from any fixed origin near the circuit to the observer, then the vector $\mathbf{r}$ from any point of integration in the circuit to the observer differs in direction from $\mathbf{r}_1$ by a negligible angle, and the magnitudes r and r_1 differ by a negligible percentage, provided r_1 is very much greater than any dimension of the circuit. Substitution of the constant r_1 in place of r in Eq. (7.102) leads only to the information that the limiting potential at great distance is zero, which we know anyway; but substitution in (7.100) for both $\mathbf{r}$ and r yields the actual potential function in the limiting case:

$$\mathbf{A}_1 = \frac{\mu_0}{4\pi} \left[\int_S d\mathbf{m} \right] \times \frac{\mathbf{r}_1}{r_1{}^3} \tag{7.103}$$

Since $\int_S d\mathbf{m}$ is a constant vector, this vector potential has the same form as the dipole potential (7.86) of Sec. 7.8. We deduce that at sufficient distance, any steady-current circuit produces the field of a magnetic dipole, and that the magnetic dipole moment appropriate to its field is $\mathbf{m} = \int_S d\mathbf{m}$, which by Eq. (7.98) is

$$\mathbf{m} \equiv I \int_S \mathbf{n}\, dS \tag{7.104}$$

This leads us to define expression (7.104) as the magnetic dipole moment of a circuit of arbitrary size and shape. Notice that the circuit need not even lie in a plane. The reader will naturally wonder whether the quantity $\mathbf{m}$ so defined is independent of the arbitrary choice of the surface S bounded by the circuit C. This must be so, for the equivalence of circuit and network from which Eq. (7.103) was derived holds without reference to the particular form of the surface on which the network lies.

It is also not very difficult to show mathematically that the integral in Eq. (7.104) has the same value for all surfaces S bounded by the same curve C. This may be done by considering two possible surfaces for the same circuit C. Let

$$\mathbf{m}' = I \int_{S'} \mathbf{n}'\, dS \tag{7.105}$$

where S' is understood to be another surface bounded by the same circuit C as bounds S of Eq. (7.104) and $\mathbf{n}'$ is understood to be the positive unit normal to S'. For simplicity of proof, consider that S and S' do not intersect, and so form a single closed surface $S + S'$. We have to show that

$$\mathbf{m}' = \mathbf{m} \qquad (7.106)$$

This will be true if and only if the components of the vectors are equal:

$$m'_x = m_x \qquad m'_y = m_y \qquad m'_z = m_z \qquad (7.107)$$

Consider the quantity

$$m'_x - m_x = \mathbf{i} \cdot (\mathbf{m}' - \mathbf{m}) = I \left(\int_{S'} \mathbf{i} \cdot \mathbf{n}' \, dS - \int_{S} \mathbf{i} \cdot \mathbf{n} \, dS \right) \qquad (7.108)$$

where $\mathbf{i}$ is unit vector in the x direction. Now let the outward normal to the combined surface $S + S'$ be $\mathbf{n}_0$. Then, depending on the sense of the current I around the circuit C, either

$$\mathbf{n} = \mathbf{n}_0 \qquad \text{and} \qquad \mathbf{n}' = -\mathbf{n}_0 \qquad (7.109a)$$

or

$$\mathbf{n} = -\mathbf{n}_0 \qquad \text{and} \qquad \mathbf{n}' = \mathbf{n}_0 \qquad (7.109b)$$

It is helpful to the understanding of what a positive normal is to verify these relations (see Sec. 7.7). Therefore

$$m'_x - m_x = \pm I \int_{S+S'} \mathbf{i} \cdot \mathbf{n}_0 \, dS \qquad (7.110)$$

Application of the divergence theorem, for which cf. Sec. 7.6, leads at once to

$$m'_x - m_x = 0 \qquad (7.111)$$

since $\mathbf{i}$ is a constant vector. In this way the other relations (7.107) are to be proved also. Equation (7.106) is thus verified, and it has been shown that the dipole moment $\mathbf{m}$ of Eq. (7.104) is a characteristic only of the circuit C and the current flowing.

7.10. Magnetic Scalar Potential. It has been shown in Sec. 7.8 that the induction $\mathbf{B}$ of a magnetic dipole has the same functional form as the electric field of an electric dipole. It must therefore be possible to derive the dipole magnetic field from a scalar potential function of the same type as the electrostatic potential of an electric dipole. We shall define the magnetic scalar potential U^* in general, for empty space, as a scalar point function which yields the magnetic induction by the formula $\mathbf{B} = -\mu_0 \, \mathrm{grad} \, U^*$, that is,

$$B_x = -\mu_0 \frac{\partial U^*}{\partial x} \qquad B_y = -\mu_0 \frac{\partial U^*}{\partial y} \qquad B_z = -\mu_0 \frac{\partial U^*}{\partial z} \qquad (7.112)$$

Comparison with the corresponding set of equations for electrostatics, Eq. (1.33), shows that we have here introduced arbitrarily the dimensional constant μ_0 where there was no constant in electrostatics. This is for the present purely a matter of convention, but it will appear reasonable after the discussion of magnetic materials in Chap. 9. Now by comparing the equations of the electric dipole in Sec. 1.13 with the field of the magnetic dipole in Sec. 7.8 it is seen that the scalar potential U^*_1 of the magnetic dipole is

$$U^*_1 = \frac{\mathbf{m} \cdot \mathbf{r}}{4\pi r^3} = \frac{m \cos \theta}{4\pi r^2} \qquad (7.113)$$

This equation has been written both in vector form and in spherical coordinates, θ being the angle between the dipole moment $\mathbf{m}$ and the radius vector $\mathbf{r}$ to the observer.

By the network theorem of the preceding section, the magnetic induction of a current loop C at any point outside the wire is expressible as a sum of dipole fields. It must therefore be possible to express the field of C in terms of a magnetic scalar potential. The form of this potential is readily found. By Eq. (7.98) the dipole moment of an element of the equivalent network is

$$d\mathbf{m} = I\mathbf{n}\, dS \tag{7.98}$$

Here dS is an element of area of the arbitrary surface S, bounded by C, in which the equivalent network lies, $\mathbf{n}$ is the unit normal to S at dS, and I is the current in C. The scalar potential of this elementary dipole is

$$dU^* = \frac{d\mathbf{m} \cdot \mathbf{r}}{4\pi r^3} = \frac{I}{4\pi}\frac{\mathbf{n} \cdot \mathbf{r}}{r^3}\, dS \tag{7.114}$$

at a point of observation whose vector position relative to the element dS is $\mathbf{r}$. The scalar potential of the entire circuit C is found by integration over S:

$$U^* = \frac{I}{4\pi}\int_S \frac{\mathbf{n} \cdot \mathbf{r}}{r^3}\, dS \tag{7.115}$$

Now the quantity $(\mathbf{n} \cdot \mathbf{r}/r^3)\, dS$ of Eq. (7.115) is the negative of the element of solid angle $d\Omega$ subtended by the area element dS at the observer:

$$d\Omega = -\frac{\mathbf{n} \cdot \mathbf{r}}{r^3}\, dS \tag{7.116}$$

This is like Eq. (1.56), Sec. 1.9, where the concept of solid angle is discussed in detail. The negative sign by which Eq. (7.116) differs from (1.56) is due to the fact that here the vector $\mathbf{r}$ is taken from dS to the observer, while there the same symbol refers to the opposite vector. Note that both here and in Chap. 1 an element dS subtends a positive solid angle when the observer is situated on the side opposite to the unit normal $\mathbf{n}$. The total solid angle subtended by the surface S is the negative of the integral in Eq. (7.115):

$$\Omega = -\int_S \frac{\mathbf{n} \cdot \mathbf{r}}{r^3}\, dS \tag{7.117}$$

In terms of the solid angle subtended by its associated surface, the magnetic scalar potential of the current circuit C may now be written

$$U^* = -\frac{I\Omega}{4\pi} \tag{7.118}$$

These functions U^* and Ω have mathematical characteristics whose consequences are of great importance in magnetic analysis. For one thing, these functions are discontinuous at any point on the surface S. Since S is an arbitrary surface bounded by C, the discontinuity of U^* at S does not imply a discontinuity of the magnetic field at S; hence U^* ceases to be a valid potential function at S, that is, it no longer yields **B** when used in Eq. (7.112). This must not surprise us, for the whole derivation of Eq. (7.115) breaks down if the observation point is located on the surface S formed by the equivalent network, inasmuch as there are then loops of the network so near the observer that their field is no longer of the dipole type. Another property of the functions U^* and Ω is that they are multiple-valued. Their value for a given observation point and circuit C depends upon the form of the surface S, not continuously but to the extent of an integral multiple of a constant. The multiple-valued property of Ω is entirely analogous to that of the trigonometric angle in a plane, whose values differ by integral multiples of the whole plane angle of 2π radians. The whole solid angle is 4π steradians, and the values of Ω differ by integral multiples of 4π steradians. This means that the values of U^* differ by integral multiples of I. Thus if we adopt principal values Ω_0 of the function Ω, for example, in the range

$$-2\pi < \Omega_0 \leqq +2\pi \quad (7.119)$$

then any value of Ω is given by

$$\Omega = \Omega_0 + n(4\pi)$$
$$n = 0, \pm 1, \pm 2, \ldots \quad (7.120)$$

Likewise the principal values U_0^* of the magnetic scalar potential would lie in the corresponding range

$$-\frac{I}{2} \leqq U_0^* < \frac{I}{2} \quad (7.121)$$

Any possible value of U^* is then

$$U^* = U_0^* + nI$$
$$n = 0, \pm 1, \pm 2, \ldots \quad (7.122)$$

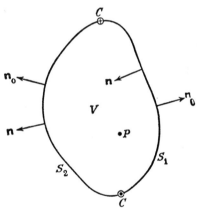

FIG. 7.12. Trace of a circuit and two different surfaces which it bounds.

We shall not attempt to give a thorough discussion of the multiple-valued functions Ω and U^*, but it may be helpful to examine some simple geometric situations. Figure 7.12 represents a circuit C and two different surfaces S_1 and S_2 bounded by C, shown as they intersect the plane of the figure. The current I in C is directed up from the page at the bottom of the figure, and down into the page at the top. The surfaces S_1 and S_2 are chosen so as not to intersect one another, and consequently they enclose a simple volume V. When the point of observation P is within V, the two surfaces yield values of Ω differing by 4π steradians:

$$\Omega_2 - \Omega_1 = 4\pi \qquad \text{observer in } V \qquad (7.123)$$

This is easily shown by reference to Sec. 1.9. If $\mathbf{n}_0$ is a unit normal to the surface of V, directed always outward to V, then we may use Eq. (1.62), remembering that the sign must be changed because of the reversed significance of the vector $\mathbf{r}$:

$$\oint_{S_1+S_2} \frac{\mathbf{n}_0 \cdot \mathbf{r}}{r^3} \, dS = -4\pi \qquad (7.124)$$

for an observer inside the closed surface $S_1 + S_2$. But on S_2 the positive normal $\mathbf{n}$ relative to the sense of the current in C is the same as $\mathbf{n}_0$, while on S_1, $\mathbf{n}$ is inward and is the negative of $\mathbf{n}_0$. Thus

$$\oint_{S_1+S_2} \frac{\mathbf{n}_0 \cdot \mathbf{r}}{r^3} \, dS = \int_{S_2} \frac{\mathbf{n} \cdot \mathbf{r}}{r^3} \, dS - \int_{S_1} \frac{\mathbf{n} \cdot \mathbf{r}}{r^3} \, dS \qquad (7.125)$$

Using Eqs. (7.117) and (7.124) in (7.125), we obtain (7.123). Q.E.D. It is left to the reader to show similarly that if the observer P is outside V, the two surfaces S_1 and S_2 yield identical values of Ω:

$$\Omega_2 = \Omega_1 \qquad \text{observer outside } V \qquad (7.126)$$

From the foregoing theorems, it follows immediately that the discontinuity of Ω at the surface used to compute Ω is 4π steradians. For, if P is conceived to pass through S_1 from the inside to the outside of V, the angle Ω_1 changes discontinuously from $\Omega_2 - 4\pi$ to Ω_2 steradians. Since Ω_2 is continuous at S_1, the discontinuity of Ω_1 is $+4\pi$ steradians as P crosses S_1 from the side of its positive normal $\mathbf{n}$ to the other side. Q.E.D.

The foregoing analysis of the functions Ω and U^* can be used to yield a rather general proof of Ampère's circuital law of Sec. 7.7. Consider the line integral of the magnetic induction $\mathbf{B}$ due to a simple circuit *in vacuo*. This may be written, for terminal points P_1 and P_2 and a path of integration L,

$$\left[\int_{P_1}^{P_2} \mathbf{B} \cdot d\mathbf{l} \right]_L = \left[\int_{P_1}^{P_2} (B_x \, dx + B_y \, dy + B_z \, dz) \right]_L \qquad (7.127)$$

Substitution of Eqs. (7.112) into (7.127) yields

$$\left[\int_{P_1}^{P_2} \mathbf{B} \cdot d\mathbf{l} \right]_L = -\mu_0 \left[\int_{P_1}^{P_2} \left(\frac{\partial U^*}{\partial x} \, dx + \frac{\partial U^*}{\partial y} \, dy + \frac{\partial U^*}{\partial z} \, dz \right) \right]_L \qquad (7.128)$$

The integrand of the right-hand member of this equation is simply the total differential dU^*, so that

$$\left[\int_{P_1}^{P_2} \mathbf{B} \cdot d\mathbf{l} \right]_L = -\mu_0 \left[\int_{P_1}^{P_2} dU^* \right]_L = -\mu_0 [U^*(P_2) - U^*(P_1)] \qquad (7.129)$$

It must be remembered that Eqs. (7.128) and (7.129) are only valid if Eq. (7.112) truly represents the vector $\mathbf{B}$ at all points of L; and hence in the use of these equations, L cannot cross the surface S used for computation of Ω. Now consider the special case where L is a closed loop, so that P_1 and P_2 coincide. If L does not link through the circuit C, it is possible to find a fixed surface S which L does not intersect. Thus the values of Ω and of U^* at the beginning and end of the path L are the same, and the result of the integration is zero:

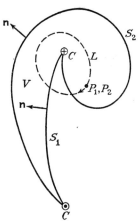

$$\oint_L \mathbf{B} \cdot d\mathbf{l} = 0 \qquad L \text{ not linking } C \qquad (7.130)$$

On the other hand if L links the circuit C once, it must cross any fixed surface S bounded by C. This case may be handled in either one of two ways. U^* may be made continuous throughout L by allowing S to be deformed continuously as the integration proceeds, so that the point of integration carries S before it around C. Figure 7.13 indicates how this may be done. S_1 and S_2 are the initial and final positions of the surface S. Notice that the starting and terminal point P_1 and P_2 of the closed loop L lies within the volume V enclosed by S_1 and S_2. It follows now from Eq. (7.123) that Ω has changed by 4π steradians during the integration. As in Fig. 7.12, it is S_2 whose positive normal is also the outward normal from V;

Fig. 7.13. Initial and final positions of a surface deformed so that the line integration never crosses it.

so we know that the signs are just as in Eq. (7.123). Hence, by Eq. (7.118),

$$U^*(P_2) - U^*(P_1) = -\frac{I}{4\pi}(\Omega_2 - \Omega_1) = -I \qquad (7.131)$$

Substitution of Eq. (7.131) into (7.129) yields now

$$\oint_L \mathbf{B} \cdot d\mathbf{l} = \mu_0 I \qquad L \text{ linking } C \qquad (7.132)$$

The sign of Eq. (7.132) is correct when, as in Fig. 7.13, the sense of integration around the loop L is related to the current sense in C by a right-handed screw relation. As a right-handed screw travels in the sense of the current along C, its threads in their motion about C link C in the positive sense for integration around L.

Another way of deducing Eq. (7.132) is to separate the starting and terminal points of the integration by a small distance Δl, and to pass a fixed surface S, which does not cross L, through Δl (see Fig. 7.14).

Now as $\Delta l \to 0$, the integral over L approaches the closed-path circuital integral over $L + \Delta l$ as its limit, for B remains finite at S. Introduction of the discontinuity of the scalar potential at S then leads to Eq. (7.132). Details are left to the reader.

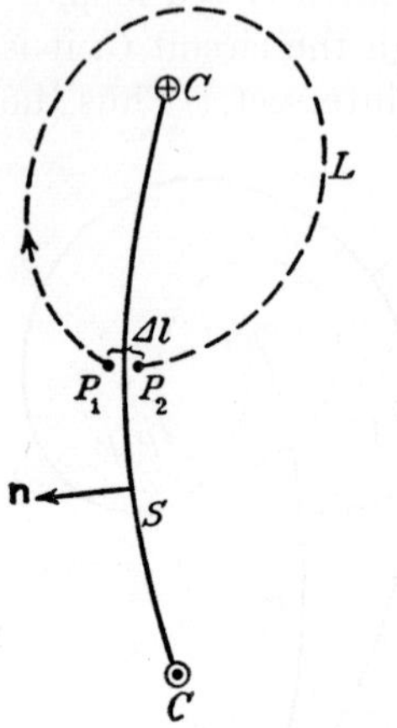

It should now be noted that Eqs. (7.130) and (7.132) are just Ampère's circuital law for empty space, of which the foregoing arguments constitute a general proof. The geometrical picture becomes complicated if the circuit C is in the form of a coil, but the theorem can be generalized by counting once for each turn of C surrounded. Thus, if N turns are linked by L,

$$\oint_L \mathbf{B} \cdot d\mathbf{l} = N\mu_0 I \qquad (7.133)$$

Fig. 7.14. A path of integration which is not quite closed, so that it never crosses the surface S.

To close this section, an example will be given of the use of the magnetic scalar potential as a method of computing the magnetic field of a current circuit. Consider the scalar potential of a circular current loop at a point on its axis. Let x be the coordinate of position on the axis of the loop, the center of the loop being at $x = 0$ (see Fig. 7.15). The sign of the x coordinate is to be such that a right-handed screw turning in the sense of the current I in the loop advances in the sense of positively increasing x. The surface S used for the computation of the scalar potential will be chosen as the plane surface bounded by the loop. The positive normal $\mathbf{n}$ to S is therefore in the direction of increasing x. An appropriate element dS of area is a ring of radius R

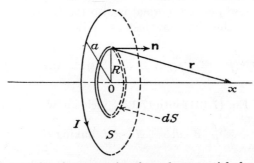

Fig. 7.15. Plane surface for computing the scalar potential of a circular loop.

and width dR. The solid angle subtended by dS at point x is found by application of Eq. (7.116):

$$d\Omega = -\frac{x}{+(x^2 + R^2)^{3/2}} 2\pi R \, dR \qquad (7.134)$$

For a loop of radius a, the solid angle at x is therefore

$$\Omega = -\pi x \int_{R=0}^{a} \frac{2R \, dR}{+(x^2 + R^2)^{3/2}} \qquad (7.135)$$

This expression is readily integrated to yield

$$\Omega = 2\pi x \left[\frac{1}{+\sqrt{x^2 + a^2}} - \frac{1}{+\sqrt{x^2}} \right] \tag{7.136}$$

Notice that the radical is positive throughout the calculation. Equation (7.136) can be rewritten in a manner which makes evident the discontinuity of Ω at the surface S, that is, at $x = 0$:

$$\Omega = 2\pi \left(\frac{x}{+\sqrt{x^2 + a^2}} \mp 1 \right) \tag{7.137}$$

Here the upper sign is to be used when x is positive, and the lower when x is negative. Equation (7.118) now gives the required magnetic scalar potential:

$$U^* = \frac{I}{2} \left(\pm 1 - \frac{x}{\sqrt{x^2 + a^2}} \right) \tag{7.138}$$

The magnetic induction on the axis of the loop has only an x component, as is evident from symmetry, and its value may be found at once by using the potential (7.138) in Eq. (7.112):

$$B_x = -\mu_0 \frac{\partial U^*}{\partial x} = \frac{\mu_0}{2} \frac{Ia^2}{(x^2 + a^2)^{3/2}} \tag{7.139}$$

This result agrees with Eq. (7.38), Sec. 7.4.

7.11. Differential Form of the Circuital Law. Ampère's circuital law implies a differential equation which is obeyed by the magnetic induction vector at every point of empty space or in a nonmagnetic medium. To derive this relation, we shall apply the circuital law first to a small rectangular path of integration C, with sides a and b parallel to the x and y axes (see Fig. 7.16). Let $P(x_0, y_0, z_0)$ be the corner point where the algebraic values of x and y are the lowest. The line integral of $\mathbf{B}$ around the path in the sense of the arrow is

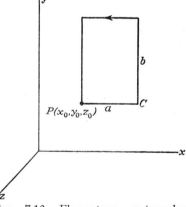

FIG. 7.16. Elementary, rectangular path of integration

$$\oint \mathbf{B} \cdot d\mathbf{l} = \int_{x_0}^{x_0+a} [B_x(x, y_0, z_0)$$
$$- B_x(x, y_0 + b, z_0)] \, dx$$
$$+ \int_{y_0}^{y_0+b} [B_y(x_0 + a, y, z_0)$$
$$- B_y(x_0, y, z_0)] \, dy \tag{7.140}$$

Now for small values of a and b the integrals of Eq. (7.140) can be evaluated by expanding the field components B_x and B_y in Taylor's series:

$$B_x = B_x(x_0, y_0, z_0) + \left(\frac{\partial B_x}{\partial x}\right)_0 (x - x_0) + \left(\frac{\partial B_x}{\partial y}\right)_0 (y - y_0)$$
$$+ \left(\frac{\partial B_x}{\partial z}\right)_0 (z - z_0) + \text{higher-order terms} \quad (7.141a)$$

$$B_y = B_y(x_0, y_0, z_0) + \left(\frac{\partial B_y}{\partial x}\right)_0 (x - x_0) + \left(\frac{\partial B_y}{\partial y}\right)_0 (y - y_0)$$
$$+ \left(\frac{\partial B_y}{\partial z}\right)_0 (z - z_0) + \text{higher-order terms} \quad (7.141b)$$

It is understood in these expansions that the derivatives are evaluated at the fixed point $P(x_0, y_0, z_0)$. Application of Eqs. (7.141) to (7.140) yields

$$\oint_C \mathbf{B} \cdot d\mathbf{l} \doteq \int_{x_0}^{x_0+a} - \left(\frac{\partial B_x}{\partial y}\right) b \, dx + \int_{y_0}^{y_0+b} \left(\frac{\partial B_y}{\partial x}\right) a \, dy = ab \left(\frac{\partial B_y}{\partial x} - \frac{\partial B_x}{\partial y}\right)$$
$$(7.142)$$

Equation (7.142) becomes exact in the limit as $a \to 0$ and $b \to 0$.

Let us now suppose that any electric current in the neighborhood of $P(x_0, y_0, z_0)$ is describable by a continuous current density function $\mathbf{J}(x, y, z)$. The current through the rectangular path over which the line integral of $\mathbf{B}$ is (7.142), is

$$I_C = \int_{y_0}^{y_0+b} \int_{x_0}^{x_0+a} J_z \, dx \, dy \quad (7.143)$$

where J_z is the z component of $\mathbf{J}$. This current has been written so as to have a positive sense relative to the sense of the line integral. Ampère's circuital law (Sec. 7.7) now states that for any region not occupied by magnetic material:

$$\oint_C \mathbf{B} \cdot d\mathbf{l} = \mu_0 I_C \quad (7.68)$$

We may evaluate I_C for the small rectangular loop by expanding J_z in a Taylor's series about the point $P(x_0, y_0, z_0)$:

$$J_z = J_z(x_0, y_0, z_0) + \left(\frac{\partial J_z}{\partial x}\right)(x - x_0) + \left(\frac{\partial J_z}{\partial y}\right)(y - y_0)$$
$$+ \left(\frac{\partial J_z}{\partial z}\right)(z - z_0) + \text{higher-order terms} \quad (7.144)$$

To obtain the limiting value of I_C as $a \to 0$ and $b \to 0$, only the zero-order term of Eq. (7.144) need be substituted into (7.143):

$$I_C \doteq J_z(x_0, y_0, z_0) \int_{y_0}^{y_0+b} \int_{x_0}^{x_0+a} dx \, dy = ab J_z \quad (7.145)$$

Finally, substitution of Eqs. (7.142) and (7.145) into (7.68) gives the differential relation we have been seeking:

$$\frac{\partial B_y}{\partial x} - \frac{\partial B_x}{\partial y} = \mu_0 J_z \qquad (7.146a)$$

This equation is not approximate but exact, since (7.145) as well as (7.142) becomes exact in the limit $a \to 0$ and $b \to 0$. It holds at any point not in a magnetic material. By symmetry we may write two similar equations, which can be obtained in the same manner by choosing loops of integration parallel to the yz and zx planes:

$$\frac{\partial B_z}{\partial y} - \frac{\partial B_y}{\partial z} = \mu_0 J_x \qquad (7.146b)$$

$$\frac{\partial B_x}{\partial z} - \frac{\partial B_z}{\partial x} = \mu_0 J_y \qquad (7.146c)$$

In vector terminology, the left-hand members of these three equations are defined as the components of the **curl** of the vector **B**. Thus

$$\text{curl } \mathbf{B} = \mu_0 \mathbf{J} \qquad (7.147)$$

For a point where there is no current density, Eqs. (7.146) reduce to

$$\frac{\partial B_y}{\partial x} - \frac{\partial B_x}{\partial y} = 0 \qquad \frac{\partial B_x}{\partial z} - \frac{\partial B_z}{\partial x} = 0 \qquad \frac{\partial B_z}{\partial y} - \frac{\partial B_y}{\partial z} = 0 \quad (7.148)$$

Equations (7.146) and (7.148) are an important commentary on our work with the magnetic scalar potential. Suppose **B** can be written as proportional to the gradient of a scalar potential function, as in Eq. (7.112), Sec. 7.10,

$$B_x = -\mu_0 \frac{\partial U^*}{\partial x} \qquad B_y = -\mu_0 \frac{\partial U^*}{\partial y} \qquad B_z = -\mu_0 \frac{\partial U^*}{\partial z} \quad (7.112)$$

Such a field then identically fulfills Eq. (7.148), as appears at once when (7.112) is substituted into (7.148). But Eqs. (7.148) hold only at points where the current density **J** is zero. It follows that the field **B** can be derived from a scalar potential function only in regions where $\mathbf{J} \equiv 0$. In addition, all our present work is limited to regions not containing magnetic materials.

The converse theorem, namely, that if Eqs. (7.148) hold in a region of space, then the magnetic induction may always be expressed by (7.112), is possible but demands somewhat detailed consideration. We used such a theorem for the electrostatic field in Sec. 1.5 but there the electric field obeyed relations like (7.148) in all space whereas here the field **B** obeys (7.146) inside a wire carrying current. It turns out that this is an important distinction, and it has the consequence that the electrostatic potential function is single-valued in all space, outside of an additive constant, while the magnetic potential function of a current circuit must be multiple-valued. The reader is referred to standard texts of advanced calculus for detailed discussion of this matter under the heading of line integrals.

7.12. Force and Torque on a Current Circuit. Let us investigate the

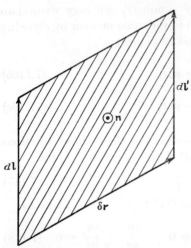

mechanical work done by a current circuit when it moves in a magnetic field. By this means, important formulas may be obtained for the magnetic force and torque on the circuit. Suppose a circuit C to be displaced, rotated or deformed to an infinitesimal extent. This is to mean that it is possible to associate with every element $d\mathbf{l}$ of the original configuration of the circuit an element $d\mathbf{l}'$ of the new configuration such that $d\mathbf{l}'$ differs from $d\mathbf{l}$ in direction at most by an infinitesimal angle, and by a second order infinitesimal in length. It will also mean that the vector $\delta\mathbf{r}$ from $d\mathbf{l}$ to $d\mathbf{l}'$ is an infinitesimal (see Fig. 7.17). If $d\mathbf{F}$ is the magnetic force on $d\mathbf{l}$, the work resulting from the displacement of $d\mathbf{l}$ into the position of $d\mathbf{l}'$ is

FIG. 7.17. Area swept out by a circuit element during a displacement or deformation of the circuit.

$$d(\delta W) = \delta\mathbf{r} \cdot d\mathbf{F} \tag{7.149}$$

But, from Sec. 7.2,

$$d\mathbf{F} = I \, d\mathbf{l} \times \mathbf{B} \tag{7.1}$$

where $\mathbf{B}$ is the magnetic induction vector at $d\mathbf{l}$ and I is the current in C. Thus

$$d(\delta W) = I \, \delta\mathbf{r} \cdot d\mathbf{l} \times \mathbf{B} \tag{7.150}$$

The combination of a cross product and dot product in Eq. (7.150) is called the scalar triple product of the three vectors. It is shown in elementary vector analysis that this quantity is unchanged by cyclic permutation of the vectors. Therefore we can write

$$d(\delta W) = I\mathbf{B} \cdot \delta\mathbf{r} \times d\mathbf{l} \tag{7.151}$$

Now the cross product $\delta\mathbf{r} \times d\mathbf{l}$ has a simple geometric interpretation. It has the magnitude of the area swept out by $d\mathbf{l}$ in the displacement $\delta\mathbf{r}$ and the direction of the unit normal $\mathbf{n}$ to this area. In Fig. 7.17 the sense of the normal n is up out of the paper. Thus $\mathbf{B} \cdot \delta\mathbf{r} \times d\mathbf{l}$ is an element of magnetic flux swept through by the circuit element $d\mathbf{l}$ in its motion. The integral over the circuit C,

$$\oint_C \mathbf{B} \cdot \delta\mathbf{r} \times d\mathbf{l} = \delta\Phi \tag{7.152}$$

represents flux $\delta\Phi$ through the ribbonlike area δA swept out by the whole circuit in its motion. This flux is related positively to the sense of current in the displaced circuit C' according to the sign rule of Sec. 7.6, as can be seen from Fig. 7.17. Now let A be a surface whose bounding curve is the circuit C in its original position. The surface $A + \delta A$ is then a surface completely bounded by the displaced circuit C'. The total magnetic flux Φ through C is that which passes through A, while the flux through C' passes through $A + \delta A$. Thus the $\delta\Phi$ of Eq. (7.152) is the additional flux through C', or the increment of flux through C due to its motion. This is to be compared with the total work done by the magnetic forces during the displacement of the circuit as obtained by integration of Eq. (7.151) over C:

$$\delta W = I \oint_C \mathbf{B} \cdot \delta\mathbf{r} \times d\mathbf{l} \tag{7.153}$$

It follows that the work done by the circuit is related to the increment of flux through it by the simple and important equation

$$\delta W = I \, \delta\Phi \tag{7.154}$$

A useful general deduction from Eq. (7.154) is that the magnetic force and torque on a current circuit are in such a direction and sense as to increase algebraically the flux through the circuit, since motion in the sense of the force or torque causes positive work δW to be done. It is understood in this statement that the positive sense for the flux is taken to correspond to the sense of current flow in the circuit by the rule of Sec. 7.6. Equation (7.154) may be used also to compute quantitatively the forces and torques on C. The flux Φ will be supposed to be expressed as a function of variables describing the position and orientation of C. In particular, let x be a coordinate describing pure translation of C in a certain direction, and let θ be an angle describing rotation of C about a certain axis. The work done by the circuit during an infinitesimal translation δx is then

$$\delta W = F_x \, \delta x = I \frac{\partial\Phi}{\partial x} \, \delta x \tag{7.155}$$

Hence the component of force in the x direction is

$$F_x = I \frac{\partial\Phi}{\partial x} \tag{7.156}$$

Similarly, the torque about the θ axis is

$$L_\theta = I \frac{\partial \Phi}{\partial \theta} \qquad (7.157)$$

Whenever Eqs. (7.156) and (7.157) are applied to a circuit carrying steady current, the magnetic field directly produced by the circuit itself may be excluded from the computation of the magnetic flux. This is possible because the circuit exerts no total force or torque on itself; all internal forces and torques balance out to zero. If this were not so, an isolated circuit carrying steady current would spontaneously develop linear or angular momentum, which is contrary to conservation of energy and is not observed to occur. It will be understood therefore in these equations that the flux Φ may be, and usually is, just that produced by sources external to the circuit. In fact, if the self-field were to be included in the computation of Φ, a more careful argument than the foregoing would be necessary, for the force law (7.1) assumes that the field of $d\mathbf{l}$ itself is excluded. Furthermore, unless a finite diameter of the wire is assumed, the self-linked flux of a circuit is infinite. We do not need to pursue such a detailed argument except for problems concerning circuit deformations, and these will not be considered.

As an example of the use of these equations, suppose a current loop to have the form of any plane figure with an area A, and to be located in a uniform external field $\mathbf{B}$. Let the loop be mounted so as to be free to rotate about an axis parallel to its plane and perpendicular to $\mathbf{B}$, and let the angle of rotation θ about this axis be measured from the position where the positive normal $\mathbf{n}$ to the circuit has the direction and sense of $\mathbf{B}$. The externally produced magnetic flux is then

$$\Phi = BA \cos \theta \qquad (7.158)$$

Hence the torque about the axis is, by Eq. (7.157),

$$L = -IBA \sin \theta \qquad (7.159)$$

The negative sign in Eq. (7.159) shows that the torque has the opposite algebraic sense to θ when $-\pi < \theta < \pi$; that is, the torque tends to bring θ to zero and hence to maximize the magnetic flux. The power of Eq. (7.157) may be appreciated by trying to check (7.159) by direct integration of the torque due to the force on each element of some particular circuit, even in such a simple case as that of a circular loop.

If the circuit C is in the form of a coil or solenoid of N turns, through every turn of which the externally produced flux has the same value ϕ, the total flux through C is

$$\Phi = N\phi \qquad (7.160)$$

Thus for instance, a solenoid of N turns and cross-sectional area a

experiences in a uniform external field **B** a torque

$$L = -INaB \sin \theta \qquad (7.161)$$

about an axis perpendicular to **B** and to the longitudinal axis of the solenoid.

7.13. Force and Couple on a Magnetic Dipole. Special equations may be written for the force and torque on a current circuit whose dimensions are small compared to the inhomogeneities of the external magnetic field in which it is located. The only characteristic of the circuit which enters these expressions is its dipole moment, as defined in Sec. 7.9:

$$\mathbf{m} \equiv I \int_S \mathbf{n} \, dS \qquad (7.104)$$

Here I is the current of the circuit, S is an arbitrary surface bounded by the circuit, and **n** is the positive unit normal to S. The circuit may therefore be called a magnetic dipole for the purposes of this section. The formulas to be developed are basic to the study of forces and torques on specimens of magnetized matter.

In the preceding section, an expression was derived for the mechanical work done by a current circuit when the magnetic flux Φ through it changes as a result of its motion:

$$\delta W = I \, \delta \Phi \qquad (7.154)$$

Let us suppose that the current I in the circuit is held constant. Equation (7.154) may then be rewritten in the form

$$\delta W = \delta(I\Phi) \qquad (7.162)$$

Now consider the quantity $I\Phi$. By definition of the magnetic flux through a circuit,

$$I\Phi = I \int_S \mathbf{B} \cdot \mathbf{n} \, dS \qquad (7.163)$$

where S is any surface bounded by the circuit and **n** is the positive unit normal to S. We shall understand **B** to be the externally produced magnetic induction only, for we are concerned with total force and torque on the circuit.

Now if the magnetic induction vector **B** varies only slightly over the surface S bounded by the circuit, it may be treated as a constant and withdrawn from the integral sign in Eq. (7.163) to yield the approximate equation

$$I\Phi \doteq \mathbf{B} \cdot \left[I \int_S \mathbf{n} \, dS \right] \qquad (7.164)$$

This operation is valid since the dot product is distributive and since an integral is the limit of a sum. The remaining vector integral multiplied by the current I is just the magnetic dipole moment of Eq. (7.104). Thus

$$I\Phi \doteq \mathbf{m} \cdot \mathbf{B} \tag{7.165}$$

Equation (7.165) becomes exact in the limit as the circuit and its associated surface S become indefinitely small in size compared to the inhomogeneities of the $\mathbf{B}$ vector in the neighborhood. This limiting case will be called that of the magnetic dipole:

$$I\Phi = \mathbf{m} \cdot \mathbf{B} \qquad \text{magnetic dipole} \tag{7.166}$$

If Eq. (7.166) is used in (7.162), it appears that the mechanical work done by a magnetic dipole during its motion is

$$\delta W = \delta(\mathbf{m} \cdot \mathbf{B}) \tag{7.167}$$

In the usual applications of Eq. (7.167), the dipole moment $\mathbf{m}$ will be considered to have a constant magnitude m and to change its direction only as a result of rotation of the entire circuit. This will be the case when the circuit is rigid, for we have already required the current I to be constant.

Let us apply Eq. (7.167) first to the case of a pure translation without rotation of the dipole. The vector $\mathbf{m}$ is then constant, but the quantity $\mathbf{m} \cdot \mathbf{B}$ is a function of the coordinates because $\mathbf{B}$ is a vector point function. Suppose an infinitesimal translation $\delta \mathbf{r}$ occurs which in terms of cartesian coordinates and unit vectors is

$$\delta \mathbf{r} = \mathbf{i}\, \delta x + \mathbf{j}\, \delta y + \mathbf{k}\, \delta z \tag{7.168}$$

The variation of the function $\mathbf{m} \cdot \mathbf{B}$ during the translation is

$$\delta(\mathbf{m} \cdot \mathbf{B}) = \frac{\partial}{\partial x}(\mathbf{m} \cdot \mathbf{B})\, \delta x + \frac{\partial}{\partial y}(\mathbf{m} \cdot \mathbf{B})\, \delta y + \frac{\partial}{\partial z}(\mathbf{m} \cdot \mathbf{B})\, \delta z \tag{7.169}$$

by the rules of the partial differential calculus. The mechanical work done by the magnetic force, $\mathbf{F} = \mathbf{i}F_x + \mathbf{j}F_y + \mathbf{k}F_z$, acting on the dipole is

$$\delta W = \mathbf{F} \cdot \delta \mathbf{r} = F_x\, \delta x + F_y\, \delta y + F_z\, \delta z \tag{7.170}$$

Substitution of Eqs. (7.169) and (7.170) into (7.167) yields

$$F_x\, \delta x + F_y\, \delta y + F_z\, \delta z = \frac{\partial}{\partial x}(\mathbf{m} \cdot \mathbf{B})\, \delta x + \frac{\partial}{\partial y}(\mathbf{m} \cdot \mathbf{B})\, \delta y$$
$$+ \frac{\partial}{\partial z}(\mathbf{m} \cdot \mathbf{B})\, \delta z \tag{7.171}$$

Since the coordinate variations δx, δy, and δz are entirely independent, their coefficients on the two sides of Eq. (7.171) must be, respectively, equal. This may be seen at once by setting any pair of the coordinate variations equal to zero and letting the third remain finite. In this way, Eq. (7.171) yields the cartesian force components

$$F_x = \frac{\partial}{\partial x} (\mathbf{m} \cdot \mathbf{B})$$

$$F_y = \frac{\partial}{\partial y} (\mathbf{m} \cdot \mathbf{B}) \qquad (7.172)$$

$$F_z = \frac{\partial}{\partial z} (\mathbf{m} \cdot \mathbf{B})$$

Since $\mathbf{m}$ is a constant vector, Eqs. (7.172) may be expanded in terms of the cartesian components of the two vectors $\mathbf{m}$ and $\mathbf{B}$, as follows:

$$F_x = m_x \frac{\partial B_x}{\partial x} + m_y \frac{\partial B_y}{\partial x} + m_z \frac{\partial B_z}{\partial x}$$

$$F_y = m_x \frac{\partial B_x}{\partial y} + m_y \frac{\partial B_y}{\partial y} + m_z \frac{\partial B_z}{\partial y} \qquad (7.173)$$

$$F_z = m_x \frac{\partial B_x}{\partial z} + m_y \frac{\partial B_y}{\partial z} + m_z \frac{\partial B_z}{\partial z}$$

It is useful for future reference to transform Eqs. (7.173) into a set of equations which is less general but is valid for a magnetic dipole situated in empty space. According to Sec. 7.11, the magnetic induction vector in empty space satisfies the differential equations

$$\frac{\partial B_y}{\partial x} = \frac{\partial B_x}{\partial y} \qquad \frac{\partial B_z}{\partial y} = \frac{\partial B_y}{\partial z} \qquad \frac{\partial B_x}{\partial z} = \frac{\partial B_z}{\partial x} \qquad (7.174)$$

If these relations are substituted into Eqs. (7.173), the resulting equations for the force components on the magnetic dipole are

$$F_x = m_x \frac{\partial B_x}{\partial x} + m_y \frac{\partial B_x}{\partial y} + m_z \frac{\partial B_x}{\partial z}$$

$$F_y = m_x \frac{\partial B_y}{\partial x} + m_y \frac{\partial B_y}{\partial y} + m_z \frac{\partial B_y}{\partial z} \qquad \text{in empty space} \quad (7.175)$$

$$F_z = m_x \frac{\partial B_z}{\partial x} + m_y \frac{\partial B_z}{\partial y} + m_z \frac{\partial B_z}{\partial z}$$

It appears from Eqs. (7.175) that any one of the force components may be derived entirely from the field component in the same direction.

Equation (7.167) may be used to compute the couple exerted by a magnetic field on a magnetic dipole by considering a pure rotation of the dipole. If there is no translation of the dipole, it is the vector $\mathbf{B}$ which now remains constant during the motion of the dipole, while the vector $\mathbf{m}$ changes its direction. If $\mathbf{m}$ is drawn from a fixed point, its tip describes a circle during a rotation of the dipole, as shown in Fig. 7.18. Let an infinitesimal rotation be described by a vector $\delta\boldsymbol{\theta}$ whose magnitude $\delta\theta$ gives the amount of the rotation in radians and which is directed along the axis of rotation in the sense of advance of a right-handed screw. It will be seen from the figure that the corresponding increment $\delta\mathbf{m}$ of the dipole moment is perpendicular to the plane of $\mathbf{m}$ and $\delta\boldsymbol{\theta}$, and has a magnitude

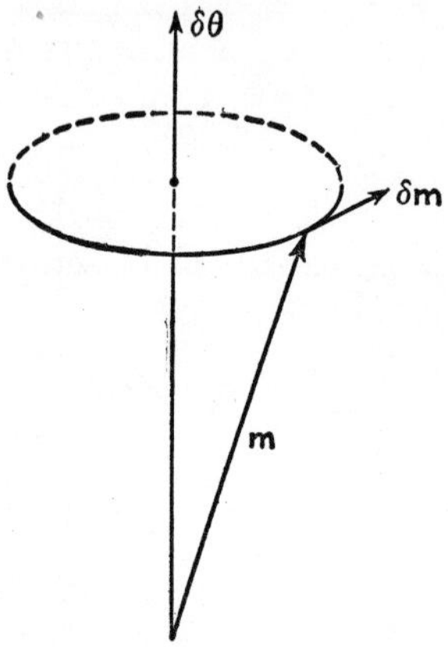

$$\delta m = m \, \delta\theta \sin (\delta\boldsymbol{\theta},\mathbf{m}) \qquad (7.176)$$

The vector $\delta\mathbf{m}$ is completely described, with the correct sense, by the cross product

$$\delta\mathbf{m} = (\delta\boldsymbol{\theta}) \times \mathbf{m} \qquad (7.177)$$

Because $\mathbf{B}$ is constant, Eq. (7.167) gives for the work done by the rotation of the dipole the expression

$$\delta W = (\delta\mathbf{m}) \cdot \mathbf{B} \qquad (7.178)$$

Using Eq. (7.177) in (7.178), we obtain

$$\delta W = \delta\boldsymbol{\theta} \times \mathbf{m} \cdot \mathbf{B} \qquad (7.179)$$

FIG. 7.18. Effect of rotation on a vector dipole moment.

This scalar triple product may be transformed by cyclic permutation of its factors into

$$\delta W = \mathbf{m} \times \mathbf{B} \cdot \delta\boldsymbol{\theta} \qquad (7.180)$$

Equation (7.180) is to be compared with the statement from mechanics that the work done by a vector couple $\mathbf{L}$ during an infinitesimal rotation $\delta\boldsymbol{\theta}$ is

$$\delta W = \mathbf{L} \cdot \delta\boldsymbol{\theta} \qquad (7.181)$$

Since Eqs. (7.180) and (7.181) must agree for any infinitesimal rotation $\delta\boldsymbol{\theta}$, the quantity $\mathbf{m} \times \mathbf{B}$ may be identified as the vector couple experienced by a magnetic dipole:

$$\mathbf{L} = \mathbf{m} \times \mathbf{B} \qquad (7.182)$$

PROBLEMS

7.1. Values of magnetic induction in air of the order of 1 mks unit are not difficult to obtain. What is the force in pounds per inch length of a wire carrying 4 amp and running perpendicular to this magnetic field?

7.2. Show how the components of the magnetic induction vector at a point can be deduced from measurements of the vector force on a current element in two fixed orientations at right angles to each other.

7.3. The vector product is not commutative but is distributive.

a. Show then how to express the product $\mathbf{a} \times \mathbf{b}$ in terms of cartesian components.

b. Deduce an expression for the square of the sine of the angle between two vectors in terms of the cartesian components of these vectors.

Ans. (b) $\sin^2\theta = 1 - \dfrac{(a_x b_x + a_y b_y + a_z b_z)^2}{(a_x{}^2 + a_y{}^2 + a_z{}^2)(b_x{}^2 + b_y{}^2 + b_z{}^2)}.$

7.4. A current element $I \, dl$ in a magnetic field is slowly rotated about its perpendicular bisector, which has a fixed direction in space at an angle θ to the magnetic induction vector **B**. What are the maximum and minimum values of the magnitude of the magnetic force on the element during a revolution? Through what angle is dl rotated between a position of minimum force and that of the next maximum?

7.5. Suppose that in a certain locality the horizontal component of the earth's magnetic induction is due north and has an intensity of 2.0×10^{-5} weber/m^2, while the magnetic inclination is 70°, that is, the **B** vector points 70° down from the horizontal. What is the magnitude and direction of the magnetic force on a 100-ft horizontal span of wire carrying 20 amp, if the wire runs (a) due north? (b) due east?

7.6. A straight wire of length L carrying current I lies on a horizontal table, subject to the uniform magnetic field **B** of the earth. Suppose that the wire can be rotated at will on the table and that the horizontal component of force on it can be measured in any position, but that the vertical component of force is not measured. Describe how to find from this apparatus the magnitude and direction of the earth's magnetic field. The direction is specified by the compass direction of the plane of the magnetic meridian, *i.e.*, the plane containing **B** and the vertical, and by the dip angle, which is the angle between **B** and the horizontal in its meridian plane.

7.7. Show mathematically that the total magnetic force is zero on any closed circuit carrying steady current and located in an external magnetic field which is uniform.

7.8. The velocity of a charged particle may be determined by allowing it to travel normally to the plane of mutually perpendicular electric and magnetic fields and adjusting the field strengths for no deviation from a straight trajectory. Suppose $B = \frac{1}{10}$ weber/m^2, while the perpendicular electric field is obtained between parallel plates $\frac{1}{2}$ cm apart at a potential difference of 300 volts. What is the speed of the undeviated particles?

7.9. Show that if a particle of charge q and relativistic mass m moves in a plane perpendicular to a uniform magnetic field with a momentum $\mathbf{p} = m\mathbf{v}$, its trajectory in the absence of other forces is a circle of radius R such that the product BR equals the ratio of the magnitude of the momentum to the charge. The dynamical equation of relativity is given as $\mathbf{f} = d\mathbf{p}/dt$, where **f** is the force on the particle. Check units through the equation $BR = p/q$.

7.10. Show that in a uniform magnetic field **B** and in the absence of an electric field or of other forces, a particle of charge q and relativistic mass m moves in a spiral such that its velocity parallel to the field is constant, while projected on a plane normal to the field it executes uniform circular motion with period $T = 2\pi m/qB$. The only relativity you need know is that the appropriate dynamical equation is $\mathbf{f} = (d/dt)(m\mathbf{v})$, where **v** is the vector velocity of the particle and **f** the force on it.

7.11. Using the result of the preceding problem, find the field strength required in order that the frequency of rotation of an electron be 10^5 cps. The electronic mass and charge are, respectively, 9.11×10^{-28} g and -1.60×10^{-19} coulomb.

7.12. Suppose that a copper conductor carrying current horizontally is in a uniform, horizontal magnetic field. What is the least magnitude of the magnetic induction required in order that the magnetic and gravitational forces may balance, if the current density is limited to 3 amp/mm^2, the mass density of copper is 8.90 g/cm^3, and the acceleration of gravity is 980 cm/sec^2?

7.13. A circular loop of radius a carrying current I is located in the yz plane with its center at the origin. Sufficiently near the x axis, and at distances from the origin for which $|x| \gg a$, the magnetic induction in the xy plane is given as

$$\mathbf{B} = \frac{\mu_0 I a^2}{2|x|^3} \left(\mathbf{i} + \frac{3y}{2x} \mathbf{j} \right)$$

Find the force due to this field on a small circular loop carrying current I' and lying in the xy plane with its center on the x axis at $x = L$, where $|L| \gg a$. The radius b of this loop is assumed small enough that the formula is valid, and also that the fractional variation in the x coordinate over the loop is negligible.

7.14. Show that in order for the force $d^2\mathbf{F}'$ on a current element dl' due to another element dl to be in the direction of the line joining the elements, it is necessary and sufficient that the element dl' be perpendicular to this line.

7.15. Suppose a current element dl' lies along the direction of the line to another element dl, the sense of dl' being away from dl.

a. Describe the direction of the magnetic force on dl' due to dl.

b. What is the magnetic force on dl due to dl'?

7.16. Show that the integrals (7.32) follow from Eq. (7.31), Sec. 7.4.

7.17. Carry through the derivation of the formula for the magnetic field on the axis of a solenoid, using the expression for the field on the axis of a circular loop.

7.18. Working backward from the expression for the field on the axis of a solenoid [Eq. (7.39), Sec. 7.4], deduce the field on the axis of a circular loop, *i.e.*, a solenoid of negligible length compared to its radius.

7.19. A solenoid of 100 turns is 12 cm long, has a radius of 2 cm, and carries a current of 4 amp. First deriving a suitable algebraic formula, find the magnetic induction on its axis (*a*) at the center and (*b*) at one end of the solenoid.

7.20. A coil of fine insulated wire is wound closely on a nonmagnetic sphere of radius R, the turns being approximately circles of constant latitude λ on the sphere. Along a circle of constant longitude, the number of turns per unit length is the constant n_1. When the coil carries current I_1, what is the resulting magnetic induction at the center of the sphere?   *Ans.* $\pi/4\mu_0 n_1 I_1$

7.21. Two parallel, straight wires carry the same current I in opposite directions. Letting the wires coincide with the lines $x = -c, y = 0$ and $x = +c, y = 0$, find the cartesian components of the magnetic induction at a general point in the xy plane.

7.22. *a.* Derive an expression for the force per unit length on each of two parallel wires *in vacuo* due to the magnetic field of the other. The wires are separated by a distance a, and carry currents I and I'. Use an algebraic convention such that like signs for I and I' indicate currents in like senses. Indicate the direction of the force.

b. Find the force per unit length if the parallel wires carry 15 amp each in the same direction and are separated by 2 cm.

7.23. A long, straight wire carrying 25 amp lies on a table of nonmagnetic material, on which is also laid a square loop 6 cm on a side, with two sides parallel to the wire and center at 10 cm from the wire. If the square carries a current of 4 amp, what is the resulting magnetic force on it? Show a direction for the currents, and give accordingly the direction of the force.

7.24. Given a solenoid of 700 turns, 40 cm long, and of small radius, carrying 0.50 amp. Let the z coordinate axis be the axis of the solenoid, and let the origin be at its center. For a region around the origin in which the magnetic induction can be assumed to be uniform, find two acceptable magnetic vector potential functions.

7.25. Show that for a magnetic induction of the type

$$\mathbf{B} = K \frac{\mathbf{r}}{r^3}$$

where K is constant and $r = \sqrt{x^2 + y^2 + z^2}$, a magnetic vector potential is

$$\mathbf{A} = \frac{Kyz}{r(x^2 + y^2)} \mathbf{i} - \frac{Kzx}{r(x^2 + y^2)} \mathbf{j}$$

where $\mathbf{i}$ and $\mathbf{j}$ are the cartesian unit vectors along the x and y axes, respectively.

7.26. *a.* Set up the integral in cartesian coordinates for the magnetic vector potential function due to an infinitely long straight wire carrying steady current I and coinciding with the z axis.

b. Although this integral diverges, assume that it is permissible to perform partial differentiations under the integral sign. Find in this way the cartesian components of the magnetic induction of the wire.

7.27. Show that the integral for the magnetic vector potential of a pair of parallel, straight, infinite wires carrying the same current I in opposite directions exists and has the value

$$\mathbf{A} = \frac{\mathbf{k}\mu_0 I}{4\pi} \ln \frac{r_2}{r_1}$$

Here r_1 and r_2 are the respective distances of the observation point from the wires carrying the current in the directions of the unit vectors $+\mathbf{k}$ and $-\mathbf{k}$.

7.28. *a.* Express the vector potential function of a pair of long, straight wires coinciding, respectively, with the lines $x = +c$, $y = 0$ and $x = -c$, $y = 0$, in the cartesian coordinates x, y of the observer. See the answer of the preceding problem.

b. By differentiation, find the cartesian components of the magnetic induction vector due to these two wires.

7.29. *a.* Express the vector magnetic induction B outside a long straight wire *in vacuo* in cartesian components and coordinates, letting the wire lie along the y axis with $+y$ as the current direction.

b. Show that this vector has a zero divergence.

7.30. Find the magnetic flux due to the field of a long, straight wire through a square loop coplanar with wire and having two sides parallel to it. The wire carries 5 amp, the side of the loop is 3 cm, and the nearest side is 4 cm from the wire.

7.31. A multilayer coil of N turns of fine wire is wound upon a cylindrical form of circular section. All layers have equal numbers of turns, and the inner and outer radii of the completed coil are, respectively, a and b. The ends of the coil are connected, and the coil is located in a uniform magnetic field whose component of induction parallel to the axis of the coil is B. Show that the total flux through the coil is

$$BN\pi \frac{b^2 + ab + a^2}{3}$$

if there are enough layers that the calculus can be used in summing up their contributions to the total flux.

7.32. Given a circular loop *in vacuo* of radius a and carrying current I, its axis being coincident with the x coordinate axis and its center being at the origin.

a. Find, by use of the divergence property of the magnetic induction, the space rate of change of the cartesian component B_y with respect to y, for a general point on the x axis.

b. From this result, write an approximate formula for B_y, valid for small enough values of y.

$$Ans.\ (b)\ B_y = \frac{3\mu_0 I a^2 x y}{4(a^2 + x^2)^{5/2}}.$$

7.33. Find the magnetic force, due to the field of the loop in the preceding problem, on a second circular loop coaxial with the first, having its center at $x = L$. This loop carries current I' in the same sense as the other, and has a radius b sufficiently small that the approximate field B_y of the preceding problem is valid.

7.34. In Prob. 7.32 the property of the magnetic induction vector that its divergence is zero was used to find the field component perpendicular to the axis of a circular current loop, at small distances from the axis. Working backward, use this result and the axial field (assumed the same as on axis) to find whether the net flux is zero through a closed, circularly cylindrical surface whose axis coincides with that of the loop. The radius b of the surface is taken much smaller than that of the current loop, so that the approximate field formulas remain valid over the cylinder; and the ends of the cylinder are taken as disks normal to the axis at arbitrary distances x_1 and x_2 from the center of the loop.

7.35. It is desired to balance the horizontal component of the earth's magnetic field with the field at the center of a Helmholtz coil. This consists of a pair of coaxial, circular loops of the same radius a, equal numbers of turns n, their centers separated by distance a, and carrying the same current in the same clock sense. If the field to be balanced is 2.00×10^{-5} weber/m², $a = 20$ cm, and $n = 50$, what must be the current in the coil?

7.36. *a.* Obtain the successive derivatives of the field on the axis of a circular current loop, with respect to the distance x from the loop. At what points do they vanish?

b. Apply these results to the Helmholtz coil defined in the preceding problem. If the field on axis of this coil is expanded in Taylor's series about the center point, what is the result to the fourth-degree term?

c. Does the approximate uniformity of the axial field at the center of a Helmholtz coil indicate anything about uniformity near the axis in the transverse plane? See Prob. 7.32.

7.37. Show that *except* at $r = 0$, a possible magnetic induction field in steady state is similar to the electric field of a point charge:

$$\mathbf{B} = K \frac{\mathbf{r}}{r^3}$$

Here K is a constant and $\mathbf{r}$ and r are, respectively, the vector and the scalar distances from the origin to the observation point. Has the exception any significance?

7.38. A toroid coil is wound uniformly about a nonmagnetic ring whose circular axis has a radius of 10 cm, while its cross section has a radius of 1 cm. The coil has 150 turns and carries a current of 2 amp. Let P be a plane perpendicular to the circular axis of the ring at two diametrically opposite points.

a. Find the component of magnetic induction normal to this plane at a general point within the material of the ring.

b. What is the maximum percentage variation of this field in this toroidal region?

7.39. Steady current I flows in a long, straight, tubular wire of circular cross section and nonmagnetic material, whose inner and outer radii are, respectively, a and b. Assuming uniform current density, find the magnetic induction vector in all regions within and near the wire.

7.40. Two current densities of equal magnitude J and opposite directions flow, respectively, in two circularly cylindrical regions of radii R_1 and R_2, with $R_1 > R_2$, and the axes of these cylinders are at a distance x apart, x being less than $R_1 - R_2$. Describe a physical realization of this system. Find the magnetic induction vector in the region common to the two currents, and show that this field is uniform.

7.41. Obtain Eq. (7.81) from Eq. (7.80), Sec. 7.8.

7.42. Derive the field of a steady magnetic dipole from its vector potential function.

7.43. Deduce the spherical components from the cartesian components of the magnetic induction of a dipole.

7.44. A coil consists of 25 turns of wire bound closely together in the form of a rectangle measuring 10×20 cm. This coil lies flat on a horizontal, nonmagnetic table, and carries a steady current of 5 amp. Evaluate the magnetic vector potential and the magnetic induction vector of the coil at a point in space 3 m below the plane of the coil and 4 m due north.

7.45. A coil is wound in the form of a symmetrical figure 8. What can you say about its distant magnetic field in a qualitative way?

7.46. A circular loop $\mathcal{L}_1$ of radius R_1 is at a distance L from a second loop $\mathcal{L}_2$ of radius R_2. L is large, so that $L \gg R_1$ and $L \gg R_2$. The axes of the two loops are coplanar and make angles θ_1 and θ_2, respectively, with the line L. What is the magnetic flux through $\mathcal{L}_2$ due to a current I in $\mathcal{L}_1$? Make a drawing, showing the direction of I and assigning a positive normal to $\mathcal{L}_2$, and showing also the angles; and give the sign of the flux accordingly.

7.47. A coil is wound in the form of a flat, tight spiral, the spacing between turns being just the diameter of the wire. The coil starts at the center and ends at the periphery with a radius of 50 cm and a total of 500 turns. If it carries a current of ½ amp, what is the magnitude of its magnetic dipole moment? *Note:* Each turn can be approximated by a circle.

7.48. Suppose an electron in a circular orbit of radius r has an orbital angular momentum (radius times linear momentum) of $(h/2\pi)\sqrt{2}$, where h is Planck's constant, 6.62×10^{-34} joule-sec. If the electron has mass $m_0 = 9.11 \times 10^{-31}$ kg and charge $e = 1.60 \times 10^{-19}$ coulomb, find the magnetic moment by considering the electron in its orbit as a circular current loop. Give an algebraic and a numerical answer. *Ans.* $(eh/4\pi m_0)\sqrt{2}$.

7.49. A nonplanar loop of wire is constructed from a single-turn square loop of side a as follows. The loop is laid on a table with a ruler across it, the edge of the ruler being parallel to one side of the square at a distance $a/3$ from that side. The wire is then bent upward 90° at the two places where the edge crosses it. From the side, the loop now looks like an L figure, with legs of $a/3$ and $2a/3$. When current I flows, find the vector magnetic dipole moment.

7.50. Find a magnetic scalar potential function continuous at all points on the axis of a circular current loop, using a surface S which changes with the position x of the point of observation. Let S be a spherical cap whose center remains always at x, bounded by the loop C and always open on the side of negative x.

7.51. Find the value of the line integral

$$\int_{x=-b}^{b} \mathbf{B} \cdot d\mathbf{l}$$

between the points $x = -b$ and $x = b$ on the axis of a circular current loop, using both a discontinuous scalar potential, Eq. (7.138), Sec. 7.10, and the continuous potential function of the preceding problem. Check by direct integration of the magnetic induction, using Eq. (7.139), Sec. 7.10.

7.52. Show that the scalar potential function given as Eq. (7.138), Sec. 7.10, has as its limiting form at large distances from the loop just the potential on the axis of a magnetic dipole.

7.53. Find the magnetic scalar potential function of a narrow rectangular circuit of length $2a$ and small width b, carrying steady current I *in vacuo*, at a general point of observation whose distance from the nearest part of the circuit is much greater than b. Let the circuit lie in the xy plane with center at the origin and long sides parallel to the x axis; and use cartesian coordinates.

Ans. $U^* = \dfrac{bIz}{4\pi(y^2 + z^2)} \left[\dfrac{a - x}{\sqrt{(a - x)^2 + y^2 + z^2}} + \dfrac{a + x}{\sqrt{(a + x)^2 + y^2 + z^2}} \right].$

7.54. Show that the magnetic scalar potential function for the narrow circuit of the preceding problem becomes the appropriate magnetic dipole potential at very large distances r from the origin, that is, when $r \gg a$.

7.55. Use the integral form of Ampère's circuital law to find the magnetic induction vector at general points both inside and outside a long, straight, cylindrical wire with circular cross section and radius R, carrying steady current I with uniform density. Assume the material of the wire to be nonmagnetic. Now take the curl of these functions, using cartesian coordinates, and check the results against the differential form of Ampère's law.

7.56. A circular loop of radius a carrying steady current I has its axis coinciding with the x coordinate axis. Near the axis of the loop, the transverse components of magnetic induction are approximately

$$B_y = \frac{3\mu_0 I a^2 xy}{4(a^2 + x^2)^{5/2}} \qquad B_z = \frac{3\mu_0 I a^2 xz}{4(a^2 + x^2)^{5/2}}$$

(See Prob. 7.32.)

a. Using these formulas, find the approximate values of the partial derivatives $\partial B_x/\partial y$, $\partial B_x/\partial z$ for small y and z.

b. From the results of (a), find an approximate expression for the longitudinal field B_x at points near the axis.

Ans. $B_x = \dfrac{\mu_0 I a^2}{2(a^2 + x^2)^{3/2}} + \dfrac{3\mu_0 I a^2(y^2 + z^2)(a^2 - 4x^2)}{8(a^2 + x^2)^{7/2}}.$

Note: See Probs. 7.35 and 7.36, and note the application of this result to the Helmholtz coil.

7.57. A single-loop rectangular circuit measuring 30 by 50 cm and carrying 5 amp rests on a horizontal table in a uniform magnetic field due to the earth. This field has a horizontal component of induction of 2×10^{-5} weber/m² and is inclined 60° below the horizontal. What is the net mechanical work required to turn the circuit over from the position where its positive normal is downward to that where the normal is upward?

7.58. A radial magnetic induction field

$$\mathbf{B} = K \frac{\mathbf{r}}{r^3}$$

where K is constant and $\mathbf{r}$ and r are the vector and scalar radii from the origin to the observer, is produced by a pole of a long, thin permanent magnet. The magnet lies along the negative branch of the x axis, and the given field does not exist within the volume of the magnet. Find the mechanical work output when a square current loop is brought up from infinity to a position with its center at the origin and its positive normal in the $+x$ direction, if the loop has side a and carries current I. What importance has the description of the magnet's location?

7.59. A magnetic field is set up in space by a circular loop $\mathcal{L}_1$ of radius a carrying current I_1. A second loop $\mathcal{L}_2$, whose radius b is much smaller than a, is located coaxially with $\mathcal{L}_1$ so that the centers of the loops are at a distance $a/2$ apart. If $\mathcal{L}_2$ carries current I_2 in the opposite clock sense to I_1, find the magnetic force between the loops.

7.60. A coil of 10 turns is wound on a cylindrical form of ½ cm radius and 1 cm length, and is located at the center of a circular loop of 50 cm radius and 3 turns. When the two coils carry a common current of 2 amp and their axes are at right angles, what is their magnetomechanical interaction?

7.61. Two similar, coaxial, circular loops have radius a and carry the same current I in like clock senses. Their centers are at a distance x apart, x being large compared with a. To the dipole approximation, what is their force interaction?

7.62. Using the approximate longitudinal field of Prob. 7.56, find as accurately as possible the force between the similar, coaxial current loops of the preceding problem.

7.63. A magnetic dipole is located in a radial, inverse-square, magnetic induction field. It experiences, in a general orientation, a magnetic force which produces a torque about the field center. Show that this torque is exactly balanced by the couple on the dipole.

7.64. Two square current loops of equal side length a and current I lie on a table, their centers being separated by a distance y which is very large compared with a. If the clock senses of the currents are opposite, find the force between them to the dipole approximation.

7.65. A magnetic dipole is located in an inverse-square, radial, magnetic induction field. If θ and ϕ are the angles, respectively, of the vector dipole moment and of the resultant force on the dipole with the radius vector from the field center to the dipole, show that

$$\tan \phi = -\tfrac{1}{2} \tan \theta$$

Sketch the directions of the vectors for several representative cases. *Hint:* Cartesian coordinates are suitable, provided the axes are simply chosen.

7.66. A coil of 200 closely bound turns is in the form of a rectangle measuring 50 by 80 cm. This coil lies on a horizontal table in the earth's magnetic field, and carries a current of 400 ma running clockwise as seen from above. If the earth's field is 2×10^{-5} weber/m^2, in the true north-south meridian, and dips at an angle of 20° below the horizontal, find the vector couple on the coil due to the magnetic field.

CHAPTER 8

ELECTROMAGNETIC INDUCTION

8.1. Motional Electromotive Force. It is a well-known experimental fact that an electromotive force appears in a conductor when the conductor is moved across a magnetic field. In this section we shall examine this motional emf in some detail and show that its existence may be deduced from the principle of conservation of energy, as well as from a microscopic picture of the conduction process.

Consider an ideal experiment as sketched in Fig. 8.1. Let a straight conductor slide on straight, horizontal, parallel rails at a distance l apart.

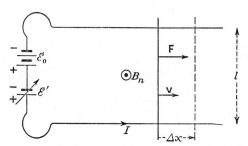

Fig. 8.1. Conductor moving in a magnetic field.

Suppose the sliding motion is entirely parallel to the rails, and for the present let the length of the conductor be normal to the rails. The rails are to serve to supply a current I to the moving conductor by means of a battery of emf $\mathcal{E}_0$ connected across them. Now let a magnetic field be present whose component of induction normal to the plane of the rails and outward in Fig. 8.1 is B_n. It is clear from the equation which we used to define $\mathbf{B}$ (Eq. 7.1) that a force F exists on the conductor in the direction of sliding:

$$F = IB_nl \tag{8.1}$$

This force is to the right in the diagram if the current sense as shown is to be positive.

In order to avoid unnecessary complications, let us suppose that the field B_n is due entirely to a permanent magnet and that it is uniform in time and over the space through which the conductor moves. In making such a statement, we have evidently neglected the field produced by our

246

circuit itself. This is important for simplifying our ideal experiment. It may be justified by noting that the force on the conductor due to an externally impressed field depends on the first power of the current I, while any force on the conductor due to the rest of the circuit depends on I^2 according to Ampère's law (Sec. 7.3). Thus by reducing the current I we may cause the effect of the field of our circuit to become negligible compared to the effect of the external field.

Now if there were no motional emf, we should have in Fig. 8.1 the priceless drawing of a perpetual motion machine. For the conductor may be allowed to move to the right through a distance Δx, during which motion it will do work if F of Eq. (8.1) is positive; and then the circuit could be broken by a switch, after which the conductor could be moved freely back to its starting position. A d-c electric motor operates in a similar way, except that its motion is one of continuous rotation. Of course there is energy loss due to Joule heat, but this again may be made negligible by reducing the current I, for the Joule heat involves I^2, while the work done per cycle, neglecting friction, would be

$$\Delta W = F \, \Delta x = I B_n l \, \Delta x \tag{8.2}$$

In any case, the battery $\mathcal{E}_0$ would merely supply the Joule heat if there were no motional emf, and the work (8.2) would be obtained free.

In order to satisfy the principle of conservation of energy, we must postulate that if I is held fixed, the battery must work harder during the motion to supply the output work ΔW. This means an additional average emf $\mathcal{E}'_{av}$ must be supplied during the motion such that, if the distance Δx is covered by the conductor in a time Δt,

$$\mathcal{E}'_{av} I \, \Delta t = \Delta W \tag{8.3}$$

Combining Eqs. (8.2) and (8.3), we find that the additional emf to be supplied is

$$\mathcal{E}'_{av} = B_n l \frac{\Delta x}{\Delta t} \tag{8.4}$$

The instantaneous emf $\mathcal{E}'$ can be deduced at once by letting $\Delta t \to 0$, so that $\Delta x/\Delta t$ becomes the derivative dx/dt which is the instantaneous velocity v of the conductor:

$$\mathcal{E}' = B_n l \frac{dx}{dt} = B_n l v \tag{8.5}$$

However, $\mathcal{E}'$ is not the motional emf itself, but its negative; for $\mathcal{E}'$ is the additional battery emf required, due to the presence of the motional emf, to keep the current at its original value. The motional emf itself is then

$$\mathcal{E} = -B_n l v \tag{8.6}$$

The significance of the negative sign in Eq. (8.6) is that the motional emf induced in the conductor tends to drive current around in the opposite sense to that which we have defined as positive in the diagram. The reader may show that if l is taken as a vector length of the conductor, then the motional emf, considered positive if in the sense of l, may be written correctly in the vector form:

$$\varepsilon = \mathbf{B} \cdot \mathbf{l} \times \mathbf{v} \tag{8.7}$$

Not only is this equation consistent with the case of Fig. 8.1, but it holds for general directions of the vectors. This is seen by drawing a more general figure in which l is not perpendicular to the rails, and by considering also the fact that components of $\mathbf{B}$ parallel to the plane of the rails have no effect on the work of Eq. (8.2) and hence no effect on the emf. It is assumed, however, that the wire keeps a constant direction, *i.e.*, its motion is purely one of translation.

The rules of vector multiplication allow us to write Eq. (8.7) in two other distinct forms. One of these may be obtained by interchange of dot and cross:

$$\varepsilon = \mathbf{B} \times \mathbf{l} \cdot \mathbf{v} \tag{8.8}$$

The significance of this form is easy to see if we remember that the magnetic force on l in a uniform field is

$$\mathbf{F}_m = I\mathbf{l} \times \mathbf{B} \tag{8.9}$$

Hence the mechanical power output as the wire moves with a vector velocity $\mathbf{v}$ is

$$P = \mathbf{F}_m \cdot \mathbf{v} = I\mathbf{l} \times \mathbf{B} \cdot \mathbf{v} \tag{8.10}$$

This is to be equated, by conservation of energy, to the electrical power $-\varepsilon I$ lost in the wire due to the induced emf:

$$-\varepsilon I = I\mathbf{l} \times \mathbf{B} \cdot \mathbf{v} \tag{8.11}$$

From this Eq. (8.8) follows immediately. In a sense we have thus briefly run through our whole derivation again, less pictorially but in general vector fashion.

Another form of the motional emf equation may be obtained by cyclic permutation of the factors in Eq. (8.8):

$$\varepsilon = \mathbf{v} \times \mathbf{B} \cdot \mathbf{l} \tag{8.12}$$

This equation is suggestive of another approach to the understanding of motional emf. The quantity $q\mathbf{v} \times \mathbf{B}$ is the force which a carrier charge q participating in the translation of the conductor would experience due to the magnetic field [see Eq. (7.12), Sec. 7.2]. Thus $q\mathbf{v} \times \mathbf{B} \cdot \mathbf{l}$ is the energy put into the electrical circuit by a reversible process when a charge

q flows through the moving conductor. Now energy per unit charge transferable into an electrical circuit from any nonelectrostatic source is the measure of an emf, according to the discussion in Sec. 5.8. We have therefore shown from a microscopic viewpoint that the emf of Eq. (8.12) must exist when a conductor moves in a magnetic field.

8.2. EMF and Magnetic Flux: Faraday's Law of Electromagnetic Induction. The results of the preceding section may be restated in quite a different form. Referring to Eq. (8.6) of that section, we may notice that lv is the area per unit time swept out by the moving conductor in the diagram. Now magnetic flux was defined in Sec. 7.6 as

$$\Phi = \int_S \mathbf{B} \cdot \mathbf{n} \, da = \int_S B_n \, da \qquad (8.13)$$

Here S is the surface across which the flux is to be computed, an element of S being da, and $\mathbf{n}$ is unit vector normal to da in a specified sense. The second form of the integral is written in terms of the normal component B_n of the magnetic induction $\mathbf{B}$, that is, the component normal to the area element da. Thus the expression $B_n lv$ of Eq. (8.6) may be considered to be the new flux added per unit time to an expanding surface S bounded by the electrical circuit. We may now rewrite that equation in the form

$$\mathcal{E} = -\frac{d\Phi}{dt} \qquad (8.14)$$

The reader should satisfy himself that the first form of Eq. (8.13) may be used with Eq. (8.7) of the preceding section to lead to this same expression. Energy conservation combined with the analysis of Sec. 7.12 leads to Eq. (8.14) in general for the motional emf in a circuit of any form. See Sec. 9.18 for detailed consideration of magnetomechanical-energy relations. It might be thought that we should specify exactly what surface bounded by the circuit should be used to compute the flux Φ, as, for instance, requiring it to be the obvious choice of a plane surface between the rails of the ideal experiment of Sec. 8.1. Actually, the importance of Eq. (8.14) results from the fact that the flux through a closed circuit C is entirely independent of what surface bounded by C is used to compute the flux. This is due to the basic nature of the $\mathbf{B}$ vector, as we showed in Sec. 7.6.

The negative sign in Eq. (8.14) is important and requires careful attention. It implies first of all that we may consider Φ and $\mathcal{E}$ to be algebraic quantities. The sign of $\mathcal{E}$ depends on the positive sense assigned to the circuit in question, $\mathcal{E}$ being positive if current flow in the positive sense causes energy to be put into the electrical circuit. The sign of Φ depends on the positive normal sense chosen for the surface S of Eq. (8.13). If S

is not plane, its elements da have positive normals **n** in different directions, but these normals are to be all in the same sense, that is, all on one side of S. To visualize this, the normals may be thought of as being like the point of a thumbtack whose head may be slid around on the surface. Now we shall agree as in Sec. 7.6 that the positive normals to the surface S are to bear a specific relation to the positive sense around its boundary curve C. If a right-hand screw is imagined to advance along C in the positive sense, its threads will move through S in the positive sense as it rotates. Another way of picturing the same relation by a right-hand screw rule is to say that for a circular circuit and plane curve the screw will advance in the sense of the positive normal when it rotates in the positive sense around the circuit. With these conventions, Eq. (8.14) is correct as written with the negative sign, as the reader may check by referring to Fig. 8.1.

Having settled the sign conventions, we now proceed to an important extension of the meaning of Eq. (8.14). It is found experimentally that this emf appears in any circuit through which the flux is changing, whether the change is caused by motion of the circuit or of its parts, or whether the circuit is fixed and the field is a function of time; or both causes may operate simultaneously. For example, if a magnet is thrust at a fixed coil of wire connected to a galvanometer, the galvanometer shows a current when the magnet is moving. Another familiar demonstration experiment shows that a current is induced in a coil of wire when current in a neighboring coil is varying. The emf of Eq. (8.14), whatever has caused the flux to change, is called an induced emf, and the phenomenon of induced emf is called electromagnetic induction. Equation (8.14) itself is called Faraday's law of electromagnetic induction, in honor of Michael Faraday (1791–1867).

It will be profitable for future reference to inquire what cause may be assigned in the microscopic conduction picture to the induced emf in a fixed coil. There must be a force on the carriers of charge to produce an emf; and we may consider this force per unit carrier charge to be due to an electric field. As usual we may distinguish a microscopic electric field from its space average which will be called the macroscopic electric field. The line integral of the macroscopic electric field around the circuit is to be identified with the induced emf $\mathcal{E}$:

$$\mathcal{E} = \oint_C \mathbf{E} \cdot d\mathbf{l} \qquad (8.15)$$

Now it is not only permissible to think of an electric field being produced by electromagnetic induction, but the phenomena of electromagnetic wave motion will require us to suppose that changing magnetic induction in general does actually produce an electric field. In order to write

Eq. (8.14) in terms of the field vectors, and for a fixed circuit C, we may use Eqs. (8.15) and (8.13), taking the time derivative inside the flux integral which extends over a fixed surface S:

$$\oint_C \mathbf{E} \cdot d\mathbf{l} = - \int_S \frac{\partial \mathbf{B}}{\partial t} \cdot \mathbf{n} \, da \qquad (8.16)$$

We shall return to this equation when we consider electromagnetic fields in general in Chap. 12. It should be remarked that there is in Eq. (8.16) no requirement that a conductor should coincide with the curve C. The electric field is not the result of the conduction process; but the presence of a conducting circuit simply makes the electric field evident through the resulting current flow. It may also be remarked that in Eqs. (8.15) and (8.16) the symbol $\mathbf{E}$ may include the field due directly to the presence of electric charge concentrations in the neighborhood, for the line integral of this quasielectrostatic field around a closed path is zero, as we noted in Sec. 5.7. In fact, Eq. (8.16) will be considered to be universally true, and it is one of the basic foundations of electromagnetic theory.

8.3. Lenz's Law. The implications of the negative sign in Faraday's law may be gathered together in a general statement called Lenz's law. This statement concerns the effect of any currents which are produced by induced emf. The effects considered fall into two classes: magnetic force or torque reactions, and production of magnetic flux. Both kinds of effects may be included in a single statement as follows: The effects of a current produced by electromagnetic induction are always in such a sense as to oppose any action which is causing the induction.

Consider force and torque reactions first. These oppose a cause of the induction if this cause is a translation or rotation, respectively. For example, the north pole of a magnet may be thrust at a coil of wire connected in a closed circuit, in order to induce a current. Lenz's law now states that the induced current causes a magnetic force reaction on the magnet opposite in sense to the motion of the magnet. The reader should check this for himself in the simple case where the circuit is a circular loop and the magnet pole is moved up along the axis, remembering that the sense of magnetic induction from the north pole is outward and that force on the north pole is in the direction of the magnetic field of the current loop. Another example which is easy to work through is that of a loop of wire which rotates about a line in its plane, the axis of rotation being normal to a uniform external magnetic field. It will be found in accordance with Lenz's law that the induced current results in a magnetic torque on the loop which opposes the rotation.

It is easy to prove that force and torque reactions are opposite to the motion causing the induced current; for this simply means that work is being done by an external agency to produce the induced currents, and this must be the case if energy is to be conserved. Otherwise, we should be able to get mechanical work out of a system as induced currents were being built up, currents which in turn could do work in producing heat or driving motors.

We have remarked that Lenz's law can also refer to the magnetic flux reaction of an induced current. This means for example that if the current is produced by an algebraic increase of flux through the circuit, that is, if $d\Phi/dt > 0$, then the flux Φ_i due to the induced current is negative. Thus the flux due to the induced current opposes the change of flux causing the current. There is therefore a mechanism tending to maintain the flux at a constant value. The reader should check this idea for the examples mentioned above.

A case of special interest is that in which the flux through a circuit is due to a current in the circuit itself, and the changing of this flux is therefore the result of a changing of this current. Lenz's law now says that the induced current produces a magnetic flux opposing the changing of the flux through the circuit. It follows that the induced current has such a sense as to oppose the change of current in the circuit. Electromagnetic induction thus provides a tendency to maintain a constant current in a circuit. Anyone who has tried opening a switch in a circuit containing magnet coils has observed a striking example of this tendency. The arc which is established when the switch blades separate effectively keeps the circuit closed and hence keeps the current flowing as long as possible.

8.4. Self-inductance. The self-inductance of a circuit is defined by

$$L \equiv \frac{d\Phi}{dI} \tag{8.17}$$

In this definition, Φ is the flux through the circuit considered as a function of the current I in the circuit.

Self-inductance bears an important relationship to Faraday's law. When the current I is changing in the circuit at a rate dI/dt, the resulting rate of change of flux is $d\Phi/dI \cdot dI/dt$. Thus, by Eq. (8.17),

$$\frac{d\Phi}{dt} = L\frac{dI}{dt} \tag{8.18}$$

Faraday's law therefore predicts an induced emf in the circuit given by

$$\mathcal{E} = -L\frac{dI}{dt} \tag{8.19}$$

This equation is frequently used to define the self-inductance, for which purpose it is just as good as Eq. (8.17). If Eq. (8.19) is made the definition of L, then (8.17) becomes an immediate deduction.

The rationalized mks unit of inductance is called the henry (plural henrys), in honor of Joseph Henry (1797–1878). From Eq. (8.17) we may identify the henry as

$$1 \text{ henry} = 1 \frac{\text{weber}}{\text{ampere}}$$

or from Eq. (8.19) we may write an equivalent expression

$$1 \text{ henry} = 1 \frac{\text{volt-second}}{\text{ampere}}$$

Up to this point, we have spoken of self-inductance as a property of a closed circuit. It is often convenient, however, to consider self-inductance as a property of a two-terminal circuit component. In such a case, we may speak of the self-inductance as being lumped at the place in the circuit occupied by the component in question. The contrary to lumped self-inductance is distributed self-inductance, which cannot be localized in the circuit, but is a property of the whole circuit. Now we cannot logically use Eq. (8.17) to define the self-inductance of anything but a closed circuit, since Φ has a definite meaning only in relation to a closed circuit. In spite of this, Eq. (8.17) is used as a basis for the derivation of formulas for computing self-inductance of coils. A helical solenoid may be considered as a good approximation to a set of circular loops all connected in series; and this or any other circuit component may be imagined to be made into a closed circuit by connecting its terminals by a short wire. It is clear, however, that to isolate the self-inductance of only a part of a circuit, we must define self-inductance in terms of this part only; and this can be done by using Eq. (8.19) as the definition appropriate to lumped self-inductance. We must, however, understand that when we try to localize self-inductance the symbol $\mathcal{E}$ takes on a different meaning than it had before. Applied to a whole circuit C, $\mathcal{E}$ means the emf around that circuit, that is,

$$\mathcal{E} = \oint_{\text{around } C} \mathbf{E} \cdot d\mathbf{l} \tag{8.15}$$

as in Sec. 8.2. We may instead take the induced emf $\mathcal{E}_{12}$ between two points 1 and 2 of a circuit, which might be the terminals of a circuit component:

$$\mathcal{E}_{12} = \int_{1}^{2} \mathbf{E}_m \cdot d\mathbf{l} \tag{8.20}$$
$$\text{along } C$$

Here $\mathbf{E}_m$ is written in place of the general symbol for electric field $\mathbf{E}$, for we mean specifically only that field resulting from the process of electromagnetic induction. The closed-loop integral (8.15) had the advantage that only $\mathbf{E}_m$ contributed to it, but in computing (8.20) we must exclude fields produced by the presence of concentration of electric charge. Now the self-inductance of the component or part of the circuit between the two points 1 and 2 may be defined as

$$L_{12} \equiv -\frac{\mathcal{E}_{12}}{dI/dt} \tag{8.21}$$

One more remark must be made about this definition of lumped self-inductance. In practice, the changing magnetic fields responsible for the production of the emf originate not only from the circuit element or part between points 1 and 2, but also from the rest of the circuit. It is convenient to specify that the $\mathcal{E}_{12}$ of Eq. (8.21) is to be due to the magnetic field of that part only of the circuit over which the integral (8.20) is taken. If there is an appreciable contribution $\mathcal{E}'_{12}$ due to the rest of the circuit, which may sometimes occur, this is taken into account by the introduction of another concept to be treated in the following section, namely, mutual inductance.

To conclude this section, some general statements may be made about the values of L encountered in practice. An application of Lenz's law of the preceding section shows that L can never be negative, at least for a complete circuit. Components are sometimes specifically designed to have small inductance, and these are called noninductive. In the absence of iron or similar nonlinear materials, L or L_{12} is independent of the magnitude of current flowing. For a circuit in which L is constant, the relationship of Φ to I is linear, and this results from a linear dependence of magnetic induction on current. The use of iron or similar materials may greatly increase L or L_{12}, but results in a dependence of these quantities on the current so that they may be far from constant.

For future use, we shall drop the cumbersome subscripts on the symbol L_{12}, and simply understand from the context whether the self-inductance is that of a component or of an entire closed circuit.

8.5. Mutual Inductance. We considered in Sec. 8.4 the relationship of flux through a circuit to current in it. The extension of these ideas to two or more circuits is the subject of the present section. Suppose we label two circuits C_1 and C_2. Let the currents be I_1 and I_2, the magnetic fluxes Φ_1 and Φ_2, and the emfs around the circuits $\mathcal{E}_1$ and $\mathcal{E}_2$, respectively. To avoid ambiguities of sign, we shall suppose that positive senses for each pair of quantities I_1 and Φ_1, and I_2 and Φ_2, are established in conformity with the right-hand rule discussed in Sec. 8.2. Likewise, positive $\mathcal{E}_1$ will be understood to put energy into the electrical circuit when I_1 is positive, and positive $\mathcal{E}_2$ will be similarly related to I_2. In order to write equations relating the quantities of one circuit to those of the other, we shall require in this section that the positive senses of I_1 and I_2 be consistent with each other. This is to mean that a positive change of current ΔI_1 produces a positive change of flux $\Delta \Phi_2$.

Now in general the flux Φ_2 is some function of both the currents I_2 and I_1. We shall define as the mutual inductance of circuit C_2 with respect to C_1 the partial derivative

$$M_{21} \equiv \frac{\partial \Phi_2}{\partial I_1} \tag{8.22}$$

This symbol implies that I_2 is to be held constant, and the limit of the ratio $\Delta \Phi_2 / \Delta I_1$ is to be found as the current change $\Delta I_1 \to 0$. It is a consequence of our sign conventions that M_{21} must be positive or zero.

There is evidently another mutual inductance between the pair of circuits C_1 and C_2, namely, that of circuit C_1 with respect to C_2:

$$M_{12} \equiv \frac{\partial \Phi_1}{\partial I_2} \tag{8.23}$$

It will be possible to show that the two mutual inductances are equal after we consider the subject of magnetic energy, provided that suitable care is taken in handling the case where ferromagnetic materials are present (see Sec. 8.9). Ordinarily, therefore, we omit the subscripts on the symbols for mutual inductance, and write

$$M = M_{21} = M_{12} \tag{8.24}$$

Suppose now that the current in one of the circuits, say C_1, is varying with time at the rate dI_1/dt, while I_2 is held constant. The resulting rate of change of Φ_2 is

$$\frac{d\Phi_2}{dt} = \frac{\partial \Phi_2}{\partial I_1} \frac{dI_1}{dt} = M_{21} \frac{dI_1}{dt} \tag{8.25}$$

There is therefore an emf induced in C_2 which by Faraday's law is

$$\mathcal{E}_2 = -M_{21} \frac{dI_1}{dt} \qquad I_2 = \text{constant} \tag{8.26}$$

If I_2 also is allowed to vary, the total emf in C_2 is a sum of two terms, one for the current in each circuit:

$$\mathcal{E}_2 = -\frac{d\Phi_2}{dt} = -\frac{\partial \Phi_2}{\partial I_1} \frac{dI_1}{dt} - \frac{\partial \Phi_2}{\partial I_2} \frac{dI_2}{dt} \tag{8.27}$$

But $\partial \Phi_2 / \partial I_2 = L_2$, the self-inductance of C_2 under the condition that I_1 be held constant. Thus for a pair of circuits, the general induced emf $\mathcal{E}_2$ due to current changes in both circuits may be written

$$\mathcal{E}_2 = -M_{21} \frac{dI_1}{dt} - L_2 \frac{dI_2}{dt} \qquad \text{pair of circuits} \tag{8.28}$$

Two circuits for which M_{21} is not zero are said to be inductively coupled. Evidently their mutual inductance is of equal importance with their self-inductance in the analysis of transient or alternating current conditions. Units of mutual and self-inductance are the same. Thus in the rationalized mks system, mutual inductance is measured in henrys.

Equation (8.26) may be made the definition of mutual inductance rather than Eq. (8.22). In this case we would rewrite (8.26):

$$M_{21} \equiv \frac{-\mathcal{E}_2}{dI_1/dt} \qquad I_2 = \text{constant} \qquad (8.29)$$

and (8.22) then becomes a deduction from this alternative definition. Equations (8.25) to (8.29) may of course be rewritten with interchange of subscripts, or the subscripts of M may be omitted.

Mutual inductance is frequently considered to be a property of a pair of two-terminal circuit components rather than of a pair of complete circuits. This concept presents some difficulties, but is extremely useful in many cases where the magnetic field of connecting wires and the induced emf in them is negligible by comparison with the field and emf of the circuit components. One difficulty was discussed in connection with self-inductance: that the flux through only a part of a circuit is not defined. This may be met by imagining each component to have its terminals connected by a wire for purposes of defining the flux, or by using the alternative definition (8.29) rather than (8.22). However, if Eq. (8.29) is used, it is still necessary to specify that the emf $\mathcal{E}_2$ in (8.29) be due to change of current I_1 only in the other component, and not in any connecting wires. This is not physically realizable; but the magnetic field of connecting wires may often be negligible compared to that of a circuit component.

In practice there are often more than two circuits inductively coupled together. There is then a mutual inductance between circuits C_i and C_j which may be written

$$M_{ij} \equiv \frac{\partial \Phi_i}{\partial I_j} \qquad (8.30)$$

Here the flux Φ_i is considered a function of the various currents $I_1, I_2, \ldots$ of the set of circuits; and the partial derivative symbol then implies that all these currents except I_j are held constant in forming the limit of the quotient $\Delta \Phi_i / \Delta I_j$.

In absence of ferromagnetic materials, mutual inductance is a constant, that is, it is independent of the currents flowing in the circuits. This is a consequence of the fact that in empty space, or in nonferromagnetic materials, the magnetic induction and hence the magnetic flux created by a current is proportional to that current; and for empty space, this in turn follows directly from Ampère's law (Sec. 8.3). On the other hand, the presence of iron or similar materials causes M to bear a complicated relationship to the currents and the manner in which they change. In the case of constant M, Eq. (8.22) may be integrated at once to yield that part of the magnetic flux through C_2 due to a current I_1:

$$\Phi_{21} = M_{21}I_1 \qquad \text{constant } M \qquad (8.31)$$

The constant of integration is here taken as zero, for in absence of ferromagnetic material, Φ_{21} must be zero when I_1 is zero.

8.6. Inductors. Circuit components whose prominent electrical characteristic is inductance are called inductors. Sometimes only self-inductance is present, but frequently mutual inductance is important as well. The usual form of an inductor is that of a coil of wire, for example solenoidal or toroidal, with or without a magnetic core. The symbol for an inductor is —⟋⟍⟍⟍⟍—.

It must be borne in mind that inductance is not the only electrical property of inductors. In particular, there is always an appreciable resistance except when the inductor is made of superconducting material. Now the inductance causes the appearance of an emf $\mathcal{E}$ dependent upon the rate of change of the current in the inductor and in any coupled inductors. This means that a potential difference is in general produced and that energy is transferred between the electrical circuit and the magnetic field. The energy transfer may have either direction depending on the relative sense of $\mathcal{E}$ and I. It has been our convention in the preceding sections to consider that $\mathcal{E}$ and I have the same sign when the energy transfer is into the electrical circuit. Now there is also an irreversible loss of energy from the electrical circuit into heat; this is accounted for by the resistance R of the inductor, which by its definition produces a potential difference IR and hence a power loss I^2R. The total potential at any instant appearing across an inductor is such that the total power lost or gained by the electrical circuit is accounted for by the combined effect of $\mathcal{E}$ and R. If we adopt the convention that the potential difference V across an inductor shall be positive relative to the current when the current flows through the inductor from higher to lower potential, then a positive value of IV represents a power loss to the circuit. The energy balance now yields the equation characterizing the behavior of the inductor at any instant:

$$V = IR - \mathcal{E} \qquad (8.32)$$

The simplest example of the use of Eq. (8.32) is that of an isolated inductor (see Fig. 8.2). Here the potential difference across the component is simply

$$V = L\frac{dI}{dt} + RI \qquad (8.33)$$

since

$$\varepsilon = -L \frac{dI}{dt} \qquad (8.19)$$

To illustrate Eq. (8.32) further, consider two inductors connected in series and having a mutual inductance M. See Fig. 8.3 for the sign conventions which we shall adopt. The current I is common to the two inductors. We shall say that they are positively coupled if the current I has the same sign relative to the consistent positive senses for the two coils, as defined in Sec. 8.5, and that they are negatively coupled in the

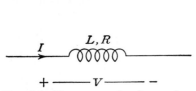

FIG. 8.2. Sign convention for an inductor.

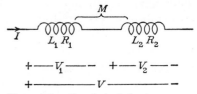

FIG. 8.3. Coupled inductors connected in series.

other case. If they are positively coupled, the flux changes through each coil due to mutual inductance are of the same sign as those due to self-inductance. For positive coupling:

$$V_1 = (L_1 + M) \frac{dI}{dt} + R_1 I \qquad (8.34)$$

and

$$V_2 = (L_2 + M) \frac{dI}{dt} + R_2 I \qquad (8.35)$$

The total potential difference is therefore

$$V = (L_1 + L_2 + 2M) \frac{dI}{dt} + (R_1 + R_2)I \qquad \text{positive coupling} \quad (8.36a)$$

In case the coupling is negative, the sign of both mutually induced emfs is changed, so that

$$V = (L_1 + L_2 - 2M) \frac{dI}{dt} + (R_1 + R_2)I \qquad \text{negative coupling} \quad (8.36b)$$

If Eqs. (8.36) are compared with (8.33), it appears that the pair of coupled inductors in series is equivalent to an isolated inductor whose self-inductance is

$$L = L_1 + L_2 \pm 2M \qquad (8.37)$$

The resistance of the pair is simply

$$R = R_1 + R_2 \qquad (8.38)$$

The foregoing example is of some interest in its laboratory application. Variable self-inductors are frequently constructed of two coils which may be rotated relative to one another so as to change the value of M as well as the sign of the coupling. These permit a continuous variation of self-inductance between the limits $(L_1 + L_2 \pm 2M_{max})$.

8.7. Limit of Mutual Inductance. Consider an inductor L which is coupled to a closed circuit of inductance L' and resistance R' by a mutual inductance M (see Fig. 8.4). If we set up the positive conventions for the two currents I and I' in a consistent manner, the equation for the potential V across L is

$$V = L\frac{dI}{dt} + M\frac{dI'}{dt} + RI \quad (8.39)$$

and the corresponding equation for the closed circuit is

$$0 = L'\frac{dI'}{dt} + M\frac{dI}{dt} + R'I' \quad (8.40)$$

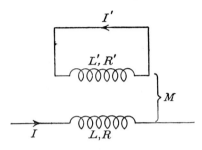

FIG. 8.4. Short-circuited, coupled inductor.

Substitution for dI'/dt into Eq. (8.39) yields

$$V = \left(L - \frac{M^2}{L'}\right)\frac{dI}{dt} + RI - \frac{R'M}{L'}I' \quad (8.41)$$

Because of the last term of this equation, the component L does not behave exactly like an isolated self-inductor. Under conditions for which the last term is negligibly small compared to the other terms of the equation, however, Eq. (8.41) is just like that for an isolated inductor having an effective self-inductance

$$L_{eff} = L - \frac{M^2}{L'} \quad (8.42)$$

It will not be worth our while here to give detailed consideration to the conditions under which the approximation involved in Eq. (8.42) is valid. In the most important case of alternating current of a definite frequency, we can handle the problem later by a more powerful method and avoid approximations. It may be noted, however, that if $R'I'$ becomes small enough and the currents change rapidly enough so that this term in Eq. (8.40) can simply be omitted, then Eq. (8.42) follows. This equation predicts that the proximity of a low-resistance closed circuit reduces the self-inductance of a coil. The effect may be observed, for example, when a nonmagnetic metal core is introduced into a solenoid, for the core then forms a circuit for induced currents.

Equation (8.42) may be used to deduce an upper limit to the mutual inductance between two inductors. L_{eff} is by Lenz's law a nonnegative quantity just as are L and L'. It follows that

$$M^2 \leqq LL' \tag{8.43}$$

This is a more severe condition than another one which we might have deduced from Eq. (8.37), namely (in our present notation),

$$M \leqq \frac{L + L'}{2} \tag{8.44}$$

The two inequalities are identical when $L = L'$, and otherwise only the more severe is worth keeping in mind. Because of the inequality (8.43), a quantity called the coefficient of coupling between two inductors is defined as follows:

$$k \equiv \frac{M}{\sqrt{LL'}} \tag{8.45}$$

Evidently the closest possible coupling occurs for $k = 1$. It might be thought that the inequality (8.43) is not rigorous, since it was deduced from an ideal case which can only be approximated in ordinary practice. Actually, (8.43) is quite general because the inductive properties are independent of resistance in their definition.

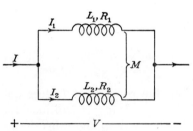

FIG. 8.5. Coupled inductors connected in parallel.

8.8. Parallel Inductors. Parallel inductors have some importance in laboratory practice, for sometimes a variable inductor is arranged to be connected in this manner. Referring to Fig. 8.5, the equations for the pair of inductors are

$$I = I_1 + I_2 \tag{8.46}$$

$$V = L_1 \frac{dI_1}{dt} \pm M \frac{dI_2}{dt} + R_1 I_1 \tag{8.47}$$

$$V = L_2 \frac{dI_2}{dt} \pm M \frac{dI_1}{dt} + R_2 I_2 \tag{8.48}$$

where the upper signs are used when the positive current senses I_1 and I_2 are consistent, that is, the coupling is positive. If we make the postulate that the resistive terms are to be negligible, it is possible to express V in terms of I in a manner similar to that in an isolated, resistanceless inductor. Omitting the resistive terms and combining these equations after differentiating (8.46), we obtain

$$V = \frac{L_1 L_2 - M^2}{L_1 + L_2 \mp 2M} \frac{dI}{dt} \tag{8.49}$$

Hence to the accuracy of our approximation, the pair of inductors in parallel behaves like a resistanceless inductor whose self-inductance is

$$L_{\text{eff}} = \frac{L_1 L_2 - M^2}{L_1 + L_2 \mp 2M} \tag{8.50}$$

Special methods for alternating current analysis will permit a rigorous discussion of this circuit connection without limitation on the values of resistance.

8.9. Energy Transformations in Inductors. Magnetic Stored Energy. In Sec. 8.6 we remarked that the power VI supplied to an inductor may be accounted for partly by the Joule heat loss in the windings of the inductor, and partly by a transfer of energy to the space or magnetic matter in the vicinity of the inductor. The Joule heat loss may always be written

$$P_J = I^2 R \tag{8.51}$$

where R is an effective resistance of the windings of the inductor, whereas the part transferred to the field may be expressed in terms of an emf ε as

$$P_F = -I\varepsilon \tag{8.52}$$

The sign is in accordance with our convention for an emf. The mechanism of energy transfer to the field is electromagnetic induction, so that ε is given by Faraday's law in terms of the flux Φ linking the inductor and its associated circuit:

$$\varepsilon = -\frac{d\Phi}{dt} \tag{8.53}$$

Substitution of Eq. (8.53) into (8.52) yields

$$P_F = +I\frac{d\Phi}{dt} \tag{8.54}$$

In a time dt therefore, the energy transferred from the electrical circuit to the field is

$$dW_F = P_F \, dt \tag{8.55}$$

Therefore

$$dW_F = I \, d\Phi \tag{8.56}$$

This is the basic equation for energy transfer in an inductor. There is in Eq. (8.56) no implication as to how this energy is disposed of. For example, an interchange of thermal energy may occur between magnetic matter near the coil and the surroundings, or the energy may all be used to establish a magnetic field in empty space. We reserve to a later section the case of systems where mechanical energy is involved, as for instance motors and generators: and we shall speak only of inductors which are fixed in size and position. Equation (8.56) is noncommittal also as to whether the energy transfer is reversible. In case the transfer is reversible, and provided also any magnetic material associated with the inductor is held at a constant temperature, it is proper to speak of the transferred energy as stored in magnetic form. The reader is referred to the discussion in Sec. 4.1 of electrostatic energy, for which the thermodynamic aspects are similar to those involved in magnetic energy.

Let us consider the question of reversibility further. The total energy transferred when the current changes from I_0 to I and the flux from Φ_0 to Φ is the integral of Eq. (8.56):

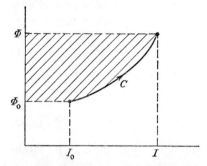

FIG. 8.6. Energy transferred out of a circuit by electromagnetic induction is represented by the shaded area.

$$W_F = \int_{\Phi_0}^{\Phi} I \, d\Phi \qquad (8.57)$$

Evaluation of this integral depends upon the characteristics of the inductor, the state of any ferromagnetic matter in its vicinity (see Chap. 9), and possibly the time-dependence of the current I; for these factors influence the functional relationship between Φ and I. This relationship may be exhibited by a curve C of Φ vs. I, as in Fig. 8.6. The area between C and the Φ axis represents graphically the energy transferred during the process of building up the current when the curve C is followed. Now if the energy transfer is to be entirely reversible, the inductor must follow this same curve C when the current is reduced again. In this case, the energy transferred to the field is all available for restoration to the electric circuit, and is therefore stored. Irreversibility may result from various causes. Ferromagnetic materials, to be studied in the next chapter, are inherently irreversible and dissipate energy as heat when their magnetic state is changed. The changing magnetic field of the inductor may produce electric currents by electromagnetic induction in neighboring conducting materials and thus produce Joule heating which is irreversible. Finally, if very rapid changes are made in the current, as when the current alternates at high frequency, there may be an appreciable irreversible loss of energy from the circuit into a traveling electromagnetic wave. This is called radiation loss. It will be neglected in our present discussion. Irreversible processes are not always undesirable, as for instance in induction heating and in radio broadcasting.

A simple case of magnetic storage of energy is presented by a linear self-inductor. The word linear means that the self-inductance L is constant:

$$L \equiv \frac{d\Phi}{dI} = \text{constant} \qquad (8.58)$$

This characteristic equation specifies the curve C of Fig. 8.6 as a straight line of slope L no matter how the current changes. The energy transfer is therefore reversible.

The integral (8.57) now becomes

$$W_F = L \int_{I_0}^{I} I \, dI = \tfrac{1}{2}L(I^2 - I_0{}^2) \qquad (8.59)$$

The energy stored when the current is I, relative to the energy at zero current, is therefore

$$W_F = U_M = \tfrac{1}{2}LI^2 \qquad \text{linear inductor} \qquad (8.60)$$

A more complex case is that of a pair of coupled inductors. There are now four variables involved in the description of a process of energy transfer: the two currents, I_1, I_2 and the two fluxes Φ_1, Φ_2. The energy transferred in a process P is, by an evident extension of the reasoning leading to Eq. (8.57),

$$W_F = \int_P (I_1 \, d\Phi_1 + I_2 \, d\Phi_2) \qquad (8.61)$$

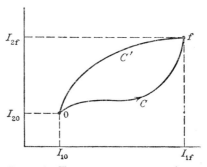

FIG. 8.7. Two processes connecting a pair of states of two inductors.

Let us first suppose that the fluxes Φ_1 and Φ_2 can each be expressed in terms of the two currents by single-valued characteristic functions $\Phi_1(I_1, I_2)$ and $\Phi_2(I_1, I_2)$. This amounts to supposing the process to be reversible, for single-valuedness implies independence of the rate or direction of change of the currents. Note, however, that this postulate does not require linearity of these functions. Now evaluation of an integral like (8.61) between two states $(I_{1,0}, I_{2,0})$ and $(I_{1,f}, I_{2,f})$ requires in general the specification of a path of integration, which may be described by a curve C in an I_2 vs. I_1 graph (see Fig. 8.7). Physically, this means that the two currents may be changed independently and the energy transferred may conceivably depend on their relation during the process. If the characteristic functions are reversible, however, the energy transferred must be independent of the path; that is the integral over any two paths C and C' between common end points must be equal. For, suppose the integral from $(I_{1,0}, I_{2,0})$ to $(I_{1,f}, I_{2,f})$ over C' to represent a larger energy transfer W'_F into the field than the energy W_F for path C. Then since C' is by hypothesis reversible, we could obtain an endless supply of energy in the electrical circuit by operating the pair of inductors around a cycle from $(I_{1,0}, I_{2,0})$ to $(I_{1,f}, I_{2,f})$ by way of C and back by way of C'. If there is no perpetual source of energy in the field, this is contrary to the principle of energy conservation; or if there is an interchange of heat energy at constant temperature occurring in surrounding magnetic matter, the deduction is contrary to the second law of thermodynamics. The statement that $W'_F = W_F$ is therefore proved. It is evident now that stating the characteristic equations of a pair of inductors to be reversible is equivalent to saying that the energy transferred from the circuits to the field when the currents are built up is all returned as the currents die down; and under these conditions it is proper to speak of storage of magnetic energy. We previously found this to hold for the single inductor also; and evidently the result may be generalized to any number of coupled circuits.

The independence of path of the integral (8.61) gives some information about the two characteristic functions Φ_1 and Φ_2. To obtain this information most directly, let us integrate (8.61) by parts between the states 0 and f, over a path specified by a curve C in the I_1 vs. I_2 plane:

$$W_F = [I_1\Phi_1 + I_2\Phi_2]_0^f - \int_C (\Phi_1\, dI_1 + \Phi_2\, dI_2) \qquad (8.62)$$

This transformation simply makes the currents rather than the fluxes the independent variables for the integral. The first term represents the difference in the function $(I_1\Phi_1 + I_2\Phi_2)$ between the initial and terminal points, and thus is patently independent of the path C. Thus if W_F is to be independent of path, it is necessary and sufficient that the integral

$$V \equiv \int_C (\Phi_1\, dI_1 + \Phi_2\, dI_2) \qquad (8.63)$$

be independent of path. According to the theory of two-dimensional line integrals, which may be found in an advanced calculus text, the necessary and sufficient condition that V be independent of path is that in addition to continuity of the functions Φ and their first derivatives,

$$\frac{\partial \Phi_1}{\partial I_2} = \frac{\partial \Phi_2}{\partial I_1} \qquad (8.64)$$

everywhere in a simply-connected region of the I_1 vs. I_2 plane containing C.

The characteristic functions must therefore satisfy Eq. (8.64) at all parts of the $I_1 - I_2$ plane, or at least in whatever regions of this plane the characteristic functions possess the postulated property of single-valuedness. The derivatives in Eq. (8.64) have been defined already in Sec. 8.5 as the mutual inductance coefficients for the two coupled circuits:

$$M_{12} \equiv \frac{\partial \Phi_1}{\partial I_2} \qquad M_{21} \equiv \frac{\partial \Phi_2}{\partial I_1} \qquad (8.65)$$

Therefore when the energy process is reversible, that is, whenever the characteristic functions are single-valued, we have demonstrated the statement given without proof in Sec. 8.5:

$$M_{12} = M_{21} \qquad (8.66)$$

Under these conditions therefore there is only one mutual inductance M for a pair of coupled circuits. This coefficient need not be a constant; it is in general a function of the two currents.

Let us evaluate the stored energy in a reversible coupled pair of inductors in terms of their mutual inductance M and their self-inductances

$$L_1 \equiv \frac{\partial \Phi_1}{\partial I_1} \qquad L_2 \equiv \frac{\partial \Phi_2}{\partial I_2} \qquad (8.67)$$

Using Eqs. (8.65) to (8.67), we may write the total differentials of Φ_1 and Φ_2:

$$d\Phi_1 = \frac{\partial \Phi_1}{\partial I_1} dI_1 + \frac{\partial \Phi_1}{\partial I_2} dI_2 = L_1 \, dI_1 + M \, dI_2$$
$$d\Phi_2 = M \, dI_1 + L_2 \, dI_2 \qquad (8.68)$$

Equation (8.61) then yields for the magnetic energy stored when the currents are I_{1f} and I_{2f}:

$$W_F = U_M = \int_0^{I_{1f}, I_{2f}} [(L_1 I_1 + M I_2) \, dI_1 + (M I_1 + L_2 I_2) \, dI_2] \qquad (8.69)$$

This is readily integrated for the special case of linear inductors, that is, the case where L_1, L_2, and M are constants:

$$U_M = L_1 \int_0^{I_{1f}} I_1 \, dI_1 + L_2 \int_0^{I_{2f}} I_2 \, dI_2 + M \int_0^{I_{1f}, I_{2f}} d(I_1 I_2) \qquad (8.70)$$

Performing the integrations and leaving off the subscript f which is no longer needed for clarity, we find as the stored energy of a pair of linear inductors carrying currents I_1 and I_2:

$$U_M = \tfrac{1}{2} L_1 I_1{}^2 + \tfrac{1}{2} L_2 I_2{}^2 + M I_1 I_2 \qquad \text{linear inductors} \qquad (8.71)$$

Extension of the foregoing paragraphs to discussion of systems of more than two reversible inductors is easily made. The basic energy transfer formula for a set of n inductors is the generalization of Eq. (8.61):

$$W_F = \sum_{i=1}^{n} \int_{\Phi_{i0}}^{\Phi_{if}} I_j \, d\Phi_j \qquad (8.72)$$

If the inductors are linear in their characteristics and consequently the energy transformation is reversible, Eq. (8.72) may be integrated at once to give the energy stored relative to the condition of zero currents and fluxes. Since this energy is independent of the process by which the final condition is attained, we are free to specify a process arbitrarily. Let us build up all currents simultaneously, so that at a given time they all have the same fraction α of their final values I_{jf}:

$$I_j = \alpha I_{jf} \quad \text{all } j \tag{8.73}$$

Because of the postulated linearity of the system, the fluxes at this stage of the process must also have the fraction α of their final values Φ_{jf}:

$$\Phi_j = \alpha \Phi_{jf} \quad \text{all } j \tag{8.74}$$

Thus the flux differentials are

$$d\Phi_j = \Phi_{jf} \, d\alpha \tag{8.75}$$

Since I_{jf} and Φ_{jf} are constants, Eq. (8.72) now becomes

$$W_F = U_M = \int_0^1 \alpha \, d\alpha \sum_{j=1}^n I_{jf}\Phi_{jf} \tag{8.76}$$

Therefore, with omission of the subscript f which is no longer needed,

$$U_M = \tfrac{1}{2} \sum_{j=1}^n I_j\Phi_j \quad \text{linear system} \tag{8.77}$$

It is to be noted that in order for Eq. (8.77) to be valid, the system must be magnetically isolated; for any externally caused magnetic field would in general produce fluxes even when all the currents of the system were zero, in contradiction to (8.74). Permanent magnets within the system, which would have the same effect, are excluded by the postulate of linearity.

The case of irreversible energy transformation is not easily treated in detail. The energy formulas (8.57), (8.61), and (8.72) remain valid, but the characteristic equations for the fluxes become multiple-valued, involving not only the currents but their rates of change and possibly also their previous time dependence. The coefficients of self- and mutual inductance are then not single-valued functions of the currents. Even though some relation between the two mutual inductances could be derived for this case, its statement could not be simple, for it would have to contain sufficient conditions to specify these coefficients uniquely. In practical cases, we often treat an irreversible component approximately, as if it were reversible. The important irreversible case of the iron-core transformer is exhaustively treated in electrical-engineering treatises. One simple statement may be made here about any irreversible system which is carried through a cyclic process so that its initial and final fluxes and currents are the same. Because of the irreversibility, there is in general a net energy transfer during the cycle. Except in the case of reception of radiation, this transfer is always a loss from the electrical circuit. The amount of energy involved per cycle for a single inductor may be written in either of two forms. By Eq. (8.57)

$$W_{cycle} = \oint_{cycle} I \, d\Phi \tag{8.78}$$

Integration by parts shows that this is equivalent to

$$W_{cycle} = -\oint_{cycle} \Phi \, dI \tag{8.79}$$

A positive sign in these expressions indicates loss of energy from the circuit. Similar expressions for a pair of inductors may be obtained at once from Eqs. (8.61) and (8.62). It may be well to note that a knowledge of the characteristic function Φ during the cycle does not permit distinguishing between stored and dissipated or radiated energy during any part of the cycle; all that is known is the total energy, all dissipated or radiated, for a complete cycle.

PROBLEMS

8.1. A square loop of No. 10 copper wire is made with a side length of 5 cm. This wire has a resistance of 3.37 ohms and a mass of 46.8 kg per kilometer. Suppose the loop to be dropped between the poles of a magnet, so that its sides are, respectively, horizontal and vertical, and so that a uniform field of 1.5 webers/m² exists over its top side while the field at the bottom side is zero. When it falls steadily, what is (a) the rate of fall? (b) the current in the loop?

8.2. Show how in a problem like the preceding, where a square loop drops in a uniform, horizontal field B normal to the top side, the velocity of fall is determined by B, by the acceleration g of gravity at the place, and by the resistivity r_1 and mass density D of the material of the wire.

8.3. A rigid, straight wire of length l rotates about an axis perpendicular to it and at one end, in a plane normal to a uniform magnetic field of magnitude B. Contact is made to the wire at the axle, and at the free end by a rail in the form of a circular arc. When the angular speed is ω, what is the induced emf in the wire?

8.4. A single-turn, plane loop of area A rotates in a uniform magnetic field about an axis parallel to its plane with uniform angular speed. If the component of induction normal to the axis is B_n, show that the resulting induced emf in the loop is

$$\mathcal{E} = B_n A \left(\frac{d\theta}{dt}\right) \sin \theta$$

where θ measures the angular position of the loop. Define θ carefully, showing it and all sign conventions in a sketch.

8.5. A plane loop of wire of area A is rotated at an angular speed ω in a uniform field about an axis making an angle a with its positive normal direction. If ϕ is the rotation angle, and if the magnetic induction B makes an angle β with the axis of rotation, find an expression for the induced emf in the loop.

8.6. A coil of 500 turns is wound on a cylindrical form with a 3-cm radius. This form rotates at 90 rpm about a vertical axis which intersects its own axis perpendicularly. The maximum induced emf is found to be 0.250 mv. What can be concluded about the earth's magnetic field in which the coil is located?

8.7. A coil of N coaxial turns of cross-sectional area A is rotated at a speed ω radians/sec about a horizontal axis which intersects its own axis perpendicularly. The maximum emf induced by the earth's uniform magnetic field B is measured as a function of compass orientation of the axis of rotation.

  a. How much can be determined, and in what way, about the earth's field?

  b. For any special orientations used in (*a*), show at what angular position of the coil the maximum emf is found.

8.8. Given two coaxial, circular loops of radius a, with a large separation x. One of them carries a steady current I and moves along the common axis with velocity $v = dx/dt$. What is the emf induced in the other loop as a result of the changing flux from the moving loop? Use the dipole approximation. Sketch the problem showing directions of current, motion, and emf.

8.9. A pole of a long magnet produces in the air a magnetic induction field which is approximately radial and spherically symmetrical, with magnitude

$$B = \frac{K}{4\pi r^2}$$

where $K = 4.0 \times 10^{-5}$ weber. This pole is moved along the axis of a coil of 200 turns bound together in the form of a circular loop of 5 cm radius. When the pole is just passing through the center of the coil with a velocity of 20 cm/sec, what is the induced emf in the coil?   *Ans.* 16 mv.

8.10. From Eq. (8.7), Sec. 8.1, the emf induced in an infinitesimal length dl of a circuit moving in a fixed magnetic field B is $d\mathcal{E} = \mathbf{B} \cdot d\mathbf{l} \times \mathbf{v}$, where **v** is the velocity of this element. Using the ideas of Sec. 7.12, show then that for any complete, rigid circuit C moving in a fixed external field B, the total emf is $-d\Phi/dt$.

8.11. Show that the self-inductance of a long solenoid of N turns, having a total length l which is very large compared with its radius a, has in the limit $a/l \to 0$ a self-inductance of

$$L = \frac{\pi\mu_0 N^2 a^2}{l}$$

Specify units to be used in this equation.

8.12. An air-core solenoid 80 cm long has 500 turns, and its circular cross section has a diameter of 2 cm.

  a. Find its approximate self-inductance. See the formula of the preceding problem.

  b. What is the self-linked flux when the current is 2 amp?

  c. What rate of change of current will produce a self-induced emf of 0.3 volt?

8.13. A coil of N turns is wound uniformly on a circular, nonmagnetic ring whose cross section is rectangular. Each turn is thus approximately a rectangular loop, and the centers of these rectangles lie on a circular axis normal to their area. Considering the ring as a section of a cylindrical shell, its inner and outer radii are, respectively, a and b, and its axial length is l. Find an algebraic formula for the self-inductance of this flat toroid coil. Reduce this to a numerical formula for inductance in microhenrys when the dimensions are given in centimeters.

8.14. A very short coil of 50 turns of fine wire is wound over the center of a long, air-core solenoid of 1,000 turns with a length of 1 m and a cross-section radius of 1 cm. Find the mutual inductance of the two coils, making a plausible approximation which should be justified by a brief argument.

8.15. Two single-turn, circular loops of wire are mounted concentrically in air. Their radii are b and c, with $c \ll b$. Find the mutual inductance of the two loops as a function of the angle θ between their normals.

8.16. Given a pair of similar coils of 400 turns in the form of circular loops of 5 cm radius. These are mounted coaxially in air, with their centers 2 m apart; and an alternating current $I = 0.10$ amp sin (377t sec^{-1}) flows in one coil, while the second coil is connected to a high-resistance circuit. Find (a) the mutual inductance of the two coils and (b) the induced emf in the second coil. Assume Ampère's law for steady-current fields to hold for this slowly varying field.

8.17. Two circular loops have parallel axes, and the distance r between their centers is sufficiently great compared with their radii that dipole approximations can be used. Show how one should be placed relative to the other so that at finite distances r their mutual inductance is zero.

Ans. r makes an angle of about 55° with the axes.

8.18. A certain air-core coil is characterized by a self-inductance of 10 mh and a resistance of 13 ohms. It is connected directly to a 2.0-volt battery of negligible internal resistance, with a switch in the circuit. Just after the switch is closed, when the current has reached one-third of its final, steady value, what is (a) the rate of change of the current? (b) the self-induced emf? (c) the rate of energy storage? (d) the rate of energy dissipation?

8.19. An inductor characterized by self-inductance L_1 and resistance R_1 has a mutual inductance M to a second inductor. Suppose that the circuit of the first inductor is closed through a resistance R and that the second inductor is connected in a circuit whose current is I_2. Show that when I_2 changes by an amount ΔI_2 between two steady values, the resulting total charge that flows in the first inductor is

$$q_1 = - \frac{M \, \Delta I_2}{R_1 + R}$$

8.20. A standard solenoid of 360 turns is 60 cm long and has a circular cross section with a diameter of 5.0 cm. A short secondary coil of 500 turns is wound with fine wire over the center of the solenoid. If the secondary coil, whose resistance is 125 ohms, has its ends connected together, what charge flows in it when the solenoid current with a steady magnitude of 1.5 amp is reversed in direction? (See the preceding problem.)

8.21. Show how a rectangular loop of wire of length a and width b can be considered as two rectangles of sides $a/2$ and b with one side in common and connected in series. Show from this that the self-inductance of the loop measuring $a \times b$ is less than twice that of a single loop measuring $a/2 \times b$.

8.22. Show how three identical circular loops, each of self-inductance L can be placed so that the mutual inductance of each pair is the same quantity M, and so that when all three loops are connected in series the total self-inductance is

a. Either $3L + 6M$ or $3L - 2M$, depending on the mode of connection
b. Either $3L - 6M$ or $3L + 2M$, depending on the mode of connection
Note: The dipole approximation may be used to check flux senses.

8.23. Show that

$$\sqrt{LL'} < \frac{L + L'}{2}$$

except in the case of $L = L'$, when these two expressions become equal.

8.24. Three coils of equal numbers of turns are wound uniformly over the same part of the same cylindrical form. Assuming unity coupling coefficient between each pair, show that when the three coils are connected in series the possible values of net self-inductance of the combination are either L or $9L$, where L is the self-inductance of each coil alone.

8.25. Fill in the steps in the derivation of Eq. (8.49), Sec. 8.8, for the potential difference across a pair of parallel, coupled inductors of negligible resistance.

8.26. An inductor is made with two identical coils of self-inductance L whose mutual inductance M is varied by changing their relative position. Show that when these coils are connected in series the total self-inductance is $2(L \pm M)$, whereas in parallel connection the total self-inductance is $\frac{1}{2}(L \pm M)$. Find the total resistances.

8.27. A pair of coupled, linear inductors isolated in space has the following characteristics: self-inductances $L_1 = 20$ mh and $L_2 = 5$ mh; coefficient of coupling $k = 0.60$. The currents are to be built up from zero to, respectively, $I_{1f} = +100$ ma and $I_{2f} = -200$ ma, where the signs are given according to a mutually consistent convention. Show in a sketch four different, simple processes for building up the currents. Find for each process the final energy, using direct integration over the path of the process.

8.28. Two coils are wound with N_1 and N_2 turns, respectively, the turns of each coil being closely bundled together and forming plane figures of areas, respectively, A_1 and A_2. These coils are laid flat on a nonmagnetic table with a distance R between them large compared with the dimensions of either coil. Find their mutual inductance, and show directly in this case that $M_{21} = M_{12}$.

8.29. The current I in a certain iron-core coil is raised from 0 to $+50$ ma during a process in which the self-inductance of the coil varies according to the expression $L = L_0 - KI$, where $L_0 = 25$ henrys, and $K = 0.2$ henry/ma. Find the following:

  a. The self-linked flux as a function of current for this process. Sketch the result qualitatively, indicating what is undetermined by the conditions of the problem.

  b. The energy which has been transferred from the electrical circuit during the process, excluding Joule heat loss in the winding.

8.30. Use an expression for the stored magnetic energy of a pair of coupled linear inductors to prove generally the inequality connecting their mutual and self-inductances, $M < \sqrt{L_1L_2}$ (see Sec. 4.7, Chap. 4).

8.31. Show that in a reversible but not necessarily linear system of current circuits, the magnetic energy stored relative to the zero-current condition can be written in the form

$$U_M = \int_0^{I_{1f}} L_1(I_1,0)\, I_1\, dI_1 + I_{1f} \int_0^{I_{2f}} M(I_{1f},I_2)\, dI_2 + \int_0^{I_{2f}} L_2(I_{1f},I_2)\, I_2\, dI_2$$

where the self- and mutual inductances have been written as functions of the two currents.

CHAPTER 9

MAGNETIC PROPERTIES OF MATTER

9.1. Macroscopic and Microscopic Analysis. The approach to a study of magnetic material is quite different in a macroscopic than in a microscopic analysis. The macroscopic approach deals only with quantities observable in experiments involving large numbers of elementary charges or of molecules of matter. Outside of the field of X and gamma rays, distances are large compared with molecular distances and outside of work with ultrahigh radio frequencies and above, times are usually long compared with most characteristic times for the motion of elementary charges. The macroscopic electromagnetic laws must therefore be concerned with space and time averages of microscopic phenomena, which means that a statistical type of analysis is required to relate the macroscopic to the microscopic phenomena. The task of microscopic analysis is to specify this statistical relationship and to predict the macroscopic laws from a microscopic model of matter, charge, and current.

In the field of electrostatics, we have found that it is not too difficult to begin with a microscopic picture of matter and from it to build up macroscopic laws, as was done in Chap. 3. A similar analysis for magnetic material is more cumbersome mathematically because of the vector nature of electric current. It seems wiser here to postpone microscopic considerations, and in fact to make it possible for the reader to skip detailed statistical analysis. We shall therefore introduce statements and definitions based on macroscopic experiment without justifying them by reference to atomic phenomena. Besides giving a simpler approach to our problem, this method has the advantage of giving the reader a contrast to the methods employed in electrostatics.

To begin a frankly macroscopic presentation of magnetism, we shall state that so far as magnetic experiments are concerned, all free electric currents may be considered to result from a macroscopic vector function called the free current density $\mathbf{J}$. In terms of $\mathbf{J}$ the current across any macroscopic surface S may be found by taking the surface integral

$$I = \int_S \mathbf{J} \cdot \mathbf{n} \, da \tag{9.1}$$

This was justified in Sec. 5.1 by a microscopic analysis, but we are not now to be concerned with such justification. Next we may lay down the experimental fact that there may be defined a macroscopic vector **B** called the magnetic induction. This vector will correctly give the force on an element of wire which was discussed in Sec. 7.2:

$$dF = I \, d\mathbf{l} \times \mathbf{B} \tag{9.2}$$

If a free current density is involved rather than a free current filament, this vector **B** is to result in a force per unit volume on the current

$$\frac{d\mathbf{F}}{dV} = \mathbf{J} \times \mathbf{B} \tag{9.3}$$

For all macroscopic purposes, it is found to be valid to assume that this vector **B** has these properties even for wires immersed in magnetic matter or for currents flowing in magnetic matter; and furthermore it is experimentally correct to ascribe to the macroscopic **B** the basic property discussed in Sec. 7.6, that at all points whether inside matter or not its divergence is zero:

$$\frac{\partial B_x}{\partial x} + \frac{\partial B_y}{\partial y} + \frac{\partial B_z}{\partial z} = 0 \tag{9.4}$$

so that

$$\oint_S \mathbf{B} \cdot \mathbf{n} \, da = 0 \tag{9.5}$$

for any macroscopic closed surface S.

Another basic property of this **B** vector function is that if Φ is the flux of the macroscopic **B** vector, so that

$$\Phi \equiv \int_S \mathbf{B} \cdot \mathbf{n} \, da \tag{9.6}$$

then an electromotive force or line integral of a macroscopic electric field **E** exists around any macroscopic loop C through which the flux is changing:

$$\varepsilon \equiv \oint_C \mathbf{E} \cdot d\mathbf{l} = -\frac{d\Phi}{dt} \tag{9.7}$$

Here Φ is computed from Eq. (9.6) by using any surface S whose boundary is C. This is Faraday's law of Sec. 8.2 stated in purely macroscopic terms. It is to be valid for any curve C, whether in or enclosing matter or not.

Now for steady-state magnetism, the **B** vector whose measurable properties are those given above is found by experiment to be expressible in terms of the free currents, the geometry, and the magnetic properties of the matter involved in any problem. When experiments are conducted with only the so-called nonmagnetic substances, then to the approximation that the magnetic characteristics of such substances may be neglected, the magnetic induction is given by Ampère's law in its various forms for free space (see Secs. 7.3 and 7.7):

$$\mathbf{B} = \frac{\mu_0 I}{4\pi} \int \frac{d\mathbf{l} \times \mathbf{r}^0}{r^2} \tag{9.8}$$

$$\mathbf{B} = \frac{\mu_0}{4\pi} \int \frac{\mathbf{J} \times \mathbf{r}^0}{r^2} \, dV \tag{9.9}$$

$$\oint_C \mathbf{B} \cdot d\mathbf{l} = \mu_0 I_c \tag{9.10}$$

Here I_c is the current linking the closed loop C of integration.

9.2. Relative Permeability. State of Magnetization. We turn now to the description of the magnetic properties of matter. Let us base our discussion on an ideal experiment. Suppose a toroid coil to be wound in such a fashion that the radius a of the ring on which it is wound is large compared with the radius b of each turn. First consider the magnetic induction inside the turns when the core is completely nonmagnetic and current I flows. This is realizable by having the turns rigid so that the coil can support itself *in vacuo*. In this case, the circuital law (9.10) shows that the field inside on a circle threading through the N turns of the coil and having radius r about the center of the coil has a component B_0 tangent to this circle, such that

$$B_0 2\pi r = \mu_0 N I \tag{9.11}$$

Therefore

$$B_0 = \frac{\mu_0 N I}{2\pi r} \tag{9.12}$$

Now r varies between $a + b$ and $a - b$ for the interior of the coil; so that if $a \gg b$, B_0 is essentially constant in this region. We shall consider only this tangential component B_0 of the field. Other components are in fact small in a well-designed coil, and furthermore are not involved in the measurements we shall be discussing.

Next suppose some material whose magnetic properties are to be investigated is introduced as the core of this coil. To the present stage of our work in magnetism, we are not in a position to calculate the tangential magnetic induction B now existing in the core when current I flows in the coil; but we can easily specify how B can be determined by experiment. A secondary coil of n turns may be wound upon the toroid, and the magnetic flux through the secondary is then

$$\Phi = n B \pi b^2 \tag{9.13}$$

Thus a change ΔB in the tangential magnetic induction causes a change in flux through the secondary

$$\Delta \Phi = n\pi b^2 \, \Delta B \tag{9.14}$$

The flux change $\Delta\Phi$ can be measured in turn by the electric charge q which passes through the secondary when $\Delta\Phi$ occurs. The current i in the secondary is, by Ohm's and Faraday's laws,

$$i = -\frac{1}{R}\frac{d\Phi}{dt} \tag{9.15}$$

if R is the resistance of the secondary. The charge that flows in infinitesimal time dt is therefore

$$dq = i\,dt = -\frac{1}{R}\,d\Phi \tag{9.16}$$

Hence, by integration, for a finite flux change there is a finite charge

$$q = -\frac{1}{R}\Delta\Phi \tag{9.17}$$

Therefore, by substitution of Eq. (9.17) into (9.14),

$$\Delta B = -\frac{R}{n\pi b^2}q \tag{9.18}$$

If now we can be sure of some starting condition for which $B = 0$, the method outlined here shows how B may be determined by measurements of electric charge which specify increments of B. It may be well to remark for the benefit of the careful reader that Eq. (9.18) remains valid even when the flux produced by the secondary itself is considered, provided the state is steady before and after the change in B is made. To be rigorous, it is only necessary to add to Φ a term Φ_s, the self-linked flux of the secondary; and since Φ_s is zero at the beginning and ending of the measurement, it does not affect the $\Delta\Phi$ or q of Eqs. (9.17) and (9.18).

We are now in position to describe the magnetic properties of the core material in terms of the original field B_0, measured by the primary current I, and the resulting induction B. The relationship of B to B_0 is, to be sure, something which is in general characteristic both of the material and of the geometry; but for the toroid geometry it is not affected by the dimensions of the toroid, so long as $a \gg b$. This is so because the specimen of material is endless, being ring-shaped; and B has essentially the same value at all points in the material, just as the initial field B_0 has the same value at all points interior to the toroid.

Suppose that we plot B vs. B_0 for a given sample of material. We shall find that for the so-called nonmagnetic materials there is a strict proportionality between these quantities, at least until B_0 becomes excessively large. This leads us to define the ratio

$$K_m \equiv \frac{B}{B_0} \tag{9.19}$$

as a quantity characteristic of the material. This is called the relative permeability, or specific permeability, of the material. For a few materials, of which iron is the most important example, K_m is found to be far from constant. In fact, the plot of B vs. B_0 for iron is not even a single-valued function, but depends in a complicated way on the past history of the specimen. Furthermore, this function may cross the B axis of the graph, so that $K_m = \infty$ at these points of the graph. This means that in our toroid experiment, there may be a residual magnetic induction even when we reduce B_0 to zero. We are led by this phenomenon to consider the difference function

$$M' \equiv B - B_0 \tag{9.20}$$

as a quantity specifically contributed to the magnetic induction by the magnetic material itself. In case M' exists when $B_0 = 0$ we say that the material has a permanent magnetization. The value of M' under any general conditions may be considered to define the state of magnetization of the material under those conditions. For this purpose, giving M' is equivalent to giving both B_0 and K_m, except that M' is definite at all times, while the description in terms of B_0 and K_m breaks down when $K_m = \infty$.

There is one feature of this discussion which we have so far neglected. It sometimes happens that a material is magnetically anisotropic. In this case the result of the experiment in the toroid coil depends upon how the crystal axes of the material are oriented relative to the tangential direction in the coil. We shall mention this anisotropic case only briefly in what follows, and for the present we shall assume that if the radius a of the toroid is very large, we can bend the crystalline material sufficiently so as to have always a definite relation between its axes and the tangential direction in the coil. We can imagine carrying out the described experiments in this manner for different directions relative to the crystal axes. The resulting description of the magnetic properties of anisotropic matter thus has a directional aspect, but is otherwise the same as for the simpler isotropic materials.

9.3. Magnetizing Force. In the experiment described in the preceding section, we have defined a quantity M' which specifies the state of magnetization of the material in the core of a toroid coil. It is natural to conceive of the initial field B_0 in the coil as being the cause of M'. In the case of permanent magnetization of the core, B_0 cannot be the sustaining cause of M'; but we may regard M' then as an effect which can remain after the cause is removed. If we look at B_0 as the cause of M', it is natural to conceive of this cause as existing in the toroid coil independently of what material forms the core. Now it is not our intention here to attach any specific physical meaning to the concept that B_0 may be regarded as the cause of the magnetized state of the material, but merely to show that it may be helpful in our thinking to use an auxiliary magnetic field function in addition to B.

It is evident that if we intend to generalize upon the quantities B, B_0, and M' which we have considered in the toroid experiment, we must consider vector rather than scalar functions. Throughout the discussion of the preceding section, we spoke of B and B_0 as tangential components of vectors $\mathbf{B}$ and $\mathbf{B}_0$, and thus in writing

$$M' \equiv B - B_0 \tag{9.20}$$

we imply that M' is also the tangential component of a vector. In other words, the state of magnetization of material has a directional aspect. Thus in general Eq. (9.20) should be replaced by

$$\mathbf{M}' \equiv \mathbf{B} - \mathbf{B}_0 \quad \text{in toroid} \tag{9.21}$$

Now if we consider the quantity $\mathbf{B}_0$ to be defined in the toroid regardless of the actual presence of core material as the field which would be there in absence of core material, then it is evident that $\mathbf{B}_0$ will always obey Ampère's circuital law for empty space:

$$\oint_C \mathbf{B}_0 \cdot d\mathbf{l} = \mu_0 I_C \quad \text{in toroid} \tag{9.22}$$

This law indeed was what we used in the preceding section for computing B_0.

We proceed to define in general an auxiliary vector like the $\mathbf{B}_0$ in the toroid, framing our definition in terms which may be applied to any situation. First, we shall regard the vector $\mathbf{M}'$, as defined for the toroid experiment, to have a unique meaning in terms of the microscopic structure of the magnetic material, so that we may speak of a vector function $\mathbf{M}'$ characteristic of any magnetic material at any place or time in a magnetic system. Just what $\mathbf{M}'$ means is a matter to be elucidated as we delve further into magnetic analysis; but it is always to mean the same thing that it did in the toroid. Thus we have given a general definition of $\mathbf{M}'$. Next we shall extend the definition of the auxiliary field vector $\mathbf{B}_0$ which we had for the toroid, in such a way that $\mathbf{B}_0$ is always to be defined for a general system not in terms of the field of a coil of wire nor as an initial field in any sense, but rather by turning Eq. (9.21) around to read

$$\mathbf{B}_0 \equiv \mathbf{B} - \mathbf{M}' \quad \text{general} \tag{9.23}$$

It is now necessary to appeal in a rather general way to the conclusions of magnetic experiments. All experiments with steady-state magnetism show that this auxiliary field B_0 still has the property (9.22) which the initial free-space field has for the toroid experiment:

$$\oint_C B_0 \cdot dl = \mu_0 I_C \quad \text{general} \quad (9.24)$$

This beautifully simple and general relation is the most important characteristic of the newly defined auxiliary vector field. It would in fact be nice if Eq. (9.24) could serve to define B_0, but it turns out mathematically that (9.24) is insufficient for a definition. However, as long as we are engaged in defining a new quantity, we can at least define our auxiliary field so as to make this basic equation as simple as possible. For this reason alone, we shall not use B_0 itself in future; but instead we define as our auxiliary vector

$$H \equiv \frac{1}{\mu_0} B_0 \quad (9.25)$$

This means that H always satisfies the simple relation

$$\oint_C H \cdot dl = I_C \quad (9.26)$$

Notice that H will in general differ from B_0 both in dimensions and in magnitude, depending on the system of units employed, although these two quantities are always proportional to one another.

To summarize the definition of H, we may now rewrite Eq. (9.25) in terms of the meaning of B_0, as given in (9.23),

$$H = \frac{1}{\mu_0} B - \frac{1}{\mu_0} M' \quad (9.27)$$

It is customary, for no other reason than convention, to replace M' also by another vector M having the dimensions of H rather than of B:

$$M \equiv \frac{1}{\mu_0} M' \quad (9.28)$$

Finally, in terms of M we may write the definition of H as

$$H \equiv \frac{1}{\mu_0} B - M \quad (9.29)$$

The auxiliary vector H which we have now defined has received various names. Perhaps the name most nearly in line with our presentation is magnetizing force. Frequently also H is called magnetic intensity or magnetic field; but these terms are rather confusing since it is magnetic induction B rather than H which is the basic force vector analogous to electric field E. The vector M defining the state of magnetization of material is called intensity of magnetization or magnetic polarization.

Appropriate units for magnetizing force are quickly deduced from the basic property (9.26). Evidently [H] = current per length. Since the current surrounded by a path C is often found by multiplying the number of turns of a coil by the current in the coil, a usual term for the unit of H is the ampere-turn per meter.

9.4. Terminology of Magnetism. The most important practical classification of magnetic materials divides them into two groups: those which exhibit the phenomenon of permanent polarization, so that M may exist in absence of H, and those which do not have this property. The former class of materials is called ferromagnetic, since iron is the chief material in this class, while the latter class is called nonferromagnetic. It happens that this same classification also separates materials into those exhibiting relatively strong magnetic properties, and those whose magnetic properties are relatively weak, respectively.

The distinction between isotropic and anisotropic materials referred to in Sec. 9.2 is a somewhat delicate matter, for a material may appear anisotropic in two very different ways. The property which we shall denote by the term isotropic is that if we start from a demagnetized condition in which M = 0 = H in the material and then proceed to build up H in a fixed direction, then the resulting M is always parallel (or antiparallel) to H, and furthermore the relation of M to H is independent of the direction of H in the material. Both of these properties are implied in saying that the material has no preferred directions of its own. Conversely, an inherently anisotropic material is one for which the above conditions are not true. In such a material, the relation of M to H depends on direction in the material, and except for certain privileged directions the M is not even parallel to H. The reason for specifying in the above remarks that the experiment is to start from a condition where M = 0 = H is that in ferromagnetic materials a permanent polarization M_0 may otherwise be present. Such a permanent polarization in effect makes the material anisotropic, for it marks one direction out from all others. If a magnetizing force is then produced in a direction different from M_0, it is evident that the resultant magnetization M will not in general be in the direction of H. In most of our work, we shall be concerned only with isotropic materials. In addition, we shall describe the magnetic properties of ferromagnetic materials only for the case where the vectors H and M remain parallel (or antiparallel); for this will be true in many practical cases where the magnetic field direction remains always the same at a given place in the material.

It is evident from Eq. (9.29) that when H and M are in the same direction, although not necessarily with the same sense, then B also has this direction. We may therefore discuss the magnetic properties of isotropic materials in terms of the relative algebraic magnitudes of these three vectors; and we may use scalar factors to express one vector in terms of another. It is customary to write

$$\frac{B}{H} \equiv \mu \tag{9.30}$$

where μ is called the permeability of the material, under the particular conditions. The vector fields are then related as follows:

$$\mathbf{B} = \mu\mathbf{H} \tag{9.31}$$

Referring to the toroid experiment of Sec. 9.2, and combining Eq. (9.19) with the scalar form of Eq. (9.25), Sec. 9.3, we see that the specific permeability K_m previously defined may be written

$$K_m = \frac{B}{\mu_0 H} \tag{9.32}$$

Comparison of Eq. (9.30) now shows that K_m and μ are related by the equation

$$K_m = \frac{\mu}{\mu_0} \tag{9.33}$$

This gives to K_m the significance of the ratio of the permeability of a given material with that of empty space, whence the name specific or relative permeability. It will be noted that K_m is dimensionless.

Sometimes it is of interest not only to use the ratio B/H, but to plot in detail the B-H curve. Such plots are basic in the discussion of ferromagnetism. The ratio of increments on this curve

$$\mu_\Delta \equiv \frac{\Delta B}{\Delta H} \tag{9.34}$$

is called the incremental permeability. The limit of μ_Δ for $\Delta H \to 0$, which is of course the slope of the B-H curve, is called the differential permeability:

$$\mu_d \equiv \frac{dB}{dH} \tag{9.35}$$

Another way in which magnetic properties are described is to give the ratio of M to H, called the magnetic susceptibility,

$$\frac{M}{H} \equiv \chi_m \tag{9.36}$$

The corresponding vector equation for isotropic cases is

$$\mathbf{M} = \chi_m \mathbf{H} \tag{9.37}$$

Notice that χ_m is a pure number, according to our definitions of $\mathbf{M}$ and $\mathbf{H}$. The susceptibility is particularly used in a microscopic discussion of the origin of the magnetic characteristics of matter. It will appear as we proceed that **M** is interpretable as a dipole moment per unit volume, so that χ_m is also a quantity whose interpretation is in terms of unit volume of material. For comparison between theory and experiment, it is convenient to minimize the dependence of χ_m on the density of material by using instead of χ_m a quantity whose interpretation is in terms of unit mass of material. This is done by defining the mass susceptibility or specific susceptibility

$$\chi_{ms} \equiv \frac{\chi_m}{d} \tag{9.38}$$

where d is the density of the material. Another useful quantity is obtained by referring χ_m to a particular number of molecules of the material. For this purpose we define the molar susceptibility, or susceptibility per mole of material

$$\chi_{m\,mol} \equiv \frac{W}{d}\,\chi_m \tag{9.39}$$

where W is the molecular weight of the material.

We may deduce from Eqs. (9.29), (9.31), and (9.37) a relation between permeability and susceptibility:

$$\chi_m = \frac{\mu}{\mu_0} - 1 \tag{9.40}$$

In terms of specific permeability,

$$\chi_m = K_m - 1 \tag{9.41}$$

9.5. Nonferromagnetic Materials. Along with absence of permanent magnetization, the isotropic nonferromagnetic materials are characterized by the existence of a single-valued functional relationship between B and H. These materials fall into two categories. According to whether their susceptibility is positive or negative, they are called paramagnetic and diamagnetic, respectively. A positive susceptibility implies that **M** has the same sense as **H**, while a negative susceptibility indicates that **M** has the opposite sense to that of **H**. The presence of a diamagnetic material in the core of a toroid coil results in a smaller magnetic induction than if the coil has a vacuum core.

Diamagnetic susceptibilities are usually independent of magnetizing force. This means that the B-H curve is a straight line through the origin. For most diamagnetic materials, the specific susceptibility is independent of temperature. The magnitude of diamagnetic susceptibility is always small. A representative but fairly large value is that of water in which $\chi_m = -9.0 \times 10^{-6}$ in the particular rationalized system of units which we have been using.

Paramagnetism frequently has a larger magnitude than diamagnetism. Strong paramagnetism is especially notable for example in iron compounds, in the rare earths and rare earth compounds, and in oxygen. Liquid oxygen will hang as a bridge between the poles of a strong electromagnet. Its susceptibility at $-183°C$ is $3,400 \times 10^{-6}$.

Under ordinary circumstances, the B-H curve for strongly paramagnetic materials is closely a straight line through the origin. For very intense magnetic fields applied to certain materials at low temperature, the phenomenon of saturation has been observed. This means that there is a falling away of the B-H curve below the straight line to which it approximates at lower magnetizing force (cf. Fig. 9.1). Theoretically, saturation results from an upper limit to the possible value of magnetization M of the material. Saturation in paramagnetic material is of purely theoretical interest, since under all ordinary conditions the proportionality of B to H holds to a high degree of accuracy. Thus we shall always consider μ and χ_m to be independent of H in practice for paramagnetic material.

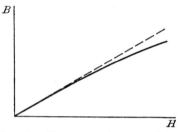

FIG. 9.1. Paramagnetic saturation.

The behavior of specific paramagnetic susceptibility as a function of temperature is of considerable theoretical importance. In general, strong paramagnetic properties become more marked as the temperature becomes lower. A useful generalization of the temperature dependence of χ_{ms} for paramagnetic materials is the Curie-Weiss law

$$\chi_{ms} = \frac{C}{T + \Delta} \tag{9.42}$$

Here C and Δ are approximately constants for a given material, at least in a restricted temperature range; and T is the absolute temperature.

Weak paramagnetism, with susceptibilities of the order of magnitude characteristic of diamagnetism, is found in many solid materials, for example in metallic and alkali elements. The paramagnetism in these cases frequently shows little dependence on temperature.

9.6. Ferromagnetism. The salient aspects of ferromagnetism are the development of permanent magnetization, the extreme importance of the magnetic past history as well as the actual magnetizing force in determining the magnetic induction, and the large permeability. Values of relative permeability of $K_m = 10^4$ or larger are not uncommon. Susceptibility χ_m is little used in describing ferromagnetism. In diamagnetism and paramagnetism, χ_m is more significant than K_m not only for theoretical purposes but because K_m is always but little different from unity.   On the other hand, in ferromagnetism the unit difference between χ_m and K_m is trivial compared to the ordinary magnitudes of K_m; and the induction B is of greater practical significance than the magnetization M.   The B-H curve and the permeability are therefore quantities most used for discussing ferromagnetic properties.

The ferromagnetic elements are iron, cobalt, and nickel, in decreasing order of permeability.   Cobalt and nickel are used chiefly in alloys with iron, as also are many other elements which are themselves nonferromagnetic.   There are certain ferromagnetic alloys whose constituents are all nonferromagnetic.   An example is Heusler's alloys which are composed of copper, manganese, and aluminum.   Ferromagnetic alloys of copper, manganese, and tin are also known.   Conversely, there are also some iron alloys having almost no ferromagnetism.

The properties of ferromagnetic materials are dependent on temperature.   For most iron alloys, however, small changes around room temperature are not important.   Ferromagnetic properties exist only below a characteristic temperature for each material.   When the temperature rises through this value, which is called the Curie point, the material ceases to be ferromagnetic and becomes paramagnetic.   For iron, the Curie point is about 790°C.

The method of preparation of ferromagnetic metals is of as great importance as their constituents in determining their magnetic characteristics.   Of particular importance is the annealing treatment.   The reader is referred to engineering handbooks for further discussion of this point.

A number of special terms are used in the description of ferromagnetic materials.   Most of these refer to the B-H curve obtained for a given specimen when H is changed in a monotonic and cyclic way from a maximum in one sense to an equal maximum in the other.   Of course this change is one of algebraic magnitude only and not of direction; for we are understanding in this discussion that **H** is not to change its direction during the course of a test, although it may change its sense. The curve obtained for such a cyclic change of H becomes a definite, closed figure if the cycle is traversed a sufficient number of times.   This figure is called a hysteresis loop.   A sample loop is shown in Fig. 9.2. The arrowheads show the sense in which the loop is traversed.   This sense is inherent in the nature of the experiment, not arbitrary.   It is impossible to drive the magnetic specimen around the curve the other way.   The word hysteresis is derived from a Greek word implying a lagging behind.   Inspection of the figure will show that the changes of B lag behind those of H.   For example, starting at the maximum positive H and reducing H to zero we do not yet reduce B to zero; but B crosses zero when H has already become negative.

The great complexity introduced into the quantitative study of magnetic properties by their dependence on the previous magnetic history of the sample must not be underestimated. The state of a sample of material is not at all uniquely specified by the representative point on the *B-H* diagram. For example, if in successive tests the same specimen of material is brought to the origin of the *B-H* curve by different magnetic processes, and then a magnetizing force *H* is built up, the representative point on the *B-H* diagram will in general follow different curves in the successive tests. The following definitions have been found sufficient to make the description of the properties of a given sample independent of its previous magnetic experiences.[1] A specimen will be said to be in its neutral state when $B = 0$ and $H = 0$ in it and when it has been

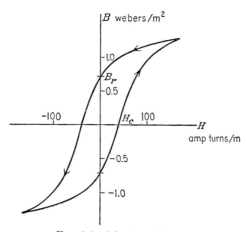

FIG. 9.2. A hysteresis loop.

brought to this condition by a standard process of demagnetization. The demagnetization process is to consist of the application of a sufficiently large magnetizing force which is to be successively reversed in direction and steadily decreased to a sufficiently low value. The term sufficiently high may have different quantitative meanings for different materials, but it indicates that experimentally the value of the maximum demagnetizing force is irrelevant so long as it exceeds a critical value for the given material. The term sufficiently low has reference to the magnitude of the magnetizing forces to be subsequently applied to the material. The lowest magnetizing forces applied in the demagnetization must be less than the values involved in subsequent experiments if it is not to affect the results of those experiments. It should be remarked that the result of a standard demagnetization procedure leaves the material in such a state that it responds equally to magnetizing forces in either direction;

[1] See C. W. Burrows, "On the Best Method of Demagnetizing Iron for Magnetic Testing," *Natl. Bur. Standards Bull.* (*U.S.*) **4**, 205 (1907–1908).

and this may be made a defining characteristic of the neutral state. The neutral state must not be confused with the virgin state of metal which subsequent to its solidifying has never been subjected to magnetizing force of appreciable intensity. The virgin state is experimentally different from the neutral state.

Now suppose that a ferromagnetic specimen in the neutral state is gradually magnetized by building up the field H. The resulting B-H curve is called the initial magnetization curve and is characterized by a certain slope with which it departs from the origin, followed by a region of increasing slope, after which the slope decreases and saturation sets in, i.e., the magnetization M approaches a maximum value. If at a certain point of this magnetization process, the magnetizing force is no longer increased beyond a certain value H', but is reversed monotonically to $-H'$, and then monotonically returned again to $+H'$, the resulting B-H curve is an almost closed loop. A closed hysteresis loop which may be repeated indefinitely results after a sufficient number of monotonic reversals. Now if the hysteresis loop is established in this manner, it is found to be symmetrical about the origin of the B-H graph. A closed hysteresis loop symmetrical about the origin is called a normal hysteresis loop.

There is of course an infinite family of normal hysteresis curves for any sample of ferromagnetic material, corresponding to different maximum magnetizing forces. These curves are the basis of technical description of the material. The values of B at the tips of the normal hysteresis loops are called the values of normal induction corresponding to the given magnetizing force. The plot of the values of normal induction against magnetizing force is called a normal magnetization curve. It shows the same general characteristics as the initial magnetization curve, but is not identical with it. The ratio of the values of B and H at a point on the normal magnetization curve is called the normal permeability at this point; and the maximum value of this ratio is the maximum permeability and is frequently used in tabulations. The term differential permeability may refer to the slope of this normal magnetization curve.

Certain terms are applied to the axis intercepts of a normal hysteresis loop. The B intercept is called the normal residual induction, while the H intercept is called the normal coercive force. High values of residual induction and coercive force are valuable characteristics in material to be used for permanent magnets. Materials capable of large residual induction are said to be retentive, or to have the property of large retentivity.

We shall investigate the subject of magnetic energy in a later section. It may be remarked here, however, that the area enclosed by a hysteresis loop is a measure of energy lost to heat during the magnetic cycle per unit volume of material. It is therefore desirable for material which is to be used in alternating current instruments to have as small a loop as possible. For use in components of communications systems, special materials have been developed whose hysteresis loop departs only slightly from a straight line through the origin so long as the magnetizing force is not too great. These materials may be said to be approximately linear, because their differential permeability is approximately constant.

9.7. Origins of Magnetic Susceptibility. The magnetic properties of matter are all to be deduced from the motion of electric charge, since experiment has failed to show the existence of such an entity as net magnetic charge. We are not concerned here as we were in Chap. 7 with the macroscopic circulation of current. The currents which give rise to diamagnetism, paramagnetism, and ferromagnetism are of three general kinds. There is first the perpetual, microscopic circulation of charge involved in orbital motion of the electrons in atoms or molecules. Presumably there is also within the structure of the electron itself a submicroscopic current associated with the spin angular momentum, for the electron possesses an intrinsic dipole moment. Finally, the conduction electrons in a solid may have their random motion influenced in a systematic way by a magnetic field, so as to produce a small dipole moment per unit volume even in the absence of macroscopic conduction. A quantum-mechanical picture of the solid state, combined with the knowledge of atomic and molecular structure derived from spectroscopy, gives an excellent account of how these microscopic currents are affected by an applied magnetic field so as to produce the phenomena of magnetization. It will be taken for granted in this section that the magnetization $\mathbf{M}$ of Sec. 9.3 is a net magnetic dipole moment per unit volume. The effects to be expected from such a dipole moment will be investigated in detail in succeeding sections. Here we are concerned rather with a brief outline of the ways in which the magnetization is produced.

Because of its negative susceptibility accompanied by a permeability less than μ_0, a diamagnetic body opposes the establishment of magnetic flux in its substance. This action finds a ready explanation in Faraday's and Lenz's laws. The production of magnetic flux is accompanied by an emf which acts upon the moving electrons of the diamagnetic material, particularly in their orbital circulation. According to Lenz's law, the reaction of these microscopic currents is such as to produce an opposing magnetic flux. Unlike macroscopic currents so induced in material of finite conductivity, these microscopic currents are not subject to decay by Joule heat loss. Thus the opposing flux remains as long as the external flux that induced it. Such reasoning might seem to imply that all materials should be diamagnetic. Indeed this process of diamagnetism must operate universally, but it may be overridden by other mechanisms producing a flux of the same sign as that externally applied.

Strong paramagnetism results from the existence of permanent dipole moments of the atoms, ions, or molecules of the material. The torque on a current circuit in an external field is in such a sense as to make the external flux through it positive, that is, to cause its own self-linked flux to have the same sign as the externally produced flux, or to turn its dipole moment toward parallelism with the field (cf. Secs. 7.12 and 7.13). Likewise, if an electronic shell of the atoms or molecules in a material has a magnetic moment, and if this shell is free to be oriented by an applied magnetic field, an alignment occurs which increases the flux through the material and produces a net component of dipole moment parallel to the field. This alignment is never perfectly complete because of the thermal energy which tends toward a random orientation of the atomic moments. The net result is a statistical distribution of orientation of the molecules, the field direction being favored for the dipole moment. It is evident that paramagnetic susceptibilities having this origin will be temperature dependent, increasing as the temperature decreases. Thus the Curie-Weiss law, Eq. (9.42), is qualitatively accounted for. The quantitative statistical analysis of strong paramagnetism was carried through by Langevin. It should be remarked that by no means all atoms or molecules in their stable electronic configurations have a permanent magnetic dipole moment. Furthermore, not all materials whose atoms have such a moment are paramagnetic, since the interaction between atoms may prevent alignment of the moments.

Weak paramagnetism in a solid material arises from alignment by the external magnetic field of the intrinsic (spin) magnetic moments of some of the conduction electrons. This effect is so small as to require an appreciable correction for concomitant diamagnetism. It is not strongly temperature dependent, as the electronic energy distribution itself changes little from absolute zero up to moderate temperatures.

Ferromagnetism requires a highly special condition of the atoms in a solid material, as is indicated by the infrequent occurrence of this striking phenomenon. This condition involves both the electronic structure of the atoms and the distance between atoms in the crystalline state. When the condition is fulfilled, it is shown by quantum mechanics that the most stable, or lowest energy, configuration of the electrons of a crystal is that in which the spin magnetic moments are parallel. The result is spontaneous and complete alignment of these spins, with a consequent enormous magnetization and flux density inside the crystal. In the unmagnetized state, an entire microcrystal of material does not polarize in a single direction. Rather it contains subregions called domains which are uniformly polarized, each in its own direction, so that the net macroscopic magnetic moment and average flux density of the crystal are zero in the unmagnetized state. Magnetic domains are affected by an externally applied field in two distinct ways. The direction of their spontaneous polarization may suddenly shift, to take any one of a number of discrete, preferred directions relative to the crystal axes. Not all these possible directions are equally favored; some are called directions of easy magnetization, others directions of hard magnetization. In addition, the domain boundaries may shift with application of a field, enlarging those domains whose polarization direction is parallel or nearly parallel to the field. The process of magnetization involves many small irreversible changes in the domains. This results in the Barkhausen effect, the occurrence of many small discontinuities in magnetization, whose presence may be detected as a hissing noise in an audio amplifier fed by induced current in a coil about the specimen. The irreversibility manifests itself on a large scale in the phenomenon of hysteresis, involving inherent loss of energy to heat during a cycle of magnetization and demagnetization.

9.8. Magnetic Polarization. We turn now to a statistical analysis of magnetic matter based upon microscopic considerations, in which the magnetic properties of matter are all to be deduced from the motion of electric charge. The currents which give rise to paramagnetism, diamagnetism, and ferromagnetism are entirely on a microscopic scale, as discussed in Sec. 9.7, except in the case of superconducting material. We may speak of closed paths in a statistical sense for these currents even though the quantum mechanics forbids a naïve concept of electron orbits. Closed currents are characterized by a magnetic dipole moment, for which see Secs. 7.8, 7.9, and 7.13. The magnetic dipole moment of a microscopic system, if nonvanishing, determines not only its field at macroscopic distances but also the force and couple which it experiences in an external magnetic field whose inhomogeneities are on a macroscopic scale. It appears therefore that the basic quantity with which a microscopic analysis of magnetic matter is concerned is the magnetic dipole moment.

The analysis to be undertaken is statistical in nature because of the vast numbers of elementary magnetic dipoles even in macroscopically small volume elements, and because these dipoles are not uniform either in magnitude or direction. To cope with this situation, a vector average may be made of the dipole moments contained in a macroscopically small volume element ΔV which still contains many dipoles. Suppose the individual dipoles in ΔV have moments $\mathbf{m}_i$ which may be all different. We shall first define the magnetic dipole moment of the material within ΔV as the vector sum

$$\Delta m \equiv \sum_{\text{in } \Delta V} m_i \tag{9.43}$$

This is a sensible definition because the magnetic field of the matter within ΔV, at large distances compared to the linear dimensions of ΔV, is just the field of a single magnetic dipole located at ΔV and having the moment Δm. A formal proof of this statement need hardly be made, for it follows at once from the basic principle of superposition, *i.e.*, that the total magnetic induction is the vector sum of the separate contributions from all sources, and from the fact that the vector dipole moment enters linearly into the formulas for the magnetic induction of a dipole.

The average dipole moment per unit volume of the matter in ΔV is now defined:

$$\overline{M} \equiv \frac{\Delta m}{\Delta V} = \frac{1}{\Delta V} \sum_{\text{in } \Delta V} m_i \tag{9.44}$$

The next step is to postulate macroscopic continuity of the magnetic material. This is to mean that a sort of limiting value of $\overline{M}$ is approached, not precisely but within whatever statistical accuracy is required, when ΔV shrinks about a point inside the material so as to become macroscopically infinitesimal while yet containing enough dipoles for good statistics. If now such a limit exists and varies continuously from point to point within the material, the material will be said to be macroscopically continuous. This limit M is then a vector point function describing the magnetic state of the material. It will be written in the notation of an ordinary limit:

$$M \equiv \lim_{\Delta V \to 0} \overline{M} = \lim_{\Delta V \to 0} \frac{1}{\Delta V} \sum_{\text{in } \Delta V} m_i \tag{9.45}$$

On boundary surfaces where the nature of the material changes macroscopically, the limit (9.45) does not exist. The function M will be considered discontinuous on such surfaces, but elsewhere it is to be continuous. It should be remarked that the same symbol M has been used in the macroscopic discussion of Sec. 9.3, to designate a quantity called the intensity of magnetization of matter. It will be shown later that that quantity, which was defined only in rather general terms, is identical with the quantity now explicitly defined by Eq. (9.45). For brevity, M will be called simply the magnetization vector. The mks unit for M is the ampere per meter, since the unit for m_i is the ampere-meter^2.

From a macroscopic viewpoint, the limit (9.45) may be expressed in the notation of the differential calculus:

$$M = \frac{dm}{dV} \tag{9.46}$$

The differential $d\mathbf{m}$ will refer to the element of dipole moment possessed by the material in the volume element dV. Thus we write

$$dm = \mathbf{M}\, dV \tag{9.47}$$

The magnetic moment $\mathbf{m}$ of an entire magnetized body of macroscopic size will be defined as the vector sum of the dipole moments of its parts. This may be written as a sum, like Eq. (9.43), but extended over the whole body, or it may be obtained in terms of the magnetization vector $\mathbf{M}$ by integration of Eq. (9.47) over the volume V of the body:

$$\mathbf{m} \equiv \int_{\text{entire body}} d\mathbf{m} = \int_V \mathbf{M}\, dV \tag{9.48}$$

Consider for example an idealized bar magnet consisting of a uniformly, axially magnetized bar of uniform cross section with its ends plane and parallel to one another. Whenever $\mathbf{M}$ is constant, Eq. (9.48) reduces to

$$\mathbf{m} = \mathbf{M}V \qquad \text{constant } \mathbf{M} \tag{9.49}$$

Now let l be the axial length of the bar magnet, and let $\mathbf{1}$ be its vector length parallel to the magnetization. The magnetization may then be written in terms of its scalar magnitude M as follows:

$$\mathbf{M} = \frac{M\mathbf{1}}{l} \tag{9.50}$$

Substitution of Eq. (9.50) into (9.49) yields

$$\mathbf{m} = M\left(\frac{V}{l}\right)\mathbf{1} \tag{9.51}$$

Finally, the quantity V/l is the cross section A of the bar, that is its section by planes perpendicular to its axis. The magnetic dipole moment of the bar magnet is therefore

$$\mathbf{m} = MA\mathbf{1} \tag{9.52}$$

9.9. Exterior Field of Magnetized Material. Magnetic Bound Charge. This section and those to follow deal with bodies of material in which the magnetization vector $\mathbf{M}$ exists. Such bodies will be called magnets, and their material will be said to be magnetized. It is to be understood that these terms have no reference to whether the magnetization is permanent. The magnetic induction produced directly by the magnetization of a body will be given the symbol $\mathbf{B}_m$ to differentiate it from the total magnetic induction $\mathbf{B}$, which may include contributions from macroscopic current in the body as well as the fields of external sources and surrounding matter.

It is easy to derive the field $\mathbf{B}_m$ of a magnet at an exterior point of observation. The material in an infinitesimal volume element dV located at (x,y,z) has a magnetic dipole moment given by Eq. (9.47):

$$dm = \mathbf{M}(x,y,z)\, dV \tag{9.53}$$

At any finite distance r of macroscopic magnitude there results a dipole field which may be expressed in terms of a scalar potential function having the form given in Eq. (7.114), Sec. 7.10,

$$dU_m^* = \frac{(dm) \cdot \mathbf{r}^0}{4\pi r^2} \tag{9.54}$$

Here $\mathbf{r}^0$ is the unit vector directed from the volume element dV toward the observer, whose coordinates we shall call (x',y',z'). The element of magnetic scalar potential due to the material in dV at the external observer is therefore

$$dU_m^* = \frac{\mathbf{M}(x,y,z) \cdot \mathbf{r}^0}{4\pi r^2}\, dV \tag{9.55}$$

Integration now gives the magnetic scalar potential of an entire magnet of volume V at an exterior point of observation:

$$U_m^*(x',y',z') = \frac{1}{4\pi} \int_V \frac{\mathbf{M} \cdot \mathbf{r}^0}{r^2}\, dV \tag{9.56}$$

As indicated, this expression is a function only of the observer's coordinates, for the coordinates of the element of volume dV have been integrated out. The magnetic induction at the observer is found by multiplying $-\mu_0$ into the gradient of the potential with respect to the observer's coordinates, according to Eq. (7.112), Sec. 7.10,

$$B_{mx} = -\mu_0 \frac{\partial U_m^*}{\partial x'} \qquad B_{my} = -\mu_0 \frac{\partial U_m^*}{\partial y'} \qquad B_{mz} = -\mu_0 \frac{\partial U_m^*}{\partial z'} \tag{9.57}$$

Now Eq. (9.56) has the same form as the electrostatic potential of a dielectric body at an exterior point of observation, as given in Eq. (3.9), Sec. 3.4. The reader is referred to a mathematical transformation given there whose result is Eq. (3.33). Transferring the notation to that appropriate for the magnetized body, and noting the absence of any factor in Eq. (9.56) to correspond to the ϵ_0, we obtain the following significant transformation of (9.56):

$$U_m^*(x',y',z') = \frac{1}{4\pi} \oint_S \frac{\mathbf{M} \cdot \mathbf{n}}{r}\, da$$

$$- \frac{1}{4\pi} \int_V \frac{1}{r} \left(\frac{\partial M_x}{\partial x} + \frac{\partial M_y}{\partial y} + \frac{\partial M_z}{\partial z} \right) dV \tag{9.58}$$

The surface integral here is extended over the entire boundary surface S enclosing the volume V of the magnet, and $\mathbf{n}$ is the unit normal to S outward from V. The advantage of Eq. (9.58) over (9.56) is that in (9.56) the source of the magnetic scalar potential is the vector point function $\mathbf{M}$, while in (9.58) the potential has scalar sources. These scalar sources will be called, respectively, the surface density of magnetic bound charge, $\sigma^*(x,y,z)$, and the volume density of magnetic bound charge, $\rho^*(x,y,z)$,

$$\sigma^*(x,y,z) \equiv \mathbf{M}(x,y,z) \cdot \mathbf{n} \tag{9.59}$$

$$\rho^*(x,y,z) \equiv -\left(\frac{\partial M_x}{\partial x} + \frac{\partial M_y}{\partial y} + \frac{\partial M_z}{\partial z}\right) = -\operatorname{div} \mathbf{M} \tag{9.60}$$

Surface and volume integrals, respectively, of these densities yield the quantity which we shall define as magnetic bound charge, q^*. Thus elements dq^* of bound charge are

$$dq^* = \sigma^* \, da \tag{9.61}$$

and

$$dq^* = \rho^* \, dV \tag{9.62}$$

In accordance with these definitions, Eq. (9.58) for the scalar potential of a magnet may be rewritten in the following forms:

$$U_m^* = \frac{1}{4\pi} \oint_S \frac{\sigma^*}{r} \, da + \frac{1}{4\pi} \int_V \frac{\rho^*}{r} \, dV \tag{9.63}$$

$$U_m^* = \frac{1}{4\pi} \int_{\text{magnet}} \frac{dq^*}{r} \tag{9.64}$$

Concentrations of magnetic bound charge are called magnetic poles. By convention, a positive concentration of charge is called a north pole while negative charge forms a south pole. This terminology arises from the use of a magnet as a compass. When a simple magnet having one pole of each sign is so mounted as to rotate freely in a horizontal plane, it is its positive pole which seeks north. The total, net magnetic bound charge of any magnet is exactly zero. This follows from the definitions that have been made as a mathematical identity:

$$q_{\text{total}}^* \equiv \oint_S \sigma^* \, da + \int_V \rho^* \, dV \equiv 0 \tag{9.65}$$

This identity is proved just as the corresponding identity for the electrostatic case in Sec. 3.4. It will be seen from Eqs. (9.59) to (9.62) that the mks unit of magnetic bound charge or pole strength is the ampere-meter, for the unit of magnetization is the ampere per meter.

The exterior field of a magnet may be obtained explicitly by applying formulas (9.57) to Eq. (9.63) or (9.64) and differentiating within the integral sign. In this process it is to be remembered that the variables of differentiation, (x',y',z'), appear only in the distance r:

$$r = \sqrt{(x' - x)^2 + (y' - y)^2 + (z' - z)^2} \tag{9.66}$$

The results of the differentiation may be expressed in vector form as follows:

$$\mathbf{B}_m = \frac{\mu_0}{4\pi} \int_V \frac{\rho^* \mathbf{r}^0}{r^2} \, dV + \frac{\mu_0}{4\pi} \oint_S \frac{\sigma^* \mathbf{r}^0}{r^2} \, da \tag{9.67}$$

$$\mathbf{B}_m = \frac{\mu_0}{4\pi} \int_{\text{magnet}} \frac{\mathbf{r}^0 \, dq^*}{r^2} \tag{9.68}$$

where $\mathbf{r}^0$ is the unit vector from the element of integration at (x,y,z) toward the observer:

$$\mathbf{r}^0 = \frac{(x' - x)\mathbf{i} + (y' - y)\mathbf{j} + (z' - z)\mathbf{k}}{\sqrt{(x' - x)^2 + (y' - y)^2 + (z' - z)^2}} \tag{9.69}$$

Algebraic details are left to the reader.

Magnetic bound charge is so useful a concept that it has dominated the treatment of permanent magnets. It provides a simple picture of the sources of the external field of a magnet, but the picture is essentially an artificial one. The external field of a magnet is not just the result of local conditions at the poles, but is more properly the superposition of the dipole fields of all the parts of the magnet. The artificial nature of magnet poles is indicated by the absence of any net magnetic charge on a magnet, as predicted in Eq. (9.65) and confirmed by experiment. This is dramatically demonstrated by cutting a bar magnet in two. Instead of obtaining one piece of matter with a net north magnetic charge and one with a net south charge, one finds that two new poles of opposite sign appear at the newly severed ends. Each piece becomes a complete bar magnet with equal north and south poles, and has no net magnetic charge.

Let us apply the concept of magnetic bound charge to an idealized bar magnet having uniform cross-sectional area A and a uniform longitudinal magnetization whose scalar magnitude is M. In this case, the magnetic bound charge appears entirely as a surface density on the two end faces of the bar, which form the poles of the magnet. By integration of Eq. (9.61) over each of the ends in turn, the north and south poles of the bar magnet are quickly found to be

$$q_N^* = +MA \qquad q_S^* = -MA \tag{9.70}$$

The magnitude of either charge, $q^* = q_N^* = -q_S^*$, is called the pole strength of the bar magnet. The magnetic scalar potential of the bar magnet is easily found for such distances from both of the poles that they may be considered as point charges.

This is the case when the variations in the distance r and the unit vector $\mathbf{r}^0$ of equations (9.64) and (9.68) are negligible over the extent of a pole. These quantities may then be withdrawn from the integrals, and the resulting potential and magnetic induction are

$$U_m^* = \frac{q_N^*}{4\pi r_N} + \frac{q_S^*}{4\pi r_S} = \frac{q^*}{4\pi}\left(\frac{1}{r_N} - \frac{1}{r_S}\right) \tag{9.71}$$

$$\mathbf{B}_m = \frac{\mu_0 q^*}{4\pi}\left(\frac{\mathbf{r}_N^0}{r_N^2} - \frac{\mathbf{r}_S^0}{r_S^2}\right) \tag{9.72}$$

In these equations, r_N and r_S are the respective distances from the north and south poles to the observer, while $\mathbf{r}_N^0$ and $\mathbf{r}_S^0$ are the corresponding unit vectors directed toward the observer. It will be noted that the magnetic scalar potential of a point pole falls off as the inverse first power of the distance, while the corresponding magnetic induction is radial and follows the inverse-square law.

The magnetic dipole moment of a magnet as defined in Eq. (9.48), Sec. 9.8, may be expressed in terms of magnetic bound charge. Consider the x component of the magnetic dipole moment of a body of volume V:

$$m_x = \int_V M_x \, dV \tag{9.73}$$

The integrand of Eq. (9.73) may be expanded in the following way:

$$M_x = \left[\frac{\partial}{\partial x}(xM_x) + \frac{\partial}{\partial y}(xM_y) + \frac{\partial}{\partial z}(xM_z)\right]$$
$$- x\left[\frac{\partial M_x}{\partial x} + \frac{\partial M_y}{\partial y} + \frac{\partial M_z}{\partial z}\right] \tag{9.74}$$

where x is a coordinate of the point of integration in an arbitrary cartesian system. By comparison of Eq. (9.60), the volume density ρ^* of magnetic bound charge may be identified as part of (9.74), so that (9.74) becomes

$$M_x = \left[\frac{\partial}{\partial x}(xM_x) + \frac{\partial}{\partial y}(xM_y) + \frac{\partial}{\partial z}(xM_z)\right] + x\rho^* \tag{9.75}$$

Substitution of Eq. (9.75) into (9.73) now yields

$$m_x = \int_V \left[\frac{\partial}{\partial x}(xM_x) + \frac{\partial}{\partial y}(xM_y) + \frac{\partial}{\partial z}(xM_z)\right] dV + \int_V x\rho^* \, dV \tag{9.76}$$

The next step is to transform the first integral of Eq. (9.76) into a surface integral by means of the divergence theorem, for which see Sec. 7.6. The vector whose divergence is the integrand here is $x\mathbf{M}$. As a result of the transformation, Eq. (9.76) takes the form

$$m_x = \oint_S x\mathbf{M} \cdot \mathbf{n} \, da + \int_V x\rho^* \, dV \tag{9.77}$$

where S is the complete boundary surface of V and $\mathbf{n}$ is the outward unit normal to S. The surface density σ^* of bound magnetic charge, as given in Eq. (9.59), can now be identified as a factor in the surface integral. Thus

$$m_x = \oint_S x\sigma^* \, da + \int_V x\rho^* \, dV \tag{9.78}$$

Similar equations for the other components m_y and m_z of the magnetic dipole moment may be combined with Eq. (9.78) into a single vector equation

$$\mathbf{m} = \oint_S \mathbf{r}\sigma^* \, da + \int_V \mathbf{r}\rho^* \, dV \tag{9.79}$$

where $\mathbf{r} = x\mathbf{i} + y\mathbf{j} + z\mathbf{k}$ is the vector distance from the origin to the point of integration. This result may finally be expressed in terms of the general element dq^* of magnetic bound charge:

$$\mathbf{m} = \int_{\text{magnet}} \mathbf{r} \, dq^* \tag{9.80}$$

Equation (9.80) relates the magnetic dipole moment of a body to its magnetic bound charge in exactly the same way as the electric dipole moment of a system is related to the electric charge (see Sec. 1.14). There is a difference, however, in that the corresponding electrostatic equation is a definition, whereas Eq. (9.80) is a deduction from a definition of different form.

As an elementary example of the use of Eq. (9.80), consider a bar magnet so thin that its poles may be treated as point charges, $\pm q^*$. Let the vector positions of the poles be $\mathbf{r}_N$ and $\mathbf{r}_S$, respectively, relative to the origin of coordinates. For this case, Eq. (9.80) yields at once

$$m = q^*(\mathbf{r}_N - \mathbf{r}_S) \tag{9.81}$$

But

$$\mathbf{r}_N - \mathbf{r}_S = \mathbf{l} \tag{9.82}$$

where $\mathbf{l}$ is the vector length of the magnet from its south to its north pole. Therefore

$$\mathbf{m} = q^*\mathbf{l} \tag{9.83}$$

Because of Eqs. (9.70), this result checks with Eq. (9.52) which was derived for a uniformly magnetized bar.

9.10. Internal Field of a Magnet. In this section we shall investigate the relationship between the microscopic and macroscopic magnetic induction within magnetic matter, making the basic assumption that the macroscopic field at a point may be identified with a sort of local mean value of the microscopic field in the neighborhood of the point. The only other postulates which need to be made concerning the microscopic field are that it possesses three of the basic properties of the field of macroscopic currents. The first of these is that it can be everywhere written in terms of a vector potential function, but that it cannot be everywhere expressed by a scalar potential function (see Sec. 7.11). Thus if **b** denotes the microscopic magnetic induction of a single, average, elementary current system in magnetic material, there exists a corresponding vector potential function **a** such that at all points of space **b** = **curl a**. In terms of cartesian components,

$$b_x = \frac{\partial a_z}{\partial y} - \frac{\partial a_y}{\partial z}$$

$$b_y = \frac{\partial a_x}{\partial z} - \frac{\partial a_z}{\partial x} \qquad (9.84)$$

$$b_z = \frac{\partial a_y}{\partial x} - \frac{\partial a_x}{\partial y}$$

We assume that the microscopic field of a single elementary system is that of a magnetic dipole at all distances large compared to the size of the system. According to Eq. (7.86), Sec. 7.8, the vector potential **a** may therefore be written in the following form for all distances r greater than some constant s:

$$\mathbf{a} = \frac{\mu_0}{4\pi} \frac{\mathbf{m}_1 \times \mathbf{r}}{r^3} \qquad r \geqq s \qquad (9.85)$$

Here **r** is the vector distance from an arbitrary origin in the elementary system to the observer, r is the magnitude of **r**, and $\mathbf{m}_1$ is the magnetic dipole moment of the system. It is understood that this dipole field is actually a time average, so that the orbital motions of electrons are smeared out into current density. The third assumption is the law of superposition: The total microscopic magnetic induction is the vector sum of independent contributions from all currents, both those which constitute the elementary systems of matter and those which constitute macroscopic current flow; and all these currents are to be treated as flowing in empty space.

In any actual sample of magnetic material the elementary current systems may not be all alike. They may fall into classes, as when the material contains various different kinds of molecules; and in addition, the members of a class will have a statistical distribution in their vector dipole moment. Without loss of generality, we may consider a material having only one class of elementary systems; for the field in a more complex situation is simply the vector sum of the fields of the various classes of systems that may be present. The statistical variation of dipole moment within the class may be taken into account most simply by supposing the actual macroscopic field to be the same as if all the systems in a macroscopically infinitesimal region had a common dipole moment.

If **M** is the magnetization vector and there are N_1 systems per unit volume, this average dipole moment $\mathbf{m}_1$ must be given by

$$\mathbf{m}_1 = \frac{1}{N_1}\mathbf{M} \tag{9.86}$$

since **M** means dipole moment per unit volume (see Sec. 9.8). It is understood that all three of the quantities in Eq. (9.86) are in general functions of position and that this equation holds point by point in the material.

We proceed now to find the microscopic magnetic induction due to a specimen of the ideal magnetic material just described at an average interior point Q, that is, a point which is located at random relative to the structure of the material. Circumscribe Q by a sphere of volume

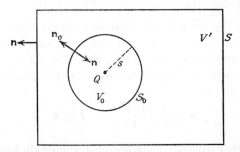

Fig. 9.3. Observation point within magnetic matter, and circumscribed sphere.

V_0 and surface S_0, with a radius s which is macroscopically infinitesimal and yet large enough that the elementary systems in the material outside V_0 have a dipole field at Q (see Fig. 9.3). The magnetic induction $\mathbf{B}_m$ produced at Q by the entire magnet may be written as the sum of the field $\mathbf{B}'$ due to the material in the region V' of the specimen outside V_0, and the field $\mathbf{B}_0$ due to the material within V_0:

$$\mathbf{B}_m = \mathbf{B}' + \mathbf{B}_0 \tag{9.87}$$

Such a division of the field into parts is allowed by the law of superposition. Now the partial field $\mathbf{B}'$ is that of a body of magnetized matter at an exterior point, since Q is exterior to the region V' by the required distance s. This field may therefore be written as in Eq. (9.67) of the preceding section, in terms of the densities ρ^* and σ^* of magnetic bound charge. These densities will appear in the region V' of the magnet outside of V_0, on the actual boundary surfaces S of the magnet, and on S_0 which forms an additional boundary to V'. Thus

$$\mathbf{B}' = \frac{\mu_0}{4\pi}\int_{V'}\frac{\mathbf{r}^0\rho^*\,dV}{r^2} + \frac{\mu_0}{4\pi}\int_S\frac{\mathbf{r}^0\sigma^*\,dS}{r^2} + \frac{\mu_0}{4\pi}\int_{S_0}\frac{\mathbf{r}^0\sigma^*\,dS}{r^2} \tag{9.88}$$

Separate consideration will be given to the last integral of Eq. (9.88) which represents the contribution to $\mathbf{B}'$ from the bound surface charge on S_0. Let us abbreviate as follows:

$$\mathbf{B}' = \mathbf{B}_1 + \mathbf{B}_2 \tag{9.89}$$

where

$$\mathbf{B}_1 = \frac{\mu_0}{4\pi} \int_{V'} \frac{\mathbf{r}^0 \rho^* \, dV}{r^2} + \frac{\mu_0}{4\pi} \int_S \frac{\mathbf{r}^0 \sigma^* \, dS}{r^2} \tag{9.90}$$

and

$$\mathbf{B}_2 = \frac{\mu_0}{4\pi} \int_{S_0} \frac{\mathbf{r}^0 \sigma^* \, dS}{r^2} \tag{9.91}$$

In Eq. (9.91), the unit vector $\mathbf{r}^0$ from dS toward the observer is the same as the unit normal $\mathbf{n}$ to the surface S_0 directed outward from the region V', and the distance r is simply the radius s of S_0 (see Fig. 9.3). The surface charge density function σ^* is given in terms of the magnetization vector $\mathbf{M}$ by Eq. (9.59), Sec. 9.7,

$$\sigma^* = \mathbf{M} \cdot \mathbf{n} \tag{9.59}$$

Equation (9.91) may thus be written in the form

$$\mathbf{B}_2 = \frac{\mu_0}{4\pi s^2} \int_{S_0} \mathbf{n}(\mathbf{M} \cdot \mathbf{n}) \, dS \tag{9.92}$$

Assuming $\mathbf{M}$ to be macroscopically continuous as specified in Sec. 9.8, we may treat $\mathbf{M}$ as a constant everywhere on the macroscopically small surface S_0, assigning to it the magnitude and direction which it has in the magnetic material at Q. The field $\mathbf{B}_2$ is readily evaluated from Eq. (9.92), and turns out to have the value $\frac{1}{3}\mu_0\mathbf{M}$, but this result will not be needed for what follows.

The next part of the analysis is to determine the field $\mathbf{B}_0$ due to the elementary current systems within V_0. Let us indicate the microscopic field of the average elementary system in V_0 by the vector function $\mathbf{b}(\xi,\eta,\zeta)$, where ξ, η, ζ are cartesian coordinates relative to some arbitrary origin in the elementary system which we may call its center. This field has an unknown form at small distances from the center; but at distances as great as s, according to our second basic postulate, it takes on as its limiting form the expression for the field of a magnetic dipole. Consider an elementary system whose center is at a position x, y, z relative to the observation point Q. The coordinates of Q relative to this system are $\xi = -x$; $\eta = -y$; $\zeta = -z$ if the x, y, z and ξ, η, ζ axes are, respectively, parallel; and the magnetic field at Q due to the system is $\mathbf{b}(-x,-y,-z)$. Now if the magnetic material has no macroscopic discontinuity at Q, and if Q is to be a randomly located point, the probable number of elementary systems whose centers lie in a microscopic volume element dV must be independent of the location of dV within the macroscopically small region V_0. This number is $N_1 dV$, where the macroscopic density N_1 of elementary systems is considered to have an essentially constant value everywhere within the small region V_0. The element $d\mathbf{B}_0$ of the field at Q due to the systems in a volume element dV lying at the position x, y, z relative to Q is therefore

$$d\mathbf{B}_0 = N_1 \mathbf{b}(-x, -y, -z)\, dV \tag{9.93}$$

The total field $\mathbf{B}_0$ at Q due to all the elementary current systems within V_0 is the integral

$$\mathbf{B}_0 = N_1 \int_{V_0} \mathbf{b}(-x, -y, -z)\, dV \tag{9.94}$$

Now the region V_0 was taken as spherical, and consequently to every volume element at $-x$, $-y$, $-z$ there is a corresponding element at x, y, z. The value of the integral is therefore unchanged by omission of the negative signs:

$$\mathbf{B}_0 = N_1 \int_{V_0} \mathbf{b}(x,y,z)\, dV \tag{9.95}$$

According to this equation, the field $\mathbf{B}_0$ is equal to N_1 times the volume integral over V_0 of the field which would be produced by a single elementary system located at the center Q of V_0.

We now make use of the assumption that the field $\mathbf{b}$ of a single elementary system may be expressed everywhere by a vector potential function $\mathbf{a}$. By substitution of Eqs. (9.84), the cartesian components of the field $\mathbf{B}_0$ of Eq. (9.95) become

$$B_{0x} = N_1 \int_{V_0} \left(\frac{\partial a_z}{\partial y} - \frac{\partial a_y}{\partial z} \right) dV \tag{9.96}$$

$$B_{0y} = N_1 \int_{V_0} \left(\frac{\partial a_x}{\partial z} - \frac{\partial a_z}{\partial x} \right) dV \tag{9.97}$$

$$B_{0z} = N_1 \int_{V_0} \left(\frac{\partial a_y}{\partial x} - \frac{\partial a_x}{\partial y} \right) dV \tag{9.98}$$

These expressions may be transformed by a vector identity into surface integrals over the surfaces S_0 enclosing V_0.

Consider for example one term of the integral in Eq. (9.98):

$$\int_{V_0} \frac{\partial a_y}{\partial x}\, dV$$

When the volume element dV is expressed in cartesian coordinates, this becomes the triple integral

$$\int_{V_0} \frac{\partial a_y}{\partial x}\, dV = \int_{-s}^{+s} \int_{y_1}^{y_2} \int_{x_1}^{x_2} \frac{\partial a_y}{\partial x}\, dx\, dy\, dz \tag{9.99}$$

Here the limits of the x integration, which may be performed first, are written x_1 and x_2. These limits are, of course, functions of y and z. When the x integration is performed, Eq. (9.99) yields

$$\int_{V_0} \frac{\partial a_y}{\partial x} \, dV = \int_{-s}^{+s} \int_{y_1}^{y_2} [a_y(x_2,y,z) - a_y(x_1,y,z)] \, dy \, dz \qquad (9.100)$$

Now the point (x_2,y,z) lies on the half S_2 of the spherical surface S_0 on which x is positive, while the point (x_1,y,z) lies on the other half S_1 of S_0; for the x integration has swept out a rod-shaped element of V_0 bounded at the ends by these two hemispheres. See Fig. 9.4, which is a section of the sphere V_0 by the z plane in which the x integration is taking place. Since the integral (9.100) is concerned with the values of the function a_y only at the surface S_0, it may be expressed as a surface integral. The differential quantity $dy \, dz$ is the cross section of the rod-shaped volume element shown in Fig. 9.4,

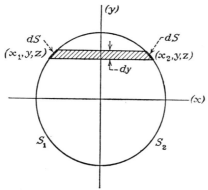

Fig. 9.4. Integration with respect to x within the sphere surrounding the observer.

and as such it is also the projection on the yz plane of the area elements dS in which the volume element cuts the surface S_0. Let n_0 be the unit vector normal to S_0 and outward from V_0, having cartesian components n_{0x}, n_{0y}, n_{0z}. Then

$$dy \, dz = -n_{0x} \, dS \quad \text{at } (x_1,y,z) \text{ on } S_1$$
$$dy \, dz = +n_{0x} \, dS \quad \text{at } (x_2,y,z) \text{ on } S_2 \qquad (9.101)$$

since n_{0x} is a negative quantity on S_1 and a positive quantity on S_2. The two terms of the integral (9.100) may now be written

$$\int_{-s}^{+s} \int_{y_1}^{y_2} a_y(x_2,y,z) \, dy \, dz = \int_{S_2} a_y(x,y,z) n_{0x} \, dS$$
$$- \int_{-s}^{+s} \int_{y_1}^{y_2} a_y(x_1,y,z) \, dy \, dz = \int_{S_1} a_y(x,y,z) n_{0x} \, dS \qquad (9.102)$$

Each surface integral here covers just half of the spherical surface S_0; thus their sum is simply the surface integral over all of S_0. Equation (9.100) therefore becomes

$$\int_{V_0} \frac{\partial a_y}{\partial x} \, dV = \oint_{S_0} n_{0x} a_y \, dS \qquad (9.103)$$

The second term of the integral (9.98) leads to a surface integral of the same type:

$$- \int_{V_0} \frac{\partial a_x}{\partial y} \, dV = - \oint_{S_0} n_{0y} a_x \, dS \qquad (9.104)$$

In this way the whole of the integral (9.98) has been transformed into the surface integral

$$B_{0z} = N_1 \oint_{S_0} (n_{0x}a_y - n_{0y}a_x) \, dS \qquad (9.105)$$

Equations (9.96) and (9.97) lead similarly to the expressions

$$B_{0x} = N_1 \oint_{S_0} (n_{0y}a_z - n_{0z}a_y) \, dS \qquad (9.106)$$

$$B_{0y} = N_1 \oint_{S_0} (n_{0z}a_x - n_{0x}a_z) \, dS \qquad (9.107)$$

These may be expressed by the single vector equation

$$\mathbf{B}_0 = N_1 \oint_{S_0} \mathbf{n}_0 \times \mathbf{a} \, dS \qquad (9.108)$$

Equations (9.105) to (9.108) have the great advantage that they involve the values of the function $\mathbf{a}(x,y,z)$ only at the boundary S_0 of the region V_0, while the former expressions for $\mathbf{B}_0$, Eqs. (9.96) to (9.98), required for their integration the values of $\mathbf{a}$ everywhere in V_0. The form of $\mathbf{a}$ is unknown at small distances from the origin; but on S_0, where the distance from the origin is the radius s, $\mathbf{a}$ becomes by hypothesis the dipole potential. By Eq. (9.85), $\mathbf{a}$ on S_0 is therefore

$$\mathbf{a}(S_0) = \frac{\mu_0}{4\pi s^2} \, \mathbf{m}_1 \times \mathbf{n}_0 \qquad (9.109)$$

where the unit normal $\mathbf{n}_0$ to the surface S_0, directed outward from V_0, has been written for the unit vector $\mathbf{r}^0$. Substitution of Eq. (9.109) into (9.108) gives for the partial field $\mathbf{B}_0$ the expression

$$\mathbf{B}_0 = \frac{\mu_0}{4\pi s^2} \int_{S_0} \mathbf{n}_0 \times (\mathbf{M} \times \mathbf{n}_0) \, dS \qquad (9.110)$$

Here Eq. (9.86) has been used to identify the product $N_1 \mathbf{m}_1$ as the magnetization $\mathbf{M}$ at Q and throughout its infinitesimal neighborhood V_0. The integrand of this equation is a vector triple product which may be expanded by a well-known and readily checked identity to yield

$$\mathbf{n}_0 \times (\mathbf{M} \times \mathbf{n}_0) = (\mathbf{n}_0 \cdot \mathbf{n}_0)\mathbf{M} - (\mathbf{n}_0 \cdot \mathbf{M})\mathbf{n}_0 = \mathbf{M} - (\mathbf{n}_0 \cdot \mathbf{M})\mathbf{n}_0 \quad (9.111)$$

After substitution of Eq. (9.111), (9.110) may be written in the form

$$\mathbf{B}_0 = \frac{\mu_0}{4\pi s^2} \int_{S_0} \mathbf{M} \, dS - \frac{\mu_0}{4\pi s^2} \int_{S_0} (\mathbf{n}_0 \cdot \mathbf{M})\mathbf{n}_0 \, dS \qquad (9.112)$$

Since $\mathbf{M}$ is constant over S_0, the first of these two integrals may be evaluated immediately. The area of S_0 is $4\pi s^2$, and thus the result is

$$\frac{\mu_0}{4\pi s^2} \int_{S_0} \mathbf{M} \, dS = \mu_0 \mathbf{M} \qquad (9.113)$$

The second term in Eq. (9.112) is to be compared with Eq. (9.92) for the partial field $\mathbf{B}_2$. At any point of the surface S_0, the unit normals $\mathbf{n}$ and $\mathbf{n}_0$ are opposite to one another, so that

$$\mathbf{n}_0 = -\mathbf{n} \tag{9.114}$$

When this substitution has been made for $\mathbf{n}$ in Eq. (9.92), it is seen that

$$\frac{\mu_0}{4\pi s^2} \int_{S_0} (\mathbf{n}_0 \cdot \mathbf{M})\mathbf{n}_0 \, dS = \mathbf{B}_2 \tag{9.115}$$

The resulting expression for the field $\mathbf{B}_0$ is now

$$\mathbf{B}_0 = \mu_0 \mathbf{M} - \mathbf{B}_2 \tag{9.116}$$

The problem of finding the magnetic induction $\mathbf{B}_m$ interior to magnetic matter is now essentially complete. Combination of Eqs. (9.87), (9.89), and (9.116) yields

$$\mathbf{B}_m = \mathbf{B}_1 + \mu_0 \mathbf{M} \tag{9.117}$$

whence, by use of Eq. (9.90),

$$\mathbf{B}_m = \frac{\mu_0}{4\pi} \int_{V'} \frac{\mathbf{r}^0 \rho^* \, dV}{r^2} + \frac{\mu_0}{4\pi} \int_S \frac{\mathbf{r}^0 \sigma^* \, dS}{r^2} + \mu_0 \mathbf{M} \tag{9.118}$$

Here $\mathbf{r}^0$ is the unit vector directed from the element of integration toward the observer, and r is the scalar distance between these two points. Before interpreting Eq. (9.118), we shall make one minor change. The volume integral

$$\int_{V'} \frac{\mathbf{r}^0 \rho^* \, dV}{r^2}$$

is formally to be extended only over the part of the magnet exterior to the surface S_0. This surface, which was only a tool for the analysis, is infinitesimal in radius on a macroscopic scale, so that in Eq. (9.118) it serves merely to keep the volume integral from becoming improper by preventing r from becoming zero. Nevertheless, the improper integral

$$\int_V \frac{\mathbf{r}^0 \rho^* \, dV}{r^2}$$

over the whole volume V of the magnet converges, and to it is assigned the limiting value of the proper integral over V' as $s \to 0$. See Sec. 1.8 for a discussion of the similar integral of electrostatics. We may therefore replace the proper integral in Eq. (9.118) by the improper integral, and we obtain the final formula

$$\mathbf{B}_m = \frac{\mu_0}{4\pi} \int_V \frac{\mathbf{r}^0 \rho^* \, dV}{r^2} + \frac{\mu_0}{4\pi} \int_S \frac{\mathbf{r}^0 \sigma^* \, dS}{r^2} + \mu_0 \mathbf{M} \tag{9.119}$$

What is gained in Eq. (9.119) is only a simplification of the limit of the volume integral of (9.118). An abbreviation of Eq. (9.119) results from the use of the differential dq^* of bound magnetic charge for both the elements of charge $\rho^* \, dV$ and $\sigma^* \, dS$:

$$\mathbf{B}_m = \frac{\mu_0}{4\pi} \int_{\text{magnet}} \frac{\mathbf{r}^0 dq^*}{r^2} + \mu_0 \mathbf{M} \tag{9.120}$$

Equations (9.119) and (9.120) may be interpreted in words as follows. The microscopic magnetic induction produced by a specimen of magnetic material at an average interior point may be considered as a sum of two terms: the field of all the bound magnetic charges of the specimen treated as though these charges were located in empty space (for note the presence of the permeability μ_0 of empty space), plus the term $\mu_0 \mathbf{M}$ which involves the local conditions in the neighborhood of the point of observation.

It is easy now to generalize so as to obtain a universal equation for the steady-state magnetic induction field. We may notice first that Eq. (9.120) holds as well outside as inside magnetic material; for when $\mathbf{M} = 0$ at the observer, this equation reduces to Eq. (9.68), Sec. 9.9. Next, the limits of integration may be extended over all space so that the "specimen" is taken to include all magnetic matter in the universe. Finally, given a formula for the induction produced by all magnetic matter, it remains only to add by the principle of superposition the magnetic induction $\mathbf{B}_i$ produced by all steady macroscopic currents in the universe without regard to the presence of magnetic matter, i.e., as though these free currents flowed in empty space. If the macroscopic currents are described by a current density function $\mathbf{J}$, their contribution to the magnetic induction is given by Ampère's law as stated in Eq. (7.27), Sec. 7.3,

$$\mathbf{B}_i = \frac{\mu_0}{4\pi} \int_{\text{all space}} \frac{\mathbf{J} \times \mathbf{r}^0}{r^2} \, dV \tag{9.121}$$

where $\mathbf{r}^0$ as usual is directed from dV toward the observer. Thus the total magnetic induction in a magnetostatic system, whether at a random point in magnetic material or outside magnetic material, is given by

$$\mathbf{B} = \mathbf{B}_m + \mathbf{B}_i = \frac{\mu_0}{4\pi} \int_{\substack{\text{all magnetic} \\ \text{matter}}} \frac{\mathbf{r}^0 \, dq^*}{r^2} + \frac{\mu_0}{4\pi} \int_{\text{all space}} \frac{\mathbf{J} \times \mathbf{r}^0}{r^2} \, dV + \mu_0 \mathbf{M} \tag{9.122}$$

The term $\mu_0 \mathbf{M}$ in Eqs. (9.120) and (9.122) is of extremely great importance. It may happen, as in an isotropic core of a toroid coil, that there is no bound magnetic charge at all, so that this term $\mu_0 \mathbf{M}$ represents the entire contribution of the magnetic material; yet this contribution may augment the magnetic induction produced by the windings by a factor of 10,000 or more.   The absence of bound magnetic charge for this case is apparent from the axial symmetry of the principal component of the magnetic field produced by the windings of the toroid, if we assume the **M** vector to share this symmetry.   Lines having everywhere the direction of **M** are then endless.   They are always tangent to the surface at the surface of the core, so that the surface density σ^* is zero.   There is no net flux of the **M** vector from any region of volume of the core; hence the divergence of $-\mathbf{M}$, which is the volume density ρ^*, is zero in the core.   See Sec. 7.6, where flux and divergence are discussed, in connection with the magnetic induction vector.

The case of the ideal toroid coil has been discussed not for illustration only, but because it was used in Secs. 9.2 and 9.3 as a basis for the discussion of the macroscopic magnetic field vectors.   We shall now take the step of identifying the random-point magnetic induction in the local neighborhood of a point in magnetic material with the macroscopic magnetic induction at that point.   This may be taken as a physical postulate, at least in the absence of a more extended statistical analysis than we have undertaken.   Equation (9.122) is thus an expression for the macroscopic magnetic induction in terms of the magnetization **M** as defined in Sec. 9.8, where **M** is related to the microscopic structure of the material as the magnetic dipole moment per unit volume.   This equation may now be made the connection between the macroscopic and microscopic points of view.   In Sec. 9.3, the contribution of the toroid core to the magnetic induction in the core was called **M′**, while from Eq. (9.122) this contribution is $\mu_0\mathbf{M}$.   The quantity $1/\mu_0\mathbf{M'}$, which was called **M** in Sec. 9.3, is therefore the same as the **M** of Eq. (9.122) and Sec. 9.8.   The macroscopic intensity of magnetization is thus identified with the magnetic dipole moment per unit volume, and the use of the same symbol for these quantities in Secs. 9.3 and 9.8 is justified.

9.11. Microscopic Analysis of Magnetizing Force.   In Sec. 9.3, a macroscopic vector field called the magnetizing force **H** was defined in terms of the macroscopic vectors **B** and **M** by the equation

$$\mathbf{H} \equiv \frac{1}{\mu_0}\mathbf{B} - \mathbf{M} \qquad (9.29)$$

Equation (9.122) of the preceding section yields a formula for **H** at any point of a magnetostatic system, now that the quantities **B** and **M** in this equation have been identified with the macroscopic vectors of the same name in Sec. 9.3:

$$\mathbf{H} = \frac{1}{4\pi}\int_{\substack{\text{all magnetic}\\\text{matter}}} \frac{\mathbf{r}^0\,dq^*}{r^2} + \frac{1}{4\pi}\int_{\text{all space}} \frac{\mathbf{J}\times\mathbf{r}^0\,dV}{r^2} \qquad (9.123)$$

The simplicity of Eq. (9.123) provides sufficient motivation for definition (9.29) in a microscopic analysis.

Notice the absence of any permeability in this equation. Notice also that a principle of superposition applies to magnetizing force: the total magnetizing force in a magnetostatic system is the vector sum of terms arising, respectively, from magnetic matter and from macroscopic currents. Calling these two terms, respectively, $\mathbf{H}_m$ and $\mathbf{H}_i$, we may write

$$\mathbf{H} = \mathbf{H}_m + \mathbf{H}_i \tag{9.124}$$

where

$$\mathbf{H}_m \equiv \frac{1}{4\pi} \int_{\substack{\text{all magnetic} \\ \text{matter}}} \frac{\mathbf{r}^0 \, dq^*}{r^2} \tag{9.125}$$

and

$$\mathbf{H}_i \equiv \frac{1}{4\pi} \int_{\text{all space}} \frac{\mathbf{J} \times \mathbf{r}^0 \, dV}{r^2} \tag{9.126}$$

Equation (9.125) shows that the elements dq^* of bound magnetic charge may be considered as the sole source of the part $\mathbf{H}_m$ of the magnetizing force. The same cannot be said about the magnetic induction $\mathbf{B}_m$ of magnetic matter because of the term $\mu_0\mathbf{M}$ in Eq. (9.122), Sec. 9.10. The relation between $\mathbf{H}_m$ and its sources is the inverse-square law, which likewise relates the electrostatic field in free space to electric charge. Because of this similarity, much of the discussion in Chap. 1 can be applied immediately to magnetic problems. For example, it follows from Sec. 1.5 that the field $\mathbf{H}_m$ can always and everywhere be derived from a single-valued, scalar potential function U^*, unique except for an arbitrary additive constant:

$$H_{mx} = -\frac{\partial U^*}{\partial x} \qquad H_{my} = -\frac{\partial U^*}{\partial y} \qquad H_{mz} = -\frac{\partial U^*}{\partial z} \tag{9.127}$$

In vector form,

$$\mathbf{H}_m = -\operatorname{grad} U^* \tag{9.128}$$

In regions devoid of magnetic material, the potential function U^* of this equation is the same as the function denoted by the same symbol in Sec. 9.9, where the magnetic induction $\mathbf{B}_m$ was expressed in terms of a scalar potential. Equation (9.57) is consistent with Eq. (9.128) of this section because of the form which definition (9.29) takes in empty space, $\mathbf{H} = 1/\mu_0\mathbf{B}$.

On the other hand, it is not possible in general to express the macroscopic magnetic induction $\mathbf{B}_m$ at an interior point of magnetic matter by a scalar potential function. This is because the term $\mu_0\mathbf{M}$ of Eq.

(9.122) cannot always be expressed by a scalar potential function. It appears therefore that the magnetic scalar potential function is particularly appropriate to the field H_m. On this account, the convention has been adopted that the magnetizing force is derived from U^* as in Eq. (9.128) without any arbitrary constant factor, while the constant μ_0 has been arbitrarily inserted whenever the magnetic induction is expressed by U^*.

Another theorem of electrostatics which can be transferred to magnetostatics because of the inverse-square law (9.125) is Gauss' law. By comparison of Sec. 1.9, it appears that the total flux of the vector H_m outward from the surface S enclosing a volume V is

$$\oint_S H_m \cdot n \, dS = \int_V dq^* \equiv q^*_{\text{inside } S} \tag{9.129}$$

Equation (9.129) may be applied for example to finding the component H_{mn} normal to an infinite, plane sheet of magnetic surface charge, σ^* (see Sec. 1.10). The result is

$$H_{mn} = \frac{\sigma^*}{2} \tag{9.130}$$

This field component is directed away from the surface charge when σ^* is positive. Equation (9.130) applies also to the field produced at any point very near to a finite, plane sheet of magnetic charge such as appears at the ends of an ideal bar magnet. Only the charge in the near neighborhood of the point then contributes to the normal component of the field of the sheet of charge. See Eq. (4.90), Sec. 4.11, and context, where this subject is discussed for the electrostatic case. In the case of the bar magnet, it must be remembered that the far pole of the magnet as well as the near one contributes to the total magnetizing force, so that the field (9.130) is in general only part of the normal component of magnetizing force at points near the end surfaces.

Equation (9.129) may be generalized to include the flux of the total magnetizing force, for the flux of the partial field H_i through any closed surface S is always zero:

$$\oint_S H_i \cdot n \, dS = 0 \tag{9.131}$$

This follows from Eq. (9.126). Aside from the absence of the factor μ_0, Eq. (9.126) is like Ampère's law for the magnetic induction of steady currents in free space. It was shown in Secs. 7.5 and 7.6 that the zero flux of the magnetic induction follows from Ampère's law, and in just the same way Eq. (9.131) follows from (9.126). Now by addition of Eq. (9.131) and use of Eq. (9.124), Eq. (9.129) is generalized:

$$\oint_S H \cdot n \, dS = q^*_{\text{inside } S} \tag{9.132}$$

Another consequence of Ampère's law in steady state is Ampère's circuital law as stated in Eq. (7.68), Sec. 7.7,

$$\oint_C \mathbf{B} \cdot d\mathbf{l} = \mu_0 I_c \qquad \text{otherwise empty space} \qquad (9.133)$$

where I_c is the total current linked by the closed path C of integration. See the context in Sec. 7.7 for discussion of the conditions under which Eq. (9.133) holds, and see Sec. 7.10 for a rather general proof of the circuital law. Now because of the similarity of form of Eq. (9.126) to Ampère's law, we may deduce that $\mathbf{H}_i$ satisfies a circuital equation similar to (9.133)

$$\oint_C \mathbf{H}_i \cdot d\mathbf{l} = I_c \qquad (9.134)$$

The validity of Eq. (9.134) is not restricted to regions devoid of magnetic matter, as is the validity of (9.133), since Eq. (9.126) is without such restriction. Equation (9.134) may be used in obtaining a very important theorem concerning the total magnetizing force. The part $\mathbf{H}_m$ of the magnetizing force, that due to magnetic matter, has a zero line integral around any closed curve C:

$$\oint_C \mathbf{H}_m \cdot d\mathbf{l} = 0 \qquad (9.135)$$

This follows at once from the fact that $\mathbf{H}_m$ satisfies Eq. (9.128) everywhere. See Sec. 1.5, for a detailed discussion of the corresponding electrostatic situation, and compare also Sec. 7.11, especially the last paragraph. Now by combining Eqs. (9.134), (9.135), and (9.124), we find that the total magnetizing force $\mathbf{H}$ satisfies the same circuital law as the part $\mathbf{H}_i$ alone:

$$\oint_C \mathbf{H} \cdot d\mathbf{l} = I_c \qquad (9.136)$$

This is true for any closed path C in a steady-state system of steady currents and magnetic matter. Equation (9.136) was stated without proof in the macroscopic discussion of Sec. 9.3. The microscopic analysis has now provided a general proof of this important relation. Notice that the circuital law belongs more properly to $\mathbf{H}$ than to the macroscopic $\mathbf{B}$ vector; for in the case of $\mathbf{B}$, the circuital law holds in general only for a path of integration which nowhere lies in magnetic matter. There is, however, a special case in which the macroscopic magnetic induction within magnetic matter satisfies a circuital relation, namely, when the path of integration lies entirely in a homogeneous, linear, isotropic medium. For such a medium,

$$\mathbf{B} = \mu \mathbf{H} \qquad (9.137)$$

where the permeability μ is a constant. Then

$$\oint_C \mathbf{B} \cdot d\mathbf{l} = \mu I_C \qquad \text{special case} \qquad (9.138)$$

There is a differential form of the circuital law (9.136) which is of importance for further work. In Sec. 7.11, a differential form of the circuital law (9.133) was found for the case when all currents are expressible in terms of a finite volume density of current $\mathbf{J}$:

$$\frac{\partial B_z}{\partial y} - \frac{\partial B_y}{\partial z} = \mu_0 J_x$$

$$\frac{\partial B_x}{\partial z} - \frac{\partial B_z}{\partial x} = \mu_0 J_y \qquad \text{otherwise empty space} \qquad (9.139)$$

$$\frac{\partial B_y}{\partial x} - \frac{\partial B_x}{\partial y} = \mu_0 J_z$$

Hence the corresponding differential equation for $\mathbf{H}$, holding for steady-state systems both inside magnetic matter and outside, is

$$\frac{\partial H_z}{\partial y} - \frac{\partial H_y}{\partial z} = J_x \qquad \frac{\partial H_x}{\partial z} - \frac{\partial H_z}{\partial x} = J_y \qquad \frac{\partial H_y}{\partial x} - \frac{\partial H_x}{\partial y} = J_z \qquad (9.140)$$

In abbreviated form,

$$\text{curl } \mathbf{H} = \mathbf{J} \qquad (9.141)$$

9.12. The Magnetic Circuit. A practical problem of magnetism is the determination of the magnetic flux produced in a closed iron core by the electric current flowing in a winding about the core. Because of the large permeability of iron, the magnetic induction within the core may greatly exceed that outside, and any magnetic flux which passes through the walls of the core may be small compared with the flux through a cross section. It is then a reasonable approximation to consider the flux as confined to the core in the same way that electric current is confined within the wires and components of an electric circuit. It is possible to consider magnetic flux as analogous to electric current in steady-state because both quantities are without sources or sinks, that is, the flux and the steady-state current through any closed surface are both zero:

$$\oint_S \mathbf{B} \cdot \mathbf{n} \, dS = 0 \qquad (9.142)$$

$$\oint_S \mathbf{J} \cdot \mathbf{n} \, dS = 0 \qquad (9.143)$$

(See Secs. 5.3 and 7.6.) If leakage flux through the walls is neglected, it follows from Eq. (9.142) that in a core composed of a single loop of iron the flux is the same through one cross section of the loop as through any other. In a core composed of a network of paths, an equation like the first law of Kirchhoff for current circuits is implied by Eq. (9.142) (see Sec. 6.4). The fluxes Φ_b in paths which meet at a common point, called a branch point or junction, of the core network must satisfy

$$\sum_b \Phi_b = 0 \tag{9.144}$$

The fluxes in this equation are algebraic quantities whose sign must be consistently determined. For example, a positive sign may be assigned to the fluxes toward the branch point and a negative sign to fluxes away from the branch point. The magnitude of the flux in a given branch may be expressed by a surface integral of the magnetic induction over any cross section A_b of the branch:

$$\Phi_b = \int_{A_b} \mathbf{B} \cdot \mathbf{n} \, dS \tag{9.145}$$

Consider next the nature of the magnetizing force $\mathbf{H}$ within a core in whose material no electric current flows. By Eq. (9.141), Sec. 9.11, the **curl** of $\mathbf{H}$ is then zero inside the core. Consequently $\mathbf{H}$ in the core can be expressed as the gradient of a scalar potential function U^*:

$$\mathbf{H} = -\left(\frac{\partial U^*}{\partial x} \mathbf{i} + \frac{\partial U^*}{\partial y} \mathbf{j} + \frac{\partial U^*}{\partial z} \mathbf{k} \right) \tag{9.146}$$

It must be remembered that this function U^* is multiple-valued if the core is linked by windings carrying electric current. See Secs. 7.10 and 7.11 for discussion of such a potential function. The difference of potential ΔU^* between two points a and b in the core, which may be obtained by line integration of the two sides of Eq. (9.146), has infinitely many discrete values corresponding to different choices of the path of integration $\mathfrak{L}$:

$$\Delta U^* \equiv U^*(b) - U^*(a) = -\left[\int_a^b \mathbf{H} \cdot d\mathbf{l} \right]_\mathfrak{L} \tag{9.147}$$

From Eq. (9.147) it follows as a special case that the values of U^* at a single point may differ by the line integral of $\mathbf{H}$ about a closed loop C starting and ending at that point. The line integral of $\mathbf{H}$ taken once around C is called the magnetomotive force, abbreviated as mmf, in the loop C of the core. This will be designated by $\mathfrak{M}_C$:

$$\oint_C \mathbf{H} \cdot d\mathbf{l} \equiv \mathfrak{M}_C \tag{9.148}$$

If the loop C links a current I_C, then, by Eq. (9.136) of the preceding section,

$$\mathfrak{M}_C = I_C \tag{9.149}$$

In particular, if I_c is carried by a winding of N_c turns of wire with a current I in each turn, then

$$I_c = N_c I \qquad (9.150)$$

It will be noted that the line integral (9.148) is named magnetomotive force by analogy to the electromotive force produced by a changing magnetic field:

$$\mathcal{E}_c = \oint_c \mathbf{E} \cdot d\mathbf{l} \qquad (9.151)$$

The existence of the scalar potential function U^* allows us to speak of equipotential surfaces in a magnet core. These will be everywhere perpendicular to the lines of magnetizing force $\mathbf{H}$; and since $\mathbf{H}$ is largely parallel to the axis of the core, the equipotential surfaces cut generally across the core. Consider two equipotential surfaces S_a and S_b so located that no branching of the core occurs in the region V of the core between S_a and S_b (see Fig. 9.5). Even though the potential in the core is not single-valued, still a unique potential difference between the end surfaces S_a and S_b of this piece of core may be defined by requiring that the path $\mathcal{L}$ of integration in Eq. (9.147) lie wholly in V. Any two such paths between a point a of S_a and a point b of S_b then form a closed loop linking no current; whence the line integrals of $\mathbf{H}$ over these two paths have the same value. Furthermore, the choice of the particular points in S_a and S_b does not affect the integral (9.147), since the line integral of H between any pair of points in one equipo-

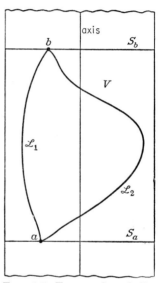

FIG. 9.5. Two paths of line integration between points on equipotential surfaces.

tential surface along a path in that surface is zero. Hence with the restrictions that $\mathcal{L}$ lie in V and that V be not branched (or more precisely speaking, multiply-connected), Eq. (9.147) gives a unique potential difference between the equipotentials at the ends of V.

Now consider a closed loop C lying along the axis of a magnet core. The core, or the part of the core, through which C passes may be divided by equipotential surfaces into sections V_k across each of which there is a definite potential difference ΔU_k^*. The algebraic sum of the ΔU_k^* about the loop C is just the negative line integral of $\mathbf{H}$ around C, so that

$$-\sum_{\substack{\text{all } k \\ \text{in } C}} \Delta U_k^* = \oint_c \mathbf{H} \cdot d\mathbf{l} \equiv \mathfrak{M}_c \qquad (9.152)$$

Equation (9.152) is the magnetic analogue of the second Kirchhoff law for current circuits. To obtain a working equation, it remains only to evaluate the ΔU_k^* in terms of the flux and the characteristics of the core. This may be done easily for a piece of core whose cross section is uniform, whose axis has no sharp bends, and which is composed of homogeneous, isotropic material. Except for end effects, the field $\mathbf{H}_k$ in such a section is approximately uniform and parallel to the axis, and equipotential surfaces are cross sections of the core. These simple properties of the field of magnetizing force may be shown to follow from the existence of a scalar potential function, as was done for an electrical conductor in Sec. 5.13. If now the axial length of such a simple section V_k of the core is l_k, the line integral of Eq. (9.147) may be evaluated immediately to yield (except for algebraic sign)

$$\Delta U_k^* = H_k l_k \tag{9.153}$$

Equation (9.145) gives for the flux in this section of the core

$$\Phi_k = B_k A_k \tag{9.154}$$

in terms of the magnetic induction B_k and cross-sectional area A_k of the section. If the material has a permeability μ_k, the flux in the section is therefore

$$\Phi_k = \mu_k H_k A_k \tag{9.155}$$

Combining Eqs. (9.153) and (9.155), we obtain the desired equation for ΔU_k^*:

$$\Delta U_k^* = \Phi_k \frac{l_k}{\mu_k A_k} \tag{9.156}$$

By analogy to the electric circuit, in which the ratio of the potential difference across a wire to the current in it is called its resistance, the ratio of ΔU_k^* to Φ_k is given a special name, the reluctance of this piece of the core:

$$\mathfrak{R}_k \equiv \frac{\Delta U_k^*}{\Phi_k} \tag{9.157}$$

In terms of this new quantity, the circuit equation (9.152) becomes

$$\sum_{\substack{\text{all } k \\ \text{in } C}} \mathfrak{R}_k \Phi_k = \mathfrak{M}_C \tag{9.158}$$

The special formula for the reluctance of a piece of core with uniform cross section, having no sharp bends, and consisting of homogeneous, isotropic material is, by comparison of Eqs. (9.156) and (9.157),

$$\mathfrak{R}_k = \frac{l_k}{\mu_k A_k} \tag{9.159}$$

Let us apply the foregoing theory first to the simplest case, that of a single-loop, closed core of uniform cross section upon which is a winding of N turns carrying current I. If l, A, and μ are, respectively, the axial length, cross-sectional area, and permeability of the core, Eqs. (9.158), (9.159), (9.149), and (9.150) together yield

$$\Phi = \frac{\mu A}{l} NI \tag{9.160}$$

Suppose next that a short air gap of length s is cut in the core. At such a gap there is spreading or "fringing" of the lines of $\mathbf{H}$, so that $\mathbf{H}$ is neither confined to just the cross section A nor is it uniform in the gap. Nevertheless, as a rather gross but useful approximation, we may neglect the fringing. There are now two sections in the core: the iron section and the air section. Their reluctances are, respectively,

$$\mathcal{R}_1 = \frac{l - s}{\mu A} \qquad \mathcal{R}_2 = \frac{s}{\mu_0 A} \tag{9.161}$$

by Eq. (9.159). Equation (9.158) now leads to the result that the flux Φ, which in our approximation is considered common to both the iron and the gap, is

$$\Phi = \frac{ANI}{[(l - s)/\mu] + (s/\mu_0)} \tag{9.162}$$

Since μ_0 may be less than μ by a factor of 10,000 or more, the presence of even a relatively short gap may reduce the flux by a large factor. A variable gap is intentionally introduced in some pieces of apparatus as a means of controlling the flux. Another reason for introducing a gap arises from the fact that the permeability of iron is variable, depending on the ·magnetizing force H, whereas the permeability of air is constant and, as assumed above, has essentially the value μ_0. Thus the reluctance $\mathcal{R}_2$ is linear, while $\mathcal{R}_1$ is not. If $\mathcal{R}_2$ is much greater than $\mathcal{R}_1$, the gap makes the total reluctance approximately linear. This is very desirable in some apparatus, as in transformers for audio amplifiers or in chokes (inductors) designed to carry direct as well as alternating current.

In concluding the discussion of the magnetic circuit, a few general remarks should be made. In the first place, there is no magnetic counterpart of a good insulator, for the ratio between the available maximum and minimum values of permeability is much more limited than the ratio of electrical conductivities. The best magnetic insulators are diamagnetic materials, but their permeability is for practical purposes the same as that of air or empty space. An exception is found in the realm of superconducting materials, where induced currents may entirely prevent the penetration of magnetic flux; but superconducting matter can hardly be considered a readily available material. The lack of a magnetic insulator implies that leakage in any magnetic circuit is relatively larger than in a well-constructed electric circuit. Even in the case of a completely closed core there may be appreciable flux carried by the air around the core. Another feature of the magnetic circuit is that in practical cases the ratio of axial length to cross-section dimensions or to axial radius of curvature is not usually as great as for wires, so that end effects are of greater significance. Furthermore, ferromagnetic materials are nonlinear; therefore magnetic reluctance is generally variable. Finally, the analysis of this section has been based on a magnetostatic analysis, and has neglected effects resulting from time variation of the magnetic fields; and yet magnetic circuit theory is chiefly used in the design of alternating current apparatus. Two effects of time-varying fields need discussion. The important effect in practice is the production of eddy currents in the core by electromagnetic induction. These currents render the entire analysis invalid, since there is then no scalar potential function for **H** in the core. In practice, eddy currents are usually undesirable, and are reduced as far as possible by using laminated or powdered material for the core. There is theoretically another effect of time variation, the direct production of a magnetic field by a changing electric field, even in the absence of electric conductivity; but this effect is of importance only when the rate of time variation is so high that electromagnetic wave analysis is appropriate for the problem. This effect may be entirely neglected in design of electromagnetic machinery for low-frequency applications.

9.13. Force and Torque on a Magnet in Terms of Bound Charge. The general problem of analyzing forces upon a magnet in a fluid magnetic medium cannot be undertaken here because of its complexity and the need for a detailed stress analysis. For practical purposes such an analysis is unnecessary because of the smallness of the magnetic susceptibility of air and indeed of almost all fluids. We must, however, give some account of the force reactions between magnets, for these are among the most obvious of magnetic phenomena. It will be shown that all forces and torques between magnets immersed *in vacuo* or in a nonmagnetic fluid can be expressed in terms of magnetic bound charge, as this charge has been defined in Sec. 9.9. In proving this statement, we forge the link between the microscopic analysis, which reduces all magnetism to phenomena associated with moving electric charge, and the classical experiments with magnet poles.

To set the problem up, consider a magnetized body, to be called the magnet, occupying a volume V and having a complete boundary surface S. Suppose there are no macroscopic currents flowing in the magnet. The total magnetic force or torque on the body is then the vector sum of the force or torque on each of its elementary current systems. Since we are not to be concerned with local stresses, the contributions of the magnet itself to the magnetic induction throughout its volume and on its surface may be subtracted off. Thus only that part $\mathbf{B}_0$ of the magnetic induction which is produced by currents or magnetic matter external to the magnet need be considered in computing the total force or torque. This field is treated as existing in empty space, for in microscopic analysis the elementary systems reside in empty space. All parts of the magnet will be assumed to be at macroscopic distances from the sources of the external field $\mathbf{B}_0$, so that $\mathbf{B}_0$ will have no structure of microscopic fineness. Each elementary current system of the magnet is therefore in an external field which changes only slightly over its extension. Under these conditions, the force and torque on each elementary system can be computed from its magnetic dipole moment by the formulas which were developed for macroscopic circuits in Sec. 7.13. This is not only a natural postulate to make concerning the microscopic systems, but it follows as a deduction if Newton's law of action and reaction is assumed to hold for steady-state magnetostatic interactions between closed current systems. See Sec. 4.12, where similar reasoning is used to establish a theorem of electrostatics. To take into account the statistical variations between the dipole moments of neighboring elementary systems of the magnet, we may use the dipole moment per unit volume, $\mathbf{M}$, introduced in Sec. 9.8 and called the magnetization vector. Thus the force on the element of volume dV of the magnet is to be computed from the differential dipole moment $\mathbf{M}\,dV$. According to Eqs. (7.175), Sec. 7.13, the cartesian components of this force will be

$$
\begin{aligned}
dF_x &= \left(M_x \frac{\partial B_{0x}}{\partial x} + M_y \frac{\partial B_{0x}}{\partial y} + M_z \frac{\partial B_{0x}}{\partial z} \right) dV \\
dF_y &= \left(M_x \frac{\partial B_{0y}}{\partial x} + M_y \frac{\partial B_{0y}}{\partial y} + M_z \frac{\partial B_{0y}}{\partial z} \right) dV \qquad (9.163)\\
dF_z &= \left(M_x \frac{\partial B_{0z}}{\partial x} + M_y \frac{\partial B_{0z}}{\partial y} + M_z \frac{\partial B_{0z}}{\partial z} \right) dV
\end{aligned}
$$

The total x component of the force on the magnet is therefore the integral over the volume of the magnet:

$$
F_x = \int_V \left(M_x \frac{\partial B_{0x}}{\partial x} + M_y \frac{\partial B_{0x}}{\partial y} + M_z \frac{\partial B_{0x}}{\partial z} \right) dV \qquad (9.164)
$$

Similar equations hold for the other force components.

Equation (9.164) will now be subjected to mathematical transformation so that it may be expressed in terms of the magnetic bound charge densities:

$$\rho^* = -\left(\frac{\partial M_x}{\partial x} + \frac{\partial M_y}{\partial y} + \frac{\partial M_z}{\partial z}\right) \tag{9.60}$$

$$\sigma^* = \mathbf{M} \cdot \mathbf{n} \tag{9.59}$$

where the unit normal $\mathbf{n}$ to the surface S of the magnet is taken outward from the volume V. First, by use of the product rule for differentiation, we obtain

$$F_x = \int_V \left[\frac{\partial}{\partial x}(M_x B_{0x}) + \frac{\partial}{\partial y}(M_y B_{0x}) + \frac{\partial}{\partial z}(M_z B_{0x})\right] dV$$
$$- \int_V B_{0x}\left(\frac{\partial M_x}{\partial x} + \frac{\partial M_y}{\partial y} + \frac{\partial M_z}{\partial z}\right) dV \tag{9.165}$$

It is apparent from comparison with Eq. (9.60) that part of the goal has already been achieved, in that the second integral contains the volume density of magnetic bound charge. Thus

$$F_x = \int_V \left[\frac{\partial}{\partial x}(M_x B_{0x}) + \frac{\partial}{\partial y}(M_y B_{0x}) + \frac{\partial}{\partial z}(M_z B_{0x})\right] dV + \int_V B_{0x}\rho^* \, dV \tag{9.166}$$

The first integral may be expressed in terms of the surface density σ^* by transforming it into a surface integral over the complete boundary S of the magnet. The integrand here is just the divergence of the vector $(B_{0x}\mathbf{M})$. By the divergence theorem, for which see Sec. 7.6, this integral is identically equal to the surface integral of the vector over the complete boundary of the region V:

$$\int_V \left[\frac{\partial}{\partial x}(M_x B_{0x}) + \frac{\partial}{\partial y}(M_y B_{0x}) + \frac{\partial}{\partial z}(M_z B_{0x})\right] dV$$
$$\equiv \oint_S (B_{0x}\mathbf{M}) \cdot \mathbf{n} \, dS \tag{9.167}$$

where $\mathbf{n}$ is the unit normal to S outward from V. Using Eq. (9.59) in (9.167) and substituting back into (9.166), we obtain the result desired, in which F_x is expressed in terms of magnetic bound charge:

$$F_x = \int_V B_{0x}\rho^* \, dV + \oint_S B_{0x}\sigma^* \, dS \tag{9.168}$$

The other components of total force may be written down immediately by symmetry, and then combined into the single vector equation for the force on the magnet:

$$\mathbf{F} = \int_V \mathbf{B}_0 \rho^* \, dV + \oint_S \mathbf{B}_0 \, \sigma^* \, dS \tag{9.169}$$

Some care must be exercised in interpreting this result. Equation (9.169) means that the total magnetic force on a body of matter may be computed correctly by postulating that each element dq^* of magnetic bound charge, whether the volume element $\rho^*\,dV$ or the surface element $\sigma^*\,dS$, experiences in the external field $\mathbf{B}_0$ a force

$$d\mathbf{F} = \mathbf{B}_0\,dq^* \qquad (9.170)$$

However, Eq. (9.170) must not be supposed to give the actual space distribution of the elements of magnetic force. This would be the case indeed if magnetic bound charge were a physical entity like free electric charge, whereas magnetic bound charge is actually just a convenient mathematical definition. It is Eqs. (9.163), not Eq. (9.170), which are a reliable statement of the space distribution of the force elements, although even this is incomplete since it neglects internal magnetic interactions; for the physical cause of magnetism lies not in magnetic charge but in elementary current circuits. Equations (9.163) and Eq. (9.170) are not identical, even though integration of them yields the same total force. The reader may convince himself of the difference between these two points of view by examining the simple case of an ideal bar magnet, with uniform axial magnetization, in the field of a point pole. Equations (9.163) yield a force on the bar magnet throughout its length, in general, while Eq. (9.170) indicates force only on the ends of the bar where the poles appear. In summary, it may be said that Eq. (9.169) is entirely correct for the total magnetic force, but (9.170) is not correct for computation of stress.

Since magnetic bound charge does not correctly represent stress distribution on a magnet, it may not be taken for granted that this quantity would be useful for computation of torque. This is actually the case, however, as we proceed to demonstrate. As defined in mechanics, the torque about an origin 0 produced by a force $\mathbf{F}$, whose point of application is at a vector position $\mathbf{r}$ relative to 0, is the vector

$$\mathbf{L}_F = \mathbf{r} \times \mathbf{F} \qquad (9.171)$$

Thus the magnetic force $d\mathbf{F}$ on the volume element dV of the magnet produces a torque element

$$d\mathbf{L}_F = \mathbf{r} \times d\mathbf{F} \qquad (9.172)$$

where $\mathbf{r}$ is now the vector position of the element dV relative to the origin. Equations (9.163) give the force components to be used in Eq. (9.172). There is, however, another source of torque on the magnet, in addition to these elements $d\mathbf{L}_F$. A magnetic dipole experiences in general a couple when it is located in a magnetic field. Now a couple, which may be represented by a pair of equal, opposite, and noncolinear forces, produces a torque which is independent of the location of the origin and is equal to the moment of the couple. This torque $d\mathbf{L}_C$ for the elementary dipole moment $\mathbf{M}\, dV$ characterizing the volume element dV of the magnet is, by Eq. (7.182), Sec. 7.13,

$$d\mathbf{L}_c = (\mathbf{M}\, dV) \times \mathbf{B}_0 \tag{9.173}$$

The externally produced magnetic induction $\mathbf{B}_0$ is used in Eq. (9.173) just as it has been throughout this section. The field due to other parts of the magnet itself can only cause internal stresses; only external causes can produce net total torque.

The total torque element due to the magnetic force and couple on the material in dV is now

$$d\mathbf{L} = d\mathbf{L}_F + d\mathbf{L}_c \tag{9.174}$$

Let us work with the x component of the torque. If $\mathbf{r}$ is written in terms of its components which are the cartesian coordinates x, y, z of the element dV, the x component dL_{Fx} of the torque element (9.172) is

$$dL_{Fx} = y\, dF_z - z\, dF_y \tag{9.175}$$

Likewise the x component dL_{cx} of the couple moment (9.173) is

$$dL_{cx} = (M_y B_{0z} - M_z B_{0y})\, dV \tag{9.176}$$

The total x component dL_x of the torque due to the magnetic matter in dV is, according to Eq. (9.174), the sum of the expressions (9.175) and (9.176). Forming the sum and at the same time substituting from Eqs. (9.163) into Eq. (9.175) for the force components, we obtain the lengthy expression

$$dL_x = \left[y\left(M_x \frac{\partial B_{0z}}{\partial x} + M_y \frac{\partial B_{0z}}{\partial y} + M_z \frac{\partial B_{0z}}{\partial z} \right) \right.$$
$$\left. - z\left(M_x \frac{\partial B_{0y}}{\partial x} + M_y \frac{\partial B_{0y}}{\partial y} + M_z \frac{\partial B_{0y}}{\partial z} \right) + (M_y B_{0z} - M_z B_{0y}) \right] dV \tag{9.177}$$

Let us collect terms in the components M_x, M_y, and M_z of the magnetization:

$$dL_x = \left[M_x\left(y\frac{\partial B_{0z}}{\partial x} - z\frac{\partial B_{0y}}{\partial x} \right) + M_y\left(y\frac{\partial B_{0z}}{\partial y} - z\frac{\partial B_{0y}}{\partial y} + B_{0z} \right) \right.$$
$$\left. + M_z\left(y\frac{\partial B_{0z}}{\partial z} - z\frac{\partial B_{0y}}{\partial z} - B_{0y} \right) \right] dV \tag{9.178}$$

Equation (9.178) may be written more compactly in the form

$$dL_x = \left[M_x\frac{\partial}{\partial x}(y B_{0z} - z B_{0y}) + M_y\frac{\partial}{\partial y}(y B_{0z} - z B_{0y}) \right.$$
$$\left. + M_z\frac{\partial}{\partial z}(y B_{0z} - z B_{0y}) \right] dV \tag{9.179}$$

Now the expression which is operated upon by the partial derivative symbols is just the x component of the vector $\mathbf{r} \times \mathbf{B}_0$:

$$(\mathbf{r} \times \mathbf{B}_0)_x = yB_{0z} - zB_{0y} \tag{9.180}$$

Thus

$$dL_x = \left[M_x \frac{\partial}{\partial x} (\mathbf{r} \times \mathbf{B}_0)_x + M_y \frac{\partial}{\partial y} (\mathbf{r} \times \mathbf{B}_0)_x \right. $$
$$\left. + M_z \frac{\partial}{\partial z} (\mathbf{r} \times \mathbf{B}_0)_x \right] dV \tag{9.181}$$

The total x component of torque on the magnet is to be found by integrating Eq. (9.181) over the volume V of the magnet:

$$L_x = \int_V \left[M_x \frac{\partial}{\partial x} (\mathbf{r} \times \mathbf{B}_0)_x + M_y \frac{\partial}{\partial y} (\mathbf{r} \times \mathbf{B}_0)_x \right. $$
$$\left. + M_z \frac{\partial}{\partial z} (\mathbf{r} \times \mathbf{B}_0)_x \right] dV \tag{9.182}$$

We may proceed now to subject this integral to exactly the same transformations which were applied to the integral (9.164); for (9.182) is identical in form to (9.164), the only difference being that the scalar function B_{0x} in (9.164) is replaced in (9.182) by the scalar function $(\mathbf{r} \times \mathbf{B}_0)_x$. Just as Eq. (9.164) led to (9.168), so now (9.182) leads to an expression involving the magnetic bound charge densities:

$$L_x = \int_V (\mathbf{r} \times \mathbf{B}_0)_x \rho^* \, dV + \oint_S (\mathbf{r} \times \mathbf{B}_0)_x \sigma^* \, dS \tag{9.183}$$

Similar expressions may be written down at once by symmetry for the components L_y and L_z of the total torque, involving the y and z components, respectively, of the vector $(\mathbf{r} \times \mathbf{B}_0)$. These three component equations are equivalent to the single vector equation for the total torque on the magnet:

$$\mathbf{L} = \int_V \mathbf{r} \times \mathbf{B}_0 \rho^* \, dV + \oint_S \mathbf{r} \times \mathbf{B}_0 \sigma^* \, dS \tag{9.184}$$

In terms of the general element dq^* of magnetic bound charge, which is either $\rho^* \, dV$ or $\sigma^* \, dS$ as the case may be, the torque is

$$\mathbf{L} = \int_{\text{magnet}} \mathbf{r} \times \mathbf{B}_0 \, dq^* \tag{9.185}$$

Equation (9.185) means that the total magnetic torque on a body in which there is no macroscopic current may be computed correctly by use of the concept of magnetic bound charge, just as we have found to be true also of the total magnetic force. The total torque is just what would arise if each element dq^* of magnetic bound charge actually experienced the force given by Eq. (9.170). Now the mechanical effect upon a rigid body of an arbitrary set of forces and couples is completely specified by the total force and the torque about an arbitrarily chosen origin. It follows that for a rigid magnet, the entire set of magnetic forces is mechanically equivalent to the set of elementary forces (9.170) computed from the magnetic bound charge. This statement is complementary to the theorem of Sec. 9.9, according to which the external field of a magnet may be computed from the magnetic bound charge. It is evident therefore that magnetic bound charge is sufficient to account for all the force and torque interactions between rigid magnets in which no macroscopic currents flow. It is no wonder that this charge appears to be a physical reality instead of the mere mathematical representation which it is. Although it is remarkable that for rigid magnets the mechanical effects of the elementary circuits are completely described in this way, one should bear in mind that magnetic bound charge is not the only correct representation of these phenomena. In succeeding sections we shall show that magnetization of rigid bodies may also be represented by a set of macroscopic currents which will be called bound currents.

The simplest example of the interaction of two magnets is the ideal case of a pair of thin bar magnets with uniform magnetization parallel to their axes. The magnetic bound charge appears then only upon the ends of the bar magnets in point poles, that is, in regions of magnetic charge whose spatial dimensions may be small compared to their distances from one another. The poles of one magnet then appear as point sources of the external magnetic induction for the other magnet, and the forces and torques on each magnet may be represented by forces just on its poles. By Eq. (9.72), Sec. 9.9, the magnetic induction *in vacuo* due to a point pole of strength q_1^* is

$$\mathbf{B}_0 = \frac{\mu_0}{4\pi} \frac{q_1^*}{r^2} \mathbf{r}^0 \qquad \text{point pole } in \ vacuo \qquad (9.186)$$

where r is the distance to the observer and $\mathbf{r}^0$ is the unit vector from the pole toward the observer. This field has been designated by the symbol $\mathbf{B}_0$ used in the present section, since it is an external field for the other magnet. Now the force $\mathbf{F}_2$ on a point pole q_2^* *in vacuo* is readily derived from integration of Eq. (9.170) over the pole, which is assumed to be contained in a small enough region that the external field $\mathbf{B}_0$ is essentially constant over the pole. Thus

$$\mathbf{F}_2 = \int_{q_2^*} \mathbf{B}_0 \, dq^* \qquad (9.187)$$

Taking $\mathbf{B}_0$ outside and performing the integration, we obtain

$$\mathbf{F}_2 = \mathbf{B}_0 q_2^* \qquad \text{point pole} \qquad (9.188)$$

Combination of Eqs. (9.186) and (9.188) gives the force on a point pole q_2^* due to a point pole q_1^* when both are *in vacuo* or in a nonmagnetic medium:

$$\mathbf{F}_{21} = \frac{\mu_0}{4\pi} \frac{q_1^* q_2^*}{r^2} \mathbf{r}^0 \qquad \text{point poles } in \ vacuo \qquad (9.189)$$

This is Coulomb's law, which forms the basis of classical magneto-statistics, which was experimentally established in 1785. Since $\mathbf{r}^0$ in Eq. (9.189) is directed from q_1^* toward q_2^*, the force $\mathbf{F}_{21}$ is a repulsion when $q_1^* q_2^* > 0$, that is, when the two poles have the same sign. The familiar rule of magnetostatics is thus given by Eq. (9.189): like poles repel, and unlike poles attract.

An important special problem is that of a rigid magnet in a uniform external field. If $\mathbf{B}_0$ is a constant, Eq. (9.170) when integrated shows that the total magnetic force on a magnet vanishes, since the total, net, magnetic bound charge of any body is zero. The entire set of magnetic forces then reduces to a couple. The moment of the couple, which is the torque about any origin point whatever, is given by Eq. (9.185) as

$$\mathbf{L} = \left(\int_{\text{magnet}} \mathbf{r} \, dq^* \right) \times \mathbf{B}_0 \qquad (9.190)$$

The integral in this expression is just the magnetic dipole moment $\mathbf{m}$ of the magnet, as was shown in Eq. (9.80), Sec. 9.9. Thus the torque is simply

$$\mathbf{L} = \mathbf{m} \times \mathbf{B}_0 \qquad \text{uniform field} \qquad (9.191)$$

This is the same expression as that for the torque on a current circuit in a uniform field [see Eq. (7.182), Sec. 7.13]. When Eq. (9.191) is applied to a bar magnet of pole strength q^* whose axial, vector length from its south to its north pole is l, the result is

$$\mathbf{L} = q^* \mathbf{l} \times \mathbf{B}_0 \qquad (9.192)$$

9.14. Exterior Field of a Magnet: Bound Current Densities. The use of the scalar potential of the elementary dipoles of a magnet led in Sec. 9.9 to the concept of magnetic bound charge. An alternative mathematical transformation presents itself if the vector potential is used. The elementary circuits in a volume element dV of the magnet have a dipole moment $d\mathbf{m} = \mathbf{M} \, dV$, where $\mathbf{M}$ is the magnetization vector. At an external point in empty space, the material in dV produces a dipole field whose magnetic vector potential is

$$d\mathbf{A}_m = \frac{\mu_0}{4\pi} \frac{\mathbf{M} \times \mathbf{r}}{r^3} dV \qquad (9.193)$$

where $\mathbf{r}$ and r are, respectively, the vector and scalar distances from the volume element dV to the observer (see Sec. 7.8). The total vector potential of the magnetized material in the volume V of the magnet, at an external point of observation, is therefore

$$A_m = \frac{\mu_0}{4\pi} \int_V \frac{\mathbf{M} \times \mathbf{r}}{r^3} dV \tag{9.194}$$

Let us work just with the z component A_z, of this potential function. To simplify the notation, the subscript m will be omitted from this component of $\mathbf{A}_m$. The cartesian coordinates of the point of integration will be called x, y, z, and those of the point of observation will be called x', y', z'. The vector $\mathbf{r}$ is then

$$\mathbf{r} = (x' - x)\mathbf{i} + (y' - y)\mathbf{j} + (z' - z)\mathbf{k} \tag{9.195}$$

and the scalar r is

$$r = \sqrt{(x' - x)^2 + (y' - y)^2 + (z' - z)^2} \tag{9.196}$$

Hence

$$A_z(x',y',z') = \frac{\mu_0}{4\pi} \int_V \frac{M_x(y' - y) - M_y(x' - x)}{r^3} dV \tag{9.197}$$

Now the reader may show by Eq. (9.196) that

$$\frac{x' - x}{r^3} = \frac{\partial}{\partial x}\left(\frac{1}{r}\right) \qquad \frac{y' - y}{r^3} = \frac{\partial}{\partial y}\left(\frac{1}{r}\right) \tag{9.198}$$

Substitution of Eqs. (9.198) into Eq. (9.197) yields

$$A_z(x',y',z') = \frac{\mu_0}{4\pi} \int_V \left[M_x \frac{\partial}{\partial y}\left(\frac{1}{r}\right) - M_y \frac{\partial}{\partial x}\left(\frac{1}{r}\right) \right] dV \tag{9.199}$$

By use of the product rule of differentiation, the integrand of Eq. (9.199) may be transformed as follows:

$$M_x \frac{\partial}{\partial y}\left(\frac{1}{r}\right) = \frac{\partial}{\partial y}\left(\frac{M_x}{r}\right) - \frac{1}{r}\frac{\partial M_x}{\partial y}$$

$$M_y \frac{\partial}{\partial x}\left(\frac{1}{r}\right) = \frac{\partial}{\partial x}\left(\frac{M_y}{r}\right) - \frac{1}{r}\frac{\partial M_y}{\partial x}$$

Therefore

$$A_z = \frac{\mu_0}{4\pi} \int_V \frac{1}{r}\left(\frac{\partial M_y}{\partial x} - \frac{\partial M_x}{\partial y}\right) dV + \frac{\mu_0}{4\pi} \int_V \left[\frac{\partial}{\partial y}\left(\frac{M_x}{r}\right) - \frac{\partial}{\partial x}\left(\frac{M_y}{r}\right)\right] dV \tag{9.200}$$

Let us abbreviate these two integrals A_{1z} and A_{2z}, respectively, so that

$$A_z = A_{1z} + A_{2z} \tag{9.201}$$

The first integral A_{1z} is in the form of the vector potential due to a volume density of current [see Eq. (7.50), Sec. 7.5]. We define a vector point function $\mathbf{J}'(x,y,z)$, to be called the volume density of bound current in the magnet, as the vector whose cartesian components are

$$J'_x \equiv \frac{\partial M_z}{\partial y} - \frac{\partial M_y}{\partial z} \qquad J'_y \equiv \frac{\partial M_x}{\partial z} - \frac{\partial M_z}{\partial x} \qquad J'_z \equiv \frac{\partial M_y}{\partial x} - \frac{\partial M_x}{\partial y} \tag{9.202}$$

In vector notation,

$$\mathbf{J}' \equiv \text{curl } \mathbf{M} \tag{9.203}$$

The integral A_{1z} then reads

$$A_{1z} = \frac{\mu_0}{4\pi} \int_V \frac{J'_z}{r} dV \tag{9.204}$$

The second integral of Eq. (9.200) may be transformed into a surface integral extended over the entire boundary S of the magnet. The labor of proving the transformation has already been done in Sec. 9.10, in passing from Eq. (9.98) to (9.105). The result is

$$A_{2z}(x',y',z') = \frac{\mu_0}{4\pi} \oint_S \left[n_y \left(\frac{M_x}{r} \right) - n_x \left(\frac{M_y}{r} \right) \right] dS \tag{9.205}$$

where n_x and n_y are the x component and y component of the unit normal $\mathbf{n}$ to S outward from the volume V of the magnet. It is assumed here that the integrand of the original volume integral is continuous throughout V. We now define a vector point function $\mathbf{K}'(x,y,z)$ to be called the surface density of bound current, existing only on the surface S of the magnet or at any surfaces of discontinuity which may occur in its material. The cartesian components of $\mathbf{K}'$ on the boundary are to be

$$K'_x \equiv M_y n_z - M_z n_y \qquad K'_y \equiv M_z n_x - M_x n_z \qquad K'_z \equiv M_x n_y - M_y n_x \tag{9.206}$$

In vector notation,

$$\mathbf{K}' \equiv \mathbf{M} \times \mathbf{n} \tag{9.207}$$

In terms of this definition, the integral A_{2z} is simply

$$A_{2z} = \frac{\mu_0}{4\pi} \oint_S \frac{1}{r} K'_z \, dS \tag{9.208}$$

Equation (9.208) is the particular form which (9.204) would take for a current confined to a layer of infinitesimal thickness b. See Sec. 5.2 for a discussion of surface current density, whence it is seen that the surface density vector is connected with the volume density vector in the layer by the crossover relation

$$\mathbf{K}' \, dS = \mathbf{J}' \, dV \tag{9.209}$$

The introduction of $\mathbf{K}'$ has been necessitated by the assumption of a sharp discontinuity in the magnetic matter at the boundary surface of the magnet, which would cause the $\mathbf{J}'$ vector to be infinite at the boundary. The integral (9.204) excludes the boundary itself, so that its integrand remains finite, while the discontinuity is accounted for by the introduction of the surface density and the addition of integral (9.208) to (9.204).

Let us now assemble and interpret the results of the foregoing mathematical transformation. Substitution of Eqs. (9.204) and (9.208) into (9.201) gives

$$A_z = \frac{\mu_0}{4\pi} \int_V \frac{1}{r} J'_z \, dV + \frac{\mu_0}{4\pi} \oint_S \frac{1}{r} K'_z \, dS \tag{9.210}$$

Similar expressions can be written down at once from symmetry for the other components of the vector potential. Combining these into a single vector equation, we obtain for the vector potential of a body of magnetic material at an external point

$$\mathbf{A}_m = \frac{\mu_0}{4\pi} \int_V \frac{1}{r} \mathbf{J}' \, dV + \frac{\mu_0}{4\pi} \oint_S \frac{1}{r} \mathbf{K}' \, dS \tag{9.211}$$

The magnetic induction due to the magnet at an external point is obtained from the vector potential $\mathbf{A}_m$ by taking its **curl** (see Sec. 7.5). The differentiations involved are with respect to the observer's coordinates x', y', z', which appear only in the function r. Differentiating inside the integral signs, we obtain Ampère integrals for the external field of the magnet:

$$\mathbf{B}_m = \frac{\mu_0}{4\pi} \int_V \frac{\mathbf{J'} \times \mathbf{r}}{r^3} dV + \frac{\mu_0}{4\pi} \oint_S \frac{\mathbf{K'} \times \mathbf{r}}{r^3} dS \qquad (9.212)$$

Equations (9.211) and (9.212) mean that the external field of the magnet is exactly equivalent to that which would be caused by macroscopic volume and surface densities of current having the values given by Eqs. (9.203) and (9.207), respectively, if these currents are considered to flow in a nonmagnetic medium. It should be emphasized, however, that the bound current densities representing the magnetization of matter are essentially only mathematical definitions. They do not imply the macroscopic transportation of electric charge which is described by actual, free current densities.

As an example of the use of bound currents, consider a right circular cylinder as shown in Fig. 9.6, having uniform magnetization $\mathbf{M}$ parallel to its axis. Since $\mathbf{M}$ is constant in the material, Eq. (9.203) gives for the volume density $\mathbf{J'}$ of bound current

$$\mathbf{J'} = 0 \qquad (9.213)$$

At the curved surface of the magnet, $\mathbf{M}$ is everywhere perpendicular to the outward normal $\mathbf{n}$. Since $\mathbf{n}$ has a unit magnitude, Eq. (9.207) then gives for the magnitude of $\mathbf{K'}$ on this surface

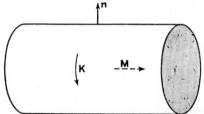

$$K' = M \qquad (9.214)$$

where M is the magnitude of $\mathbf{M}$. The direction of $\mathbf{K'}$ is everywhere normal to $\mathbf{M}$ and $\mathbf{n}$, that is, along circles around the cylinder; and the sense of $\mathbf{K'}$ is related to that of $\mathbf{M}$ as the rotation of a right-hand screw to its advance. $\mathbf{K'}$ is zero on the ends of the bar where $\mathbf{M}$ and $\mathbf{n}$ are parallel or opposite. Now a circular flow of current in a sheet around a straight axis is an ideal case which is approximated by a solenoid closely wound of fine wire. The bound current flow past a line of unit length parallel to the axis and on the curved surface of the magnet is just K', while for a solenoid of N_1 turns per unit length carrying current I, the corresponding quantity is $N_1 I$. Thus the theorem of the present section tells us that the external magnetic induction of a uniformly and axially magnetized, cylindrical bar is the same as that of an ideal solenoid of the same dimensions when

FIG. 9.6. A bar magnet of circular cross section, with its equivalent bound surface current.

$$N_1 I = K' \qquad (9.215)$$

or, by Eq. (9.214), when

$$N_1 I = M \qquad (9.216)$$

9.15. Interior Field of a Magnet in Terms of Bound Currents. The macroscopic magnetic induction within a sample of magnetic material has already been deduced in Sec. 9.10, where it was expressed partly in terms of magnetic bound charge. A somewhat similar analysis can be carried out to find the same field in terms of bound current densities. The point of observation Q is taken as the center of an imaginary sphere V_0 whose surface is S_0 (see Fig. 9.7). The radius s of the sphere is taken to be macroscopically infinitesimal, so that the magnetization vector $\mathbf{M}$ of the material may be treated as constant within V_0. The magnetic induction at Q is written as the sum of two partial fields:

$$\mathbf{B}_m = \mathbf{B'} + \mathbf{B}_0 \qquad (9.87)$$

where $\mathbf{B'}$ is due to the material in the region V' of the magnet which excludes V_0, while B_0 is due to the material in V_0. In order to identify B_m at Q with the macro-scopic magnetic induction there, the field B_0 is computed by supposing the point Q to have a random position relative to the structure of the material. The calculation of this partial field B_0 has been set up in Sec. 9.10. Equation (9.110) expresses B_0 as an integral in terms of the magnetization M at Q:

$$B_0 = \frac{\mu_0}{4\pi s^2} \oint_{S_0} n_0 \times (M \times n_0)\, dS \qquad (9.110)$$

where n_0 is the unit normal to S_0 directed outward from V_0. This integral may be evaluated by expressing the unit vectors as functions of position on S_0, and it turns out to equal $\frac{2}{3}\mu_0 M$; but we shall not need to use this result. Turning to the partial field B', we postulate first that the radius s of the sphere about Q is large enough on a microscopic scale that an elementary current system of the material in V', even though located right at the boundary S_0, produces a dipole field at Q. This sets a lower limit to s. The point Q is then external to the region V' by a sufficient distance that the analysis of Sec. 9.14 may be used, and the magnetic induction B' may be expressed in terms of volume and surface densities of bound current as in Eq. (9.212). It must

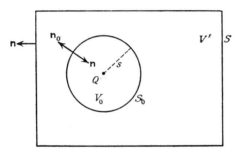

FIG. 9.7. Observation point within magnetic matter, and circumscribed sphere.

be remembered in setting up this expression that S_0 is a boundary surface of V' in addition to the natural surfaces S of the magnet. The field B' is therefore the sum of the three Ampère integrals

$$B' = \frac{\mu_0}{4\pi} \int_{V'} \frac{J' \times r}{r^3}\, dV + \frac{\mu_0}{4\pi} \int_{S} \frac{K' \times r}{r^3}\, dS + \frac{\mu_0}{4\pi} \int_{S_0} \frac{K' \times r}{r^3}\, dS \qquad (9.217)$$

The bound current densities J' and K' in Eq. (9.217) are defined in terms of the magnetization M by the relations

$$J' = \text{curl } M \qquad (9.203)$$

and

$$K' = M \times n \qquad (9.207)$$

It is understood in Eq. (9.217) that the vector distance r is directed from the element of integration to the observer at Q and in (9.207) that the unit normal n to S or S_0 is always directed outward from V'.

Notice now that in the last integral of Eq. (9.217), which extends over the artificially introduced boundary S_0, the quantity r/r may be identified with the unit normal n, for it has unit magnitude and the inward radial direction:

$$\frac{r}{r} = n \qquad (9.218)$$

By substitution of Eqs. (9.207) and (9.218), this term of (9.217) becomes

$$\frac{\mu_0}{4\pi} \int_{S_0} \frac{\mathbf{K'} \times \mathbf{r}}{r^3} \, dS = \frac{\mu_0}{4\pi} \int_{S_0} \frac{(\mathbf{M} \times \mathbf{n}) \times \mathbf{n}}{r^2} \, dS \qquad (9.219)$$

But on S_0, the distance r has the constant value s and $\mathbf{n} = -\mathbf{n}_0$. Hence

$$\frac{\mu_0}{4\pi} \int_{S_0} \frac{\mathbf{K'} \times \mathbf{r}}{r^3} \, dS = \frac{\mu_0}{4\pi s^2} \int_{S_0} (\mathbf{M} \times \mathbf{n}_0) \times \mathbf{n}_0 \, dS \qquad (9.220)$$

Equation (9.220) is now to be compared with (9.110). Since reversal of the order of a vector product changes the algebraic sign of the result, it appears that

$$\frac{\mu_0}{4\pi} \int_{S_0} \frac{\mathbf{K'} \times \mathbf{r}}{r^3} \, dS = -\mathbf{B}_0 \qquad (9.221)$$

When Eq. (9.221) is substituted into (9.217) and then (9.217) is substituted into (9.87), the partial field $\mathbf{B}_0$ cancels out, and the macroscopic magnetic induction due to the magnet at the interior point Q is expressed entirely in terms of bound currents:

$$\mathbf{B}_m = \frac{\mu_0}{4\pi} \int_{V'} \frac{\mathbf{J'} \times \mathbf{r}}{r^3} \, dV + \frac{\mu_0}{4\pi} \int_{S} \frac{\mathbf{K'} \times \mathbf{r}}{r^3} \, dS \qquad (9.222)$$

Equation (9.222) still involves the sphere V_0 which was introduced in the analysis, since V' is not the entire volume of the magnet, but excludes V_0. It is possible, however, to replace the proper volume integral in Eq. (9.222) by an improper integral over the entire volume V of the magnet:

$$\int_V \frac{\mathbf{J'} \times \mathbf{r}}{r^3} \, dV$$

An integral of this form can be shown to be convergent by a method similar to that used in Sec. 1.8. As the radius s of V_0 approaches zero, the limit of the integral over V_0 approaches zero:

$$\lim_{s \to 0} \int_{V_0} \frac{\mathbf{J'} \times \mathbf{r}}{r^3} \, dV = 0 \qquad (9.223)$$

Therefore

$$\int_V \frac{\mathbf{J'} \times \mathbf{r}}{r^3} \, dV = \lim_{s \to 0} \int_{V'} \frac{\mathbf{J'} \times \mathbf{r}}{r^3} \, dV \qquad (9.224)$$

since for any value of s

$$\int_V \frac{\mathbf{J'} \times \mathbf{r}}{r^3} \, dV = \int_{V'} \frac{\mathbf{J'} \times \mathbf{r}}{r^3} \, dV + \int_{V_0} \frac{\mathbf{J'} \times \mathbf{r}}{r^3} \, dV \qquad (9.225)$$

Now in the derivation of Eq. (9.222), s was macroscopically infinitesimal by hypothesis. The volume integral in Eq. (9.222) therefore has already its limiting value given in (9.224), so that (9.222) may be written

$$\mathbf{B}_m = \frac{\mu_0}{4\pi} \int_V \frac{\mathbf{J'} \times \mathbf{r}}{r^3} \, dV + \frac{\mu_0}{4\pi} \int_S \frac{\mathbf{K'} \times \mathbf{r}}{r^3} \, dS \qquad (9.226)$$

Equation (9.226) shows that the magnetic induction produced at an interior point by a body of magnetized matter is just that which would result from the current densities $\mathbf{J'}$ and $\mathbf{K'}$ of Eqs. (9.203) and (9.207) if these actually flowed in nonmagnetic material.

This is the same conclusion which was reached in the preceding section for a point of observation exterior to the magnet, for Eq. (9.212) of that section is identical with (9.226). Therefore a body of magnetized matter may be represented, so far as concerns the magnetic induction which it produces at any point of observation, by the system of bound currents. The field (9.226) may of course be expressed as the curl of the vector potential function given as Eq. (9.211) of Sec. 9.14:

$$\mathbf{A}_m = \frac{\mu_0}{4\pi} \int_V \frac{\mathbf{J}'}{r} \, dV + \frac{\mu_0}{4\pi} \int_S \frac{\mathbf{K}'}{r} \, dS \qquad (9.211)$$

If free, macroscopic current densities $\mathbf{J}$ and $\mathbf{K}$ exist in the magnetostatic system, and possibly within the magnet itself, the total macroscopic field $\mathbf{B}$ is, according to the principle of superposition, the vector sum of the field (9.226) due to the magnetic material and the field $\mathbf{B}_i$ due to the macroscopic currents as though these flowed in nonmagnetic matter:

$$\mathbf{B} = \mathbf{B}_m + \mathbf{B}_i \qquad (9.227)$$

To emphasize the symmetry between bound and free current, we may generalize Eq. (9.121) used for $\mathbf{B}_i$ in Sec. 9.10 by adding a surface density $\mathbf{K}$ of free current:

$$\mathbf{B}_i = \frac{\mu_0}{4\pi} \int \frac{\mathbf{J} \times \mathbf{r}}{r^3} \, dV + \frac{\mu_0}{4\pi} \int \frac{\mathbf{K} \times \mathbf{r}}{r^3} \, dS \qquad (9.228)$$
$$\text{all space} \qquad\qquad \text{all surfaces}$$

When Eqs. (9.226) and (9.228) are substituted into (9.227), the resultant magnetic induction may be written

$$\mathbf{B} = \frac{\mu_0}{4\pi} \int \frac{(\mathbf{J} + \mathbf{J}') \times \mathbf{r}}{r^3} \, dV + \frac{\mu_0}{4\pi} \int \frac{(\mathbf{K} + \mathbf{K}') \times \mathbf{r}}{r^3} \, dS \qquad (9.229)$$
$$\text{all space} \qquad\qquad\qquad \text{all boundaries}$$

In writing Eq. (9.229), the limits of the integrals in (9.226) have been extended over all magnetic matter and boundaries of a system, so that this equation may give the total magnetic induction at any point in the system. Notice that this total field may be considered to result from the sum of the free and bound currents flowing in nonmagnetic space.

As an application of Eq. (9.226), the example given in the preceding section may be used. There it was shown that the external magnetic induction of a uniformly and axially magnetized bar magnet is the same as that of a uniformly wound, ideal solenoid of the same dimensions, provided the current I and the turns density N_1 of the solenoid are related to the magnetization M of the bar by

$$N_1 I = M \qquad (9.216)$$

Now according to the results of the present section, the macroscopic magnetic induction interior to the magnet is also the same as that in the solenoid. Consider next the case of an ideal toroid coil, one in which the core may be treated as a uniformly magnetized, endless bar with a negligibly curved axis. The bound currents of the core are then like those of the bar magnet, and produce within the core the magnetic induction which would result from an ideal toroid winding characterized by the constants N_1 and I of Eq. (9.216). This induction has the value

$$B_m = \mu_0 M \qquad (9.230)$$

See Eq. (9.12), Sec. 9.2, where the field in a toroid is given, and note that N_1 is the quantity which is there written $N/2\pi r$. The total magnetic induction in the core of a toroid carrying a winding is by Eq. (9.227) the sum of the term (9.230) and the magnetic induction B_i which the actual winding would produce in a nonmagnetic core. Now in Secs. 9.2 and 9.3, the scalar contribution of the toroid core to the magnetic induction in the core was designated M'. Therefore

$$M' = \mu_0 M \tag{9.231}$$

The vector contribution of the core, the quantity $\mathbf{M}'$ of Sec. 9.3, is consequently

$$\mathbf{M}' = \mu_0 \mathbf{M} \tag{9.232}$$

Comparing Eq. (9.232) with (9.28) of Sec. 9.3, we see that the magnetization vector $\mathbf{M}$ of our present microscopic analysis is identical with the vector of the same name and symbol which was defined in Sec. 9.3 from a purely macroscopic point of view. This identity has already been demonstrated by an alternative method in Sec. 9.10, by use of the concept of magnetic bound charge.

Equation (9.229) has important theoretical applications. It shows that in any steady-state system, the magnetic induction depends on the free plus bound current densities in just the same manner as the magnetic induction in a system of nonmagnetic matter depends on free current alone. We may therefore generalize Ampère's circuital law of Sec. 7.7 by adding the bound current to the free current:

$$\oint_C \mathbf{B} \cdot d\mathbf{l} = \mu_0 (I_C + I'_C) \tag{9.233}$$

Here C is any closed path of integration, and $(I_C + I'_C)$ is the total free plus bound current flowing through any surface bounded by C. The differential form of this equation may be found at once by using the result of Sec. 7.11, where the differential form of Ampère's law for nonmagnetic space was deduced. It is only necessary to add the volume density of bound current $\mathbf{J}'$ to the free density $\mathbf{J}$. In condensed notation, then,

$$\text{curl } \mathbf{B} = \mu_0 (\mathbf{J} + \mathbf{J}') \tag{9.234}$$

This is true at all points of any steady-state system of free currents and magnetic matter except on boundaries where $\mathbf{K}$ or $\mathbf{K}'$ might exist. Let us now substitute Eq. (9.203) for $\mathbf{J}'$ into (9.234) and collect terms under the derivatives represented by the **curl** operation. The result is

$$\text{curl } (\mathbf{B} - \mu_0 \mathbf{M}) = \mu_0 \mathbf{J} \tag{9.235}$$

If therefore we form the vector

$$\mathbf{H} \equiv \frac{1}{\mu_0} \mathbf{B} - \mathbf{M} \tag{9.236}$$

which in Secs. 9.3 and 9.11 has been called the magnetizing force, we obtain a quantity which in a steady-state system, at all points except on a boundary, satisfies the relation

$$\text{curl } \mathbf{H} = \mathbf{J} \tag{9.141}$$

In integral form, Eq. (9.141) becomes

$$\oint_C \mathbf{H} \cdot d\mathbf{l} = I_C \tag{9.136}$$

where I_C is the free current through any surface bounded by the arbitrary closed curve C. Equations (9.141) and (9.136) have already been deduced in another way in Sec. 9.11.

The general steady-state, magnetostatic field (9.229) may be expressed as the curl of a vector potential $\mathbf{A}$:

$$\mathbf{B} = \operatorname{curl} \mathbf{A} \qquad (9.237)$$

This function $\mathbf{A}$ may be written down immediately from (9.211) simply by the addition of the free current densities $\mathbf{J}$ and $\mathbf{K}$ to the respective bound densities. It follows from (9.237), as in Sec. 7.6 for the field of steady-state steady free currents alone, that the general magnetostatic field (9.229) always has a zero divergence and a zero net flux through any closed surface S:

$$\operatorname{div} \mathbf{B} = 0 \qquad (9.238)$$

$$\oint_S \mathbf{B} \cdot \mathbf{n} \, dS = 0 \qquad (9.239)$$

9.16. Force and Torque on a Magnet in Terms of Bound Currents.
The two preceding sections have been devoted to the representation of a magnetized body by a set of fictitious currents flowing in nonmagnetic space. It has been shown that these so-called bound currents are adequate in all cases to give both the external and the internal macroscopic magnetic induction produced by the magnet. It remains to be shown that the bound currents also give correctly the total magnetic force and torque on a magnet not immersed in a magnetic fluid, even though they do not in general give the correct space distribution of the local stresses. This means that the representation of a rigid body of magnetized matter by bound currents is complete so far as magnetostatic, mechanical experiments are concerned. This result is to be expected from Newton's third law (action and reaction) which holds for closed steady-current systems *in vacuo* and consequently must hold for magnetized matter whose properties derive from its composition by such systems on a microscopic scale. To carry through a formal proof, let α be a magnet carrying no macroscopic free current. When α is subjected to the field of a system $\mathfrak{B}$ of other magnets and possibly steady free currents as well, its magnetization vector will be designated by $\mathbf{M}$. Let α' be a nonmagnetic body of the same shape as α, in which we suppose current densities equal to the bound current densities $\mathbf{J}'$ and $\mathbf{K}'$ of α to flow. These densities are given by Eqs. (9.203) and (9.207), Sec. 9.14,

$$\mathbf{J}' = \operatorname{curl} \mathbf{M} \qquad (9.203)$$
$$\mathbf{K}' = \mathbf{M} \times \mathbf{n} \qquad (9.207)$$

where $\mathbf{n}$ is the outward unit normal to the surface S of the magnet. Now by Sec. 9.14, the external magnetic induction of α' is identical with that of α. The substitution of α' for α thus leaves the magnetic force and torque on $\mathfrak{B}$ unchanged. The total force on α' is therefore the same as that on α, both being the negative of that on $\mathfrak{B}$; and similarly the torques on α' and α are the same when computed relative to a given origin, both being the negative of the torque about that origin on $\mathfrak{G}$. Q.E.D.

It follows from the foregoing theorem that correct expressions for the total force and torque on a magnet, when not immersed in a magnetic fluid, may be written out in terms of the bound current densities by assuming these to experience the same forces as if they were free current densities in nonmagnetic matter. The element of force $d\mathbf{F}$ on the volume element dV is thus to be taken as

$$d\mathbf{F} = \mathbf{J}' \times \mathbf{B}\, dV \qquad (9.240)$$

[See Eq. (7.6), Sec. 7.2.] The corresponding form for the force on an element of surface dS in which a bound surface current of density $\mathbf{K}'$ flows is obtained by using the equivalence

$$\mathbf{J}'\, dV = \mathbf{K}'\, dS \qquad (9.209)$$

(See Sec. 9.14.)   The force on dS is therefore to be taken as

$$d\mathbf{F} = \mathbf{K}' \times \mathbf{B}\, dS \qquad (9.241)$$

It is understood in Eqs. (9.240) and (9.241) that $\mathbf{B}$ excludes the field of the elements of current themselves. In fact, since stresses are not of present concern and are not given by bound currents anyway, we may and shall let $\mathbf{B}$ mean only that part of the magnetic induction produced directly by sources external to the magnet, that is, by the system called $\mathfrak{G}$ in the theorem above. The subscript used in Sec. 9.13 to designate the external field will be dispensed with here in the interest of simplifying the notation. The total force on the magnet due to its magnetization is now to be found by integrating Eqs. (9.240) and (9.241) over the volume V and complete boundary surface S of the magnet, respectively,

$$\mathbf{F} = \int_V \mathbf{J}' \times \mathbf{B}\, dV + \oint_S \mathbf{K}' \times \mathbf{B}\, dS \qquad (9.242)$$

The torque $\mathbf{L}$ about a given origin produced by the magnetic force is to be computed as though Eqs. (9.240) and (9.241) gave the correct space distribution of the force elements on the magnet. Thus

$$\mathbf{L} = \int_V \mathbf{r} \times (\mathbf{J}' \times \mathbf{B})\, dV + \oint_S \mathbf{r} \times (\mathbf{K}' \times \mathbf{B})\, dS \qquad (9.243)$$

Here $\mathbf{r}$ is the vector position of the element of integration, dV or dS as the case may be, relative to the origin.

It is quite possible, even though tedious, to prove without the use of Newton's third law that Eqs. (9.242) and (9.243) give correct values for the total force and torque on a magnet. These proofs, which are based upon Eqs. (7.173) and (7.182), Sec. 7.13, will be omitted.

The equivalence of the set of bound currents to the magnetization of a body of material, which has now been shown to be complete except for stress analysis, is a matter of theoretical interest rather than an aid in computing force and torque on a magnet, for Eqs. (9.242) and (9.243) are complicated in form. The theorem has a practical use in reverse, however, for it may be applied to state the equivalence of a magnet to a set of free, macroscopic current densities. For example, we noticed in Sec. 9.14 that a solenoid of N_1 turns per unit length carrying current I represents a uniformly and axially magnetized bar of the same dimensions in which the intensity of magnetization is

$$M = N_1 I \tag{9.216}$$

In reverse, the bar magnet can represent the solenoid. The force and torque which the solenoid experiences in an external magnetic field are therefore the same as those which would be exerted on the bar magnet, and these may be computed from the relatively simple integrals of Sec. 9.13 in terms of magnetic bound charge. Thus a rigid solenoid behaves as though it had magnetic poles at its ends.

9.17. Magnetic Energy. Hysteresis Loss. The transfer of energy out of a set of electric circuits by the mechanism of electromagnetic induction has been considered in Sec. 8.9. There the currents I_j and the linking fluxes Φ_j of the circuits were taken as the variables describing the process. For a set of n inductors, the basic equation for the energy lost to the circuits is Eq. (8.72) of that section:

$$W_F = \sum_{j=1}^{n} \int_{\Phi_{j0}}^{\Phi_{jf}} I_j \, d\Phi_j \tag{9.244}$$

The integration is to be carried from the initial to the final configuration of the system, as specified by the variables of the system, using the relations between the variables expressed by the characteristic functions $\Phi_j(I_1, I_2, \ldots, I_n)$. The path, specified by the ratios of the currents as they change, is in general involved in the answer but was found to be irrelevant in the reversible cases. Now in case the currents do not vary too rapidly, the magnetic field in the near vicinity of a set of inductors may be considered as quasi-static, that is, to be specified by the instantaneous values of the currents just as if these currents were stationary. This statement will be taken for granted here, because its proof requires use of the complete Maxwell equations to be developed in Chap. 12. See the discussion of small systems in Sec. 12.12. In this quasi-static case, Eq. (9.244) may be transformed so as to express the transferred energy entirely in terms of the magnetic field variables. We proceed to give this transformation in the simple case of an ideal toroid coil, and then to generalize without formal proof.

Consider then an ideal toroid coil such as was used in the discussion of Secs. 9.2 and 9.3. It is to be wound with N turns about a circular axis of radius a, each turn having a radius $b \ll a$. The magnetic field of such a coil is almost all in the region V enclosed by the windings. The magnetizing force at a point inside V is approximately uniform and parallel to the circular axis, if the core material is isotropic and homogeneous, and has a magnitude easily found by use of Ampère's circuital law, Eq. (9.26), Sec. 9.3. When the current in the coil is I,

$$H = \frac{NI}{2\pi a} \tag{9.245}$$

The external field $\mathbf{H}$ of the toroid has circuital integrals like those of a single turn carrying current I around the circular axis; hence if N is large, this external field is small compared with the internal, as stated above. Likewise, the flux turns self-linking the toroid are due almost entirely to the internal magnetic induction, which links all N turns. Let us consider the turns of the coil to be circular loops, each of area πb^2, all connected in series. Under the assumption of isotropic, homogeneous core material, the magnetic induction has a uniform magnitude B in V, and being parallel to the circular axis it is normal to the loops of the winding. The flux linkage is then

$$\Phi = N\pi b^2 B \tag{9.246}$$

Equations (9.245) and (9.246) can now be substituted into the energy expression (9.244), written for only one circuit:

$$W_F = \int_{\Phi_0}^{\Phi_f} I \, d\Phi \tag{9.247}$$

Therefore the energy transfer during the change of induction from B_0 to B_f is

$$W_F = (2\pi a)\pi b^2 \int_{B_0}^{B_f} H \, dB \tag{9.248}$$

But the volume V of the torus is just

$$V = (2\pi a)\pi b^2 \tag{9.249}$$

Thus the transferred energy is

$$W_F = V \int_{B_0}^{B_f} H \, dB \tag{9.250}$$

Consider two simple applications of Eq. (9.250). In the linear, isotropic, homogeneous case,

$$B = \mu H \tag{9.251}$$

with the permeability μ a constant. The energy W_F is then all stored magnetically, and relative to the zero-current condition its magnitude is

$$U_M = V\mu \int_0^{H_f} H \, dH = \frac{1}{2}\mu H_f^2 V \qquad (9.252)$$

Here the subscript f simply distinguishes the final H from the variable H, and is unnecessary in a resulting formula. Alternative forms of Eq. (9.252) are

$$U_M = \frac{1}{2\mu} B^2 V = \frac{1}{2} HBV \qquad \text{linear case} \qquad (9.253)$$

One may define an energy density function in the toroid, an energy per unit volume $u_M \equiv U_M/V$:

$$u_M = \frac{1}{2}BH \qquad \text{linear case} \qquad (9.254)$$

More will be said of this later.

Another application of Eq. (9.250) was referred to in Sec. 9.6. If the toroid coil has a ferromagnetic core, the energy given by Eq. (9.250) for a complete cycle around an established hysteresis loop is all lost to heat. The hysteresis loss per cycle per unit volume is thus

$$\frac{W_{\text{hist. cycle}}}{V} = \oint_{\text{cycle}} H \, dB \qquad (9.255)$$

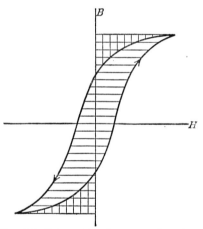

The integral (9.255) represents the area in BH units enclosed by the hysteresis loop of the B-H diagram for the core material, and is always positive for the counterclockwise sense in which the hysteresis loop is necessarily traversed. This may be seen by considering the partial areas between segments of the loop and the B axis. In Fig. 9.8, these

FIG. 9.8. Integration for energy loss during a hysteresis cycle.

areas are shown with horizontal or vertical shading according as their contribution to the integral is positive or negative. The same result follows from the more familiar consideration of areas between the curve and the H axis, after Eq. (9.255) has been integrated by parts:

$$\oint_{\text{cycle}} H \, dB = [HB] - \oint_{\text{cycle}} B \, dH \qquad (9.256)$$

Since HB has the same value at the end as at the beginning of a cycle, the first term on the right of Eq. (9.256) vanishes; hence

$$\frac{W_{\text{cycle}}}{V} = -\oint_{\text{cycle}} B \, dH \qquad (9.257)$$

An empirical formula was found by Steinmetz to relate this hysteresis loss approximately to the maximum magnetic induction B_{max} attained by a magnetic material during the hysteresis cycle:

$$\frac{W_{\text{cycle}}}{V} = \eta B_{\text{max}}{}^{k} \qquad (9.258)$$

where η is called the hysteresis coefficient of the material, and k is an exponent having a value of about 1.6 for ordinary values of B_{max}. Values of η are tabulated by engineering handbooks.

The natural generalization of Eq. (9.250) to the case of nonuniform fields is

$$W_F = \int_{\text{all space}} \int_{B_0}^{B_f} \mathbf{H} \cdot \delta\mathbf{B} \, dV \qquad (9.259)$$

where the integration is formally carried to infinity, but it is understood that a finite system of currents is involved. This equation expresses the energy transferred, by electromagnetic induction, out of a set of circuits in a small system. Its general proof will be omitted. Consider the linear case in which the energy W_F is reversibly transferred to the field where it may be said to be stored. To find an expression for the stored magnetic energy of a general linear system we may imagine the currents causing the field to build up simultaneously so that at any time they all have the same fraction α of their final values. The fields B and H will then have at every point of space just the same fraction α of their final values, because of the linearity of the system. Thus at any stage of the process

$$\mathbf{H} = \alpha \mathbf{H}_f \qquad \mathbf{B} = \alpha \mathbf{B}_f \qquad \delta\mathbf{B} = \mathbf{B}_f \, \delta\alpha$$

Equation (9.259) now gives for the stored magnetic energy relative to the condition of no currents or fields

$$U_M = \int_0^1 \alpha \, \delta\alpha \int_{\text{all space}} \mathbf{H}_f \cdot \mathbf{B}_f \, dV = \tfrac{1}{2} \int_{\text{all space}} \mathbf{H}_f \cdot \mathbf{B}_f \, dV \qquad \text{linear} \qquad (9.260)$$

This reduces in the isotropic case to

$$U_M = \tfrac{1}{2} \int_{\text{all space}} \mu H_f{}^2 \, dV = \tfrac{1}{2} \int_{\text{all space}} \frac{1}{\mu} B_f{}^2 \, dV \qquad \text{linear, isotropic} \qquad (9.261)$$

and in the case of a homogeneous material filling the region occupied by the field

$$U_M = \frac{\mu}{2} \int_{\text{all space}} H_f{}^2 \, dV \qquad \text{linear, isotropic, homogeneous} \qquad (9.262)$$

A space density of magnetic energy can be defined in general by use of the integrand of Eq. (9.260):

$$u_M \equiv \tfrac{1}{2} \mathbf{H}_f \cdot \mathbf{B}_f \qquad (9.263)$$

As in the similar electrostatic problem, such an energy distribution is not unique and its significance is open to question.

9.18. Magnetomechanical Energy Relations. In Sec. 8.9 the energy transferred by electromagnetic induction from an electric circuit was shown to be

$$\delta W = I \, \delta \Phi \qquad (9.264)$$

in terms of the flux change $\delta \Phi$ and the current I. The discussion given there of the disposition of this energy by storage, dissipation, or radiation was appropriate only for systems of rigid inductors in which no mechanical motion occurs. When mechanical motion does occur, the magnetic forces on current circuits result in input or output of mechanical work. Let us consider the energy relations in such magnetomechanical systems. Equation (9.264) is still basic for the energy transferred out of a circuit. A similarly basic expression for mechanical energy produced by motion of a circuit relative to a coordinate frame in which there is a steady magnetic field was deduced in Sec. 7.12, where see Eq. (7.154):

$$\delta W_M = I \, \delta_M \Phi \qquad (9.265)$$

For present purposes, we have distinguished this energy from that of Eq. (9.264) by the subscript M. The sign of δW_M is taken as positive for mechanical energy output from the moving circuit. A subscript has also been put on the variation symbol in Eq. (9.265) to remind us that this variation is only that due directly to the motion of the circuit and not to a time variation of the magnetic induction vector. If the magnetic induction does actually vary in time, or is dependent on the position of the circuit, then the flux variation in Eq. (9.265) must be considered as that resulting from a virtual motion of the circuit, not a real one, that is, a motion unaccompanied by changes in the field. The proper self-field of a circuit, that is, the field which the circuit would produce if it were isolated as distinguished from external fields even when these are induced by the circuit, contributes to the variation $\delta_M \Phi$ only in the case of deformations of the circuit. In no case is variation of the self-field with the current I to be included in computing $\delta_M \Phi$. In the discussion that follows we shall consider only rigid circuits. For these the proper self-field may always be omitted from the computation of the flux.

As a simple example of a magnetomechanical system, consider a pair of isolated rigid circuits C_1 and C_2 *in vacuo*, whose currents I_1 and I_2 are held constant. Let C_1 be given some finite displacement relative to C_2 which results in a flux change $\Delta\Phi_1$ through C_1. Notice that the symbol Δ is used here for an arbitrarily large charge, by contrast to the differential variation symbol δ of Eqs. (9.264) and (9.265). These equations imply an integration in order to yield the work involved in a finite process, during which the current of course may in general be variable. The integration is trivial in our present case of constant current. Assuming C_2 to be held fixed, the mechanical work output during the process is done entirely by C_1, and is given by Eq. (9.265) as

$$W_M = I_1\,\Delta\Phi_1 \qquad\qquad (9.266)$$

By Eq. (9.264), the battery which supplies the constant current I_1 does just this same amount of work:

$$W_{F1} = I_1\,\Delta\Phi_1 = W_M \qquad\qquad (9.267)$$

This is not the whole story, however; for the relative displacement of the two circuits produces in general a change of flux $\Delta\Phi_2$ in C_2, and hence the battery supplying the constant current I_2 must contribute the work

$$W_{F2} = I_2\,\Delta\Phi_2 \qquad\qquad (9.268)$$

In order to compare this amount of work with that of Eqs. (9.266) and (9.267), it may be noted that the relative displacement of the two circuits completely determines the mechanical work. They have been supposed to form an isolated system, so there are no externally produced magnetic forces; and consequently only internal motions, not motion of the system as a whole, cause the magnetic forces to do work. Thus if C_1 is held fixed and C_2 moves while the same relative displacement as before occurs, the same mechanical work as before is done. By Eq. (9.265) this work is then

$$W_M = I_2\,\Delta\Phi_2 \qquad\qquad (9.269)$$

Comparison with Eq. (9.268) shows that the battery maintaining the current I_2 supplies work W_M, just like the battery maintaining I_1:

$$W_{F2} = W_M \qquad\qquad (9.270)$$

The batteries together therefore contribute the double work

$$W_F = 2W_M \qquad\qquad (9.271)$$

The difference W_M between the work W_F supplied by the batteries and the mechanical output work W_M is stored in the magnetic field, for the whole process is reversible. If U_M represents stored magnetic energy, the situation can be summed up by writing

$$W_M = +\Delta U_M \tag{9.272}$$

The foregoing example is a special case of a more general theorem, that Eqs. (9.271) and (9.272) hold for any linear and magnetically isolated system of constant-current circuits. Such a system may of course include more than two circuits, and linear magnetic matter as well. The theorem may be demonstrated by use of Eq. (8.77), Sec. 8.9, according to which the magnetic energy reversibly stored in the field of a linear, isolated system containing n circuits is

$$U_M = \tfrac{1}{2} \sum_{j=1}^{n} I_j \Phi_j \tag{9.273}$$

Suppose now that a linear isolated system of constant-current circuits and magnetic matter has an initial mechanical configuration in which the fluxes through the circuits are Φ_j and that after certain mechanical displacements take place the fluxes become Φ_j'. The changes of flux are then

$$\Delta \Phi_j = \Phi_j' - \Phi_j \tag{9.274}$$

The work W_F done by all the batteries during the process is given by Eq. (9.264) after summation over all the circuits and integration:

$$W_F = \sum_{j=1}^{n} I_j \, \Delta \Phi_j \tag{9.275}$$

Thus

$$W_F = \sum_{j=1}^{n} I_j (\Phi_j' - \Phi_j) \tag{9.276}$$

Comparison of Eq. (9.273) shows that the work of the batteries is twice the change ΔU_M of magnetic stored energy:

$$W_F = 2 \, \Delta U_M \tag{9.277}$$

But according to the conservation of energy, the mechanical output W_M during the process must be

$$W_M = W_F - \Delta U_M \tag{9.278}$$

for the input energy W_F must be fully accounted for. Combining Eqs. (9.278) and (9.277), we obtain (9.271) and (9.272) again, Q.E.D. This theorem may be compared with a corresponding result in Sec. 4.13 for a linear electrostatic system in which all conductors are held at constant potentials.

By way of contrast, consider a nonlinear system containing a single circuit C carrying constant current I together with an ideal permanent magnet having constant magnetization. On the assumption of no induced magnetization, the field of the magnet is unchangeable. If the circuit and the magnet form an isolated system in space, it is irrelevant whether the magnet or the circuit is held at rest during a mechanical process: the mechanical work output W_M depends only on their relative displacement. If the circuit is considered the element which moves, Eq. (9.265) is applicable and yields the mechanical work output in terms of the flux change through the circuit:

$$W_M = I \, \Delta\Phi \tag{9.279}$$

The work put in by the battery is, according to Eq. (9.264),

$$W_F = I \, \Delta\Phi \tag{9.280}$$

Evidently for this case

$$W_M = W_F \tag{9.281}$$

The process is reversible; thus no energy is dissipated. The conservation of energy in connection with Eq. (9.281) therefore implies that there is no change in magnetic stored energy:

$$\Delta U_M = 0 \tag{9.282}$$

Equations (9.281) and (9.282) are to be contrasted with (9.271) and (9.272). General systems of several ideal magnets and circuits would require individual analysis.

It may be well in conclusion to carry to the limit the progression from Eqs. (9.271) and (9.272) to (9.281) and (9.282). Suppose a system of ideal permanent magnets only, with no circuits. There being no dissipation of energy in ideal magnets, the conservation of energy requires that any mechanical output work resulting from a displacement within the system should equal the loss of potential energy of the system. If we believe in the general validity of the formulas of Sec. 9.17 of this chapter for storage of magnetic energy, we should expect to be able to write

$$W_M = -\Delta U_M = - \int_{\text{all space}} \int_{\text{process}} \mathbf{H} \cdot \delta\mathbf{B} \, dV \tag{9.283}$$

This is in fact correct, although its proof will not be given.

PROBLEMS

9.1. A toroid coil of 500 turns is wound about an iron ring of circular cross section. The ring has outer and inner radii of 5.10 and 3.90 cm, respectively. A secondary coil of 30 turns also wound around the ring is connected to a ballistic galvanometer, and the resistance in the secondary circuit totals 600 ohms. When the toroid current is changed from 0 to 100 ma, a charge of 1.25×10^{-6} coulomb is found to flow in the secondary circuit. What is (a) the change of magnetic induction in the ring, (b) the change of the field B_0, computed as if there were no iron, (c) the ratio $\Delta B/\Delta B_0$, and (d) the change of the quantity M' in the iron?

9.2. Suppose that 900 turns of No. 18 wire can be wound per meter in a single layer and that this wire can safely carry 3 amp. What is the maximum value of magnetizing force available in a single-layer solenoid or toroid wound of this wire, due to the current in the coil? If the coil has an air core, what is the maximum magnetic induction?

9.3. Find the ratio of the intensity of magnetization to the magnetic induction in the nonferromagnetic manganese steel whose relative permeability is 1.20, deriving a suitable algebraic formula first.

9.4. A certain nonferromagnetic iron alloy containing chromium and nickel has a relative permeability of 1.01 and a specific gravity of 7.89. Find its permeability, susceptibility, and mass susceptibility in the rationalized mks system.

9.5. The magnetic susceptibility of copper is -9.60×10^{-6}, and its specific gravity is 8.89. Find (a) the relative permeability of copper, (b) the mass susceptibility of copper, and (c) the intensity of magnetization and the magnetizing force in copper when the magnetic induction is 2 webers/m².

9.6. The maximum relative permeability in the normal induction curve of a certain kind of cast iron is 700, at the point of the normal magnetization curve where the induction is 0.60 weber/m². What are the values of the intensity of magnetization and magnetizing force at this point?

9.7. An alloy of 78.5 per cent nickel and 21.5 per cent iron has, when properly processed, the unusually high relative permeability of 100,000 at a magnetizing force of 4.4 amp-turns/m. At this point on its normal magnetization curve, what fraction of the total magnetic induction is provided by the local magnetization of the material?

9.8. A certain steel for permanent magnets has a normal residual induction of 0.73 weber/m² and a coercive force of 3.5×10^4 amp-turn/m. Find the intensity of magnetization of the steel at the points in the normal hysteresis loop for which these data apply, and indicate its sense relative to **B** or **H** as the case requires.

9.9. Within pure iron, the local magnetization can contribute as much as 2 webers/m² to the magnetic induction.

a. What is the magnetic moment of 1 cm³ of iron under these conditions?

b. One electron can contribute one Bohr magneton, 0.927×10^{-23} amp-m², to the magnetic moment in a given direction due to its spin. How many electrons are needed to produce the moment (a) of 1 cm³ of iron, if each contributes one magneton?

c. Compare (b) with the number of atoms of iron per cubic centimeter. Data: Avogadro number 6.02×10^{23}/mole; density 7.85 g/cm³; atomic weight 55.8 g/mole.

9.10. A thin sheet S of steel of constant thickness s has a uniform magnetization M_0 everywhere normal to its faces. Show that the magnetic induction due to the sheet at an exterior point in space, whose distance r from any point of the shell is large compared with s, is the same as that of a circuit C which coincides with the edge of the sheet S and carries steady current $I = M_0 s$ in the proper sense (see Sec. 7.10). Such a sheet is called a magnetic shell. Use the magnetic scalar potential, and represent the magnetic matter by magnetic bound charge.

9.11. A bar magnet is said to be in the Gauss A position for an observer colinear with the magnet and in the Gauss B position for an observer on its perpendicular bisector. Suppose the magnet has moment m, and let its poles be considered point magnetic charges of equal magnitude separated by distance l. Show that to the second order in l/r, where r is the observer's distance from the center of the magnet, the fields in the two positions are

$$B_A = \frac{\mu_0 m}{2\pi r^3}\left(1 + \frac{1}{2}\frac{l^2}{r^2}\right) \qquad B_B = \frac{\mu_0 m}{4\pi r^3}\left(1 - \frac{3}{8}\frac{l^2}{r^2}\right)$$

9.12. Suppose the field of a point pole is radial and proportional to $(1/r)^n$. Show that n is given by the ratio of the fields at equal distances from a bar magnet in the two Gauss positions (see the preceding problem), to the first degree in l/r, where l is the distance between poles of the bar magnet. (This method was used by Gauss to establish the inverse-square law.)

9.13. Given a solid steel sphere with uniform magnetization parallel to the polar axis. Find the magnetic moment of the sphere in two ways: (a) by integration of the magnetization vector and (b) by integration over the bound magnetic charge.

9.14. A bar magnet of circular cross section, with plane ends normal to the axis of the bar, has a diameter of 1 cm and a length of 20 cm. The magnetic induction on the axis just outside one end of the magnet has a magnitude of 0.2 weber/m². Supposing uniform axial magnetization of the bar, and treating the far end as a point pole, find (a) the magnetization, (b) the surface densities of bound magnetic charge, (c) the pole strength, and (d) the magnetic moment of the bar.

9.15. Given a region of magnetic material in which the induction and the magnetizing force always have the same (or the opposite) direction, so that the constitutive equation $\mathbf{B} = \mu\mathbf{H}$ can be used. Express the volume density of bound charge in this region in terms of $\mathbf{B}$ and μ, and show that this density can exist only when both $\mathbf{B}$ exists and μ is a function of position. Are these conditions also sufficient?

9.16. A thin disk of steel is uniformly magnetized normally to its faces, with permanent magnetization M. Neglecting edge effects, and assuming that in the process of magnetizing the disk it was carried around a normal hysteresis loop, show at what point of the loop it is after the magnetizing field is removed.

9.17. Suppose a spherical steel shell having inner and outer radii a and b, respectively, were magnetized in a spherically symmetrical way with an intensity of magnetization $\mathbf{M} = k\mathbf{r}$, k being a constant and $\mathbf{r}$ the spherical radius vector.

a. Find the magnetic charge densities of the shell.

b. Show by integration of these densities that the net magnetic charge is zero.

c. Find the magnetizing force and the magnetic induction at a general point in each of the three regions of the system.

9.18. A bar magnet is 15 cm long and 3 mm in diameter. At the center, the axial magnetic induction is 0.60 weber/m². If the entire magnet had a uniform intensity of magnetization, what would its magnetic moment be?

9.19. Given a solid circular cylinder of steel with ends cut normal to the axis, and with uniform axial magnetization of magnitude M. Let the cylinder have radius R and length $2L$. Use magnetic bound charge to find both the magnetizing force and the magnetic induction at general points on the axis, both inside the magnet and outside.

Ans. $$B_z = \frac{\mu_0 M}{2} \left(\frac{L - z}{\sqrt{(L - z)^2 + R^2}} + \frac{L + z}{\sqrt{(L + z)^2 + R^2}} \right)$$

if z is a coordinate along the axis with origin at the center of the magnet.

9.20. A steel sphere of radius R has a uniform magnetization $\mathbf{M} = 4.0 \times 10^5 \, \mathbf{k}$ amp/m, where $\mathbf{k}$ is a cartesian unit vector. Find the magnetic intensity and induction at its center, using magnetic bound charge.   *Ans.* $\mathbf{H} = -\frac{1}{3}\mathbf{M}$; $\mathbf{B} = \frac{2}{3}\mu_0\mathbf{M}$.

9.21. Show that in an isolated system of stationary permanent magnets and other magnetic matter, but without any current flow, the magnetic scalar potential is single-valued and satisfies a Poisson type of equation everywhere except on a boundary, where $\mathbf{M}$ may be discontinuous (see Sec. 2.2).·

9.22. Apply the discussion of electrostatic boundary conditions in Secs. 3.9 and 3.10 to the magnetizing force vector $\mathbf{H}$ and the magnetic scalar potential U^* in systems containing no currents, representing magnetic matter entirely by magnetic bound charge.

$Ans.\ H_{2n} - H_{1n} = \sigma^*$ $H_{2p} = H_{1p}$

$$U_1^* = U_2^*\qquad \frac{\partial U_1^*}{\partial n_1} - \frac{\partial U_2^*}{\partial n_1} = \sigma^*$$

9.23. Consider the problem of an isolated steel sphere of radius R with uniform permanent magnetization M parallel to the polar axis. Show that the boundary conditions on H (see Prob. 9.22) at the surface of the sphere are satisfied by a suitable uniform field inside the sphere and the dipole field outside which is necessary to be correct at large distances. Express these two fields in terms of M, R, and polar coordinates (spherical coordinates without the need of an azimuth angle). [A uniqueness theorem similar to that for electrostatics (Sec. 2.3) guarantees that these fields are the actual ones.]

9.24. *a.* A current of $\frac{3}{4}$ amp flows in a solenoid 1 m long with 1,100 turns, having a cross-sectional area of $\frac{1}{4}$ cm^2. What is its magnetic moment?

b. An iron wire 80 cm long is now placed along the axis of the solenoid, with its center at the center of the solenoid. If the wire has a cross-sectional area of 0.025 cm^2 and a relative permeability of 1,200 under the conditions of the problem, what is the magnetic moment of solenoid plus wire? (The demagnetizing field of H in the wire due to its own poles is to be neglected because of its large ratio of length to diameter.)

9.25. When a permanent magnet is not in use, its poles, if appreciably separated, are joined by a keeper consisting of a piece of iron of high permeability and low coercive force, so that the magnet becomes a part of a closed magnetic circuit. Explain the effect of such a keeper, and the reason for the magnetic characteristics mentioned.

9.26. An electromagnet has a U-shaped core with a length of 20 cm and a circular cross section 1 cm in diameter. An iron strap 2 mm thick and 1 cm wide bridges the gap of 5 cm between the pole faces. Let the permeabilities of the core and strap be, respectively, 3,000 and 2,000 relative to air. If a flux density of 0.80 weber/m^2 is to exist in the strap, find (a) the total reluctance of the circuit; (b) the flux; (c) the induction in the core; (d) the mmf of the windings; (e) the number of turns required if the windings are to carry a current of $\frac{1}{2}$ amp; (f) the magnetic potential difference across the strap.

9.27. The core of a small transformer is built up of sheet steel 0.014 in. thick, punched out in pieces shaped like a letter E in which all legs are equal and equally spaced; 100 such pieces are stacked to form the core, successive pieces having their legs pointing in opposite directions and completely overlapping. The width of all branches of the core is $\frac{3}{4}$ in. and the completed shell is square with an outside dimension of $4\frac{1}{4}$ in. What current is needed in a coil of 300 turns about the central branch of the shell in order that the flux density there shall be 1.0 weber/m^2, if the relative permeability of the steel is taken as 5,000?

9.28. A permanent magnet has the form of a single loop, closed except for a small air gap with parallel faces. Suppose for simplicity that the steel path has a constant cross section except for a small region near the pole faces. Neglecting fringing and flux leakage, show that

$$B_g^2 V_g = -\mu_0(B_m \bar{H}_m) V_m$$

Here B_g and V_g are, respectively, the induction in and volume of the gap; and B_m, $\bar{H}_m$, and V_m are the induction, mean magnetizing force, and volume of the iron. (Notice from this result that the maximum obtainable value of $-BH$ in a magnet steel is a criterion of its suitability for use in permanent magnets.)

9.29. Two equal bar magnets are 10 cm long of small diameter and have pole strengths of 4 amp-m. Find the force between them when they are colinear with a distance of 30 cm between centers, when their magnetic moments are (a) in the same sense and (b) in opposite senses. Treat the poles as point magnetic charges at the ends of the magnets, and neglect the influence of each magnet on the magnetization of the other.

9.30. A long, straight wire in air carries a steady current of 20 amp. Parallel to it and at a distance of 1 cm there is mounted a compass needle 2 cm long, with a cross-sectional area of 1 mm^2 and a uniform, axial magnetization of $\frac{1}{4} \times 10^6$ amp/m. Find the torque on the needle due to the current in the wire.

9.31. Given two similar thin, uniformly and axially magnetized bars, one lying along the perpendicular bisector of the other. Find (a) the torque on each about its center; (b) the total torque on the system about the center of one of the magnets.

9.32. Use Eq. (9.164) to compute the force on a thin, uniformly and axially magnetized bar in the field of a point pole colinear with the bar. Check the result by use of Coulomb's law.

9.33. Use the integral of Eq. (9.177) to find the torque about its center on a thin, uniformly and axially magnetized bar due to a point pole lying on its perpendicular bisector. Check the result by use of Coulomb's law.

9.34. A point pole q^* of a long bar magnet is moved with velocity $v = dx/dt$ along the x axis, which is also the axis of a circular current loop of radius a at the origin.

a. Calculate the induced current I, assuming Ohm's law to hold in the loop which has resistance R.

b. Find the force on the magnet pole due to the induced current.

c. Show that the power required to move the magnet is just accounted for by Joule heat loss in the loop.

9.35. *a.* The force interactions by pairs of a set of three magnet poles are observed qualitatively. Show that there are just two possible cases, depending on the signs of the poles: either there are three repulsions or else there are two attractions and one repulsion.

b. Examine similarly the possible qualitative force interactions by pairs of a set of 4 magnet poles.

9.36. Given a solenoid of N_1 turns per unit length carrying current I *in vacuo*, so shaped that its length L greatly exceeds its radius a. From the formula for the axial field of a solenoid in Sec. 7.4 obtain the limiting form by binomial expansion of the axial field at a point whose distances X_1 and X_2 from the ends of the solenoid are both large compared with a, but not necessarily large compared with L. Show thus that the ends of the coil appear as point poles of strength $\pm N_1 I \pi a^2$.

9.37. Repeat Prob. 9.10 on the equivalence of the exterior field of a magnetic shell to the field of a current circuit coinciding with its periphery, using the representation of the magnetic matter of the shell by bound current densities.

9.38. Use the representation of magnetic matter by bound current density to find the magnetic induction and the magnetizing force at general points on the axis of a bar magnet of circular cross section, uniformly magnetized in the axial direction. Take representative points both inside and outside the magnet. Let the magnet have length $2L$ and radius R, with plane ends cut normally to the axis. The answer may be compared with that of Prob. 9.19.

9.39. Find a general boundary condition on the normal component for the magnetic induction vector at any boundary in any static system of magnetic matter and steady currents (see Sec. 3.9).   *Ans.* B_n is continuous.

9.40. Use the equivalence of the uniformly magnetized bar and the solenoid, so far as the magnetic induction is concerned, to show that the axial component of the magnetic induction in an end plane of a long, thin solenoid is constant over this plane. *Hint:* See some of the discussion of Sec. 4.11.

9.41. A solid steel sphere of radius R is uniformly magnetized in a direction parallel to the polar axis, the intensity of magnetization being $\mathbf{M}$. Using the representation by bound currents, find the resulting induction and magnetizing force at the center of the sphere. The answer may be compared with that of Prob. 9.20.

9.42. Suppose that in a long, straight iron wire of circular cross section with radius R, the magnetization vector has a magnitude $M = br$, where b is a constant and r is the cylindrical radius from the axis of the wire to the observer's position. Let M have a tangential direction always perpendicular to r and to the axis of the wire, *i.e.*, the direction corresponding to increase of the cylindrical angle coordinate.

a. Write $\mathbf{M}$ in cartesian coordinates.

b. Find the volume and surface densities of bound current.

c. Find the magnetic induction inside and outside the wire.

d. Find the magnetizing force inside and outside the wire, using (*c*).

e. Check (*d*) by finding the magnetic bound charge densities.

9.43. Two solenoids of circular cross section are coaxially placed in air. The larger has radius $R_1 = 4$ cm and length $l_1 = 20$ cm, while the smaller has radius $R_2 = 2$ mm and length $l_2 = 10$ cm. A current of 2 amp flows in the $n_1 = 200$ turns of the larger coil, and a current of $\frac{1}{2}$ amp flows in like clock sense in the $n_2 = 300$ turns of the smaller coil. When the two ends corresponding to south poles of the equivalent bar magnets coincide, find the force action between the coils.

9.44. The power loss due to hysteresis in a certain transformer steel is 0.68 watt/lb at 60 cps when the maximum induction is 1.0 weber/m.². The specific gravity of the steel is 7.8. Find the following:

a. The Steinmetz coefficient in mks units

b. The power loss at 30 cps and 1.0 weber/m²

c. The power loss at 60 cps and 0.80 weber/m²

$$Ans. \ (a) \ \eta = 194 \ \frac{\text{joules}}{m^3(\text{weber/m}^2)^{1.6}}.$$

9.45. A circuit is completed through the inner and outer conductors of a long concentric cable of circular cross section, with nonmagnetic insulation. The inner conductor is a solid wire with radius a, and the outer is a cylindrical shell of negligible thickness with radius b. Assuming uniform current densities in the conductors, find (*a*) the magnetic energy stored per unit length when current I flows in the cable and (*b*) the self-inductance of the cable per unit length (see Sec. 8.9).

9.46. *a.* Given a pair of rigid, stationary-current circuits in empty space or a linear medium, show that the force in the x direction on one of them is

$$F_x = I_1 I_2 \frac{\partial M}{\partial x}$$

where $\partial M/\partial x$ is the rate of change of the mutual inductance with x displacement of the given circuit and I_1 and I_2 are the two currents.

b. Generalize this result for the x component of force on a circuit C_1 which is one of a set of n circuits in a linear system (cf. Sec. 7.12).

9.47. A point magnet pole whose charge is $+5$ amp-m is moved along the axis of a coil of 500 turns bound in the form of a circular loop of 3 cm radius. A constant-current battery maintains 800 ma in the coil. When the pole moves from the center of the coil to a point 10 cm from the center in the direction of the positive normal to the coil's area, find (*a*) the mechanical work output, by direct integration of force into distance; (*b*) the work done by the battery in excess of Joule heat, using an equation based on Faraday's law; (*c*) the change in stored magnetic energy.

CHAPTER 10

TRANSIENT CURRENTS

10.1. Circuit Components. We shall be concerned here with the time variation of current in circuits composed of two-terminal components and batteries. The circuit components may be characterized by resistance, capacitance, self-inductance, and mutual inductance. We shall deal with ideal circuit components: resistors characterized by pure resistance, capacitors by pure capacitance, and inductors by pure self-inductance and perhaps mutual inductance. Actual circuit components may be represented by networks of ideal components, so that we do not thus lose generality. Only for inductors do high-grade components deviate very greatly from the ideal in any case, except when the current varies extremely rapidly.

The electrical characteristics of a circuit component are specified by an equation for the instantaneous potential difference across its terminals. For ideal resistors, this equation looks just like the direct-current relationship:

$$V = IR \tag{10.1}$$

where R is the resistance of the component and I the instantaneous value of the current through it. Equation (10.1) may be considered as defining a pure resistance.

The characteristic equation of an isolated ideal inductor is

$$V = L \frac{dI}{dt} \tag{10.2}$$

This is written with the sign convention of Sec. 8.6, namely, that V is considered positive when the positive sense for the current I is from higher to lower potential through the inductor; and this is the same convention as applies to Eq. (10.1). We shall consider Eq. (10.2) to define a pure self-inductance. If another inductor carrying current I' is coupled to L with a mutual inductance M, then the instantaneous potential across L is

$$V = L \frac{dI}{dt} \pm M \frac{dI'}{dt} \tag{10.3}$$

Here the upper sign is used when the positive senses assigned to I and I' are mutually consistent, as discussed in Sec. 8.5.

The concept of capacitance is developed in detail in Chap. 4. Sections 4.9 and 4.10 are devoted to circuit components having capacitance. Components whose chief characteristic is capacitance are called condensers or capacitors. We shall define an ideal capacitor as a two-terminal component for which the instantaneous potential difference across the terminals depends solely upon the instantaneous value of the charge q which has been transferred from one terminal to the other through the external circuit. Letting the zero of q correspond to a zero potential difference, we write

$$V = \frac{q}{C} \tag{10.4}$$

where C is the capacitance. Since charge does not flow spontaneously when a conducting path is provided between terminals of an uncharged condenser, the terminal to which positive charge is transferred is at higher potential than the terminal from which the charge has been removed. We shall fix the sign conventions for the V and q of a condenser so that the capacitance C is always positive.

It is frequently important to know the current flow to and from the terminals of a condenser. This is not properly a flow of current through the condenser, but is indistinguishable from a flow through a circuit component since the same charge always flows to one terminal as flows away from the other. We may properly use the term "current of a condenser." If the positive sense for I is taken such as to build up positive charge, then I and q are related by

$$I = \frac{dq}{dt} \tag{10.5}$$

It will be seen that positive I is then such as to increase the potential of the terminal into which it flows, or positive I is such as to flow into the higher potential terminal when V is also positive. Combining Eqs. (10.5) and (10.4), we find that

$$I = C \frac{dV}{dt} \tag{10.6}$$

Nothing has been said in the foregoing equations concerning the possibility of variation of the circuit parameters R, L, M, and C with the current or the rate of variation of the current. For purposes of this chapter, we shall consider all these parameters to be constants, that is, we shall restrict the analysis to circuits of linear components.

The batteries in the circuit will for simplicity be assumed to be ideal emfs. Of course a practical battery has an internal resistance as we discussed in Sec. 5.10; but if this is important to the problem, it may be exhibited in the circuit as a separate component in series with the pure emf. Now an ideal emf maintains a potential difference across its terminals numerically equal to the emf. The sign conventions we have been using lead to the relation

$$V = -\varepsilon \qquad (10.7)$$

for a battery; since ε is positive in relation to the current if it supplies energy to the circuit, that is, when current flows through it from its lower to its higher potential side, while V is positive in relation to current when the current flows through from higher to lower potential.

In previous work we have introduced units for all the quantities involved in the equations of this section. It might be well to summarize these for the rationalized mks system that we are using:

Charge............................	Coulomb
Potential difference or emf..........	Volt
Current...........................	Ampere
Time..............................	Second
Resistance........................	Ohm
Inductance........................	Henry
Capacitance.......................	Farad

10.2. Circuit Theorems for Transient Conditions.

We shall assume that Kirchhoff's laws for circuits will apply at every instant in the analysis of transient currents, provided the potential differences across the various types of circuit components are used with the proper sign conventions. The conventions of the preceding section are in harmony with those used in Chap. 6, except for the sign of Eq. (10.7). The reader should refer to that chapter for background material and definition of terms.

The first law of Kirchhoff for transient currents is in appearance exactly like that for direct currents, but it is to apply to all instants of time as the currents vary. At any branch point, the algebraic sum of all currents flowing to the branch point is zero:

$$\sum_j I_j = 0 \qquad \text{at a branch point} \qquad (10.8)$$

There is another form of this first-law equation which is useful in circuits containing condensers. If Eq. (10.8) is integrated with respect to time, it gives a relation between the algebraic quantities of charge q_j flowing to any branch point in any given interval of time:

$$\sum_j q_j = 0 \qquad \text{at a branch point} \qquad (10.9)$$

It is assumed that both I_j and q_j are characteristic of a whole branch of the circuit rather than of any one point in the branch, that is, that the same charge and current flow past all points in one branch at the same time. Naturally the interior of a condenser is excepted in this statement. All that we have said concerning this first law of Kirchhoff depends upon and is a consequence of the postulate that no appreciable currents are required to build up concentrations of charge at any point of the circuit with the exception of the interior parts of condensers. When such concentrations of charge are significant, they may be accounted for by introducing the concepts of distributed capacitance and stray capacitance.

The second law of Kirchhoff applies to any closed loop of the circuit. Suppose this loop contains various circuit elements across which the potential differences are V_k at a given instant of time, the V_k being given by the formulas of the preceding section for different types of ideal circuit components including batteries. Now in terms of potential differences, the second law of Kirchhoff states that at every instant of time the algebraic sum of the potential differences around any closed loop of the circuit is zero:

$$\sum_k V_k = 0 \qquad \text{any closed loop} \qquad (10.10)$$

The reason for the validity of this equation is the single-valued character of the quasi-electrostatic potential function, as discussed carefully in Sec. 5.7.

For the use of Eqs. (10.8) to (10.10), we may lay down rules similar to those suggested in Chap. 6. The signs of the potential differences V_k are not usually all known at the start of a problem since the currents or charges are not usually known. If the currents or charges are the unknowns, the procedure is to assign symbols and consistent but otherwise arbitrary positive senses to all currents or charges, and to consider the V_k to have the sign appropriate to these arbitrary senses. The first- and second-law equations of the network are then written down and solved. The actual sense of currents or potential differences follows from the algebraic sign of the solutions in accordance with the arbitrary positive senses that were assigned.

10.3. Simple _R-L_ Circuits. Figure 10.1 shows a circuit containing an inductor in series with a resistor. A battery $\mathcal{E}$ may be placed in the circuit by closing switch S_1 while S_2 is left open. If the battery is then short-circuited by closing S_2 (which ought not to be done in laboratory practice!), we have simply the inductor and resistor connected together with an initial current I_0 flowing in them. Consider first the equation of the circuit with the battery shorted:

$$L \frac{dI}{dt} + IR = 0 \qquad (10.11)$$

This is a simple differential equation which may be integrated directly to yield

$$\ln I = -\frac{R}{L}t + a \tag{10.12}$$

where a is a constant of integration. Taking both sides of this equation as exponents of e, and introducing a new constant $A = e^a$, we obtain the form

$$I = Ae^{-(R/L)t} \tag{10.13}$$

The constant A is determined by the boundary conditions of the problem. Physically, it means the current I_0 at $t = 0$, so we shall write for our final form of the solution

$$I = I_0 e^{-(R/L)t} \tag{10.14}$$

Figure 10.2 shows the graph of this function, which decays asymptotically from the initial value to zero. The rate of decay is measured

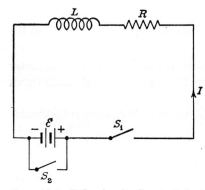

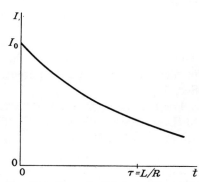

FIG. 10.1. R-L circuit for transient current.

FIG. 10.2. Exponential decay of current in an R-L circuit.

by the time constant τ of the circuit, which is that time in which the current decays to e^{-1} or $1/2.7 \ldots$ of its initial value:

$$\tau = \frac{L}{R} \tag{10.15}$$

The reader should check for himself that henrys/ohms = seconds.

It may be worth remarking that in Eq. (10.12) the current is treated as a pure number rather than as a dimensional quantity. This is a convenience in the integration, but it involves the inconsistency of using the same symbol I in two ways. The difficulty could be avoided by working from the outset with a ratio of I to a unit current I_1.

Now let us consider the building up of current in the circuit of Fig. 10.1. Starting with both switches open, suppose that S_1 is closed at

$t = 0$. The Kirchhoff second-law equation now reads

$$L\frac{dI}{dt} + RI - \varepsilon = 0 \qquad (10.16)$$

This equation may be solved by direct integration or by other methods:

$$I = \frac{\varepsilon}{R} - Ae^{-(R/L)t} \qquad (10.17)$$

The constant of integration A is determined for our problem by specifying that $I = 0$ when $t = 0$. This requires that

$$0 = \frac{\varepsilon}{R} - A \qquad (10.18)$$

Substituting this expression for A into Eq. (10.17) we obtain the solution subject to the given initial condition:

$$I = \frac{\varepsilon}{R}(1 - e^{-(R/L)t}) \qquad (10.19)$$

It will be seen that the difference between the momentary value of I and its asymptotic final value of ε/R decreases by the factor $e^{-1} = 1/2.7$ . . . in a time L/R. This is the same time constant as for the decay

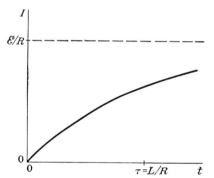

FIG. 10.3. Rise of current in an R-L circuit.

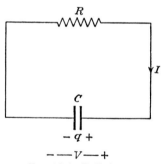

FIG. 10.4. R-C circuit.

problem when no battery was in the circuit. The battery affects the time constant only if it has an internal resistance which is appreciable compared with R, in which case we should exhibit its internal resistance as a circuit component. The behavior of the current in Eq. (10.19) is sketched in the graph of Fig. 10.3.

10.4. Simple R-C Circuits. Let us first consider the circuit containing just a condenser and resistor. Adding potential differences in Fig. 10.4 we have

$$\frac{q}{C} + IR = 0 \qquad (10.20)$$

Since $I = dq/dt$, we obtain a differential equation for q:

$$R\frac{dq}{dt} + \frac{q}{C} = 0 \qquad (10.21)$$

This may be integrated immediately to yield

$$\ln q = -\frac{t}{RC} + a \qquad (10.22)$$

where a is a constant of integration. Using both sides as exponents of e we obtain

$$q = e^{-(t/RC)+a} \qquad (10.23)$$

A more useful form is obtained if we notice that at $t = 0$, the value of q is e^a. If we write $e^a = q_0$, then our solution takes the form

$$q = q_0 e^{-t/RC} \qquad (10.24)$$

Equation (10.24) shows that the initial charge of the condenser falls off to zero asymptotically as indicated in Fig. 10.5. The rate of decay of the charge is determined by the product RC. RC is dimensionally a time, and is defined as the time constant τ of the circuit:

$$\tau = RC \qquad (10.25)$$

In terms of the time constant, the charge of the condenser is

$$q = q_0 e^{-t/\tau} \qquad (10.26)$$

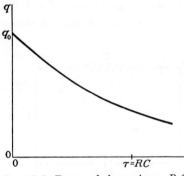

FIG. 10.5. Decay of charge in an R-C circuit.

The meaning of τ may be expressed by saying that in a time $t = \tau$ the charge decays by the factor $e^{-1} = 1/2.7 \ldots$. It would be a worthwhile exercise in units for the reader to show that ohms times farads equal seconds. It is often convenient to remember also that megohms times microfarads equal seconds.

A complete discussion of the circuit of Fig. 10.5 involves consideration of the current. We may obtain the current at once by differentiating the solution (10.24) for charge:

$$I = -\frac{q_0}{RC} e^{-t/RC} \qquad (10.27)$$

Thus the current follows a curve of exponential decay similar to that for the charge, and the magnitude of the current is inversely as the time constant. The negative sign in Eq. (10.27) is a consequence of our convention for the relative signs of q and I. A rather useful form of Eq. (10.27) is obtained by putting

$$q_0 = CV_0 \qquad (10.28)$$

where V_0 is the potential to which the condenser is charged at $t = 0$:

$$I = -\frac{V_0}{R} e^{-t/RC} \qquad (10.29)$$

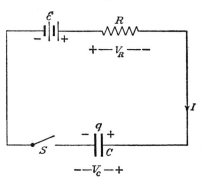

Once written, Eq. (10.29) is quite obvious; for it says that the potential difference across the resistor IR equals that across the capacitor at $t = 0$, as at all times.

Let us consider next an R-C circuit containing a battery of emf ε and a switch, the condenser being initially uncharged and the switch being closed at $t = 0$. Kirchhoff's second law for the circuit of Fig. 10.6 reads

FIG. 10.6. R-C circuit with battery.

$$\varepsilon - IR - \frac{q}{C} = 0 \qquad (10.30)$$

Therefore

$$R\frac{dq}{dt} + \frac{q}{C} = \varepsilon \qquad (10.31)$$

This differential equation is readily solved by direction integration or by other methods:

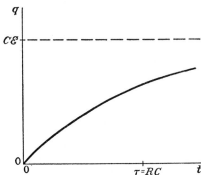

$$q = \varepsilon C - Ae^{-t/RC} \qquad (10.32)$$

Here A is the constant of integration, which may be evaluated by reference to the given conditions of the problem (called boundary conditions). In this case we have specified that $q = 0$ at $t = 0$, so that

$$0 = \varepsilon C - A \qquad (10.33)$$

FIG. 10.7. Charging of a condenser through a resistor.

Substituting this value of A into Eq. (10.32), we find the solution fitting our conditions:

$$q = \varepsilon C(1 - e^{-t/RC}) \qquad (10.34)$$

A graph of this solution is sketched in Fig. 10.7, showing that there is an asymptotic increase of q to the limit εC. The time constant RC is not affected by the presence of the battery so long as the internal resistance of the battery is negligible. It is the difference between q and its asymptote which decreases by a factor e^{-1} in a time $t = RC$.

Differentiation of Eq. (10.34) gives an expression for the current in the circuit

$$I = \frac{\mathcal{E}}{R} e^{-t/RC} \tag{10.35}$$

Notice that this current is positive, for it represents a charging up of the condenser. The current follows an exponential decay law like that illustrated in Fig. 10.5. Its initial value is the same as though the condenser were not present in the circuit, as is obvious from the fact that the initial potential difference across the condenser is zero.

We may write a differential equation representing the behavior of the current in the two circuits of this section. Term-by-term differentiation of Eqs. (10.21) and (10.31) for the charge of the condenser yields the same equation for each circuit:

$$R \frac{dI}{dt} + \frac{I}{C} = 0 \tag{10.36}$$

This equation can be solved directly to yield

$$I = I_0 e^{-t/RC} \tag{10.37}$$

where the constant of integration has been written I_0 to suggest its meaning as the initial current. It will be seen that Eq. (10.37) is a general expression which gives both Eq. (10.27) and (10.35) when the proper boundary value for I_0 is introduced.

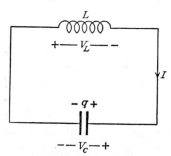

FIG. 10.8. *L-C* circuit.

10.5. Ideal *L-C* Circuit. The transient circuits discussed so far have been non-oscillatory in character. Perhaps the greatest interest in transient circuits lies in the possibility of their producing oscillating electric currents. The simplest case to consider is the circuit of Fig. 10.8 consisting of an ideal inductor connected across an ideal capacitor. The word ideal will imply that we are neglecting resistance in these components. This restriction will be removed in the next section.

The Kirchhoff equation for the circuit of Fig. 10.8 is

$$L \frac{dI}{dt} + \frac{q}{C} = 0 \tag{10.38}$$

Using $I = dq/dt$, we obtain

$$L \frac{d^2q}{dt^2} + \frac{q}{C} = 0 \qquad (10.39)$$

Equation (10.39) is the equation of simple harmonic variation of q with time. Its solution is well known, and the reader may check it at once by substitution of the trial solution

$$q = A \cos (\omega t - \phi) \qquad (10.40)$$

Here A and ϕ are arbitrary constants of integration, but ω must have the value

$$\omega = \frac{1}{\sqrt{LC}} \qquad (10.41)$$

We shall take only the positive value of ω, for no generality is to be gained by admitting the negative value. The interpretation of the constants of the solution (10.40) is easy. It represents a sinusoidal variation of q between limits $\pm A$ with a period

$$T = \frac{2\pi}{\omega} = 2\pi \sqrt{LC} \qquad (10.42)$$

or a frequency

$$f = \frac{\omega}{2\pi} = \frac{1}{2\pi \sqrt{LC}} \qquad (10.43)$$

The constant ϕ is called the phase angle, and is concerned with the part of the cycle which occurs at $t = 0$. The maximum positive value of q occurs at times

$$t = \frac{\phi}{\omega} + 2\pi n \text{ radians} \qquad (10.44)$$

where n is any integer.

The current in the circuit may be deduced by differentiation of Eq. (10.40):

$$I = -A\omega \sin (\omega t - \phi) \qquad (10.45)$$

We might have found I from solution of its differential equation, which is identical with that for q, as may be seen by differentiating Eq. (10.38) or (10.39); but (10.45) is useful in that I is expressed in terms of the same constants as Eq. (10.40).

10.6. Series L-C-R Circuit. The circuit of Fig. 10.9 corresponds more closely to actual laboratory conditions than that of the preceding section. Let us investigate the transient conditions here. Kirchhoff's second law for the circuit of Fig. 10.9 is

$$L \frac{dI}{dt} + \frac{q}{C} + RI = 0 \qquad (10.46)$$

Rearranging Eq. (10.46) and writing it in terms of q, we have

$$L\frac{d^2q}{dt^2} + R\frac{dq}{dt} + \frac{q}{C} = 0 \tag{10.47}$$

The differential equation for the current is obtainable by differentiation of Eq. (10.47), and has the same form:

$$L\frac{d^2I}{dt^2} + R\frac{dI}{dt} + \frac{I}{C} = 0 \tag{10.48}$$

Equations (10.47) and (10.48) are well known in mechanics. If a spring of stiffness k is loaded by a bob so that its effective mass is m, and if its motion experiences a viscous resistance proportional to the velocity of the bob, then the differential equation for the position x of the bob is

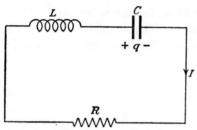

FIG. 10.9. Series L-C-R circuit.

$$m\frac{d^2x}{dt^2} + r\frac{dx}{dt} + kx = 0 \tag{10.49}$$

Here r is a positive constant such that $(-r\,dx/dt)$ gives the viscous force. Evidently R corresponds to r, L to m, and C to $1/k$.

It is known that the solution of the differential equation (10.47) is obtainable in the form

$$q = Ae^{-bt} \cos(\omega t - \phi) \tag{10.50}$$

where A and ϕ are arbitrary constants of integration. Substituting Eq. (10.50) into (10.47) as a trial solution, we obtain

$$Ae^{-bt}\left\{\left[L(b^2 - \omega^2) + \frac{1}{C} - Rb\right]\cos(\omega t - \phi) \right.$$
$$\left. + \omega[2Lb - R]\sin(\omega t - \phi)\right\} = 0 \tag{10.51}$$

Now a differential equation is a sort of identity: it must hold not only at one particular value of the independent variable t but for all values. Evidently a trivial solution is obtained when $A = 0$, which corresponds to the quiescent state of the system. For other solutions the expression in the curly brackets must vanish at all times. Since the cosine and sine functions each pass through zero, but at different times, their coefficients must both be zero. Thus the expressions in the two square brackets must equal zero:

$$2Lb - R = 0 \tag{10.52}$$

and

$$L(b^2 - \omega^2) + \frac{1}{C} - Rb = 0 \tag{10.53}$$

Equation (10.52) determines the value that the constant b must take in our solution:

$$b = \frac{R}{2L} \tag{10.54}$$

Substitution of this value into Eq. (10.53) yields the value of ω:

$$\omega = \sqrt{\frac{1}{LC} - \frac{R^2}{4L^2}} \tag{10.55}$$

There is no loss of generality in taking only the positive sign of the radical, although the negative sign also gives a solution. Now with these values of b and ω, and arbitrary values of A and ϕ, it is seen that Eq. (10.50) is a solution of (10.47). It is the general solution, for it contains two independent and arbitrary constants.

It will be noticed from Eq. (10.55) that there is a possibility that no real value of ω exists. In fact, ω is real and not zero only if

$$\frac{1}{LC} > \frac{R^2}{4L^2} \qquad \text{oscillatory} \tag{10.56}$$

If the inequality (10.56) holds for the circuit, the solutions are oscillatory, for q periodically changes sign. On the other hand, if

$$\frac{1}{LC} = \frac{R^2}{4L^2} \qquad \text{critically damped} \tag{10.57}$$

then the solution (10.50) apparently reduces to a simple exponential decay; but this solution is no longer general. The circuit is said to be critically damped in this case. If, however,

$$\frac{1}{LC} < \frac{R^2}{4L^2} \qquad \text{general aperiodic} \tag{10.58}$$

then the form of solution which we have adopted is no longer convenient at all. We shall discuss these last two cases later.

Before discussing the solution for q further, let us consider the current in the circuit for the oscillatory case. Differentiation of Eq. (10.50) gives a rather complex result:

$$\frac{dq}{dt} = I = -Ae^{-bt}[b \cos (\omega t - \phi) + \omega \sin (\omega t - \phi)] \tag{10.59}$$

We know, however, that the current is a solution of Eq. (10.48) and hence may be written

$$I = A'e^{-bt} \cos (\omega t - \phi') \tag{10.60}$$

where b and ω are as before, but A' and ϕ' are new constants. The connection between the constants in Eq. (10.59) and those in (10.60) is readily established by the use of trigonometric identities. It is illuminating to rewrite Eq. (10.60) first in the form

$$I = A'e^{-bt} \cos (\omega t - \phi - \alpha) \qquad (10.61)$$

so that the angular distance α between zeros of q and the succeeding zeros of I is explicitly used. Now comparison of Eqs. (10.61) and (10.59) leads to

$$A' = -A \sqrt{b^2 + \omega^2} \qquad (10.62)$$

$$\alpha = \tan^{-1}\frac{\omega}{b} \qquad (10.63)$$

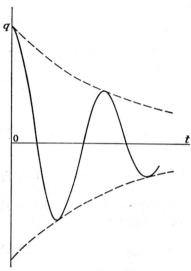

In order to determine the constants A and ϕ, boundary conditions must be specified for the problem. As an example, it may be given that the condenser is first given a charge q_0 and then connected into the circuit of Fig. 10.9. At the moment of connection, say $t = 0$, we then have $q = q_0$ and $I = 0$. We shall not carry through the details of application of the boundary conditions.

The graph of the oscillatory solution has the general appearance of Fig. 10.10. The curve is bounded by the exponential envelope $\pm Ae^{-bt}$.

Fig. 10.10. Damped oscillation in a series L-C-R circuit.

Zeros of q are spaced by a time $T/2 = \pi/\omega$, and this is also the time between zeros of I which are extreme values of q. The time

$$T = \frac{2\pi}{\omega} \qquad (10.64)$$

is called the natural period of the oscillating circuit, and its reciprocal is the natural frequency. T may be described as the time between successive maxima of q, or between successive minima.

In describing the damped oscillations of a circuit, it is of interest to know how successive maxima of charge are related. The ratio of any maximum to the next one is evidently

$$\frac{e^{-bt}}{e^{-b(t+T)}} = e^{bT} \qquad (10.65)$$

The natural logarithm of this ratio is called the logarithmic decrement δ

of the circuit or of the train of oscillations. Thus

$$\delta = bT \tag{10.66}$$

If $R^2/4L^2 \ll 1/LC$, the logarithmic decrement is approximately

$$\delta = \pi R \sqrt{\frac{C}{L}} \tag{10.67}$$

We shall examine only briefly the critically damped or aperiodic solutions corresponding to the cases of Eq. (10.57) and inequality (10.58). For the critically damped case, the general solution for q is

$$q = Ae^{-bt} + Bte^{-bt} \tag{10.68}$$

where b must have the value (10.54), while A and B are arbitrary constants of integration.   In the general aperiodic solution for which inequality (10.58) holds, the solution becomes

$$q = Ae^{-a_1t} + Be^{-a_2t} \tag{10.69}$$

Here the exponents have the values

$$a_1 = \frac{R}{2L} + \sqrt{\frac{R^2}{4L^2} - \frac{1}{LC}} \qquad a_2 = \frac{R}{2L} - \sqrt{\frac{R^2}{4L^2} - \frac{1}{LC}} \tag{10.70}$$

The reader is left to set up for himself the problem of the L-C-R circuit including a battery ε.   Nothing essentially new arises here, and a simple change of variable reduces the differential equation for the charge of the circuit to the one we have just studied.

10.7. Transient Balance. Consider a bridge network made up of two uncoupled inductors L_1 and L_2 together with four resistors as in Fig. 10.11.   The resistances R_1 and R_2 are to include the internal resistances of the inductors, but may also include external resistance; g represents any detector of current or charge. We shall investigate the conditions under which the detector current $I_g = 0$ at all times, regardless of the magnitude or

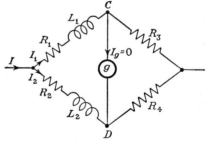

FIG. 10.11. Inductance bridge.

change of the current I to the bridge. This requirement means that a current I_1 is common to both upper arms of the bridge, and a current I_2 to the lower arms.   Furthermore, $I_g \equiv 0$ will imply a zero potential difference between points C and D, provided that g has finite values of resistance, inductance, and perhaps capacitance, but no independent **emf.**

Now the second law of Kirchhoff gives

$$R_1 I_1 + L_1 \frac{dI_1}{dt} - L_2 \frac{dI_2}{dt} - R_2 I_2 = 0 \tag{10.71}$$

$$R_3 I_1 - R_4 I_2 = 0 \tag{10.72}$$

From Eq. (10.72), we have

$$I_2 = \frac{R_3}{R_4} I_1 \tag{10.73}$$

Differentiation of Eq. (10.73) gives

$$\frac{dI_2}{dt} = \frac{R_3}{R_4} \frac{dI_1}{dt} \tag{10.74}$$

Substitution of Eqs. (10.73) and (10.74) into (10.71) leads to

$$\left(R_1 - \frac{R_2 R_3}{R_4}\right) I_1 + \left(L_1 - \frac{L_2 R_3}{R_4}\right) \frac{dI_1}{dt} = 0 \tag{10.75}$$

By hypothesis this condition is to hold at all times, so that the coefficients of both I_1 and dI_1/dt must vanish. In this way we obtain two conditions for the transient balance of the network:

$$\frac{R_1}{R_2} = \frac{R_3}{R_4} \tag{10.76}$$

$$\frac{L_1}{L_2} = \frac{R_3}{R_4} \tag{10.77}$$

If and only if these two balance conditions are satisfied, the detector current will always be zero.

A bridge circuit like that of Fig. 10.11 is useful for comparing an unknown self-inductor with a standard. An external resistor may be used with one of the inductors to make possible the satisfaction of Eq. (10.76). A similar circuit may be used to compare two capacitors, but the details of the analysis are left to the reader.

10.8. Mutual Inductance Bridge of Carey Foster. The Carey Foster bridge for mutual inductance, shown in Fig. 10.12, gives an interesting example of transient analysis. The net total flow of charge through a ballistic galvanometer g is to be zero during the transient conditions arising when the switch is opened or closed. It is understood that the galvanometer is characterized by a resistance R_g in series with a self-inductance L_g. Positive conventions for the currents are shown in the diagram, and it is required that the inductors be so coupled that the positive current senses of I_p and I_s as shown are mutually consistent.

We shall carry out just enough analysis to lead to the balance conditions. Kirchhoff's first law at point A gives

$$I_g - I_s - I_c = 0 \tag{10.78}$$

The total charges that flow in these circuits are therefore related by

$$q_g - q_s - q_c = 0 \tag{10.79}$$

Let us refer all these charges to a reference time $t = 0$ when the condenser is discharged, so that q_c also represents the charge on the condenser.

Next we write the second law of Kirchhoff for the circuit containing the secondary coil L_s and the galvanometer g:

$$(R_s + R_2)I_s + L_s \frac{dI_s}{dt} + M \frac{dI_p}{dt} + R_g I_g + L_g \frac{dI_g}{dt} = 0 \qquad (10.80)$$

We are interested in total flow of charge through g when the switch is closed; therefore let us integrate Eq. (10.80) with respect to time from $t = 0$, at the moment the switch is closed, to $t = \infty$:

$$(R_s + R_2)q_s(\infty) + L_s[I_s(\infty) - I_s(0)] + M[I_p(\infty) - I_p(0)]$$
$$+ R_g q_g(\infty) + L_g[I_g(\infty) - I_g(0)] = 0 \qquad (10.81)$$

Here the currents and total charges are written as functions of the time, and $q_s(0) = q_g(0) = 0$ is understood as we agreed above. Consideration of the steady

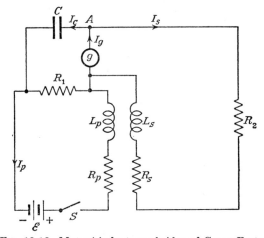

FIG. 10.12. Mutual inductance bridge of Carey Foster.

conditions at $t = 0$ and $t = \infty$ now shows, without the need of a formal analysis, that

$$I_p(0) = I_s(0) = I_g(0) = 0 \qquad (10.82)$$
$$I_s(\infty) = I_g(\infty) = 0 \qquad (10.83)$$
$$I_p(\infty) = \frac{\varepsilon}{R_1 + R_p} \equiv I \qquad (10.84)$$

In this last equation, I is simply used as an abbreviation for the final steady primary current. Substituting Eqs. (10.82) through (10.84) into Eq. (10.81), we obtain

$$(R_s + R_2)q_s(\infty) + MI + R_g q_g(\infty) = 0 \qquad (10.85)$$

Now in the final steady condition the potential difference across the resistor R_1 is IR_1, and this equals the final potential difference across the condenser. Thus

$$\frac{q_c(\infty)}{C} = IR_1 \qquad (10.86)$$

Combining this with Eq. (10.79) written for $t = \infty$ gives

$$q_s(\infty) = q_g(\infty) - IR_1C \qquad (10.87)$$

Equation (10.87) permits elimination of $q_s(\infty)$ from (10.85), and leads to

$$q_g(\infty) = \frac{I}{R_s + R_2 + R_g} [CR_1(R_s + R_2) - M] \tag{10.88}$$

Evidently we may make $q_g(\infty) = 0$ if we fulfill the balance condition

$$M = CR_1(R_s + R_2) \tag{10.89}$$

Conversely, when balance is attained, Eq. (10.89) determines the mutual inductance between the coils in terms of values of resistance and capacitance.

If the switch is opened after the steady primary current has been established, the process just described is reversed. The same balance condition (10.89) is necessary and sufficient for no net charge to flow through the galvanometer while the condenser discharges.

10.9. Moving-coil D-C Galvanometers.

The most frequently used device for measurement of direct currents is the moving-coil, or d'Arsonval, galvanometer. The coil, which carries the current to be measured,

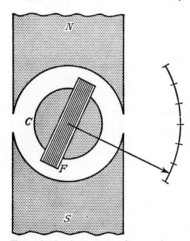

FIG. 10.13. Armature of a moving-coil galvanometer.

rotates in the field of a strong permanent magnet. Its steady deflection is determined by the balance between the magnetic torque and a restoring torque provided by a hairspring or torsion fiber. Figure 10.13 shows how a cylindrical piece C of soft iron is used inside the form F on which the coil is wound, so as to produce a strong, radial distribution of the magnetic field. The d'Arsonval galvanometer is used both for rugged portable meters and for sensitive research instruments. In the former case, the moving coil is mounted on pivots, and the angular position of the coil is indicated by a pointer and scale. The coil of a sensitive galvanometer is suspended by a fine metal ribbon so as to eliminate bearing friction and provide a very small restoring torque. Readings are made by observing the deviation of light reflected from a small mirror attached to the coil.

A moving-coil galvanometer is a complex system with electromagnetic coupling between the mechanical rotation and the current circuit. The problems of its design and operation involve transient conditions; for in addition to the final deflection for a given current, it is of interest to find the time required for a steady condition to be reached. Consider the electric circuit first. Suppose the network connected to the galvanometer has a steady emf $\mathcal{E}_0$ and an equivalent d-c resistance R_0, and let the galvanometer coil have a d-c resistance R_g. Now the galvanometer coil certainly has some self-inductance L_g, and the external network also may have in general some inductive or capacitive components. In the discussion of this and the following section, we shall assume the condition which is usually very well fulfilled in practice that the electrical time constants of the circuit including the galvanometer are much shorter than the period or time constant of the mechanical motion. Thus the purely electrical transients will be assumed to exist only when the circuit is just closed and only for a short time in which the galvanometer coil turns through a negligible angle. Only during this same interval will there be any impulsive motion of the coil, with its accompanying rapid change of the angular velocity of the coil. In examining the course of the motion, we shall accordingly suppose that the emf $\mathcal{E}_g$ produced by electromagnetic induction in the moving coil varies slowly by comparison to the electrical time constants. The current in the circuit will then be determined only by the resistance and the sum of the emfs $\mathcal{E}_0$ and $\mathcal{E}_g$:

$$I = \frac{1}{R_0 + R_g} (\mathcal{E}_0 + \mathcal{E}_g) \tag{10.90}$$

Consider the coupling between the electrical and mechanical systems, which is represented by the emf $\mathcal{E}_g$. Let the magnetic flux through the coil form F be $\phi(\theta)$, a function of the angular position θ of the coil, and usually a nearly linear function because of the radial magnetic field. $\phi(\theta)$ is to include no self-linked flux, but only that due to the steady field of the permanent magnet. Effects of self-linked flux have already been disposed of during consideration of the purely electrical transients. If there are n turns in the galvanometer coil, the pertinent flux linkage is $n\phi(\theta)$ and the induced emf resulting from the coil's motion is

$$\mathcal{E}_g = -\frac{d}{dt} n\phi(\theta) = -n\phi' \frac{d\theta}{dt} \tag{10.91}$$

Here we have written as an abbreviation

$$\frac{d}{d\theta} \phi(\theta) \equiv \phi' \tag{10.92}$$

This quantity is in general a function of the angle θ, but if $\phi(\theta)$ is truly linear it becomes a constant of the galvanometer. Equation (10.90) now reads

$$I = \frac{1}{R_0 + R_g} \left(\mathcal{E}_0 - n\phi' \frac{d\theta}{dt} \right) \tag{10.93}$$

which gives the explicit relation between the two dependent variables, I and θ, of the system.

Next let us write the differential equation of the mechanical motion. If N is the total torque on the moving coil and A is the moment of inertia of the coil, both referred to the axis of rotation, the basic mechanical equation is

$$A\frac{d^2\theta}{dt^2} = N \tag{10.94}$$

The torque N is made up of several terms. There is the elastic restoring torque

$$N_1 = -k\theta \tag{10.95}$$

The torsional stiffness k will be assumed to be constant, although for a coil spring this is likely to be only approximately true. We shall neglect bearing friction, which is always undesirable since its presence makes final, steady readings uncertain, but we shall include a mechanical damping term for air resistance. This term is ordinarily taken to be proportional to the angular velocity

$$N_2 = -a\frac{d\theta}{dt} \tag{10.96}$$

where a is a constant. Lastly, the magnetic torque on the coil is given by using Eq. (9.265), Sec. 9.18, according to which the mechanical work done by the magnetic torque is

$$\delta W_M = I\delta_M[n\phi(\theta)] \tag{10.97}$$

Therefore

$$\delta W_M = In\phi' \, \delta\theta \tag{10.98}$$

Here our expression $n\phi(\theta)$ has been used for the flux linkage. As required by the symbol δ_M, the varying self-linked flux is excluded by the definition of $\phi(\theta)$. Now during an infinitesimal displacement $\delta\theta$, the magnetic torque N_3 does work

$$\delta W_M = N_3 \, \delta\theta \tag{10.99}$$

By comparison of Eqs. (10.98) and (10.99), the magnetic torque is

$$N_3 = In\phi' \tag{10.100}$$

Addition of the torques N_1, N_2, and N_3 yields the total torque N to be substituted into Eq. (10.94). The resulting differential equation is

$$A\frac{d^2\theta}{dt^2} + a\frac{d\theta}{dt} + k\theta = In\phi' \tag{10.101}$$

We may now use Eq. (10.93) to separate the dependent variables. Elimination of I yields the equation for θ:

$$A\frac{d^2\theta}{dt^2} + \left(a + \frac{n^2\phi'^2}{R_0 + R_g}\right)\frac{d\theta}{dt} + k\theta = \frac{n\phi'\mathcal{E}_0}{R_0 + R_g} \tag{10.102}$$

The quantity $\mathcal{E}_0/(R_0 + R_g)$ may be called the current to be measured. It is the current through the galvanometer produced by the external emf $\mathcal{E}_0$, and it does not include the current produced by the galvanometer emf $\mathcal{E}_g$. We shall call this current to be measured I_0, to distinguish it from the total instantaneous current I:

$$I_0 \equiv \frac{\mathcal{E}_0}{R_0 + R_g} \tag{10.103}$$

The final, steady deflection θ_f of the galvanometer may be read off from Eq. (10.102) by putting the time derivatives to zero:

$$\theta_f = \frac{n\phi'\mathcal{E}_0}{k(R_0 + R_g)} = \frac{n\phi'}{k} I_0 \tag{10.104}$$

Thus the sensitivity of the instrument depends on the quantity $n\phi'/k$. In practice, the length of the optical or mechanical lever arm is also important because of its influence on the linear deflection per unit current. For sensitive galvanometers, it is standard to place the scale 1 m from the galvanometer mirror and normal to the optical path. This results in an optical lever arm effectively 2 m long, since the reflected beam turns through twice the angle of deflection of the mirror. The figure of merit of the galvanometer is defined as the current required for a 1-mm deflection under these conditions.

Let us now assume that ϕ' is a constant, that is, not dependent on θ. The coefficient of the first derivative term in Eq. (10.102) is then a constant, which will be designated by r:

$$r \equiv a + \frac{n^2\phi'^2}{R_0 + R_g} \tag{10.105}$$

Equation (10.102) may now be solved explicitly. According to usual procedure, it is first reduced to a homogeneous equation by a change of variable:

$$\alpha \equiv \theta - \theta_f \tag{10.106}$$

where the constant θ_f is the final deflection for a given applied emf as given by Eqs. (10.104). The differential equation is then

$$A \frac{d^2\alpha}{dt^2} + r \frac{d\alpha}{dt} + k\alpha = 0 \tag{10.107}$$

whose solutions were discussed in Sec. 10.6. The motion is oscillatory or underdamped, critically damped, or overdamped according as the coefficient r is less than, equal to, or greater than a critical value r_c, which for our present equation takes the form

$$r_c = 2 \sqrt{Ak} \tag{10.108}$$

In the underdamped case, the galvanometer coil overshoots its final mark and oscillates, somewhat as shown in Fig. 10.14, which assumes that the coil starts from rest at some initial deflection $a(0)$. An algebraic expression for the solution is

$$a = C_1 e^{-(r/2A)t} \cos (\omega t - \phi) \qquad \text{underdamping} \qquad (10.109)$$

where the constant ω is 2π divided by the period T of the oscillation, and has the value

$$\omega = \sqrt{\frac{k}{A} - \frac{r^2}{4A^2}} \qquad (10.110)$$

The period T in turn is twice the time between successive zeros or successive extreme values of a, the latter points being zeros of da/dt or of

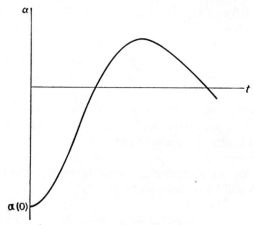

Fig. 10.14. Typical response of an underdamped galvanometer.

$d\theta/dt$. The constants C_1 and ϕ in Eq. (10.109) are determined by the boundary conditions, that is, the initial values $a(0)$ and $(da/dt)_0$ at $t = 0$. In ordinary practice, the interesting case is that for which $(da/dt)_0 = 0$, that is, when the coil starts from rest. The time required to reach the first extreme value of a after overshooting zero is then just $T/2$. The galvanometer is convenient to use if this first extremum after zero is already negligibly small compared with $a(0)$, say $-10^{-3}a(0)$. The time interval required for a reading is then less than $T/2$, for one need only wait until the coil is at $+10^{-3}a(0)$, that is, before zero is crossed, to read to the required accuracy. The ratio between the magnitudes of successive extreme values is just $e^{-(r/4A)T}$, as appears from Eq. (10.109), since the cosine function has the same absolute value at all extrema. One may rewrite the equations pertinent to the speed of galvanometer response for the underdamped case in terms of the damping constant r, the critical value r_c of this constant, and the free period T_0, that is, the period for zero damping which is

$$T_0 = 2\pi \sqrt{\frac{A}{k}} \tag{10.111}$$

In these terms, the damped period is

$$T = T_0 \frac{r_c}{\sqrt{r_c^2 - r^2}} \tag{10.112}$$

while the ratio between successive extreme values is

$$e^{-rT/4A} = \exp \frac{-\pi r}{\sqrt{r_c^2 - r^2}} \tag{10.113}$$

These equations are in a form convenient for calculating the effect of varying the damping constant r while leaving the other characteristics of the galvanometer unchanged.

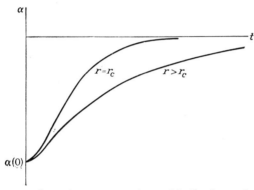

FIG. 10.15. Response of a galvanometer when critically damped or overdamped.

The critically damped case, occurring when $r = r_c$, and the overdamped case $r > r_c$ are both aperiodic and produce an asymptotic approach of α to its final zero value. See Fig. 10.15, where two such solutions are sketched. For reference, we give the general solutions of Eq. (10.107) in these cases, using again the quantities r_c and T_0,

$$\alpha = C_1 e^{-2\pi t/T_0} + C_2 t e^{-2\pi t/T_0} \qquad \text{critical damping, } r = r_c \tag{10.114}$$

$$\alpha = C_1 \exp\left[\frac{-2\pi}{T_0}\left(\frac{r}{r_c} + \sqrt{\frac{r^2}{r_c^2} - 1}\right)t\right]$$
$$+ C_2 \exp\left[\frac{-2\pi}{T_0}\left(\frac{r}{r_c} - \sqrt{\frac{r^2}{r_c^2} - 1}\right)t\right] \qquad \text{overdamping, } r > r_c \tag{10.115}$$

The critically damped case is often considered the desideratum, and it is very satisfactory for speedy reading although slightly slower than the ideal periodic case described above. The difference between the values of the damping constant r in the ideal periodic and the critically damped cases is only of the order of 10 per cent. The equivalent resistance R_0 of the external galvanometer circuit may be adjusted until the desired damping is obtained by using an appropriate shunt (or occasionally a series) resistance with the galvanometer. The value R_c of R_0 which produces critical damping is frequently written by the manufacturer on the galvanometer tag, and is sometimes called CDRX (critical external damping resistance). Sometimes when maximum sensitivity is desired in a galvanometer which is to operate in a high-resistance circuit, damping is achieved by mounting a single, short-circuited turn of heavy copper wire to turn with the galvanometer coil. Supposing this turn to have a resistance R_d and to be linked by the same steady flux $\phi(\theta)$ as the coil, the reader can readily show that this turn will increase the damping constant r from its value in Eq. (10.105) to

$$r = a + \frac{n^2\phi'^2}{R_0 + R_g} + \frac{\phi'^2}{R_d} \tag{10.116}$$

10.10. The d'Arsonval Ballistic Galvanometer. An interesting and important application of the d-c galvanometer is to the measurement of the total electric charge in a current pulse of short duration. Let us suppose that, due possibly to rapid flux change in a coil or discharge of a condenser, a current $I(t)$ flows in the galvanometer for a very short time τ, after which no more current flows except such as may result from the emf $\mathcal{E}_g$ resulting from motion of the galvanometer coil. The general dynamical equation of the galvanometer deflection θ during τ is, from the preceding section,

$$A \frac{d^2\theta}{dt^2} + a \frac{d\theta}{dt} + k\theta = In\phi' \tag{10.101}$$

Notice that Eq. (10.102) is not suitable during τ. That equation applies for a steady external emf $\mathcal{E}_0$ after purely electrical transients have died out, but now we are considering just those transients. Let us integrate all terms of Eq. (10.101) over the time interval $(0,\tau)$, considering ϕ' to be a constant of the galvanometer,

$$A \frac{d\theta}{dt}\bigg]_{t=0}^{\tau} + a\theta \bigg]_{t=0}^{\tau} + k \int_{t=0}^{\tau} \theta \, dt = n\phi' \int_{t=0}^{\tau} I \, dt \tag{10.117}$$

The integral of the current is the electric charge q that flows during τ:

$$q = \int_{t=0}^{\tau} I \, dt \tag{10.118}$$

The right-hand member of Eq. (10.117) is the angular impulse

$$G = \int_0^{\tau} N_3 \, dt$$

due to this charge [cf Eq. (10.100)], and is seen to be proportional to q:

$$G = n\phi'q \qquad (10.119)$$

Now it is well known in mechanics that the result of such an impulse is an angular momentum, so that during τ the coil acquires an angular velocity. Let this angular velocity be called $\dot{\theta}_\tau$, and suppose the coil to be initially at rest. The first term of Eq. (10.117) is thus

$$A \frac{d\theta}{dt}\bigg]_{t=0}^{\tau} = A\dot{\theta}_\tau \qquad (10.120)$$

The second term of Eq. (10.117) is the angular distance traveled by the coil in the time τ, and this may be written as the product of τ into the average value $\langle d\theta/dt \rangle_{\text{av}}$ of $d\theta/dt$ during τ:

$$a\theta\bigg]_{t=0}^{\tau} = a \left\langle \frac{d\theta}{dt} \right\rangle_{\text{av}} \tau \qquad (10.121)$$

This term approaches zero if τ approaches zero while $d\theta/dt$ remains finite, and $d\theta/dt$ must remain finite if finite energy is given to the galvanometer. We shall in fact assume that τ is small enough so that term (10.121) is negligible compared with term (10.120). The third term in Eq. (10.117) may likewise be made negligible by reducing τ to a sufficiently small value, for this integral may be written as an average angular position $\langle \theta_\tau \rangle_{\text{av}}$ during τ times the time τ:

$$k \int_{t=0}^{\tau} \theta \, dt = k\langle \theta_\tau \rangle_{\text{av}}\tau \qquad (10.122)$$

Incidentally, if the pulse comes in when θ is zero, $\langle \theta_\tau \rangle_{\text{av}}$ is itself nearly zero by the zero limit of term (10.121). Finally then, for sufficiently small τ, Eq. (10.117) reduces to

$$A\dot{\theta}_\tau = n\phi'q \qquad (10.123)$$

Equation (10.123) shows that in the postulated case of small enough τ, the result of a current pulse through the galvanometer is simply the acquisition by the coil of an angular velocity $\dot{\theta}_\tau$, which becomes the initial velocity in the problem of the subsequent motion with no impressed current. This motion is described by Eq. (10.102) of the preceding section when the impressed emf $\mathcal{E}_0$ is set to zero:

$$A \frac{d^2\theta}{dt^2} + \left(a + \frac{n^2\phi'^2}{R_0 + R_g} \right)\frac{d\theta}{dt} + k\theta = 0 \qquad (10.124)$$

As before, let us abbreviate by introducing the damping constant

$$r \equiv a + \frac{n^2\phi'^2}{R_0 + R_g} \qquad (10.105)$$

The differential equation of the motion is then

$$A \frac{d^2\theta}{dt^2} + r \frac{d\theta}{dt} + k\theta = 0 \qquad (10.125)$$

The ballistic galvanometer is used by observing the maximum deflection θ_m in the first swing caused by the current pulse. We shall suppose that $\theta = 0$ when the pulse occurs. For simplicity in finding θ_m, let us set a new origin of time by taking $t = 0$ now at the end of the pulse interval τ rather than at its beginning. This shift of origin is actually negligible since τ is small compared with times significant in the swing, but it may help to clarify the reasoning. We have now to solve Eq. (10.125) subject to the initial conditions

$$\theta(0) = 0 \qquad (10.126a)$$

$$\left(\frac{d\theta}{dt}\right)_0 = \dot\theta_\tau \qquad (10.126b)$$

These suffice to determine the constants in whichever general solution of Eq. (10.125) is appropriate for the condition of damping. The maximum swing θ_m occurs at the first time t_m following the current pulse when the angular velocity of the coil becomes zero:

$$\frac{d\theta}{dt} = 0 \qquad (10.127)$$

Substitution into Eq. (10.127) of the solution of (10.125) subject to conditions (10.126) yields an equation determining the times of all extreme swings; and the shortest of these, if there are more than one, is the required time t_m. Finally, t_m may be inserted into the solution of Eq. (10.125) to yield θ_m. We are not greatly concerned, in our study of basic principles, with the details of this analysis. The important equations for the underdamped case only will be given.

The general solution of Eq. (10.125) for the underdamped case, $r < 2\sqrt{Ak}$, is similar to Eq. (10.109), Sec. 10.9,

$$\theta = C_1 e^{(-r/2A)t} \cos(\omega t - \phi) \qquad \text{underdamped} \qquad (10.128)$$

where ω is the frequency of oscillation multiplied by 2π. The value of ω as given in the preceding section is

$$\omega = \sqrt{\frac{k}{A} - \frac{r^2}{4A^2}} \qquad (10.110)$$

From boundary condition (10.126a), it follows that

$$\phi = \pm 90° \qquad (10.129)$$

aside from an arbitrary multiple of 360°. Choosing $\phi = +90°$ loses no generality, and yields

$$\theta = C_1 e^{(-r/2A)t} \sin \omega t \qquad (10.130)$$

From boundary condition (10.126b),

$$C_1 = \frac{\dot\theta_\tau}{\omega} \qquad (10.131)$$

The first time of maximum swing is

$$t_m = \frac{1}{\omega} \tan^{-1} \frac{2A\omega}{r} \qquad (10.132)$$

where the capital letter in Tan^{-1} indicates the angle between 0 and 90°. By use of Eqs. (10.131), (10.123), and (10.132) in (10.130) the maximum swing is found, after some reduction, to be

$$\theta_m = q \frac{n\phi'}{\sqrt{Ak}} \exp\left[-\frac{r}{2A\omega} \text{Tan}^{-1} \frac{2A\omega}{r} \right] \tag{10.133}$$

Thus θ_m is proportional to q. Of the parameters appearing in Eq. (10.133), only ω is readily observable. The other constants may, however, be expressed in terms of observable characteristics of the galvanometer and its external network. From Eq. (10.104) of the preceding section,

$$\frac{n\phi'}{k} = \frac{\theta_f}{I_0} \tag{10.134}$$

where θ_f is the steady deflection for a current I_0. On open circuit, the damping of a research type of galvanometer is usually very small when no damping loop is used, so that the undamped period T_0 may be directly observed to good accuracy without making any correction for damping. This gives $\sqrt{A/k}$ according to Eq. (10.111):

$$\omega_0 = \sqrt{\frac{k}{A}} \tag{10.135}$$

where ω_0 is 2π times the undamped frequency, that is, $\omega_0 \equiv 2\pi/T_0$. Thus

$$\frac{n\phi'}{\sqrt{Ak}} = \frac{\omega_0\theta_f}{I_0} \tag{10.136}$$

Finally, the observed ratio of two successive extreme values during the underdamped motion may be used. This ratio D is, as shown in Sec. 10.9,

$$D = e^{-rT/4A} \tag{10.137}$$

where T is the damped period. In terms of ω, D is then

$$D = e^{-\pi r/2A\omega} \tag{10.138}$$

Thus the quantity $r/2A\omega$ is determined as

$$\frac{r}{2A\omega} = -\frac{1}{\pi} \ln D \tag{10.139}$$

Measurement of the three quantities θ_f/I_0, ω_0, and D therefore suffices for the calibration of the instrument, so long as its motion on open circuit is little damped.

PROBLEMS

10.1. A certain ideal inductor has a self-inductance of 100 mh. At what rate must the current in this component change to produce a potential difference of 800 volts across it?

10.2. In a certain oscillograph for very high frequency work, the voltage across the sweep deflecting plates of the cathode-ray tube must change at the rate of 1.2×10^{11} volts/sec, and the effective capacitance between the plates is about 15 $\mu\mu\text{f}$. Find the instantaneous current required for the sweep.

10.3. Choose positive senses for the branch currents in the circuit shown on page 368, and write a complete set of Kirchhoff equations for the instantaneous currents and their time derivatives.

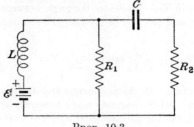

PROB. 10.3.

10.4. A 2-volt battery of negligible resistance, a 100-ohm resistor, a 4-henry ideal inductor, and a switch are all connected in series. When the current has built up to one-half its final value after the switch is closed, (a) what is the rate of change of the current? (b) What time has elapsed since the closing of the switch?

10.5. An ideal inductor with a self-inductance of 200 mh is in series with a resistance of 50 ohms and a 10-volt battery of negligible internal resistance. If the battery is short-circuited, find the total charge that flows through the inductor during the decay of current.

10.6. (a) Show that henrys/ohms = seconds. (b) Show that ohms $\times$ farads = seconds.

10.7. A 3-μf condenser is charged to 400 volts and then discharged through a 100,000-ohm resistor. After $1\frac{1}{2}$ sec of discharge, find the current in the circuit and the charge remaining on the condenser.

10.8. A certain condenser and resistor in series are connected across an ideal 500-volt power supply. If the time constant of the combination is $\frac{1}{4}$ sec and the initial current is 40 ma, what are the values of capacitance and resistance?

10.9. Carry through a time integration of the Joule heat developed in a resistor R through which (a) a condenser C of initial potential difference V is discharged and (b) a condenser C is charged from a battery of constant emf $\mathcal{E}$ and no internal resistance. Compare these results with the stored energy of the fully charged condenser.

10.10. Show that the time constant of a leaky condenser on open circuit is the same as the relaxation time of its dielectric (see Secs. 5.11 and 5.12).

10.11. A condenser C is charged to a potential difference V and then connected across an inductor L. Assuming negligible resistance in the circuit, find an expression for the maximum current during the subsequent oscillations.

10.12. An ideal L-C circuit has an inductance of 300 mh and oscillates with a frequency of 1000 kc/sec. Supposing that at $t = 0$ the potential difference across the condenser is +15 volts and the current through it is zero, find the potential difference and current at $t = \frac{4}{3} \times 10^{-6}$ sec.

10.13. In the oscillations of an ideal L-C circuit, find expressions for the stored energies associated with the inductor and with the capacitor at a general instant of time. Show that the sum of these energies is constant and that maxima of one energy coincide with zeros of the other, and conversely.

10.14. a. What capacitance is required with a 400-μh inductance to produce oscillations with a frequency of 800 kc/sec, assuming negligible resistance in the circuit?

b. What is the percentage frequency change if a series resistance of 80 ohms is included in the circuit?

10.15. Given an inductor of 4 henrys with an effective series resistance of 2,000 ohms. If this is to form an oscillatory circuit with a condenser but no additional resistance, in what range of capacitance must the condenser lie?

10.16. It is required to design a series L-C-R circuit using a condenser of 0.01 μf, such that the natural frequency is 50,000 cps and the damping causes the amplitude of oscillation to fall by the factor $1/e$ during 1,000 complete cycles. Find the inductance and resistance needed.

10.17. Given a series L-C-R circuit with no battery, whose components have the values of $\frac{1}{4}$ henry, 30 μf, and 100 ohms. Suppose that at zero time the potential difference across the condenser is 90 volts and the current is zero. Find (a) the time for the first zero of charge on the condenser and (b) the current at this time.

10.18. *a.* In an oscillatory, series L-C-R circuit, find the times t_1 of extreme values of current in terms of circuit parameters.

b. Show that these times do not coincide with the nearest times t_0 of zeros of charge, except in a limiting case, but come earlier in general.

$$Ans.\ (a)\ \omega t_1 = \phi + \tan^{-1}\frac{1}{2}\left(\frac{\omega}{b} - \frac{b}{\omega}\right).$$

10.19. A circuit is made up of an ideal inductor L, capacitor C, resistor R, and battery $\mathcal{E}$, all in series with a switch. The switch is thrown closed at zero time. Find solutions for the charge and current in which all constants are evaluated in terms of the given quantities.

10.20. A 1-μf condenser is charged to a potential difference of 100 volts and then at zero time is connected across the series combination of an 0.01-henry inductor and a 400-ohm resistor.

a. Using the differential equation of the circuit, find the initial rate of change of the current.

b. Find the solutions for charge on the condenser and for current, evaluating all constants.

10.21. Demonstrate Eqs. (10.62) and (10.63), Sec. 10.6.

10.22. In a certain series L-C-R circuit, the resistance has one-half of the value required for critical damping. Find, by exact equations, the logarithmic decrement and the ratio of successive charge maxima.

10.23. *a.* Find the value of logarithmic decrement required in a series L-C-R circuit in order that successive charge maxima may be in a 2:1 ratio.

b. For this case, find the relation between L, C, and R, and show that the approximate equation (10.67) is good almost to slide-rule approximation.

10.24. Let a critically damped series circuit be subjected to the initial conditions $q = q_0 > 0$, $I = 0$, at $t = 0$.

a. Find the algebraic signs of the constants A and B of the solution for q, Eq. (10.68).

b. Show that I is always negative while dI/dt changes sign from negative to positive.

c. Find an expression for the time at which the current is maximum.

d. Sketch the rough form of the solutions for q and I on the same graph with a common time scale.

10.25. Check the solutions given in the text for the critically damped and the aperiodic cases of the series L-C-R circuit.

10.26. Given two inductors, having self inductances of 0.10 and 0.25 henrys and effective internal series resistances of 6 and 5 ohms, respectively. These are to be connected in a bridge circuit like that of Sec. 10.7 in which one of the purely resistive branches has a resistance of 100 ohms. Show the circuit of the bridge arranged so as to be balanced, giving the value of each component.

10.27. Sketch a bridge for transient balance, having two resistive ratio arms and having in each of the other two arms a series-connected capacitor and resistor. Deduce balance conditions.

10.28. Find by Kirchhoff's laws for transient currents the conditions for balance of the Maxwell bridge shown in the figure.

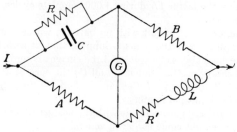

PROB. 10.28.

10.29. Work through in detail, so as to check the balance condition, the operation of the mutual inductance bridge of Carey Foster when the switch is opened after a steady primary current is attained.

10.30. If one adds a resistor R_2 in series with the condenser of the bridge of Carey Foster, he obtains what is called Heydweiller's bridge. Show that if R_2 has the right value, and if the balance condition of the Carey Foster bridge is also satisfied, then the galvanometer current remains zero at all times.

10.31. Show that in the solution of a critically damped system, the constant in the exponent is simply related to the frequency that would characterize the system in the absence of damping.

10.32. Suppose the magnetic induction in the air gap of a galvanometer to be perfectly radial with a uniform magnitude of 0.6 newton/amp-m, and suppose that the coil has 1,000 turns in a form measuring 1 by 3 cm.

a. Sketch the lines of induction from one magnet pole to the other.

b. Deduce the flux linkage $n\phi(\theta)$ and its derivative $n\phi'$.

c. Find the torsion constant k of the coil suspension if the galvanometer has a figure of merit of 10^{-10} amp.

10.33. Suppose that the total conducting cross section of copper in a galvanometer coil is fixed by design considerations, but that by using different wire gages the designer has at his disposal the number of turns. Show that the coil resistance is then proportional to the square of the number of turns.

10.34. Show from the result of the preceding problem that, under the conditions postulated, the angular deflection is proportional to the square root of the power dissipated in the galvanometer coil.

10.35. Show from the result of the preceding problem that, under the given conditions, the galvanometer coil yielding the best sensitivity for a given application is one whose resistance equals the effective resistance of the external circuit.

10.36. Under the conditions of Prob. 10.33 and by its result, show that the part of the damping constant arising from the emf induced in a moving galvanometer coil (*a*) increases steadily from zero to a constant asymptotic value as the resistance of the galvanometer coil increases, for a constant external resistance; (*b*) is independent of the resistance of the galvanometer coil when the external resistance is always the same as the coil resistance.

10.37. Deduce the effect on the galvanometer damping constant of a single-turn, shorted damping loop of resistance R_d, as given in Eq. (10.116).

10.38. *a.* Find the exact ratio of the critical damping constant of a galvanometer to the actual damping constant which results in an amplitude of the first overshoot which is 10^{-3} times the steady reading.

b. What is the ratio of the galvanometer period with the actual damping of part (a) to the undamped period T_0? *Ans.* (a) 1.098; (b) 2.42.

10.39. Suppose a certain galvanometer with negligible damping on open circuit has a resistance of 1,000 ohms and a CDRX of 500 ohms. What external circuit resistance will produce the ratio of critical to actual damping constant found in the preceding problem?

10.40. A certain galvanometer with an undamped period of 3.0 sec is damped according to the conditions of Prob. (10.38) so that the first overshoot is 10^{-3} times the steady deflection.

a. Apply boundary conditions to obtain a formula for the phase constant ϕ of the solution (10.109), assuming that the coil starts from rest.

b. Find the time required to reach the first zero of a and compare with the damped period. See the results of Prob. (10.38).

Ans. (a) $\tan \phi = rT/4\pi A$; (b) $t = 0.432T$

10.41. a. For a critically damped galvanometer, evaluate the constants C_1 and C_2 in solution (10.114) in terms of the steady deflection $-a(0)$. Assume the coil to be initially at rest.

b. Obtain an approximate time, in terms of the undamped period T_0, for a deflection $a = 10^{-3}a(0)$.

10.42. Assuming the damping constant of a galvanometer on open circuit to be negligibly small, find separate expressions for the basic constants of flux linkage per radian, coil moment of inertia, and torsional stiffness in terms of the measurable quantities of angular sensitivity, undamped angular frequency, coil resistance, and critical external damping resistance.

$$\text{Ans. } n\phi' = \frac{2I_0(R_c + R_g)}{\theta_f\omega_0} \qquad A = \frac{2(R_c + R_g)}{\omega_0{}^3}\left(\frac{I_0}{\theta_f}\right)^2$$
$$k = \frac{2(R_c + R_g)}{\omega_0}\left(\frac{I_0}{\theta_f}\right)^2$$

10.43. Correct the expressions of the preceding problem by taking account of the open-circuit damping constant and adding to the experimental data a measurement of the ratio of successive swings on open circuit.

Note: The approximation of the observed undamped frequency to the true value may still be justified even when the open-circuit damping constant is not negligible.

10.44. Follow through the steps in the deduction of Eq. (10.133) for the swing of an underdamped ballistic galvanometer.

10.45. Show that if $-\ln D \ll \pi$, where D is the ratio of the magnitudes of successive extreme swings of an underdamped ballistic galvanometer, then Eq. (10.133) may be approximated by

$$\theta_m = \omega_0\left(\frac{\theta_f}{I_0}\right)\left(1 + \frac{1}{2}\ln D\right)q$$

10.46. A student took the following data with a ballistic galvanometer. Steady deflection X_f and swings X_m are measured on a scale at fixed distance, and may be taken as proportional to angles. $X_f = 10.0$ cm for current 2.42×10^{-7} amp; period is 17.0 sec. In 20 half swings, X_m falls from 52.0 cm to 13.5 cm. A condenser charged to 2.10 volts gives on discharge through the galvanometer $X_m = 43.5$ cm. Find the capacitance of the condenser, using the approximate equation of Prob. 10.45.

CHAPTER 11

ANALYSIS OF ALTERNATING-CURRENT CIRCUITS

11.1. Series Circuit with A-C Generator. Transient and Steady-state Currents. We have to consider in this chapter the analysis of circuits containing one or more periodically varying emfs. The circuit of Fig. 11.1, which contains constant values of inductance, capacitance, and resistance in series with a generator of alternating emf $\mathcal{E}$, will serve to introduce some of the concepts involved in the analysis. The symbol

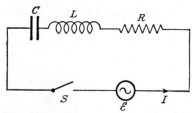

FIG. 11.1. Series L-C-R circuit with a-c generator.

$-\bigcirc-$ will stand for the generator. Unless specifically indicated otherwise, we shall assume a particular type of periodic variation of the emf $\mathcal{E}$ with time: a sinusoidal or simple harmonic variation, of which a general form is

$$\mathcal{E} = \mathcal{E}_0 \cos (\omega t - a) \qquad (11.1)$$

Here $\mathcal{E}_0$, a, and ω are all to be constant in time. $\mathcal{E}_0$ is called the peak value of the emf, a is a phase angle, while ω is related to the frequency and the period of the emf by

$$\omega = 2\pi f = \frac{2\pi}{T} \qquad (11.2)$$

ω is properly speaking an angular velocity. The angle $(\omega t - a)$, which is the instantaneous phase of the emf, is understood to be measured in radians so that the simple rules of differentiation and integration are valid. The emf $\mathcal{E}$ will be called simply an alternating emf.

The theoretical foundations for analysis of a-c circuits were laid in Chap. 10, where we studied transient conditions, especially in Secs. 10.1 and 10.2. The only fundamentally new feature of this chapter is the introduction of alternating quantities like the emf of Eq. (11.1). The sign convention for the instantaneous value of an alternating emf relative to the current is to be the same as that for batteries as specified in Sec. 10.1.

Adopting an arbitrary positive sense for instantaneous current in Fig. 11.1, we can at once write the Kirchhoff law for the circuit:

$$RI + L\frac{dI}{dt} + \frac{q}{C} - \mathcal{E} = 0 \qquad (11.3)$$

The current is ordinarily of greater interest than the charge, so we shall differentiate and rearrange Eq. (11.3):

$$L\frac{d^2I}{dt^2} + R\frac{dI}{dt} + \frac{I}{C} = \frac{d\mathcal{E}}{dt} \tag{11.4}$$

To solve this equation, we must introduce the functional form (11.1) of $\mathcal{E}$. Let us simplify our work by putting $a = 0$. This amounts merely to a simple choice of the zero time. Then

$$L\frac{d^2I}{dt^2} + R\frac{dI}{dt} + \frac{I}{C} = -\omega\mathcal{E}_0 \sin \omega t \tag{11.5}$$

The solving of an inhomogeneous differential equation such as (11.5) may be done in two steps. First, a particular solution is sought, and then the general solution is the sum of this particular solution and the solution of the corresponding homogeneous equation. Here the corresponding homogeneous equation is one which we have treated at length in Sec. 10.6:

$$L\frac{d^2I}{dt^2} + R\frac{dI}{dt} + \frac{I}{C} = 0 \tag{11.6}$$

The solutions of Eq. (11.6) yield transient currents, either oscillating or aperiodic, but always dying away exponentially with the time. These transients may be of extreme importance in practice while they last; but if the circuit is allowed to operate for a short time, the transients disappear and leave the condition called steady state which will be our present interest. We turn therefore to the problem of finding the steady-state, particular solution of Eq. (11.5).

The simplest guess that can be made for the steady-state solution of Eq. (11.5) is that I has an alternating form similar to that of $\mathcal{E}$ with the same frequency as $\mathcal{E}$:

$$I = I_0 \cos (\omega t - \phi) \tag{11.7}$$

Let us substitute Eq. (11.7) into (11.5) as a trial solution, and at the same time let us use trigonometric expansion to express the result in terms of $\sin \omega t$ and $\cos \omega t$. When this is done, we obtain

$$\left(-L\omega^2 \cos \phi + R\omega \sin \phi + \frac{1}{C} \cos \phi\right) I_0 \cos \omega t$$
$$+ \left[\left(-L\omega^2 \sin \phi - R\omega \cos \phi + \frac{1}{C} \sin \phi\right) I_0 + \omega\mathcal{E}_0\right] \sin \omega t = 0 \tag{11.8}$$

Now a solution of our differential equation must satisfy the equation at all times. Since there are times when $\cos \omega t = 0$ but $\sin \omega t \neq 0$, and other times when $\sin \omega t = 0$ but $\cos \omega t \neq 0$, it is easy to see that if

Eq. (11.7) is to be a solution of (11.5) then the coefficient of cos ωt as well as the coefficient of sin ωt in (11.8) must be zero. Setting the coefficient of cos ωt to zero, we obtain a condition on the angle ϕ:

$$\tan \phi = \frac{L\omega - (1/C\omega)}{R} \tag{11.9}$$

We may express the coefficient of sin ωt partly in terms of tan ϕ when we equate it to zero, by division by $-R\omega \cos \phi$:

$$(\tan^2 \phi + 1)I_0 - \frac{\mathcal{E}_0}{R \cos \phi} = 0 \tag{11.10}$$

Since $\tan^2 \phi + 1 = 1/\cos^2 \phi$, Eq. (11.10) yields

$$\mathcal{E}_0 \cos \phi = I_0 R \tag{11.11}$$

This equation completes the specification of the phase angle ϕ, and in addition it determines the peak current I_0. Equation (11.9) left an ambiguity of π in the value of ϕ, in addition to the trivial ambiguity of multiples of 2π which will always be present. If $\mathcal{E}_0$ and I_0 are understood as being both positive, which simply means that consistent positive conventions are assumed for the instantaneous values of $\mathcal{E}$ and I, and if R is positive, then Eq. (11.11) tells us that cos ϕ is never negative. This means that we may restrict ϕ to lie in the range

$$-\frac{\pi}{2} \leqq \phi \leqq \frac{\pi}{2} \tag{11.12}$$

Negative values of resistance R can occur in certain operating ranges of certain circuit components, as for instance in vacuum tubes and arcs; but this phenomenon is always associated with nonlinearity, which we have been excluding.

Now from Eq. (11.9) with the help of (11.12) it is easy to write the value of cos ϕ:

$$\cos \phi = \frac{R}{+ \sqrt{[L\omega - (1/C\omega)]^2 + R^2}} \tag{11.13}$$

Substitution of Eq. (11.13) into (11.11) gives the peak current:

$$I_0 = \frac{\mathcal{E}_0}{+ \sqrt{[L\omega - (1/C\omega)]^2 + R^2}} \tag{11.14}$$

It will be noticed that in Eq. (11.14) the radical takes the place which in a d-c circuit is occupied by the resistance. Because of its importance, we shall give this quantity a special name, the impedance of the circuit. Using the symbol Z for the impedance, we have for our series circuit

$$Z = \sqrt{\left[L\omega - \left(\frac{1}{C\omega}\right)\right]^2 + R^2} \tag{11.15}$$

Equations (11.13) and (11.14) now take the simple form

$$\cos \phi = \frac{R}{Z} \tag{11.16}$$

$$I_0 = \frac{\mathcal{E}_0}{Z} \tag{11.17}$$

The circuit of Fig. 11.1 is now essentially solved. By means of the characteristic equations of the components, as given in Sec. 10.1, the steady-state potential difference across any part of the circuit may be determined, for the current is known. We proceed in succeeding sections to develop general methods for treating the steady state of a-c networks without the necessity of solving a set of differential equations for each circuit.

11.2. Alternating-current Characteristics of Uncoupled Linear Circuit Components. The example of Sec. 11.1 leads us to examine the characteristic equations for ideal circuit components when the current through them is alternating sinusoidally with a given frequency. Let us consider an alternating current described by

$$I = I_0 \sin \omega t \tag{11.18}$$

In writing such a simple equation without any phase constant, we are not losing generality but merely choosing arbitrarily the position of zero time in the cycle. If this current is flowing in a pure resistor, then, by the characteristic equation for instantaneous values of potential difference and current of a resistor, we obtain immediately

$$V_R = IR = I_0 R \sin \omega t \tag{11.19}$$

See Sec. 10.1 for the transient characteristic equations of the various ideal circuit components, together with a discussion of sign conventions. We shall consider only linear components, that is, those for which the circuit parameters R, L, and C are constants. For an ideal uncoupled inductor carrying the current I of Eq. (11.18),

$$V_L = L \frac{dI}{dt} = I_0 L \omega \cos \omega t \tag{11.20}$$

It will be convenient to write the expression for V_L in the form

$$V_L = I_0 L \omega \sin \left(\omega t + \frac{\pi}{2} \right) \tag{11.21}$$

For an ideal capacitor whose current is I,

$$V_C = \frac{1}{C} \int I \, dt = -\frac{I_0}{C\omega} \cos \omega t + A \tag{11.22}$$

Here A is a constant of integration. We shall agree, however, that the average potential on the condenser is to be zero, for in alternating-current analysis we are not interested in any constant potentials which may be superposed on the alternating ones. We shall therefore put $A = 0$, and also rewrite the variable term of the equation

$$V_c = \frac{I_0}{C\omega} \sin \left(\omega t - \frac{\pi}{2} \right) \tag{11.23}$$

It will be noted that Eqs. (11.19), (11.21), and (11.23) are all expressed in the form

$$V_j = V_{0j} \sin (\omega t + \phi_j) \tag{11.24}$$

where V_{0j} is a constant, while ϕ_j is a phase angle. The angle ϕ_j is that by which the potential difference leads the current, or conversely the angle by which the current lags behind the potential difference for the particular circuit component. Any particular phase such as a positive peak which is reached by the potential difference at a time t_1 is reached by the current at time $t_1 + \phi_j/\omega$, which is later than t_1 if ϕ_j is positive. Equation (11.21) shows that for an ideal self-inductor

$$\phi_L = \frac{\pi}{2} \tag{11.25}$$

while for an ideal capacitor we see from Eq. (11.23) that

$$\phi_c = - \frac{\pi}{2} \tag{11.26}$$

For a pure resistor, evidently

$$\phi_R = 0 \tag{11.27}$$

Consider next the peak values of the potential difference across the simple circuit components. These are the constants V_{0j} of Eq. (11.24). Comparison of Eq. (11.24) with Eqs. (11.19), (11.21), and (11.23) gives the value of these constants:

$$V_{0R} = I_0 R \tag{11.28}$$
$$V_{0L} = I_0 L\omega \tag{11.29}$$
$$V_{0C} = \frac{I_0}{C\omega} \tag{11.30}$$

In each case, these peak potential differences are proportional to the peak current. The proportionality factors in Eqs. (11.29) and (11.30) which occupy the place of resistance in Eq. (11.28) are called the reactances of the ideal circuit components. These are given the symbols X_L and X_C and are termed inductive and capacitive reactance, respectively.

Thus

$$X_L \equiv \frac{V_{0L}}{I_0} = L\omega \qquad (11.31)$$

$$X_C \equiv \frac{V_{0C}}{I_0} = \frac{1}{C\omega} \qquad (11.32)$$

We now proceed to extend these ideas by defining a general linear two-terminal circuit component, excluding mutual inductance for the present. To indicate this exclusion where necessary the term "uncoupled" may be used. We shall also exclude generators from present consideration. An uncoupled linear element of an a-c circuit will be defined as one for which, when its current is in the form of Eq. (11.18), the potential difference has the form

$$V = I_0 Z \sin(\omega t + \phi) \qquad (11.33)$$

where Z and ϕ are constants. The phase angle ϕ may take any value from $-\pi/2$ to $+\pi/2$. Energy considerations to be developed later exclude values of ϕ for which $\cos\phi < 0$, so long as there is no generator in the circuit element. The quantity Z is called the impedance of the circuit element. If V_0 is the peak potential difference across the element, Z is defined by

$$Z \equiv \frac{V_0}{I_0} \qquad (11.34)$$

The reader may well find the terminology which we have introduced somewhat cumbersome. It is, however, firmly established usage that the ratio of peak potential difference to peak current for a circuit element is called impedance in general; but if the phase angle is zero, it becomes resistance, while if $\phi = \pm\pi/2$ it becomes reactance. The mks unit of impedance in any case is the ohm. The utility of these various terms will become more evident with use.

The example of Sec. 11.1 shows that an arbitrary uncoupled linear element may be produced or represented by the series combination of an ideal inductor, capacitor, and resistor. The quantities Z and ϕ of that discussion are identical with those of Eqs. (11.33) and (11.34), in spite of the difference in the choice of zero time between that section and this.

11.3. Power. Consider the energy transformations involved when an alternating current flows in a linear uncoupled circuit component not containing a generator. If V is the instantaneous potential difference across the component, and I is the instantaneous current, the product

$$P = IV \qquad (11.35)$$

is the instantaneous power transfer, by the definition of potential difference. Furthermore, our sign conventions make P the power lost to the electric circuit if its value is positive (cf. Sec. 10.1).

Let us now take for the current the expression used in Sec. 11.2:

$$I = I_0 \sin \omega t \tag{11.18}$$

For the potential difference across a linear uncoupled component we have, from Sec. 11.2,

$$V = V_0 \sin (\omega t + \phi) \tag{11.36}$$

Here

$$V_0 = ZI_0 \tag{11.37}$$

Z being the impedance of the component. Substitution of Eqs. (11.18) and (11.36) into Eq. (11.35) now gives

$$P = I_0 V_0 \sin (\omega t) \sin (\omega t + \phi) \tag{11.38}$$

It will be convenient to transform Eq. (11.38) by the trigonometric identity

$$\sin \alpha \sin \beta \equiv \tfrac{1}{2}[\cos (\alpha - \beta) - \cos (\alpha + \beta)] \tag{11.39}$$

Putting $\alpha = \omega t + \phi$ and $\beta = \omega t$, we obtain, for the power of Eq. (11.38),

$$P = \tfrac{1}{2}I_0 V_0[\cos \phi - \cos (2\omega t + \phi)] \tag{11.40}$$

Equation (11.40) shows immediately that the average power dissipation is

$$\bar{P} = \tfrac{1}{2}I_0 V_0 \cos \phi \tag{11.41}$$

since the variable term has a zero average over a cycle. By use of Eq. (11.37) we may rewrite (11.41) in two other forms

$$\bar{P} = \frac{1}{2} I_0^2 Z \cos \phi = \frac{1}{2} \frac{V_0^2}{Z} \cos \phi \tag{11.42}$$

It will be noted that there is no average power dissipation in ideal self-inductors or capacitors where $\phi = \pm \pi/2$. For an ideal resistor $\phi = 0$, so that the power dissipation is

$$\bar{P} = \frac{1}{2} I_0^2 R = \frac{1}{2} \frac{V_0^2}{R} \qquad \text{resistor} \tag{11.43}$$

Power may be put into an a-c circuit by a generator. If we consider an ideal generator having emf $\mathcal{E}$, the instantaneous power put into the circuit is, by the definition of emf,

$$P = \mathcal{E}I \tag{11.44}$$

If the current has the form (11.18) while the emf has an instantaneous value

$$\mathcal{E} = \mathcal{E}_0 \sin (\omega t + \phi) \tag{11.45}$$

then the instantaneous power put into the electric circuit is found by an analysis exactly like that above to be

$$P = \tfrac{1}{2}I_0\mathcal{E}_0[\cos \phi - \cos (2\omega t + \phi)] \tag{11.46}$$

It follows that the average power flow from the generator is

$$\bar{P} = \tfrac{1}{2}I_0\mathcal{E}_0 \cos \phi \tag{11.47}$$

The universal appearance of the factor $\tfrac{1}{2}$ in the foregoing formulas for power suggests that we may profitably define effective values of the alternating current, potential difference, and emf as follows:

$$I_e \equiv \frac{I_0}{\sqrt{2}} \qquad V_e \equiv \frac{V_0}{\sqrt{2}} \qquad \mathcal{E}_e \equiv \frac{\mathcal{E}_0}{\sqrt{2}} \tag{11.48}$$

In these terms, the average power dissipation becomes

$$\bar{P} = I_e V_e \cos \phi = I_e^2 Z \cos \phi = \frac{V_e^2}{Z} \cos \phi \tag{11.49}$$

and the average energy supplied by a generator is

$$\bar{P} = I_e \mathcal{E}_e \cos \phi \tag{11.50}$$

Effective values rather than peak values of alternating currents and voltages are nearly always used in practice, and we shall understand them except in discussions involving instantaneous values. Evidently relation (11.37) may be rewritten in terms of effective values without alteration of the meaning of impedance Z:

$$V_e = ZI_e \tag{11.51}$$

Effective values are frequently called root-mean-square values, and this in turn is abbreviated rms. The mean of the square of a sinusoidally alternating quantity is one-half the square of its peak value, and the square root of this mean is then $1/\sqrt{2}$ times the peak value. The reader may show this by direct integration over a cycle, or by comparing Eq. (11.43) with the instantaneous power $I^2R = V^2/R$ dissipated in a pure resistance.

The factor $\cos \phi$ in the expressions for average power is evidently of fundamental importance to electrical engineering. It has therefore been given a special name, the power factor. Power factor may characterize a single component or any two-terminal network.

It is helpful to our understanding of a-c power to rewrite Eq. (11.40) by expanding the variable term. Using effective values of current and potential difference, we obtain

$$P = I_e V_e[(1 - \cos 2\omega t) \cos \phi + \sin 2\omega t \sin \phi] \tag{11.52}$$

The first term of the square brackets represents the fluctuating power dissipated into heat, for this term is nonnegative and exists alone if the component is a pure resistor. The second term represents the power alternately stored in the component and released to the circuit, for this term changes sign and is the only term present if the component has a pure reactance. An ideal inductor stores energy in the form of a magnetic field, an ideal capacitor in an electric field. The reader may show for himself that this interpretation of the two terms of Eq. (11.52) holds also for a general phase angle, if the component be considered as represented by a series L-C-R combination of simple components. Alternate energy storage and release also occurs in a generator, as may be seen by throwing Eq. (11.46) into a form like that of (11.52).

The peak power involved in energy storage is

$$P_s = I_e V_e \sin \phi \tag{11.53}$$

or for a generator,

$$P_s = I_e \mathcal{E}_e \sin \phi \tag{11.54}$$

This is called reactive power, or wattless power. To distinguish reactive power from average power, different units are used. For average power, the units are watts or kilowatts. The watt is the joule per second, and is obtained, for example, in Eqs. (11.41), (11.49), and (11.50) when current is expressed in amperes and potential difference or emf is expressed in volts. Instantaneous power likewise is given in watts. Reactive power, on the other hand, is left expressed in volt-amperes or kilovolt-amperes (kva). Engineers use the specific unit reactive-volt-ampere to distinguish the reactive power from the simple product $I_e \mathcal{E}_e$ or $I_e V_e$ which is also measured in volt-amperes and which is used in rating electrical equipment.

11.4. Vector Representation of A-C Variables. In the preceding sections we have considered sinusoidally varying currents, potentials, and emfs. These variables differ only dimensionally. In order to study their mathematical properties, let us call them by a generic term, a-c variables. Throughout this discussion, it is to be understood that a single frequency is specified for all a-c variables of a given circuit.

The general a-c variable may be written

$$A = A_0 \sin (\omega t + \alpha) \tag{11.55}$$

Evidently this variable is distinguished by its peak value A_0 and its phase angle α. The phase angle may be regarded as the constant angular difference between the variable A and another a-c variable arbitrarily chosen as having standard phase. Here the reference variable is $\sin \omega t$. There is another and completely equivalent way of specifying an a-c variable, for an alternative general form is

$$A = a_1 \sin \omega t + a_2 \cos \omega t \tag{11.56}$$

Thus the values of a_1 and a_2 determine and characterize the variable just as well as A_0 and α. The relation between the pairs (a_1a_2) and $(A_0\alpha)$ is quickly found by trigonometric expansion of Eq. (11.55):

$$a_1 = A_0 \cos \alpha \tag{11.57}$$
$$a_2 = A_0 \sin \alpha \tag{11.58}$$

$$\alpha = \tan^{-1}\frac{a_2}{a_1} \tag{11.59}$$
$$A_0 = \sqrt{a_1{}^2 + a_2{}^2} \tag{11.60}$$

Suppose we consider how two a-c variables of the same dimensions combine when their instantaneous values are added. This is what we shall mean by addition of the two variables. Let a variable

$$B = b_1 \sin \omega t + b_2 \cos \omega t = B_0 \sin (\omega t + \beta) \tag{11.61}$$

be added to the variable A of Eqs. (11.55) and (11.56). If C stands for the sum of A and B, we shall write

$$C = A + B \tag{11.62}$$

Evidently if we use the form of Eq. (11.56), the addition is easy:

$$C = (a_1 + b_1) \sin \omega t + (a_2 + b_2) \cos \omega t \tag{11.63}$$

From Eq. (11.63) it appears that C is itself an a-c variable. If we write C in the standard forms

$$C = c_1 \sin \omega t + c_2 \cos \omega t = C_0 \sin (\omega t + \gamma) \tag{11.64}$$

it follows at once that

$$c_1 = a_1 + b_1 \qquad c_2 = a_2 + b_2 \tag{11.65}$$

It is a little more difficult to express C_0 and γ in terms of the peak values and phase angles of A and B, but with a little algebra and trigonometry we obtain

$$C_0 = \sqrt{A_0{}^2 + B_0{}^2 + 2A_0B_0 \cos (\beta - \alpha)} \tag{11.66}$$

$$\gamma = \sin^{-1}\left[\frac{B_0}{C_0} \sin (\beta - \alpha)\right] + \alpha \tag{11.67}$$

All of the foregoing relationships between the characteristic constants of the three a-c variables are suggestive of the description of two-dimensional vectors in a plane and of their manner of addition. Let us define vectors **A**, **B**, and **C** to correspond to the a-c variables A, B, and C, respectively,

$$\begin{aligned}
\mathbf{A} &\equiv a_1\mathbf{i} + a_2\mathbf{j} \\
\mathbf{B} &\equiv b_1\mathbf{i} + b_2\mathbf{j} \\
\mathbf{C} &\equiv c_1\mathbf{i} + c_2\mathbf{j}
\end{aligned} \tag{11.68}$$

Here **i** and **j** are unit vectors in a plane system of cartesian coordinates, along the x and y axes, respectively; and the values of a_1, etc., are those of Eqs. (11.56), (11.61), and (11.64). These vectors then have absolute values or magnitudes A_0, B_0, and C_0, and trigonometric angles α, β, and γ, respectively, which are identical to the peak values and phase angles of the three corresponding a-c variables. Furthermore, by the process of ordinary vector addition the three corresponding vectors are related by

$$\mathbf{C} = \mathbf{A} + \mathbf{B} \tag{11.69}$$

We have here a most important method of steady-state analysis of a-c circuits. In Kirchhoff's first law, alternating currents are to be added, while in his second law alternating potential differences and emfs are to be added. We now learn that a-c variables can be added by adding their corresponding vectors, and the vector sum will then correspond to the sum of the a-c variables. The analysis of a-c circuits is thus reduced to a problem involving plane vectors. This in turn permits both the graphical and the analytical methods which are well known in treating plane vectors to be used in circuit analysis.

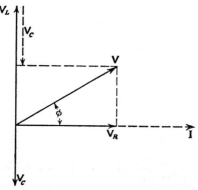

FIG. 11.2. Vector diagram for a series *L-C-R* circuit.

In practice, the components and magnitudes of corresponding vectors are often chosen to represent effective values of current, potential difference, or emf. This alters nothing except the scale of the vector diagram.

As a simple example of a vector diagram, Fig. 11.2 shows vectors corresponding to the potential differences in the series circuit of Sec. 11.1. $\mathbf{V}_R$, $\mathbf{V}_L$, and $\mathbf{V}_C$ represent the separate potential differences across the resistor, inductor, and capacitor, respectively, while $\mathbf{V}$ is their vector sum and corresponds to the total potential difference. The current is arbitrarily taken as having zero phase angle; therefore the potential difference across the resistor is represented by a vector along the x axis. Sometimes currents as well as potential differences are shown in the same diagram, as we have included in Fig. 11.2 the vector **I** representing the current. However, vectors of different dimensions are never to be added together; and the relative lengths of two vectors of different kinds is meaningless since their scales are different.

It should be remarked, in order to orient the reader to other treatments of a-c circuit analysis, that frequently the concept of rotating vectors is employed. If a plane vector of fixed length A_0 starting at the origin of coordinates is conceived to rotate with a uniform angular velocity ω about the origin, then its projection upon either of the cartesian axes is a sinusoidally varying quantity mathematically identical with a general a-c variable of frequency $\omega/2\pi$. The angular position of the rotating vector at $t = 0$ specifies the phase angle for its projection. The rotating vector therefore corresponds to the a-c variable and may be used as a representation for it. Rotating vectors of the same angular velocity add like ordinary vectors and their sum represents the sum of the a-c variables they represent. Any fixed vector diagram showing a-c currents or potential differences may be made into a rotating diagram by imagining the diagram as a whole to rotate with the angular speed ω. One advantage of the concept of rotating diagrams is that they facilitate the visualization of the instantaneous values of the a-c variables of the circuit.

11.5. Impedance Operators and Impedance Vectors. In Sec. 11.2 we have noted the relation between the two a-c variables for an uncoupled linear circuit component not including a generator. The potential difference may be obtained from the current by multiplying the magnitude of the current by the impedance Z and adding an angle ϕ to the phase of the current. Now that we propose to represent a-c variables by vectors, it is convenient to introduce a vector operator which has the power to transform the current vector into the potential difference vector by a process which may be formally called multiplication. This process may be considered to involve change of the magnitude of the current vector by the factor Z and rotation of it through the angle ϕ. We shall use the symbol Z for an impedance operator. An equation may now be written between the potential difference and current vectors of an uncoupled linear circuit component characterized by the impedance operator Z:

$$\mathbf{V} = \mathsf{Z}\mathbf{I} \tag{11.70}$$

An impedance operator for a linear component is always linear, that is, for any current vectors $\mathbf{I}$, $\mathbf{I}_1$, and $\mathbf{I}_2$,

$$\mathsf{Z}(k\mathbf{I}) = k\mathsf{Z}\mathbf{I} \tag{11.71}$$

where $k = $ constant; and

$$\mathsf{Z}(\mathbf{I}_1 + \mathbf{I}_2) = \mathsf{Z}\mathbf{I}_1 + \mathsf{Z}\mathbf{I}_2 \tag{11.72}$$

The reader should convince himself that Eq. (11.71) follows directly from the definition of Z and the meaning of multiplication of a vector by a scalar. To prove (11.72), the vector sums may be written in polar form using Eqs. (11.66) and (11.67) of Sec. 11.4. We are more concerned at the moment with another property of the impedance operator, namely, the manner in which addition of two operators may be defined. If two impedance operators are Z_1 and Z_2, we shall define their sum Z so that for any arbitrary current vector **I**

$$ZI \equiv Z_1I + Z_2I \tag{11.73}$$

Ordinary algebraic notation will be used for the sum of two operators

$$Z = Z_1 + Z_2 \tag{11.74}$$

Comparison of Eqs. (11.74) and (11.73) indicates that we may now use distributive notation

$$(Z_1 + Z_2)I = Z_1I + Z_2I \tag{11.75}$$

Definition (11.73) has been made in such a way that if two circuit components are connected in series, the impedance operator for the combination is the sum of the separate operators of the components. For in series connection, the currents are common while the potential differences are additive. Thus if the common current vector is **I** and the separate and total potential differences are, respectively, **V₁**, **V₂**, and **V**, Eq. (11.73) is a statement that

$$V = V_1 + V_2 \tag{11.76}$$

because of the nature of an impedance operator according to (11.70).

The next question is how the impedances and angles of rotation of the three impedance operators in a sum are related. This is readily determined by taking an arbitrary vector **I** of magnitude I_0 and phase angle ψ and substituting it into Eq. (11.73). Let us use a notation (A_0,α) for a plane vector **A** in polar form, A_0 denoting its magnitude and α its trigonometric angle. The current vector is thus to be written

$$I = (I_0,\psi) \tag{11.77}$$

Now let the three impedance operators of Eqs. (11.73) and (11.74) be characterized by impedances Z, Z_1, and Z_2, and by angles of rotation ϕ, ϕ_1, and ϕ_2, respectively. Then Eq. (11.73) may be written in the form

$$(ZI_0, \psi + \phi) = (Z_1I_0, \psi + \phi_1) + (Z_2I_0, \psi + \phi_2) \tag{11.78}$$

The sum of the vectors in the right-hand member of this equation may be found in polar form by using Eqs. (11.66) and (11.67) of Sec. 11.4. Equation (11.78) then becomes

$$(ZI_0, \psi + \phi) = \left\{ I_0 \sqrt{Z_1^2 + Z_2^2 + 2Z_1Z_2 \cos(\phi_2 - \phi_1)}, \right.$$
$$\left. \sin^{-1}\left[\frac{Z_2}{\sqrt{Z_1^2 + Z_2^2 + 2Z_1Z_2 \cos(\phi_2 - \phi_1)}} \sin(\phi_2 - \phi_1) \right] \right.$$
$$\left. + (\psi + \phi_1) \right\} \tag{11.79}$$

Identification of the magnitudes and angles on the two sides of Eq. (11.79) yields our answers:

$$Z = \sqrt{Z_1{}^2 + Z_2{}^2 + 2Z_1 Z_2 \cos (\phi_2 - \phi_1)} \qquad (11.80)$$

$$\phi = \sin^{-1}\left[\frac{Z_2}{Z} \sin (\phi_2 - \phi_1)\right] + \phi_1 \qquad (11.81)$$

Comparison of these equations with (11.66) and (11.77) shows that impedances and angles of rotation combine upon addition of operators in exactly the same manner as magnitudes and trigonometric angles of plane vectors. We now reach the important conclusion that impedance operators may be described in the same terms and added in the same way as plane vectors. The stretching factor or impedance Z behaves like the magnitude of a vector, and the angle of rotation behaves like the angle of a vector. The corresponding vector (Z,ϕ) may now represent the impedance operator z. We shall call this vector the impedance vector, and shall write it in ordinary vector notation **Z**. Impedance operators may be added by performing vector addition of their corresponding vectors, and the sum of the vectors then corresponds to the sum of the operators. Impedance vector diagrams are frequently used in analysis of a-c circuits.

A simple example is the impedance diagram for the series circuit of Sec. 11.1. The impedance vectors for the ideal inductor, capacitor, and resistor are found from Eqs. (11.21), (11.23), and (11.19), Sec. 11.2, to be

$$\mathbf{Z}_L = \left(X_L, \frac{\pi}{2}\right) \qquad (11.82)$$

$$\mathbf{Z}_C = \left(X_C, -\frac{\pi}{2}\right) \qquad (11.83)$$

$$\mathbf{Z}_R = (R,0) \qquad (11.84)$$

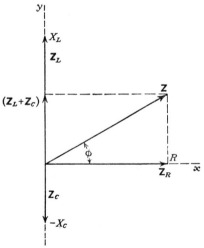

Figure 11.3 shows the addition of these three impedance vectors to form the resultant vector impedance **Z**. The usual convention is followed according to which the x axis has zero phase angle. Thus pure resistance is plotted along the x axis, inductive reactance along

FIG. 11.3. Impedance vector diagram for a series L-C-R circuit.

positive y, and capacitive reactance along negative y. One can almost read off from Fig. 11.3 the magnitude and phase angle of **Z**:

$$Z = \sqrt{(X_L - X_C)^2 + R^2} \tag{11.85}$$

$$\phi = \tan^{-1}\frac{X_L - X_c}{R} = \cos^{-1}\frac{R}{Z} \tag{11.86}$$

These agree with Eqs. (11.15), (11.13), and (11.9), Sec. 11.1.

Component form is convenient for vectors which are to be added. Any impedance vector may be considered to be the vector sum of two components, a resistive one along the x axis and a reactive one along the y axis. Thus if $\mathbf{i}$ and $\mathbf{j}$ are unit vectors along x and y, any impedance vector may be written

$$\mathbf{Z} = R\mathbf{i} + X\mathbf{j} \tag{11.87}$$

The corresponding statement for an a-c circuit is that any linear uncoupled component not containing a generator may be considered as a series combination of a pure resistance and a pure reactance. The values of R and X are obtained from the quantities Z and ϕ by simple projection:

$$R = Z \cos \phi \tag{11.88}$$
$$X = Z \sin \phi \tag{11.89}$$

11.6. Admittance. It is convenient for analysis of parallel circuits to define a quantity called admittance which is the reciprocal of impedance. If a two-terminal circuit component not including a generator has current and potential difference variables whose peak values are I_0 and V_0, respectively, the admittance of the component is defined to be

$$Y \equiv \frac{I_0}{V_0} \tag{11.90}$$

Thus in terms of the impedance Z of the component,

$$Y = \frac{1}{Z} \tag{11.91}$$

Special names are given to admittance in the special cases where Z is a pure resistance or pure reactance. In case Z is a pure resistance, its reciprocal becomes a conductance, while the reciprocal of a pure reactance is a susceptance. It should be noted that definition (11.90) could equally well be written in terms of effective values I_e and V_e. In vector analysis of a-c circuits it is useful to extend these ideas in the same way as is done for impedance. We shall define the admittance operator $\mathcal{Y}$ of an uncoupled two-terminal component not including a generator as having the power to transform the voltage vector $\mathbf{V}$ into the current vector $\mathbf{I}$:

$$\mathbf{I} = \mathcal{Y}\mathbf{V} \tag{11.92}$$

Since $\mathbf{I}$ and $\mathbf{V}$ are vectors of different magnitudes and generally are in different directions, the $\mathcal{Y}$ operator has the power to change the magnitude and the angle of the vector on which it acts. Since the current lags behind the potential difference by the phase angle ϕ, $\mathcal{Y}$ must rotate **V** through the angle

$$\theta = -\phi \tag{11.93}$$

The factor by which $\mathcal{Y}$ changes the magnitude of the current is the admittance Y of Eq. (11.90). A reciprocal relationship exists between the $\mathcal{Y}$ operator and the $\mathcal{Z}$ operator for a given component, such that the stretching factors and the angles are related by Eqs. (11.91) and (11.93), respectively.

The sum of two admittance operators $\mathcal{Y}_1$ and $\mathcal{Y}_2$ is defined to be that operator $\mathcal{Y}$ for which the vector equation

$$\mathcal{Y}\mathbf{V} = \mathcal{Y}_1\mathbf{V} + \mathcal{Y}_2\mathbf{V} \tag{11.94}$$

is identically true. Since admittance operators have the same nature as impedance operators, it follows by reasoning exactly like that of Sec. 11.5 that they may be represented by plane vectors and that they add like plane vectors. The vector corresponding to $\mathcal{Y}$ is

$$\mathbf{Y} \equiv (Y,\theta) = \left(\frac{1}{Z}, -\phi\right) \tag{11.95}$$

If **Y**, **Y**$_1$, and **Y**$_2$ are the vectors corresponding to $\mathcal{Y}$, $\mathcal{Y}_1$, and $\mathcal{Y}_2$ of Eq. (11.94), then these admittance vectors are related by the equation

$$\mathbf{Y} = \mathbf{Y}_1 + \mathbf{Y}_2 \tag{11.96}$$

The extension of Eq. (11.96) to the case of more than two admittance vectors is obvious.

The application of these ideas may be illustrated by considering two components connected in parallel. Let their vector currents and potential differences be $\mathbf{I}_1$, $\mathbf{V}_1$, $\mathbf{I}_2$, and $\mathbf{V}_2$, respectively. Then the parallel connection guarantees that the total current **I** is

$$\mathbf{I} = \mathbf{I}_1 + \mathbf{I}_2 \tag{11.97}$$

and that the two potential differences are the same. Writing the common potential difference vector as **V**, we have

$$\mathbf{V} = \mathbf{V}_1 = \mathbf{V}_2 \tag{11.98}$$

Now in terms of the separate admittance operators $\mathcal{Y}_1$, and $\mathcal{Y}_2$, and the admittance operator $\mathcal{Y}$ of the pair of components in parallel, we have as an expression of Eq. (11.97)

$$\mathcal{Y}\mathbf{V} = \mathcal{Y}_1\mathbf{V} + \mathcal{Y}_2\mathbf{V} \tag{11.99}$$

This is the same as Eq. (11.94), which means that the admittance operators of parallel components add to give the total admittance operator:

$$\mathcal{Y} = \mathcal{Y}_1 + \mathcal{Y}_2 \tag{11.100}$$

The addition may be performed by adding the corresponding vectors. As an example, consider the parallel combination of an ideal resistor R and an ideal capacitor C as shown in Fig. 11.4.   The impedance of the resistor is represented by the vector $(R,0)$; hence its admittance vector is

$$\mathbf{Y}_R = \left(\frac{1}{R}, 0\right) \tag{11.101}$$

The vector impedance of the condenser is $(1/C\omega, -\pi/2)$.   The admit-

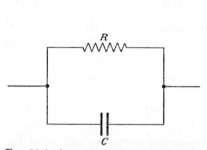

FIG. 11.4. An example of a parallel combination of components.

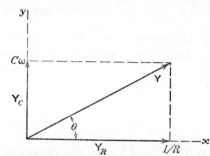

FIG. 11.5. Admittance vector diagram for the parallel combination of resistor and capacitor.

tance vector is therefore the one with the reciprocal magnitude and the negative angle

$$\mathbf{Y}_C = \left(C\omega, \frac{\pi}{2}\right) \tag{11.102}$$

We must now add these two vectors to find the total admittance vector

$$\mathbf{Y} = \mathbf{Y}_R + \mathbf{Y}_C \tag{11.103}$$

Figure 11.5 shows this addition graphically.   Conductance is here plotted along the x axis and capacitive susceptance along the positive y axis.   Evidently

$$\mathbf{Y} = \left(\sqrt{\frac{1}{R^2} + C^2\omega^2},\ \tan^{-1} RC\omega\right) \tag{11.104}$$

If desired, the impedance of this parallel combination may be obtained at once as the reciprocal vector

$$\mathbf{Z} = \left(\frac{1}{\sqrt{(1/R^2) + C^2\omega^2}},\ -\tan^{-1} RC\omega\right) \tag{11.105}$$

11.7. Complex Numbers. The Exponential Function of a Complex Variable. We have presented the vector method of analyzing a-c circuits. This method is very useful as an aid to visualization of a circuit problem, and leads to algebraic formulas for the circuit. The use of complex numbers and complex variables permits a still more elegant analytical solution which is so convenient as to be almost indispensable.

A complex number is one which can be written in the form

$$z = x + jy \tag{11.106}$$

where x and y are real numbers, and j is simply an abbreviation for $\sqrt{-1}$:

$$j \equiv \sqrt{-1} \tag{11.107}$$

It is the introduction of this quantity j which distinguishes complex analysis. The first and second terms of the right-hand member of Eq. (11.106) are called, respectively, the real and imaginary parts of the complex number z. The word imaginary is to be taken in a purely technical, not a mystical, sense. It will be noted that two data are required to specify a complex number. Two complex numbers are said to be equal if and only if both their real parts are equal and their imaginary parts are equal. Thus if

$$z_1 = x_1 + jy_1 \qquad z_2 = x_2 + jy_2 \tag{11.108}$$

then the equality

$$z_1 = z_2 \tag{11.109}$$

implies the two real equations

$$x_1 = x_2 \qquad y_1 = y_2 \tag{11.110}$$

Sums and products of complex numbers are defined according to the usual algebraic operations. Performing indicated operations and collecting terms, we obtain

$$z_1 + z_2 = (x_1 + x_2) + j(y_1 + y_2) \tag{11.111}$$
$$z_1 z_2 = (x_1 x_2 - y_1 y_2) + j(x_1 y_2 + y_1 x_2) \tag{11.112}$$

It can be seen that sums and products of complex numbers are complex numbers. Division can be defined as the inverse of multiplication. If

$$\frac{z_1}{z_2} = z \tag{11.113}$$

then z is such a number that

$$z_1 = z z_2 \tag{11.114}$$

On the assumption that z may be expressed in form (11.106), the two real equations implied by (11.114) may be solved simultaneously to yield

$$x = \frac{x_1 x_2 + y_1 y_2}{x_2^2 + y_2^2} \qquad y = \frac{y_1 x_2 - x_1 y_2}{x_2^2 + y_2^2} \tag{11.115}$$

Thus we may write

$$\frac{x_1 + jy_1}{x_2 + jy_2} = \frac{x_1x_2 + y_1y_2}{x_2{}^2 + y_2{}^2} + j\,\frac{y_1x_2 - x_1y_2}{x_2{}^2 + y_2{}^2} \tag{11.116}$$

The quotient of two complex numbers is therefore a complex number.

This process of expressing the quotient z_1/z_2 in standard form (11.106) may be done in another way which is useful in practice. We define the complex conjugate to $z_2 = x_2 + jy_2$ as

$$\bar{z}_2 \equiv x_2 - jy_2 \tag{11.117}$$

This is a complex number such that its product with z_2 is

$$z_2\bar{z}_2 = x_2{}^2 + y_2{}^2 \tag{11.118}$$

The process of reducing the quotient z_1/z_2 to standard form may now be performed by multiplying numerator and denominator by $\bar{z}_2$:

$$\frac{z_1}{z_2} = \frac{z_1\bar{z}_2}{z_2\bar{z}_2} = \frac{z_1\bar{z}_2}{x_2{}^2 + y_2{}^2} \tag{11.119}$$

The reader should show that this leads again to Eq. (11.116).

It is easy to see that the complex variable is an analytical representation of a two-dimensional vector, the vector from the origin to the point (x,y) in cartesian coordinates. Not only is there a one-to-one correspondence between complex numbers and plane vectors, but the law of addition is the same. Let us consider how to express a complex number in terms of the polar form of its corresponding vector, that is, in terms of the absolute value or magnitude and the angle of the vector. The vector from the origin to the point x, y has a magnitude

$$r = \sqrt{x^2 + y^2} \tag{11.120}$$

The trigonometric angle θ with the positive x axis is

$$\theta = \tan^{-1}\frac{y}{x} = \cos^{-1}\frac{x}{r} \tag{11.121}$$

The converse relations are

$$x = r\cos\theta \qquad y = r\sin\theta \tag{11.122}$$

Evidently then we may write a complex number in terms of r and θ as follows:

$$z = r(\cos\theta + j\sin\theta) \tag{11.123}$$

In the terminology of complex variable analysis, r may be called the modulus or absolute value of the complex number z, while θ may be called its angle.

It is important to examine the product and the quotient of two complex numbers as expressed in terms of modulus and angle. Let

$$z_1 = r_1(\cos \theta_1 + j \sin \theta_1) \qquad z_2 = r_2(\cos \theta_2 + j \sin \theta_2) \qquad (11.124)$$

A straightforward application of algebra and trigonometry shows that the product z is given by

$$z = r_1 r_2 [\cos (\theta_1 + \theta_2) + j \sin (\theta_1 + \theta_2)] \qquad (11.125)$$

Thus the modulus and angle of the product are

$$r = r_1 r_2 \qquad \theta = \theta_1 + \theta_2 \qquad (11.126)$$

For the quotient of two complex numbers we obtain the result by finding a number z which multiplied by z_2, according to the rule of Eq. (11.125), yields z_1:

$$z = \frac{z_1}{z_2} = \frac{r_1}{r_2} [\cos (\theta_1 - \theta_2) + j \sin (\theta_1 - \theta_2)] \qquad (11.127)$$

A very elegant notation for the polar form of a complex number makes use of the exponential function of a complex variable. We shall not discuss in detail how analytic functions of a complex variable are to be defined or evaluated; the reader is referred to standard mathematical texts on the subject. A particularly concise and clear treatment is found in "Analytic Functions of a Complex Variable" by D. R. Curtiss.[1] It is shown that the exponential function e^z is a complex number which may be written

$$e^z = e^x(\cos y + j \sin y) \qquad (11.128)$$

Equation (11.128) is easy to believe, since it implies that the function e^z obeys the basic functional relation for the exponential function, namely,

$$e^{z_1} e^{z_2} = e^{z_1 + z_2} \qquad (11.129)$$

for any two complex numbers z_1 and z_2. The reader may readily carry through this demonstration by using Eq. (11.125) in the process of multiplication. As a special case of Eq. (11.129), note that if $z = x + jy$, then

$$e^z = e^x e^{jy} \qquad (11.130)$$

It follows by comparison with Eq. (11.128) that

$$e^{jy} = \cos y + j \sin y \qquad (11.131)$$

If we now compare Eq. (11.123) with (11.131) we see that a complex number may be written in the form

$$z = re^{j\theta} \qquad (11.132)$$

[1] One of the Carus Mathematical Monographs published by the Mathematical Association of America.

This form makes it easy to remember the multiplication rule (11.125) and the division rule (11.127).

11.8. Complex Circuit Analysis. In Sec. 11.7 complex numbers were introduced as pure numbers without any mention of the possibility of their having physical dimensions. Nothing is altered in that section, however, if complex quantities are introduced having any desired physical dimensions, such as those of current or potential difference; only the argument of a transcendental function (trigonometric or exponential) must always be dimensionless. Since all terms of a sum must have like dimensions, the real and imaginary parts of a complex quantity must have like dimensions which will also be those of the absolute value of the quantity. We shall now introduce complex current, potential difference, emf, and impedance and admittance, and proceed to restate the a-c circuit theorems of the earlier sections of the chapter in these terms.

Fixed vectors have been introduced to correspond to a-c variables. We may now use constant complex quantities to represent these fixed vectors, and hence in their turn to correspond to a-c variables. Thus if a current vector is (I_e, ψ), I_e being the effective value of its magnitude and ψ its phase angle relative to some arbitrarily chosen standard of phase, the complex effective current will be defined as the quantity $\mathbf{I}$:

$$\mathbf{I} \equiv I_e e^{j\psi} = I_e(\cos \psi + j \sin \psi) \tag{11.133}$$

There seems no need of distinguishing the complex current $\mathbf{I}$ from the corresponding vector $\mathbf{I}$ by adopting a different symbol, for the context should make it clear which meaning of the symbol is meant. Equations with simple sums of current will be identical whether the vectors or complex quantities are intended, since addition of the complex quantities corresponds to addition of the vectors. Where products occur, a simple product of complex quantities has no multiplication symbol and thus cannot be confused with either type of vector multiplication. Division is not defined for vectors; therefore any equation involving division must be in terms of complex quantities.

It will be noted that the effective value of current was used in Eq. (11.133). This is an arbitrary matter, for a complex peak current could just as well be used in a circuit analysis. One must be consistent, however, in using either peak or effective values in a given analysis. The effective values are customary besides being simpler for the computation of power.

Complex effective potential difference and emf will be defined in the same way as complex effective current:

$$\mathbf{V} \equiv V_e e^{j\phi} = V_e(\cos \phi + j \sin \phi) \tag{11.134}$$
$$\boldsymbol{\mathcal{E}} \equiv \mathcal{E}_e e^{j\phi'} = \mathcal{E}_e(\cos \phi' + j \sin \phi') \tag{11.135}$$

where V_e and $\mathcal{E}_e$ are effective magnitudes and ϕ and ϕ' are phase angles. Furthermore, we shall introduce the complex impedance and complex admittance to correspond to the vector impedance and vector admittance:

$$\mathbf{Z} \equiv Ze^{j\phi} = Z(\cos\phi + j\sin\phi) \tag{11.136}$$
$$\mathbf{Y} \equiv Ye^{j\theta} = Y(\cos\theta + j\sin\theta) \tag{11.137}$$

where Z and Y are impedance and admittance, respectively, and ϕ and θ are the angles of rotation. Since $Y = 1/Z$ and $\theta = -\phi$ for a given circuit component, it follows that

$$\mathbf{Y} = \frac{1}{\mathbf{Z}} \tag{11.138}$$

Let us now survey what can be done with these complex quantities. First, they may be added according to the rules of complex algebra, and the sum will correspond to the sum of their separately corresponding vectors. This vector sum in turn corresponds to the sum of the corresponding a-c variables. Therefore the addition of a-c variables is represented by addition of the corresponding complex quantities. For example, Kirchhoff's first law for the instantaneous currents in an a-c network now implies a similar equation in the complex effective currents:

$$\sum_i \mathbf{I}_i = 0 \tag{11.139}$$

for all complex currents $\mathbf{I}_i$ flowing toward a branch point. Similarly, Kirchhoff's second law may be written for the complex effective potential differences $\mathbf{V}_k$ and total emf $\mathcal{E}$ of any closed loop of a network:

$$\sum_k \mathbf{V}_k = \mathcal{E} \tag{11.140}$$

Next, let us notice the remarkable fact that the complex effective potential difference and the complex effective current of any uncoupled circuit component not including a generator are related by the complex impedance and complex admittance as follows:

$$\mathbf{V} = \mathbf{Z}\mathbf{I} \tag{11.141}$$
$$\mathbf{I} = \mathbf{Y}\mathbf{V} \tag{11.142}$$

These relations may be written also in terms of complex division:

$$\mathbf{V} = \frac{\mathbf{I}}{\mathbf{Y}} \qquad \mathbf{I} = \frac{\mathbf{V}}{\mathbf{Z}} \tag{11.143}$$

Equations (11.141) and (11.142) follow immediately from the multiplication law (11.125) of Sec. 11.7 and the discussion of Secs. 11.5 and 11.6. The operation of complex multiplication or division produces exactly the stretching and rotation required to transform a complex current into a potential difference or conversely.

We have now in Eqs. (11.139), (11.140), and (11.141) or (11.142) a sufficient set of relations to solve a linear a-c network not having inductive coupling. This method of solution corresponds to the direct use of Kirchhoff's laws in treating a d-c circuit. Inductive coupling may readily be taken into account by drawing the induced emfs as generators in the circuit, but we shall defer discussion of this point.

Simple circuits involving series and parallel connections of uncoupled components not containing generators are easily handled by the complex analysis. If components are in series, their impedance vectors have been shown to add to yield the total vector impedance. The corresponding complex impedances must therefore be similarly related:

$$\mathbf{Z} = \mathbf{Z}_1 + \mathbf{Z}_2 + \cdots \tag{11.144}$$

Likewise, the complex admittances of components in parallel add to produce the total complex admittance:

$$\mathbf{Y} = \mathbf{Y}_1 + \mathbf{Y}_2 + \cdots \tag{11.145}$$

Because of the reciprocal relationship between complex impedance and complex admittance, Eq. (11.145) may be written as

$$\frac{1}{\mathbf{Z}} = \frac{1}{\mathbf{Z}_1} + \frac{1}{\mathbf{Z}_2} + \cdots \tag{11.146}$$

For only two components, we may solve for $\mathbf{Z}$ to obtain the equation

$$\mathbf{Z} = \frac{\mathbf{Z}_1 \mathbf{Z}_2}{\mathbf{Z}_1 + \mathbf{Z}_2} \tag{11.147}$$

which is formally the same as the real number equation for a pair of resistors in parallel.

Let us write the complex impedances for ideal circuit components. Referring to Eqs. (11.82) to (11.84), Sec. 11.5, and comparing Eq. (11.136), we see that these are

$$\mathbf{Z}_R = R \tag{11.148}$$

for a resistor,

$$\mathbf{Z}_L = j\omega L = jX_L \tag{11.149}$$

for an inductor, and

$$\mathbf{Z}_C = \frac{-j}{\omega C} = -jX_C \tag{11.150}$$

for a capacitor. We noted in Sec. 11.5 that a general uncoupled linear component not including a generator may be considered as the series combination of a pure resistance and pure reactance and that this corresponds to the resolution of the impedance vector into its rectangular components along the x and y axes. A corresponding statement is now that a general complex impedance can be written as the sum of a real term and an imaginary term which are to be called resistance and complex reactance, respectively,

$$\mathbf{Z} = R + jX \qquad (11.151)$$

We write similar equations for admittances:

$$\mathbf{Y}_R = \frac{1}{R} \equiv G \qquad (11.152)$$

for a resistor,

$$\mathbf{Y}_L = \frac{1}{jL\omega} = \frac{-j}{L\omega} = \frac{-j}{X_L} \equiv -jB_L \qquad (11.153)$$

for an inductor, and

$$\mathbf{Y}_C = \frac{1}{-j/C\omega} = jC\omega = \frac{j}{X_C} \equiv jB_C \qquad (11.154)$$

for a capacitor. In general

$$\mathbf{Y} = G - jB \qquad (11.155)$$

The symbols G and B have been used for conductance and susceptance, respectively. The negative sign in Eq. (11.155) follows an arbitrary convention so that B, like X in Eq. (11.151), will have a positive sign for an inductor.

The following sections will give many applications of the material of this section, for from now on we shall use the complex analysis.

11.9. Resonance. Consider a series connection of inductance, capacitance and resistance. The complex impedance of the combination is

$$\mathbf{Z}_s = R + j\left(L\omega - \frac{1}{C\omega}\right) \qquad (11.156)$$

The phase angle of this complex impedance is given by

$$\phi_s = \tan^{-1}\left[\frac{L\omega - (1/C\omega)}{R}\right] \qquad (11.157)$$

It will be noted that it is possible for the circuit to have a zero phase angle. This occurs when L, C, and ω are related by

$$\omega = \omega_s = \frac{1}{\sqrt{LC}} \qquad (11.158)$$

Equation (11.158) is called the resonance condition for the series combination. In general, a two-terminal network is said to exhibit the phenomenon of resonance if the angle of its complex or vector impedance is a function of frequency which passes through zero at least once. The frequency or frequencies at which this occurs are the resonant frequencies of the network. Evidently the angle θ of the complex admittance may equally well be used as a criterion for resonance. Figure 11.6 illustrates the relation (11.157) between ϕ_s and ω for the series circuit.

At resonance, the series combination has a minimum impedance whose value is just R. The reader may verify this by inspection of the absolute value of the complex impedance:

$$Z_s = \sqrt{R^2 + \left(L\omega - \frac{1}{C\omega}\right)^2} \qquad (11.159)$$

Suppose an a-c generator of constant emf ε and variable frequency is connected across the series combination. The current I and hence the power dissipation I^2R then will be maximum at the resonant frequency.

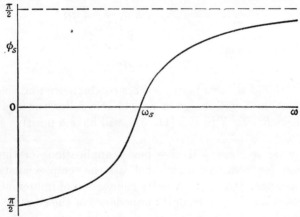

FIG. 11.6. Dependence of phase angle on frequency for a series L-C-R circuit.

Another interesting consideration in connection with series resonance is the potential difference across parts of the circuit. In laboratory practice, the resistance may be almost wholly associated with the inductor, unless an external resistor is used in the network. Let us therefore investigate the potential difference V_1 across the condenser and the potential difference V_2 across the combination of the inductor and resistor, expressing these as fractions of the total potential difference V. The current is common; thus the potential differences are proportional to the impedances. For either rms or peak values, the ratios are

$$\frac{V_1}{V} = \frac{1/C\omega}{\sqrt{R^2 + [L\omega - (1/C\omega)]^2}} \qquad (11.160)$$

$$\frac{V_2}{V} = \frac{\sqrt{R^2 + L^2\omega^2}}{\sqrt{R^2 + [L\omega - (1/C\omega)]^2}} \qquad (11.161)$$

These ratios do not have their maxima precisely at the resonant frequency, but at least their denominators have their minima there so that we should expect fairly large values of the ratios at resonance. At resonance we obtain

$$\left(\frac{V_1}{V}\right)_{res} = \frac{1}{RC\omega_s} = \sqrt{\frac{L}{R^2C}} \tag{11.162}$$

$$\left(\frac{V_2}{V}\right)_{res} = \sqrt{1 + \frac{L^2\omega_s^2}{R^2}} = \sqrt{1 + \frac{L}{R^2C}} \tag{11.163}$$

These ratios may both be much greater than unity, and $(V_2/V)_{res}$ must be at least somewhat greater than unity. If the reader is surprised to find the parts of the potential difference greater than the whole, he may find it profitable to construct the vector diagram for the potential differences of the network.

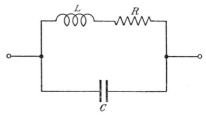

FIG. 11.7. A circuit exhibiting parallel resonance.

The parallel network of Fig. 11.7 exhibits resonance, but its properties are quite different from those of the series network. The complex admittance between the two terminals is readily found to be

$$\mathbf{Y}_p = \frac{R + j[\omega C(R^2 + L^2\omega^2) - L\omega]}{R^2 + L^2\omega^2} \tag{11.164}$$

The phase angle of $\mathbf{Y}_p$ will vanish when and only when the imaginary part of $\mathbf{Y}_p$ is zero. Therefore the condition for resonance is

$$\omega C(R^2 + L^2\omega^2) - L\omega = 0 \tag{11.165}$$

Now we shall not allow the root $\omega = 0$ as a resonance condition, for ω is never negative and hence the phase angle cannot be said to pass through zero at this point. This leaves only one resonant frequency:

$$\omega_p = \sqrt{\frac{1}{LC} - \frac{R^2}{L^2}} \tag{11.166}$$

It will be noticed that if R is appreciable, ω_p is sensibly different from ω_s of Eq. (11.158).

The admittance of the parallel network is relatively small at the resonant frequency, for the absolute value of the numerator of Eq. (11.164) has a minimum there. The exact problem of minimizing the admittance with respect to frequency is rather complicated algebraically. The results are not worth quoting except to remark that the frequency yielding a minimum Y_p approaches the same limit as the resonant frequency ω_p when the resistance R approaches zero. At the resonant frequency ω_p, the admittance of the parallel circuit becomes

$$Y_p = \frac{R}{R^2 + L^2\omega_p{}^2} \tag{11.167}$$

which reduces upon substitution of Eq. (11.166) to

$$Y_p = \frac{RC}{L} \tag{11.168}$$

The impedance at resonance is therefore

$$Z_p = \frac{L}{RC} \tag{11.169}$$

It is interesting to note that this impedance varies inversely as the resistance R. Furthermore, if R is small, the impedance Z_p may be much greater than the impedances

$$Z_1 = \frac{1}{C\omega} \tag{11.170}$$

and

$$Z_2 = \sqrt{R^2 + L^2\omega^2} \tag{11.171}$$

of the two branches of the network. This means that the total current entering the network may be much less than the separate currents of the two branches. A vector diagram for the currents makes it clear why this may be so, but the construction is left to the reader.

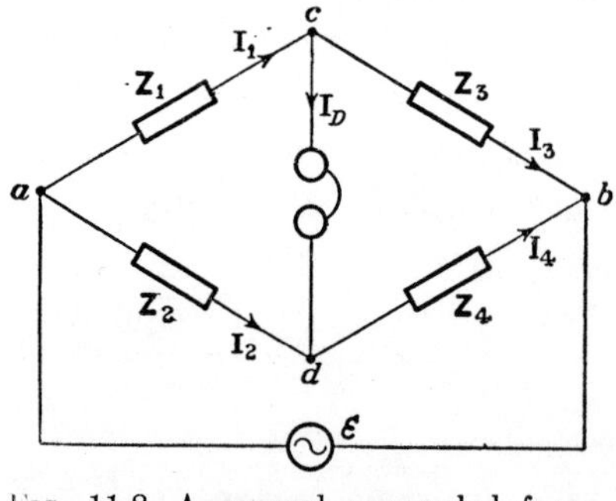

Fig. 11.8. A general uncoupled four-impedance bridge.

11.10. A-C Bridges without Coupling. The familiar Wheatstone bridge for direct current can be generalized into the four-impedance a-c bridge of Fig. 11.8. The bridge current is supplied by an a-c generator whose emf $\mathcal{E}$ is sinusoidal with a frequency $\omega/2\pi$. The detector is drawn as a pair of headphones, but may be any indicating device of good sensitivity. The condition for no current I_D in the detector, assuming no generator to be included in the detector, may be obtained at once by the use of Kirchhoff's laws in complex form. If $I_D = 0$, then the first law yields

$$I_1 = I_3 \tag{11.172}$$
$$I_2 = I_4 \tag{11.173}$$

Likewise, $I_D = 0$ and absence of emf in the detector imply that the potential difference across the detector is zero. Kirchhoff's second law for loops acd and cbd then reads

$$I_1Z_1 - I_2Z_2 = 0 \qquad (11.174)$$
$$I_3Z_3 - I_4Z_4 = 0 \qquad (11.175)$$

Combination of Eqs. (11.172) to (11.175) gives the complex balance condition

$$Z_1Z_4 = Z_2Z_3 \qquad (11.176)$$

Sometimes it may be more convenient to work with complex admittances, in which case

$$Y_1Y_4 = Y_2Y_3 \qquad (11.177)$$

the Y's being the reciprocals of the corresponding Z's. Forms of these equations involving both impedances and admittances may be useful also.

The formal equivalence of this complex analysis with the solution of a d-c bridge must not be allowed to conceal the fact that the a-c case is essentially more complicated than the d-c case as well as being much richer in variety and interest. The new features introduced by the a-c bridge are first the variety of impedance components which may be used, and second that the balance condition, being complex, implies

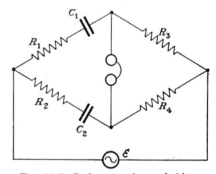

FIG. 11.9. Series-capacitance bridge.

two real equations which must be satisfied simultaneously. Obtaining balance is thus a two-dimensional sort of adjustment and two of the bridge parameters must be variable. It will be worth while to examine several four-impedance bridges in order to illustrate two general classifications of bridge types. It is not our concern to give a complete list of the bridges used in practice. Figure 11.9 shows a simple series-capacitance bridge. The impedance of branch 1 is

$$Z_1 = R_1 - \frac{j}{\omega C_1} \qquad (11.178)$$

Z_2 has a similar form, while Z_3 and Z_4 are simply R_3 and R_4, respectively. The balance condition (11.176) then implies the two real equations

$$R_1R_4 = R_2R_3$$
$$C_2R_4 = C_1R_3 \qquad (11.179)$$

It is to be noted first that these real balance equations do not contain ω, that is, the balance is independent of frequency so long as the resistance and capacitance values are independent of frequency. A bridge for which this is true may be operated from a generator having any wave-form whatever, or even by transient currents obtained from switching of a d-c source of emf. Another point of interest is to consider what bridge parameters are to be varied in order to obtain balance. It would be possible to satisfy Eqs. (11.179) by adjustment of R_1 and R_3, given the other parameters as constant, but under these conditions the process of balancing the bridge may be tedious since a change of R_3 affects both the equations. In this case the two balance conditions are dependent upon one another. The bridge is much more convenient to use if one of the condensers, say C_2, is variable and if the other adjustment is R_1 or R_2. It is then possible to satisfy Eqs. (11.179), so that an adjustment made to improve the approximation to either one of these equations does not affect the approximation to the other. In this case the balance conditions are mutually independent.

A critical reader may wonder whether the discussion of mutual dependence of the balance conditions is physically relevant. He might remark that instead of the balance equations (11.179) we may write a mathematically equivalent pair of equations

$$C_2 R_2 = C_1 R_1$$
$$C_2 R_4 = C_1 R_3 \qquad (11.180)$$

It would then seem as if the above discussion could be reversed, and that it would be preferable to balance the bridge by variation of R_1 and R_3 rather than by variation of R_2 and C_2.

To get at the root of the matter, it is necessary to solve the unbalanced bridge and examine the approach to balance. This is not very difficult for the usual case where the generator impedance is negligible. The detector current comes out in the form

$$\mathbf{I} = \frac{(\mathbf{Z}_1 \mathbf{Z}_4 - \mathbf{Z}_2 \mathbf{Z}_3)\boldsymbol{\mathcal{E}}}{\mathbf{D}} \qquad (11.181)$$

where $\mathbf{D}$ is a complex quantity depending on the bridge impedances and the detector impedance. When balance is already rather closely approached, the further changes to be made in the bridge parameters will be so small as to have a negligible percentage effect upon the magnitude or phase of the denominator $\mathbf{D}$. The complex detector current is therefore proportional to the complex quantity

$$\mathbf{Z}_1 \mathbf{Z}_4 - \mathbf{Z}_2 \mathbf{Z}_3 \equiv r + js \qquad (11.182)$$

The final steps of the balancing process then involve reducing the complex quantity (11.182) to zero. Most detectors are not phase sensitive; therefore this is usually done by observation of the absolute value

$\sqrt{r^2 + s^2}$.   The process of reducing $\sqrt{r^2 + s^2}$ to zero is quickly done if r and s can be independently adjusted, but otherwise in general it will proceed by successive approximations.

Let us apply this theory to the series-resistance condenser bridge of Fig. 11.9.   Here the quantities r and s are

$$r = R_1R_4 - R_2R_3$$
$$s = \frac{1}{\omega}\left(\frac{R_3}{C_2} - \frac{R_4}{C_1}\right) \tag{11.183}$$

Evidently if R_2 and C_2 are variable, r and s may be independently reduced to zero so the balancing is quick.   On the other hand if it is R_1 and R_3

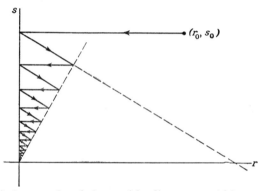

FIG. 11.10.   Typical approach to balance with adjustments which are not independent.

which are to be varied, the situation is more complex; for variation of R_1 affects r only, while variation of R_3 affects both r and s.   In fact, variation of R_3 causes the point in the complex plane which represents the quantity $(r + js)$ to move along a straight line whose slope is

$$\frac{ds}{dr} = \frac{\partial s/\partial R_3}{\partial r/\partial R_3} = -\frac{1}{\omega C_2 R_2} \tag{11.184}$$

The process of minimizing $\sqrt{r^2 + s^2}$ by successive adjustments of R_1 and R_3, starting at an arbitrary point (r_0, s_0) of the complex plane, proceeds by a zigzag path of successive approximations as shown in Fig. 11.10.

As an important example of a frequency dependent balance, consider the Wien bridge shown in Fig. 11.11.   To calculate the complex balance condition, it is convenient to rewrite Eq. (11.176) in the form

$$Z_1Z_4Y_3 = Z_2 \tag{11.185}$$

since branch 3 involves a parallel connection.   Equation (11.185) leads quickly to the real conditions

$$\frac{R_1}{R_3} + \frac{C_3}{C_1} = \frac{R_2}{R_4}$$
$$\omega^2 C_1 C_3 R_1 R_3 = 1 \tag{11.186}$$

Frequency dependence is not necessarily undesirable. The Wien bridge, for example, is useful for precise determination of capacitance in terms of frequency and resistance, for accurate standards of these two latter quantities are readily available. Another use of a frequency-dependent bridge is for the measurement of frequency.

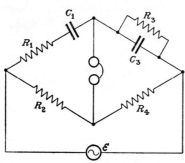

FIG. 11.11. Wien bridge.

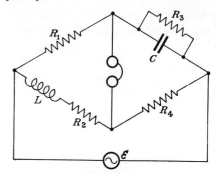

FIG. 11.12. Maxwell bridge.

As a last illustration of four-impedance bridges, we show in Fig. 11.12 the Maxwell bridge. This is an example of a bridge containing both inductance and capacitance. The complex balance condition in form (11.185) is very convenient again for this bridge, and the resulting pair of real equations is

$$R_2 = \frac{R_1 R_4}{R_3}$$
$$L = R_1 R_4 C \tag{11.187}$$

Clearly this bridge is frequency-independent. It would be convenient to have C and R_3 as variable elements if L and R_2 are the unknowns to be measured.

11.11. Inductive Coupling in Complex Analysis. General Theorems.
The instantaneous potential difference across an inductor of self-inductance L which is coupled by a mutual inductance M to a second inductor is given by Eq. (10.3), Sec. 10.1,

$$V_{LM} = L\frac{dI}{dt} \pm M\frac{dI'}{dt} \tag{11.188}$$

Here I is the current in the inductor itself while I' is that in the second inductor. The positive sign is to be taken if the currents I and I' have mutually consistent positive conventions. In what follows we shall assume consistent conventions and omit the lower sign. There is also a conventional relation between positive senses of V_{LM} and I, according to which positive current flows through the component from higher to lower potential when V_{LM} is also positive.

Now suppose we are dealing with the steady condition in an a-c network and that the currents are sinusoidal with a common frequency $\omega/2\pi$. Let

$$I = I_0 \sin (\omega t + \alpha) \tag{11.189}$$
$$I' = I'_0 \sin (\omega t + \alpha') \tag{11.190}$$

Substitution of Eqs. (11.189) and (11.190) in Eq. (11.188) then leads to

$$V_{LM} = I_0 L\omega \sin \left(\omega t + \alpha + \frac{\pi}{2} \right) + I'_0 M\omega \sin \left(\omega t + \alpha' + \frac{\pi}{2} \right) \tag{11.191}$$

Thus V_{LM} is the resultant of two alternating quantities, one of which depends on I and leads I by $\pi/2$, while the other depends on I' and leads I' by $\pi/2$. In vector notation, we may write

$$\mathbf{V}_{LM} = \mathcal{Z}_L\mathbf{I} + \mathcal{Z}_M\mathbf{I}' \tag{11.192}$$

Here, $\mathbf{V}_{LM}$, $\mathbf{I}$, and $\mathbf{I}'$ are the vectors corresponding to the alternating potential difference and currents, respectively. $\mathcal{Z}_L$ and $\mathcal{Z}_M$ are operators whose stretching factors are $L\omega$ and $M\omega$, respectively, and whose rotation angles are both $\pi/2$. Corresponding to the operators we have impedance vectors

$$\mathbf{Z}_L = \left(L\omega, \frac{\pi}{2} \right) \tag{11.193}$$

$$\mathbf{Z}_M = \left(M\omega, \frac{\pi}{2} \right) \tag{11.194}$$

The operator $\mathcal{Z}_M$ and its associated vector $\mathbf{Z}_M$ are to be called the transfer impedance operator and vector for the pair of components which are inductively coupled. The quantity $M\omega$ may be called the transfer impedance which couples the two components. The operator $\mathcal{Z}_L$ and its vector $\mathbf{Z}_L$ are the ordinary impedance operator and vector of a self-inductor.

Following the procedure of Sec. 11.8, we may rewrite the description of the coupled inductor in a complex form:

$$\mathbf{V}_{LM} = \mathbf{Z}_L\mathbf{I} + \mathbf{Z}_M\mathbf{I}' \tag{11.195}$$

In Eq. (11.195) it is understood that $\mathbf{V}$, $\mathbf{I}$, and $\mathbf{I}'$ are the complex (and usually effective) potential difference and currents, while the complex impedance and complex transfer impedance are, respectively,

$$\mathbf{Z}_L = L\omega e^{j\pi/2} = jL\omega \tag{11.196}$$
$$\mathbf{Z}_M = M\omega e^{j\pi/2} = jM\omega \tag{11.197}$$

An example of the application of these equations will be found in the elementary transformer theory of Sec. 11.13.

It will be evident to the reader how to generalize the above equations in case the inductor is coupled by different mutual inductances to more than one other inductor. Each other coupled inductor simply contributes its term to the potential difference across the component in question, so that

$$\mathbf{V}_{LM} = \mathbf{Z}_L \mathbf{I} + \sum_k \mathbf{Z}_{Mk} \mathbf{I}_k \qquad (11.198)$$

where $\mathbf{Z}_{Mk}$ are the complex transfer impedances to other coils in which the complex currents are respectively $\mathbf{I}_k$.

It is worth noting that inductive coupling may be introduced into the circuit equations from a different point of view. It will be seen from Eq. (11.195) that $\mathbf{V}_{LM}$ may exist even when $\mathbf{I} = 0$, which may be accounted for by considering the coupled component to have a complex alternating emf $\mathcal{E}_M$. The sign convention for emf being opposite to that for potential difference in our work, we should then write in place of Eq. (11.195)

$$\mathbf{V}_{LM} = \mathbf{Z}_L \mathbf{I} - \mathcal{E}_M \qquad (11.199)$$

where the induced emf is

$$\mathcal{E}_M = -\mathbf{Z}_M \mathbf{I}' = -jM\omega \mathbf{I}' \qquad (11.200)$$

In writing the complex Kirchhoff equations for a network, we may use Eq. (11.195) to express the potential difference across the coupled component. On the other hand, we may take only the term with the self-impedance

$$\mathbf{V}_L = \mathbf{Z}_L \mathbf{I} \qquad (11.201)$$

provided we add the emf of Eq. (11.200) to the emfs in writing Kirchhoff's second law for any loops containing the inductor in question. These two procedures are mathematically identical, as appears at once from the form of the Kirchhoff second law:

$$\sum_k \mathbf{V}_k = \sum_l \mathcal{E}_l \qquad \text{any loop} \qquad (11.202)$$

Equation (11.202) is the same as (11.140), Sec. 11.8, except that the total emf $\mathcal{E}$ of the loop has been written as a sum of all the separate emfs which the loop may contain.

Equation (11.199) shows that a coupled inductor may be considered as a series combination of an ideal generator having emf $\mathcal{E}_M$ and an inductive impedance $\mathbf{Z}_L$. By an ideal generator, we mean one maintaining a potential difference numerically equal to its emf regardless of the current through it. It will be useful to define a general class of circuit components which we may call linear generators, of which the coupled inductor is a particular case. A linear generator will be defined as a circuit component whose complex potential difference has the form

$$V = Z_0 I - \mathcal{E}_0 \qquad (11.203)$$

where Z_0 and $\mathcal{E}_0$ are independent of the current I and it is understood that $\mathcal{E}_0$ is not zero. The quantity Z_0 is to be called the complex internal impedance of the generator, and $\mathcal{E}_0$ is the complex emf. The linear generator may be only an approximation to an actual generator, but it is usually a useful approximation.

Evidently we could use Eq. (11.203) to describe a general single-valued relationship between V and I if the restriction on the constancy of Z_0 were removed. A circuit component for which Z_0 varies with I may be called a nonlinear generator. In this case, it is a purely arbitrary matter to define the emf $\mathcal{E}_0$ of the generator as numerically equal to its open-circuit voltage and then to consider the emf to be independent of the current; but this convention is as good as any. The reader is referred to Sec. 5.10 for further discussion of this point in the d-c case. It should be noted, however, that different sign conventions are used there.

At this point it may be well to take stock of what we have covered in a-c circuit theory. Networks of linear impedances and generators have been brought under an analysis formally like the Kirchhoff laws of d-c networks, by means of the powerful tool of the complex variable. The complex equations of an a-c network are only more involved than the real equations of a similar d-c network in the possible addition of terms describing inductive coupling between branches. They retain the same form of simultaneous linear equations in the currents and emfs, the coefficients being impedances. Naturally the algebraic details of a final solution are more complicated in the a-c case, but only because of the greater variety of components to be considered and because of the manipulations required to give answers in one of the standard forms for complex quantities.

A number of elegant and useful theorems follow as consequences of Kirchhoff's laws. Some of these theorems for d-c circuits were developed in the text and problems of Chap. 6. Examples are the use of loop currents, Thévenin's theorem, and the $T - \Pi$ transformation. These results are readily generalized to a-c circuits, their proofs being essentially unchanged. The reader may feel free to use these theorems of Chap. 6, expressing them of course in complex notation. An exception is the power-transfer theorem, which requires a slight revision. The maximum power which can be drawn into a load from two terminals of a linear network is obtained when the load impedance is the complex conjugate of the internal impedance of the network. The general question of how to express average power in terms of complex variables requires careful consideration. The reader is referred in this connection to the problems for Chap. 11.

11.12. Practical Circuit Components. Frequency Dependence. Ideal resistors, inductors, and condensers are abstractions. The phase angle of actual inductors and condensers is never exactly $\pm\pi/2$, and actual resistors may deviate from the ideal of a zero phase angle. Furthermore, all the characteristics of circuit components are subject to variation with frequency. We shall consider some of these matters briefly under separate headings.

Resistors. The a-c resistance of a conductor is not in general the same as its d-c resistance but is larger and increases with frequency. This effect is largely the result of self-induced emfs which are different for different paths in the conductor. These emfs increase with frequency, since by Faraday's law they depend on the rate of change of the magnetic flux; and they are least for conducting paths linked by the least flux. The result is that the current density distribution is altered from its d-c pattern; and this in turn implies an increase of resistance, for the d-c current distribution is such as to minimize resistance. In isolated wires, the a-c current density is greatest at the surface of the wire, giving rise to the term "skin effect," while in coils the effect may be even larger and is more complex because of the magnetic field of the entire coil.

Skin effect may also be related to the fact that high-frequency electromagnetic waves are strongly absorbed in a good conductor. Their amplitude falls to $1/2.7 \ldots$ in a distance which we may call the penetration depth s:

$$s = \sqrt{\frac{2}{\mu g \omega}} \tag{11.204}$$

where μ is the permeability and g the conductivity of the material, while $\omega/2\pi$ is the frequency. Now if the conductor is a solid wire of circular cross section, we may expect a large increase in resistance when the penetration depth becomes smaller than the radius of the wire. Thus skin effect is more pronounced the larger the radius of the solid conductor; and for this reason very fine wire is appropriate in resistors for use at high frequency.

All resistors involve capacitance which may be considered to shunt them. This arises partly from capacitance between terminals and leads, and in wire-wound resistors results also from proximity of turns to each

other.   In addition, a wire-wound resistance possesses a certain inductance.   Its equivalent circuit will be that of Fig. 11.13.   The inductance
can be reduced to a small value by suitable methods of winding.   Often
the windings of high-grade resistors are made on flat insulating cards
for this purpose.   The combined effect of the inductance and capacitance
may make the phase angle of the resistor either positive or negative.
If the inductive reactance of L is small compared with the resistance R,
then the phase angle is approximately

$$\phi = \tan^{-1} \frac{\omega(L - CR^2)}{R} \tag{11.205}$$

Note that if L, C, and R bear the proper relation, a zero phase angle can
be maintained as ω varies.   Compare Eqs. (11.164) and (11.165).

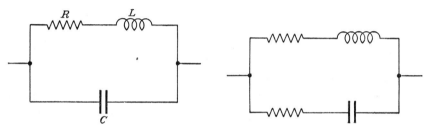

Fig. 11.13. Representation of an actual   Fig. 11.14. Representation of an actual
resistor.   inductor.

Inductors.   An inductor may be fairly accurately represented by the
same equivalent circuit shown in Fig. 11.13 for a resistor, although it is
perhaps more illuminating to indicate as in Fig. 11.14 that the distributed
capacitance frequently has high loss.   The distributed capacitance arises
between each turn of the coil and every other turn, as well as between
the coil and its surroundings.   Poor dielectric quality of the wire insulation and coil form materials may then contribute greatly to the effective
resistance of the coil, which is considered to be the value of R in the
equivalent circuit of Fig. 11.13.   The resistance R is also due to the d-c
resistance of the wire, aggravated by the large skin effect which is characteristic of coils.   For iron-core coils, R is further increased by the
hysteresis loss in the core; and unless the core is subdivided into laminae
or grains, eddy currents in the core are an important cause of a-c resistance.   Evidently, R will in general be frequency-dependent, and will
increase with increasing frequency.   If the reactance of the capacitance C
is large compared with that of the inductance L, and if the latter reactance
is larger than the resistance R, then the equivalent circuit of Fig. 11.13
may be replaced for a given frequency by that of Fig. 11.15 in which the

apparent inductance and resistance are approximately[1]

$$L_a \doteq \frac{L}{1 - \omega^2 LC} \tag{11.206}$$

$$R_a \doteq \frac{R}{(1 - \omega^2 LC)^2} \tag{11.207}$$

These approximate formulas are limited in their validity to frequencies much below the resonant frequency of the circuit of Fig. 11.13. Evidently at sufficiently high frequencies, that is, above the resonant frequency, a coil may behave like a capacitor rather than an inductor.

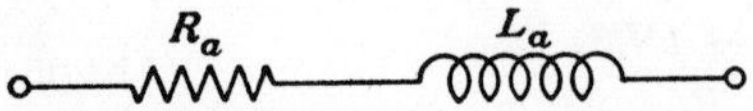

FIG. 11.15. Simplified representation of an inductor at a given frequency.

A useful index of the merit of an inductor for use in a tuned circuit is the Q value, the ratio of apparent reactance to resistance:

$$Q \equiv \frac{X_a}{R_a} = \frac{L_a \omega}{R_a} \tag{11.208}$$

The larger the Q, the sharper is the resonance obtained when the coil is used with a condenser in a tuned circuit. Since R_a increases with ω, Q may vary rather slowly with ω. Practical tuning coils in ordinary radio receivers often have Q values of several hundred.

Condensers. Good air condensers approach rather closely to ideal capacitors. For this reason, it is usual to speak of the phase defect of a condenser rather than its phase angle. The phase defect δ is the difference between the phase angle ϕ and the ideal value of $-\pi/2$ radians:

$$\delta \equiv \phi - \left(-\frac{\pi}{2} \right) = \phi + \frac{\pi}{2} \tag{11.209}$$

Other names for δ are loss angle and phase difference. The power factor of the condenser bears a simple relation to δ:

$$PF \equiv \cos \phi = \sin \delta \tag{11.210}$$

This means that when δ is very small, as is frequently the case, its numerical value is very nearly equal to the power factor:

$$PF \doteq \delta \qquad \text{when } \delta \ll 1 \tag{11.211}$$

The a-c losses in a condenser at a given frequency may be taken into account by representing the condenser either as a series combination of ideal capacitance C_s and resistance R_s or as a parallel combination of ideal components C_p and R_p. These equivalent circuits are shown in Figs.

[1] See *Natl. Bur. Standards (U.S.) Cir.* 74, p. 133, 1936.

11.16 and 11.17. Investigation of the phase angle of the equivalent circuits shows that the phase difference δ is given by

$$\tan \delta = \omega C_s R_s \qquad (11.212)$$

or by

$$\cot \delta = \omega C_p R_p \qquad (11.213)$$

Equating the real part of the complex impedances of the two combinations, we obtain the crossover relation

$$R_s = R_p \sin^2 \delta \qquad (11.214)$$

Likewise, by equating the imaginary parts of the two susceptances, we find that

$$C_p = C_s \cos^2 \delta \qquad (11.215)$$

It should be noted that when δ is a small angle, C_p and C_s are nearly the same, while R_p and R_s are very different.

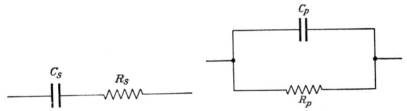

FIG. 11.16. Series-resistance representation of a capacitor.

FIG. 11.17. Parallel-resistance representation of a capacitor.

All condensers suffer from leakage of charge between their electrodes, both through the volume and over the surface of the dielectric material; therefore there is a high resistance in parallel with the electrodes. The electrodes themselves contribute a series resistance, which may be quite small but is certainly appreciable at high frequencies. An important phenomenon observed in condensers having solid or liquid dielectrics is dielectric absorption. Dielectric absorption produces a slow increase of the charge taken up by a condenser when its electrodes are held at a constant d-c potential difference. If the electrodes are then short-circuited, only a part of the charge absorbed is returned at once, and the rest flows so slowly that many minutes may be required in order to discharge the condenser completely. A potential builds up again across the electrodes if the fully charged condenser is only momentarily shorted. This rather strange phenomenon has the result that the d-c value of the capacitance of a condenser,

$$C_{dc} = \frac{q}{V} \qquad (11.216)$$

is larger than the a-c value

$$C_{ac} = \frac{dq}{dV} \qquad (11.217)$$

Furthermore, the a-c capacitance is a function of frequency, decreasing as the frequency increases. The limit which the a-c capacitance approaches as the frequency increases is, however, rather definite, and is called the geometrical capacitance of the condenser. Another result of dielectric absorption is an increase of the losses of the condenser. The slow absorption current is in phase with the potential difference, so that it results in energy dissipation. Experiment shows that the phase difference due to dielectric absorption is rather constant as the frequency varies. Dielectric absorption is often the major cause of condenser losses, and then the phase difference of the condenser is essentially independent of frequency.

Sometimes the figure of merit Q is applied to condensers. It is defined, just as for inductors, as the ratio of reactance to equivalent series resistance. Thus, for a condenser,

$$Q = \frac{1}{\omega C_s R_s} \qquad (11.218)$$

Comparison with Eq. (11.212) shows that Q may be expressed in terms of the phase difference:

$$Q = \cot \delta \qquad (11.219)$$

If δ is small, its value in radians is approximately the same as tan δ, so that

$$Q \doteq \frac{1}{\delta} \qquad \delta \ll 1 \qquad (11.220)$$

Q may be as high as 10,000 for a well-designed air condenser.

11.13. Transformers. A pair of rather closely coupled coils which is used to transfer electrical energy from one circuit to another is called a transformer. Transformers may have either an iron core or an air core. They are basic components both in power transfer and communications equipment, and find applications in all frequency ranges. In this section, we shall survey rapidly their functions and their characteristics.

In the circuit of Fig. 11.18, the four transformer terminals are marked *abcd*. The coil which is connected to the generator is called the primary winding of the transformer, while the coil connected to the load is called the secondary. An important characteristic of a transformer is its turn ratio

$$a \equiv \frac{N_2}{N_1} \qquad (11.221)$$

where N_1 and N_2 are the number of turns of the primary and secondary coils, respectively. The primary and secondary impedances Z_1 and Z_2 are those impedances which are exhibited by each of these coils, respectively, when the other coil is open-circuited. The transfer impedance Z_m is in general both resistive and inductive in character, but for an air-core transformer is entirely inductive, having the value

$$Z_m = j\omega M \tag{11.222}$$

where M is the mutual inductance between the windings (see Sec. 11.11). There may also exist an appreciable capacitance between the primary and secondary, but we shall neglect this possibility in the present discussion.

A transformer may be used to couple two circuits for one or more of the following purposes: d-c isolation, voltage transformation, current transformation, impedance transformation, and selective frequency response. The first purpose needs no further discussion, and the last requires detailed treatment

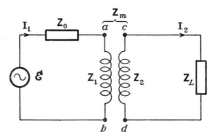

FIG. 11.18. A transformer between generator and load.

which we shall omit. The other three purposes give the transformer its name, and should be clearly understood.

Let us consider transformer theory first on the basis of circuit analysis. Kirchhoff's laws in complex form written for the circuit of Fig. 11.18 are

$$(Z_0 + Z_1)I_1 + Z_m I_2 = \mathcal{E} \tag{11.223}$$
$$(Z_2 + Z_L)I_2 + Z_m I_1 = 0 \tag{11.224}$$

Here $\mathcal{E}$ and Z_0 are the emf and impedance of the generator, Z_L is the load impedance, and I_1 and I_2 are the primary and secondary currents. Equations (11.223) and (11.224) are readily combined to give separate equations for the primary and secondary currents:

$$\left[(Z_0 + Z_1) - \frac{Z_m^2}{Z_2 + Z_L}\right]I_1 = \mathcal{E} \tag{11.225}$$

$$\left[(Z_2 + Z_L) - \frac{Z_m^2}{Z_1 + Z_0}\right]I_2 = -\frac{Z_m}{Z_1 + Z_0}\mathcal{E} \tag{11.226}$$

A characteristic feature of transformers appears when Eq. (11.225) is rewritten in the form

$$\left[Z_0 + \frac{Z_1 Z_2 - Z_m^2}{Z_2 + Z_L} + \frac{Z_1}{Z_2 + Z_L}Z_L\right]I_1 = \mathcal{E} \tag{11.227}$$

Suppose that we can satisfy the following conditions:

$$Z_1 Z_2 - Z_m{}^2 \doteq 0 \tag{11.228}$$

$$|Z_2| \gg |Z_L| \tag{11.229}$$

If these conditions hold, Eq. (11.227) reduces to the approximate equation

$$\left(Z_0 + \frac{Z_1}{Z_2} Z_L\right) I_1 \doteq \mathcal{E} \tag{11.230}$$

This means that so far as the primary circuit is concerned, the transformer plus the load is represented just by $Z_L Z_1 / Z_2$. We may say that the transformer has performed the function of multiplying the load impedance by the ratio Z_1/Z_2 and transferring this impedance into the primary circuit and that this is its entire effect so far as the primary circuit is concerned.

In a similar way, Eq. (11.226) may be rewritten in the form

$$\left[Z_L + \frac{Z_1 Z_2 - Z_m{}^2}{Z_1 + Z_0} + \frac{Z_2}{Z_1 + Z_0} Z_0\right] I_2 = -\frac{Z_m}{Z_1 + Z_0} \mathcal{E} \tag{11.231}$$

If in addition to condition (11.228) we now require that

$$|Z_1| \gg |Z_0| \tag{11.232}$$

then Eq. (11.231) reduces approximately to

$$\left[Z_L + \frac{Z_2}{Z_1} Z_0\right] I_2 \doteq -\frac{Z_m}{Z_1} \mathcal{E} \tag{11.233}$$

Equation (11.233) shows that under the supposed conditions the transformer plus the primary circuit is represented, so far as the secondary circuit is concerned, by an impedance $Z_0 Z_2 / Z_1$ in series with an emf $-\mathcal{E} Z_m / Z_1$. The transformer has therefore performed the function of multiplying the generator impedance by Z_2/Z_1 and the generator emf by $-Z_m/Z_1$, and transferring these quantities to the secondary circuit. This is its only function from the viewpoint of the secondary circuit.

Elimination of the emf $\mathcal{E}$ between Eqs. (11.230) and (11.233) shows that the secondary and primary currents bear a fixed relation, provided our conditions (11.228), (11.229), and (11.232) are valid:

$$\frac{I_2}{I_1} \doteq -\frac{Z_m}{Z_2} \tag{11.234}$$

From this viewpoint, the transformer coupling between primary and secondary circuits is a guarantee that the currents maintain the ratio $-Z_m/Z_2$. From Eq. (11.234) we can obtain also the ratio between the terminal potential differences V_{ab} and V_{cd} of primary and secondary terminals, respectively. For, by reference to Fig. 11.18,

$$\mathbf{V}_{ab} = \mathcal{E} - \mathbf{Z}_0 \mathbf{I}_1 \qquad \mathbf{V}_{cd} = \mathbf{Z}_L \mathbf{I}_2 \qquad (11.235)$$

Combination of Eqs. (11.235) with (11.230) and (11.234) yields

$$\frac{\mathbf{V}_{cd}}{\mathbf{V}_{ab}} \doteq - \frac{\mathbf{Z}_m}{\mathbf{Z}_1} \qquad (11.236)$$

It should be pointed out that the transformation ratios appearing in the approximate Eqs. (11.230), (11.233), (11.234), and (11.236) are all simply related. If we define a transformation ratio

$$\mathbf{A} \equiv \frac{\mathbf{Z}_m}{\mathbf{Z}_1} \qquad (11.237)$$

then the other ratios are simply related to $\mathbf{A}$, as may be shown by use of condition (11.228)

$$\frac{\mathbf{Z}_m}{\mathbf{Z}_2} \doteq \frac{1}{\mathbf{A}} \qquad \frac{\mathbf{Z}_2}{\mathbf{Z}_1} \doteq \mathbf{A}^2 \qquad (11.238)$$

In terms of $\mathbf{A}$, the approximate transformer equations become

$$\left(\mathbf{Z}_0 + \frac{\mathbf{Z}_L}{\mathbf{A}^2} \right) \mathbf{I}_1 \doteq \mathcal{E} \qquad (11.239)$$

$$(\mathbf{Z}_L + \mathbf{A}^2 \mathbf{Z}_0) \mathbf{I}_2 \doteq -\mathbf{A} \mathcal{E} \qquad (11.240)$$

$$\frac{\mathbf{I}_2}{\mathbf{I}_1} \doteq - \frac{1}{\mathbf{A}} \qquad (11.241)$$

$$\frac{\mathbf{V}_{cd}}{\mathbf{V}_{ab}} \doteq -\mathbf{A} \qquad (11.242)$$

The foregoing remarks illustrate why a transformer is so named and for what purposes it may be employed. The reader may be concerned to know whether the conditions (11.228), (11.229), and (11.232) may be sufficiently well achieved to make the approximate equations on which the discussion hinges of any practical use. The answer is affirmative. We define an ideal transformer as one for which condition (11.228) is to hold exactly and for which, to any accuracy desired,

$$\frac{\mathbf{Z}_0}{\mathbf{Z}_1} = 0 = \frac{\mathbf{Z}_L}{\mathbf{Z}_2} \qquad (11.243)$$

so that our approximate equations become exact; and we further require the ratio $\mathbf{A}$ to be real and constant, having a value A. Such an abstraction can be closely enough approximated to be highly useful in rough circuit analysis; and furthermore, the performance of an actual transformer may be described very accurately and conveniently as being equivalent to that of an ideal transformer plus a few associated impedances. Our first concern will be to describe a model for an ideal transformer which is not too different from a good iron-core transformer; and then we shall briefly consider how to take account of the imperfections of actual transformers.

As a model of an ideal transformer, we may imagine two coils each having many turns wound about a common core of high permeability. Suppose the core material to be linear and hence free from hysteresis losses and to be free also of eddy-current losses, and suppose the windings to have negligible wire resistance. Primary and secondary coils will then be ideal inductors of large reactance. Let the self- and mutual inductances of the coils be L_1, L_2, and M, respectively. The transformer impedances are thus

$$\mathbf{Z}_1 = j\omega L_1 \qquad \mathbf{Z}_2 = j\omega L_2 \qquad \mathbf{Z}_m = j\omega M \qquad (11.244)$$

We shall assume that these impedances are large enough to fulfill conditions (11.243) to any desired accuracy. Let N_1 and N_2 be the numbers of turns of primary and secondary, respectively, their ratio being $a \equiv N_2/N_1$. Lastly, we assume that all the magnetic flux ϕ in the core links all turns of both windings. The fluxes linking primary and secondary coils are then, respectively,

$$\Phi_1 = N_1\phi \qquad \Phi_2 = N_2\phi \qquad (11.245)$$

The self-inductances of the coils are now

$$L_1 \equiv \frac{\partial \Phi_1}{\partial I_1} = N_1 \frac{\partial \phi}{\partial I_1} \qquad L_2 \equiv \frac{\partial \Phi_2}{\partial I_2} = N_2 \frac{\partial \phi}{\partial I_2} \qquad (11.246)$$

By the hypothesis of a linear medium, L_1 and L_2 are constants. The mutual inductance between coils may be computed in two ways:

$$M = \frac{\partial \Phi_2}{\partial I_1} = \frac{\partial \Phi_1}{\partial I_2} \qquad (11.247)$$

Thus, from Eqs. (11.245),

$$M = N_2 \frac{\partial \phi}{\partial I_1} = N_1 \frac{\partial \phi}{\partial I_2} \qquad (11.248)$$

Using Eqs. (11.246), we obtain

$$M = \frac{N_2}{N_1} L_1 = \frac{N_1}{N_2} L_2 \qquad (11.249)$$

It follows that for our model transformer

$$M = \sqrt{L_1 L_2} \qquad (11.250)$$

Equation (11.250) shows that the model transformer has unit coefficient of coupling as defined in Sec. 8.7, and comparison with Eqs. (11.244) shows that condition (11.228) is fulfilled. Conditions (11.228) and (11.243) being satisfied, the model we have described is an ideal transformer.   Its transformation ratio is

$$\mathbf{A} = \frac{\mathbf{Z}_m}{\mathbf{Z}_1} = \frac{j\omega M}{j\omega L_1} = \sqrt{\frac{L_2}{L_1}} \qquad (11.251)$$

From Eq. (11.249) we have

$$\sqrt{\frac{L_2}{L_1}} = \frac{N_2}{N_1} \qquad (11.252)$$

whence $\mathbf{A}$ is identified with the turn ratio a:

$$\mathbf{A} = a \qquad (11.253)$$

It must be remembered that these equations apply just to our particular model of an ideal transformer.

An actual iron-core transformer may be designed and operated in such a way as to approximate very closely to the foregoing model of an

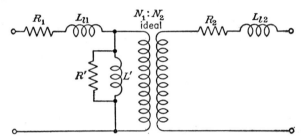

FIG. 11.19. Representation of an actual transformer.

ideal transformer. A detailed physical analysis is indispensable in the treatment of actual transformers; mere circuit analysis is not sufficient.   The reader is referred to "Magnetic Circuits and Transformers" by the staff of the Massachusetts Institute of Technology (Wiley, 1943), especially Chaps. XII, XIII, and XVII.   It turns out that an actual transformer is excellently represented by the equivalent circuit of Fig. 11.19 if capacitances are neglected.   In this representation, there is no longer any restriction on the values of generator or load impedances relative to transformer characteristics.   The ideal transformer in Fig. 11.19 has the turn ratio of the actual transformer.   The resistances R_1 and R_2 are due to the a-c resistance of the windings, but exclude core losses.   The series inductances L_{l1} and L_{l2} are called leakage inductances, and they result from fluxes which link only one of the two windings. These inductances are nearly constant even for iron-core transformers in which the self- and mutual inductances vary.   Finally, the shunt inductance L' and resistance R' together carry what is termed the magnetizing current. L' accounts for the finite self-inductance of the coils, while R' accounts for core losses. L' and R' are the only parts of the equivalent circuit which vary with the magnitude of the currents.

PROBLEMS

11.1. An inductance of 0.02 henry, a capacitance of 0.01 μf, and a resistance of 500 ohms in series are connected to a generator whose frequency is 10,000 cps. If the potential difference across the resistance has a peak value of 10 volts and passes through zero from minus to plus at $t = 0$, write expressions for the alternating potential difference across each element of the circuit including the generator. Use a consistent set of sign conventions, and show these on a diagram of the circuit.

11.2. An alternating potential difference V is impressed across the series combination of a resistor R and a capacitor C. Show that (a) for any frequency in a certain range, the potential difference across the resistor is approximately the time derivative of V; (b) for any frequency in a certain range, the potential difference across the capacitor is the time integral of V.

11.3. Show how to use a series-connected resistance and ideal inductance to obtain (a) an output potential difference which is the time derivative of the input potential difference, for the proper frequency range; (b) an output potential difference which is the time integral of the input potential difference, for the proper frequency range. See Prob. 11.2.

11.4. An a-c motor has a power factor of 0.60, with the current lagging the potential difference, and it draws 3 amp from a 220-volt 60-cycle line.

a. Find the average power drawn by the motor.

b. Find the wattless power in the motor.

Note: Potential difference, emf, and current will be rms values throughout the problem set except where otherwise indicated.

11.5. An ideal full-wave rectifier delivers a pulsating d-c voltage of the form shown in the figure, simply inverting the negative loops of the input sine wave. Compare both the peak and the rms input voltage with (a) the effective or rms value of the d-c output voltage; (b) the average value of the d-c output voltage.

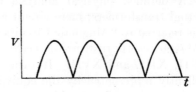

PROB. 11.5.

11.6. What capacitance in parallel with the motor of Prob. 11.4 will produce a net power factor of unity? What is then the current drawn from the line?

11.7. A 120-volt a-c motor is connected through a pure resistance to a 220-volt power line. The resistance is adjusted to make the motor voltage correct; and under these conditions the current is 10 amp and the power factor of motor plus resistor is 0.90. Find (a) the power dissipated in the resistor; (b) the power used in the motor; (c) the power factor of the motor alone.

11.8. A variable inductor is often used in place of a resistor to control the brightness of auditorium lights operated on an a-c circuit. Suppose that such a dimmer drops the line voltage of 120 down to 100 volts across the resistive load, and in so doing dissipates one-half as much power as would a resistor. Find the phase angle of the dimmer and both the rms and peak potential difference across it. A vector diagram is very helpful in solving the problem.

11.9. The circuit shown is used as a phase-shifting network. Show by a vector diagram that for no load the output voltage V_0 has half the magnitude of the input V_i, and that V_0 differs from V_i in phase by an angle between zero and 180° depending on the setting of the resistor R.

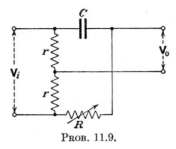

PROB. 11.9.

11.10. The three-voltmeter method of measuring average a-c power involves connecting a pure resistance R in series with the load. Show that if the effective potential difference across the resistance is V_1, across the load is V_2, and across the series combination is V_3, then the power in the load is

$$\bar{P} = \frac{V_3{}^2 - V_1{}^2 - V_2{}^2}{2R}$$

Draw a vector diagram of this situation.

11.11. Give in detail the demonstration of Eqs. (11.66) and (11.67) for the amplitude and angle of a sum of a-c variables.

11.12. In plane geometry one learns that an angle inscribed in a semicircle is always 90°. Apply this theorem to the development of a graphical construction for a series-connected inductance and resistance at a given frequency, to solve the following problems:

a. Given the potential difference V_0 across both elements, and the potential difference V_R across the resistance alone; to find the potential difference V_L across the inductor, and the phase angle.

b. Given V_0 and the phase angle, to find V_R and V_L.

11.13. Use a vector diagram to find graphically the impedance and phase angle of a series combination of an inductance of 4 henrys, a resistance of 600 ohms, and a capacitance of 1 μf, at a frequency of 60 cps. (The symbol μf stands for microfarad.)

11.14. Use vector diagrams to find graphically the admittance of a parallel combination of a pure inductance with a series-connected capacitance and resistance. The values are $L = \frac{1}{4}$ henry, $C = \frac{1}{2}\mu f$, $R = 500$ ohms. The frequency is 400 cps.

11.15. The four quantities ± 1 and $\pm j$ are readily shown to be fourth roots of unity in the system of complex numbers. Similarly, find the three cube roots of -8, both in polar form and in the form of real plus imaginary parts. *Hint:* This problem is easily done by using the exponential form for a complex number.

11.16. Show that the T and Π networks shown are equivalent if

$$Z_1 = \frac{Z_b Z_c}{Z_a + Z_b + Z_c}$$

$$Z_2 = \frac{Z_c Z_a}{Z_a + Z_b + Z_c}$$

$$Z_3 = \frac{Z_a Z_b}{Z_a + Z_b + Z_c}$$

The proof may be made by connecting a generator of emf $\mathcal{E}$ and internal impedance Z_0 to the input and a load Z_L to the output terminals, and computing the load current. This theorem is very useful in the reduction of complex networks to simpler ones.

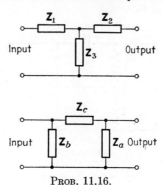

PROB. 11.16.

11.17. Show that at frequencies whose fractional deviation $\Delta\omega/\omega_0$ from the resonant frequency ω_0 of a series L-C-R circuit is small, the complex impedance of the circuit is approximately

$$Z = R + j\left(\omega_0 L + \frac{1}{C\omega_0}\right)\frac{\Delta\omega}{\omega_0}$$

11.18. Draw a graph of phase angle vs. 2π times frequency for the parallel circuit of Fig. 11.7, taking values of 800 mh, 0.20 μf, and 40 ohms for the components.

11.19. Draw a graph of impedance vs. 2π times frequency for the parallel circuit of Prob. 11.18.

11.20. An experimenter has an inductor of 200 mh which he wishes to tune to resonance at 9,000 cps by an ideal, parallel capacitance. When he has done so, he finds the impedance of the parallel circuit to be 0.500 megohm. What is (a) the effective series resistance of the inductor and (b) the tuning capacitance?

11.21. Suppose a parallel circuit is made up of an ideal variable capacitor C, and an inductor having apparent series inductance L and resistance R. If the angular frequency ω is constant and the circuit is tuned for minimum admittance by variation of C, show that this minimum occurs when

$$C = \frac{L}{R^2 + L^2\omega^2}$$

Compare the condition for phase resonance.

11.22. For a parallel resonant circuit having a perfect capacitor C and an inductor characterized by apparent inductance L and series resistance R, find the angular frequency for which the admittance is a minimum.

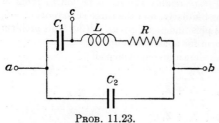

PROB. 11.23.

$$Ans. \; \omega^2 = \frac{1}{LC}\sqrt{1 + \frac{2R^2C}{L}} - \frac{R^2}{L^2}.$$

11.23. Find the resonant frequency and the admittance at resonance for the circuit shown when connection is made to terminals a and b. Compare with the corresponding quantities for terminals c and b.

11.24. Given a parallel combination having in one branch an ideal inductor and in the other an imperfect condenser represented by its equivalent series capacitance and resistance, find the frequency for phase resonance.

11.25. Find the condition for phase resonance in a parallel circuit having a series combination of inductance L and resistance R_1 in one branch and a series combination of capacitance C and resistance R_2 in the other branch.

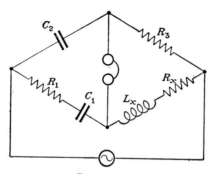

PROB. 11.26.

11.26. Deduce balance conditions for the Owen bridge shown in the figure. If L_x and R_x are the unknowns, what pair(s) of components could be variable to allow independence in balancing?

11.27. The figure shows a Schering bridge, used to measure the effective series components C_x and R_x of a condenser.

a. Find balance conditions.

b. Show that C_2 can be calibrated to read directly the power factor of the unknown condenser.

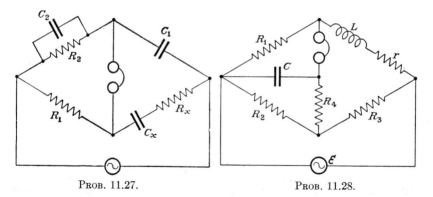

PROB. 11.27.   PROB. 11.28.

11.28. Find balance conditions for the Anderson bridge shown in the figure. (This bridge is used for measurement of inductance.)

11.29. *a.* Solve the balance conditions of the Wien bridge for the capacitances.

b. A student took the following data on a Wien bridge with two high-quality standard capacitors: frequency = 60 cps, $R_1 = 8,850$ ohms, $R_2 = 1,445$ ohms, $R_3 = 20,000$ ohms, $R_4 = 1,000$ ohms. These components are numbered according to Fig. 11.11. Find the two capacitances.

11.30. Suppose the resistors R_1 and R_3 in the arms containing the condensers are the adjustable elements in balancing the Wien bridge of Prob. 11.29. Describe by a graph the process of balancing, finding the slopes of the lines involved near balance.

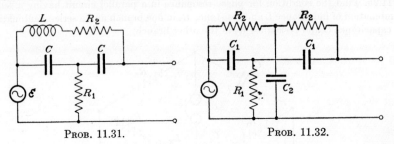

PROB. 11.31. PROB. 11.32.

11.31. Show that the alternating potential difference across the output terminals of the bridged-T network shown is zero when the following balance conditions are met:

$$\omega L = \frac{2}{\omega C} \qquad R_2 = \frac{1}{R_1(\omega C)^2}$$

11.32. The circuit shown is called a parallel-T null network. Show that for no output potential difference the balance conditions are

$$\frac{2}{\omega C_1} = R_2{}^2 \omega C_2 \qquad \frac{1}{R_1(\omega C_1)^2} = 2R_2$$

11.33. The figure shows a bridge involving self-inductance and mutual inductance. Find balance conditions. Specify consistent positive directions for the currents in the coupled coils in order to permit balance.

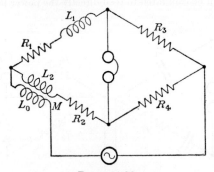

PROB. 11.33.

11.34. *a.* Use the a-c form of Thévenin's theorem to find an expression for the detector current in the general four-impedance bridge without inductive coupling. Assume negligible internal impedance in the generator.

b. Apply the formula obtained in part (*a*) to the series-capacitance bridge of Fig. 11.9.

11.35. A current $I = a_1 \sin \omega t + a_2 \sin 2\omega t + a_3 \sin 3\omega t$ flows through a resistor R. Find the instantaneous power and the average power dissipated in the resistor.

11.36. A certain coil has a Q of 200 and an apparent series inductance of 400 μh at 500 kc/sec. At this frequency, find its effective series resistance, impedance, and phase angle.

11.37. A certain condenser at 60 cps is equivalent to a perfect capacitance of 0.500 μf in series with a resistance of 40 ohms. Find (a) the values of the equivalent parallel resistance and capacitance at this frequency, (b) the phase angle and phase defect, and (c) the power factor of the condenser.

11.38. a. Show that at the resonant frequency of a parallel circuit, in which the capacitor is considered ideal, the impedance is larger than the reactance of the capacitor by the factor of the Q of the coil.

b. Show that in a series circuit composed of an ideal capacitor and an inductor of figure of merit Q, the potential difference across the capacitor at resonance is Q times the potential difference across the series combination.

11.39. Given a series circuit with an inductor whose figure of merit is $Q \gg 1$ and an ideal capacitor. By the result of Prob. 11.17, show that the impedance of the circuit rises by a factor of $\sqrt{2}$ when the frequency departs from the resonant frequency by $\Delta\omega/\omega_0 = 1/2Q$.

11.40. Prove Eqs. (11.212) to (11.215), Sec. 11.12.

11.41. Compute the penetration depth of electromagnetic waves in copper at a frequency of 1,000 kc/sec, taking the permeability as that of free space and the resistivity as 1.72×10^{-8} ohm-m. Compare with the diameter of, say, No. 24 B. and S. gage wire.

11.42. An ideal transformer couples a 1,000 cps generator, having an emf of 25 volts and an internal resistive impedance of 10,000 ohms, to a load consisting of the series combination of an 0.10 μf capacitance and a 400-ohm resistance. If the secondary to primary turns ratio is ¼, find the primary and secondary currents in complex form, and the complex potential difference across primary and secondary terminals.

11.43. An air-core transformer with ideal self- and mutual inductances L_p, L_s, and M has a perfect condenser C connected across its secondary terminals. Find from basic circuit theory the complex impedance across its primary terminals.

$$Ans.\ \mathbf{Z} = j\left(\omega L_p - \frac{\omega^2 M^2}{\omega L_s - (1/\omega C)}\right).$$

11.44. An ideal transformer with turn ratio a couples a generator into a load. The generator has a frequency $\omega/2\pi$, an emf $\mathcal{E}$, and a resistive internal impedance R_0; the load is an inductance L in series with a resistance R.

a. Find an expression for the load power.

b. By differentiation with respect to part (a), show what turn ratio maximizes the load power. What is then the impedance seen by the generator across the primary of the transformer?

11.45. Show that the average power transferred out of an a-c circuit by a two-terminal component whose complex effective current and potential difference are I and V, respectively, is the real part of the product of one of these quantities with the complex conjugate of the other.

CHAPTER 12

MAXWELL'S EQUATIONS. ELECTROMAGNETIC WAVES

12.1. Introduction. The Maxwell equations are a set of differential equations describing the sources and relationships of the electromagnetic field vectors. It would be incorrect to say that we can derive these equations from the experimental material which has been presented and analyzed in the earlier chapters of this book. We have dealt so far only with electrostatics, magnetostatics, and electromagnetic induction; it remains for us to examine the interesting phenomena of electromagnetic wave motion and radiation. These phenomena show that a basic physical postulate must be added to those which have already been made. We shall introduce this postulate, and at the same time collect the differential equations of the electromagnetic field in a form which is perfectly general. The analysis of the electrostatic or steady state, or of a-c circuits at moderately low frequencies, will then appear as special applications of the general equations.

12.2. Differential Form of Faraday's Law of Electromagnetic Induction. It was remarked in Sec. 8.2 that the phenomenon of electromagnetic induction implies the creation of an electric field by a time-varying magnetic field and that these are related by Eq. (8.16) of that section:

$$\oint_C \mathbf{E} \cdot d\mathbf{l} = -\int_S \frac{\partial \mathbf{B}}{\partial t} \cdot \mathbf{n} \, da \tag{12.1}$$

Here C is any fixed, closed path of integration which is the boundary of a surface S, and $\mathbf{n}$ is the positive unit normal vector to S, consistent with the sense of the line integration. We noticed also that Eq. (12.1) remains true even if part (or all, for that matter) of the electric field $\mathbf{E}$ is produced by the presence of net charge distributions. The general nature of this equation qualifies it to be a basic law of electromagnetism. We now postulate its universal validity, and proceed to write an equivalent equation in differential form.

A process by which the differential equation implied by (12.1) may be found is to evaluate the two sides of the equation for rectangular paths of integration lying in the coordinate planes, and then to pass to the limit as the sides of the rectangles approach zero. Exactly this same mathematical process has already been followed through in detailed

422

fashion in Sec. 7.11. There it was shown essentially that the similar integral equation

$$\oint_C \mathbf{B} \cdot d\mathbf{l} = \mu_0 \int_S \mathbf{J} \cdot \mathbf{n} \, da \qquad (12.2)$$

implies the differential equations:

$$\frac{\partial B_z}{\partial y} - \frac{\partial B_y}{\partial z} = \mu_0 J_x \qquad \frac{\partial B_x}{\partial z} - \frac{\partial B_z}{\partial x} = \mu_0 J_y \qquad \frac{\partial B_y}{\partial x} - \frac{\partial B_x}{\partial y} = \mu_0 J_z \qquad (12.3)$$

Equations (12.3) hold at every point of a region, provided Eq. (12.2) holds in the region for any curve C bounding a surface S. It follows now that the universal validity of Eq. (12.1) implies that at all points of space, at least where the field vectors are continuous,

$$\begin{aligned}
\frac{\partial E_z}{\partial y} - \frac{\partial E_y}{\partial z} &= -\frac{\partial B_x}{\partial t} \\[4pt]
\frac{\partial E_x}{\partial z} - \frac{\partial E_z}{\partial x} &= -\frac{\partial B_y}{\partial t} \\[4pt]
\frac{\partial E_y}{\partial x} - \frac{\partial E_x}{\partial y} &= -\frac{\partial B_z}{\partial t}
\end{aligned} \qquad (12.4)$$

Equations (12.4) together form one of the Maxwell equations. In the compact notation of vector analysis, this equation is

$$\text{curl } \mathbf{E} = -\frac{\partial \mathbf{B}}{\partial t} \qquad (12.5)$$

Here **curl E** is simply an abbreviation for the vector derived from **E** by differentiation according to the formula:

$$\text{curl } \mathbf{E} \equiv \left(\frac{\partial E_z}{\partial y} - \frac{\partial E_y}{\partial z} \right) \mathbf{i} + \left(\frac{\partial E_x}{\partial z} - \frac{\partial E_z}{\partial x} \right) \mathbf{j} + \left(\frac{\partial E_y}{\partial x} - \frac{\partial E_x}{\partial y} \right) \mathbf{k} \qquad (12.6)$$

where **i**, **j**, and **k** are the cartesian unit vectors.

The special case of the electrostatic field is obtained from Eq. (12.5) by putting $\mathbf{B} \equiv 0$:

$$\text{curl } \mathbf{E}_{\text{static}} = 0 \qquad (12.7)$$

The equivalent integral equation for the electrostatic field is derived at once from Eq. (12.1) by putting $\mathbf{B} \equiv 0$:

$$\oint_{\text{any } C} \mathbf{E}_{\text{static}} \cdot d\mathbf{l} = 0 \qquad (12.8)$$

From these equations it follows at once that a scalar potential function, single-valued except for an arbitrary additive constant, may be set up for the electrostatic field. See Sec. 1.5 where this argument was based on the inverse-square law for the electrostatic field. The reader can see from this example something of the elegance and power of the Maxwell equations, if they are taken not as deductions from other laws but as the fundamental postulates of electromagnetism.

12.3. Divergence of Magnetic Induction. The Maxwell equation (12.5) of Sec. 12.2 makes a statement by implication concerning the nature of the **B** vector. If the quantity

$$\frac{\partial}{\partial x}\frac{\partial B_x}{\partial t} + \frac{\partial}{\partial y}\frac{\partial B_y}{\partial t} + \frac{\partial}{\partial z}\frac{\partial B_z}{\partial t} \equiv \operatorname{div}\frac{\partial \mathbf{B}}{\partial t} \tag{12.9}$$

is evaluated by the use of Eqs. (12.4) it will be found to be identically zero:

$$\operatorname{div}\frac{\partial \mathbf{B}}{\partial t} \equiv 0 \tag{12.10}$$

Now the order of the partial derivatives in Eq. (12.10) may be changed without altering the value of the terms. Therefore

$$\frac{\partial}{\partial t}\operatorname{div}\mathbf{B} \equiv 0 \tag{12.11}$$

This states that the quantity called the divergence of **B**,

$$\operatorname{div}\mathbf{B} \equiv \frac{\partial B_x}{\partial x} + \frac{\partial B_y}{\partial y} + \frac{\partial B_z}{\partial z} \tag{12.12}$$

never changes with time. But the magnetic induction vector itself is subject to time variation; and hence the value of div **B** can have no significant relation to the **B** function. In particular, the value of **B** may be made zero throughout a region, at least to a good approximation. Then div **B** is necessarily zero also in that region; and Eq. (12.11) states that it will forever remain zero, and in fact must always have been zero in that region. Hence the deduction we may make from Eq. (12.11) is that always and everywhere

$$\operatorname{div}\mathbf{B} = 0 \tag{12.13}$$

This property of the **B** vector was shown in Sec. 7.6 to be true for the steady state, on the assumption that all steady-state fields are produced ultimately by a steady current or moving charge (including charges in the constitution of matter) in accordance with Ampère's law. Furthermore, the integral form of Eq. (12.13)

$$\oint_{\text{any closed } S} \mathbf{B} \cdot \mathbf{n}\, da = 0 \tag{12.14}$$

was involved in setting up Faraday's law, in Sec. 8.2; so there we essentially assumed that Eq. (12.13) holds also for time-varying fields. From the present viewpoint, we see that if Eq. (12.5) is postulated, (12.13) follows as a deduction. Nevertheless, Eq. (12.13) is so important that it is usually listed as one of the Maxwell equations.

12.4. Displacement Current. The magnetic induction in steady state has been shown in Sec. 7.11 to satisfy the following differential equations in empty space or nonmagnetic material:

$$\left(\frac{\partial B_z}{\partial y} - \frac{\partial B_y}{\partial z}\right)\mathbf{i} + \left(\frac{\partial B_x}{\partial z} - \frac{\partial B_z}{\partial x}\right)\mathbf{j} + \left(\frac{\partial B_y}{\partial x} - \frac{\partial B_x}{\partial y}\right)\mathbf{k} = \mu_0 \mathbf{J} \quad (12.15)$$

Here $\mathbf{J}$ is the current density vector due to free charge only. The left-hand member is defined as **curl B**; thus, more briefly,

$$\operatorname{curl} \mathbf{B} = \mu_0 \mathbf{J} \quad\quad\quad (12.16)$$

The corresponding equation for regions which may be occupied by magnetic material is, still for steady state,

$$\operatorname{curl} \mathbf{H} = \mathbf{J} \quad\quad\quad (12.17)$$

The magnetizing force $\mathbf{H}$ is a macroscopic vector which we found it convenient to introduce in the study of magnetic materials (see Secs. 9.3 and 9.11). The definition of $\mathbf{H}$,

$$\mathbf{H} \equiv \frac{1}{\mu_0}\mathbf{B} - \mathbf{M} \quad\quad\quad (12.18)$$

expressed in terms of the macroscopic magnetic induction $\mathbf{B}$ and the magnetization $\mathbf{M}$ of the material, is just as valid for nonsteady as for steady state, provided the problem involves only dimensions which are large on an atomic scale. The magnetization vector $\mathbf{M}$ is the magnetic dipole moment per unit volume, a quantity which is defined in terms of the motion, orientation, and the intrinsic properties of the ultimate particles of the material.

Now it is impossible to suppose that Eq. (12.17) is universally valid in nonsteady states. The conservation of electric charge is stated in differential form by the equation of continuity in Sec. 5.3:

$$\operatorname{div} \mathbf{J} + \frac{\partial \rho}{\partial t} = 0 \quad\quad\quad (12.19)$$

Now if $\mathbf{J}$ is substituted from Eq. (12.17) into (12.19), it appears that (12.17) implies that

$$\frac{\partial \rho}{\partial t} = 0 \quad\quad\quad (12.20)$$

This is indeed true by definition for steady state, but not in general. Every time a condenser charges or discharges, charge density (actually in the form of a surface layer) changes with time. Equation (12.17) therefore needs some extension, and this involves an additional physical postulate.

The generalization of Eq. (12.17) was achieved by J. C. Maxwell (1831–1879), for whom the Maxwell equations are named. The equation is altered by the addition to $\mathbf{J}$ of the term $\partial \mathbf{D}/\partial t$, called the displacement current:

$$\operatorname{curl} \mathbf{H} = \mathbf{J} + \frac{\partial \mathbf{D}}{\partial t} \tag{12.21}$$

Here $\mathbf{D}$ is understood to mean the electric displacement vector whose general definition has been already given in Sec. 3.6:

$$\mathbf{D} \equiv \epsilon_0 \mathbf{E} + \mathbf{P} \tag{12.22}$$

where $\mathbf{P}$ is the electric polarization, or electric dipole moment per unit volume. Of course, $\mathbf{D}$ and $\mathbf{P}$ are only appropriate to problems involving dimensions of macroscopic magnitude. Subject to this restriction, Eq. (12.22) is a definition which is independent of whether or not the state is steady.

Let us examine Eq. (12.21) to see why it is reasonable to try such a form. In the first place, it evidently reduces to Eq. (12.17) for steady state, because in steady state there are no changing electric fields. Next, it does not require, as Eq. (12.17) did, that the charge densities be independent of time. Solving Eq. (12.21) for $\mathbf{J}$ and substituting into Eq. (12.19), we obtain

$$-\operatorname{div} \frac{\partial \mathbf{D}}{\partial t} + \frac{\partial \rho}{\partial t} = 0 \tag{12.23}$$

After interchange of order of partial differentiation, Eq. (12.23) reads

$$\frac{\partial}{\partial t} (\rho - \operatorname{div} \mathbf{D}) = 0 \tag{12.24}$$

This is always satisfied if we assume that in general

$$\operatorname{div} \mathbf{D} = \rho \tag{12.25}$$

Equation (12.25) has been demonstrated to hold for static fields in Sec. 3.6. It now appears as a general equation implied by Eqs. (12.19) and (12.21). The reader may object that Eq. (12.24) does not of itself imply (12.25), but only that the quantity $(\rho - \operatorname{div} \mathbf{D})$ is independent of time. However, it is possible to make both ρ and $\mathbf{D}$ zero in a region of space by evacuation and shielding, so that $(\rho - \operatorname{div} \mathbf{D}) = 0$ in the region. Equation (12.24) then tells us that $(\rho - \operatorname{div} \mathbf{D})$ has always been zero, and always will be; whence (12.25) follows. Compare the discussion of a similar situation for the magnetic induction vector in Sec. 12.3.

One final consideration which makes Eq. (12.21) seem reasonable is the symmetry which it introduces into electromagnetic equations. A time-varying magnetic field produces an electric field, according to Faraday's law and the Maxwell equation of Sec. 12.2, and now we postulate that the converse phenomenon also occurs. Notice however that the algebraic signs for the two phenomena differ. Also notice that there is no magnetic current density in Eq. (12.5), Sec. 12.2, just as there is no magnetic charge density in Eq. (12.13), Sec. 12.3, whereas the equations of the present section involve both electric current density and charge density.

Now of course the foregoing considerations have not proved that Eq. (12.21) is true, *i.e.*, that it is in accord with observation in the non-steady state. An equation stating a physical postulate is verified only by comparing its predictions with experiment. Equation (12.21) is abundantly confirmed by experiment not only in the realm of electromagnetic apparatus as such, but also in the realm of optics. It is understood, however, that not only Eq. (12.21) but the entire system of classical electrodynamics needs modification in accordance with the principles of the quantum mechanics, in order to treat interactions between radiation and atomic systems. It will also be evident that a macroscopic theory may be usefully applied to the treatment of electromagnetic waves in matter only when the wavelength is much greater than atomic dimensions.

Equation (12.25) is usually considered to be one of the Maxwell equations, even though it may be deduced from Eq. (12.21) and the equation of continuity. A logically possible alternative is to consider Eqs. (12.21) and (12.25) to be independent, basic postulates, and then the equation of continuity (12.19) becomes a deduction from them.

It is instructive to use Eq. (12.22) to elucidate the meaning of the displacement current, $\partial \mathbf{D}/\partial t$:

$$\frac{\partial \mathbf{D}}{\partial t} = \epsilon_0 \frac{\partial \mathbf{E}}{\partial t} + \frac{\partial \mathbf{P}}{\partial t} \tag{12.26}$$

The first term is the essentially new feature of Maxwell's postulate; for it means that a time-dependent electric field becomes a source of a magnetic field. In other words, the quantity $\epsilon_0(\partial \mathbf{E}/\partial t)$, which exists in space, is equivalent so far as its magnetic effect is concerned to a current density due to motion of free charge. The second term of Eq. (12.26) is only what we should expect from the microscopic analysis of dielectric matter. It represents an actual flow of electric charges, not free charges such as the term $\mathbf{J}$ of Eq. (12.21) represents, but those charges in the molecular constitution of matter which undergo only slight relative displacements under the action of an applied electric field. We proceed to verify this statement by referring to the microscopic picture.

For simplicity, consider the dielectric to contain just one molecular species. Let the average molecule in the macroscopically infinitesimal neighborhood of a point of observation have an electric dipole moment $\bar{\mathbf{p}}$. If the number of molecules per unit volume at the point of observation is N_1, then the polarization vector there is

$$\mathbf{P} = N_1\bar{\mathbf{p}} \tag{12.27}$$

(See Sec. 3.2.) Next, consider the average molecule to be composed of a set of point charges q_i, which are in fact its electrons and nuclei. These charges are in ceaseless motion, the orbital motion of electrons and the thermal vibration of nuclei; but to each particle there corresponds an average position vector $\bar{\mathbf{r}}_i$, averaged over such natural motion. We shall assume that the period of time variation of the macroscopic electric field is large compared with these molecular periods, so that such an average yields the macroscopically significant dipole moment of the molecule. This moment is then found by using the $\bar{\mathbf{r}}_i$ in the form of Eq. (1.105), Sec. 1.14, which is appropriate for a system of point charges:

$$\bar{\mathbf{p}} = \sum_{\text{molecule}} q_i\bar{\mathbf{r}}_i \tag{12.28}$$

Substitution of Eq. (12.28) in (12.27) yields

$$\mathbf{P} = N_1 \sum_{\text{molecule}} q_i\bar{\mathbf{r}}_i \tag{12.29}$$

We are now ready to find $\partial\mathbf{P}/\partial t$:

$$\frac{\partial\mathbf{P}}{\partial t} = N_1 \sum_{[\text{molecule}} q_i\bar{\mathbf{v}}_i \tag{12.30}$$

where

$$\bar{\mathbf{v}}_i \equiv \frac{\partial\bar{\mathbf{r}}_i}{\partial t}$$

are the drift velocities of the particles of the molecule as they readjust their positions under the action of the applied electric field. Comparison of Eq. (12.30) with (5.9), Sec. 5.1,

$$\mathbf{J} = \sum_i n_i q_i\mathbf{v}_i \tag{12.31}$$

which expresses the current density due to macroscopic drift velocity $\mathbf{v}_i$ of charges q_i of density n_i, shows that $\partial\mathbf{P}/\partial t$ is just the current density due to the intramolecular displacements of charge under the applied field, Q.E.D.

12.5. The Maxwell Equations.   The Wave Equation in Insulating Material.   The Maxwell equations, discussed in Secs. 12.2 to 12.4, are the following four differential equations:

$$\text{curl } \mathbf{E} = -\frac{\partial \mathbf{B}}{\partial t} \tag{12.5}$$

$$\text{div } \mathbf{B} = 0 \tag{12.13}$$

$$\text{curl } \mathbf{H} = \mathbf{J} + \frac{\partial \mathbf{D}}{\partial t} \tag{12.21}$$

$$\text{div } \mathbf{D} = \rho \tag{12.25}$$

It is understood always that $\mathbf{J}$ and ρ are the current and charge densities due to free charges only.   In order to combine these equations in such a way as to describe the space and time dependence of each of the four field vectors separately, it is necessary to add to them a statement of the characteristics of the medium in which the fields exist.   The electrical characteristics consist of relations between the electric field $\mathbf{E}$ and the electric displacement $\mathbf{D}$, or between $\mathbf{E}$ and the current density $\mathbf{J}$.   The magnetic properties of matter determine the relation between $\mathbf{B}$ and $\mathbf{H}$. Such relations, called constitutive equations, have been discussed in some detail in Chaps. 3, 5, and 9.   The constitutive relations have a simple mathematical form only in matter which is homogeneous, linear, and effectively isotropic.   There is much that can be done in the more complex cases, as for instance analysis of the physical optics of anisotropic crystals; but these are matters for more extended or more specialized treatises.   We shall explore only the simple case, in which

$$\mathbf{D} = \epsilon \mathbf{E} \tag{12.32}$$

$$\mathbf{J} = g \mathbf{E} \tag{12.33}$$

$$\mathbf{H} = \frac{1}{\mu} \mathbf{B} \tag{12.34}$$

where ϵ, g, and μ are constant in both space and time.   In empty space these equations will be

$$\mathbf{D} = \epsilon_0 \mathbf{E} \tag{12.35}$$

$$\mathbf{J} = 0 \tag{12.36}$$

$$\mathbf{H} = \frac{1}{\mu_0} \mathbf{B} \tag{12.37}$$

The use of Eq. (12.33) is necessary only in the treatment of electromagnetic fields in conducting material.   For many actual materials, g is so nearly zero that often Eq. (12.36) may be used.   No such simplification occurs in Eqs. (12.32) and (12.34) since the dielectric constant ϵ is never below its empty-space value ϵ_0, while the permeability μ is at best only very slightly below μ_0.

We shall consider first the case of insulating material, for which

Eq. (12.36) holds; and in addition we shall suppose that there is no free charge density, so that $\rho = 0$. The Maxwell equations may now be written in terms of only two of the field vectors, by use of Eqs. (12.32) and (12.34). Choosing **E** and **B** arbitrarily as these two vectors, we obtain, in place of Eqs. (12.21) and (12.25),

$$\text{curl } \mathbf{B} = \mu\epsilon \frac{\partial \mathbf{E}}{\partial t} \tag{12.38}$$

$$\text{div } \mathbf{E} = 0 \tag{12.39}$$

Now we may eliminate either **B** or **E** from the pair of Eqs. (12.5) and (12.38) by taking the curl of either equation and combining it with the other. For instance, Eq. (12.5) yields, after interchange of the order of partial differentiation

$$\text{curl (curl } \mathbf{E}) = -\frac{\partial}{\partial t}\text{ curl } \mathbf{B} \tag{12.40}$$

Substitution of Eq. (12.38) into (12.40) gives a differential equation in **E** only:

$$\text{curl (curl } \mathbf{E}) = -\mu\epsilon \frac{\partial^2 \mathbf{E}}{\partial t^2} \tag{12.41}$$

The reduction of the vector **curl (curl E)** is somewhat complicated, but it presents no difficulties in principle and is well known in vector analysis. It will be sufficient to work out one component of the vector in order to see how it goes. For example, the x component is

$$\text{curl}_x \text{ (curl } \mathbf{E}) = \frac{\partial}{\partial y}\text{ curl}_z \text{ } \mathbf{E} - \frac{\partial}{\partial z}\text{ curl}_y \text{ } \mathbf{E}$$

$$= \frac{\partial}{\partial y}\left(\frac{\partial E_y}{\partial x} - \frac{\partial E_x}{\partial y}\right) - \frac{\partial}{\partial z}\left(\frac{\partial E_x}{\partial z} - \frac{\partial E_z}{\partial x}\right)$$

Therefore

$$\text{curl}_x \text{ (curl } \mathbf{E}) = \left(\frac{\partial^2 E_y}{\partial y \, \partial x} + \frac{\partial^2 E_z}{\partial z \, \partial x}\right) - \left(\frac{\partial^2 E_x}{\partial y^2} + \frac{\partial^2 E_x}{\partial z^2}\right) \tag{12.42}$$

Interchange of the order of differentiation in Eq. (12.42) yields

$$\text{curl}_x \text{ (curl } \mathbf{E}) = \frac{\partial}{\partial x}\left(\frac{\partial E_y}{\partial y} + \frac{\partial E_z}{\partial z}\right) - \left(\frac{\partial^2 E_x}{\partial y^2} + \frac{\partial^2 E_x}{\partial z^2}\right) \tag{12.43}$$

Now Eq. (12.39) may be used to achieve a simpler form. That equation implies that

$$\frac{\partial E_y}{\partial y} + \frac{\partial E_z}{\partial z} = -\frac{\partial E_x}{\partial x} \tag{12.44}$$

Therefore Eq. (12.43) becomes

$$\text{curl}_x \text{ (curl } \mathbf{E}) = -\left(\frac{\partial^2 E_x}{\partial x^2} + \frac{\partial^2 E_x}{\partial y^2} + \frac{\partial^2 E_x}{\partial z^2}\right) \tag{12.45}$$

Finally, the vector equation (12.41) implies that the x components of its two members are equal. The x component of $\partial^2\mathbf{E}/\partial t^2$ is $\partial^2 E_x/\partial t^2$; thus Eqs. (12.45) and (12.41) yield

$$\left(\frac{\partial^2 E_x}{\partial x^2} + \frac{\partial^2 E_x}{\partial y^2} + \frac{\partial^2 E_x}{\partial z^2}\right) - \mu\epsilon\frac{\partial^2 E_x}{\partial t^2} = 0 \qquad (12.46)$$

This is a wave equation for the component E_x, for its solutions represent wave motion in which E_x is the dependent variable. It is remarkable that E_x obeys a differential equation which is perfectly independent of the existence or behavior of other cartesian components of the electric field. The reader may guess, and correctly so, that E_x is no more privileged than the other components of the $\mathbf{E}$ vector. The isotropic character postulated for the material in which the field exists guarantees that the other components E_y and E_z obey exactly the same equation. Furthermore, it is shown by a similar process that each cartesian component of $\mathbf{B}$ also satisfies an equation of the form of (12.46). For example, the reader is asked in the problem set to show that in insulating material which is isotropic, homogeneous, and linear:

$$\left(\frac{\partial^2 B_y}{\partial x^2} + \frac{\partial^2 B_y}{\partial y^2} + \frac{\partial^2 B_y}{\partial z^2}\right) - \mu\epsilon\frac{\partial^2 B_y}{\partial t^2} = 0 \qquad (12.47)$$

The three scalar equations for the components of $\mathbf{E}$ can be summarized in the single vector equation

$$\left(\frac{\partial^2\mathbf{E}}{\partial x^2} + \frac{\partial^2\mathbf{E}}{\partial y^2} + \frac{\partial^2\mathbf{E}}{\partial z^2}\right) - \mu\epsilon\frac{\partial^2\mathbf{E}}{\partial t^2} = 0 \qquad (12.48)$$

Likewise for $\mathbf{B}$,

$$\left(\frac{\partial^2\mathbf{B}}{\partial x^2} + \frac{\partial^2\mathbf{B}}{\partial y^2} + \frac{\partial^2\mathbf{B}}{\partial z^2}\right) - \mu\epsilon\frac{\partial^2\mathbf{B}}{\partial t^2} = 0 \qquad (12.49)$$

The use of the constitutive equations (12.32) and (12.34) leads immediately to equations of the same form in $\mathbf{D}$ and $\mathbf{H}$. Thus all the field vectors satisfy the same differential equation under the special assumptions of this section.

It may be well to stress that Eq. (12.48) is correct only because, in a dielectric and in absence of free charge, the electric field obeys (12.39). Thus any solutions of (12.48) which do not satisfy (12.39) are solutions of an incorrect differential equation, and hence are not possible electric fields. It is true, however, that all simultaneous solutions of Eqs. (12.39) and (12.48) are possible electric fields in a dielectric where $\rho = 0$. Similarly all simultaneous solutions of Eqs. (12.13) and (12.49) are possible magnetic fields for the systems discussed.

12.6. Plane Waves in Dielectric Material. The wave equation (12.48) for the electric field in isotropic, homogeneous, dielectric materials where there is no charge density has infinitely many solutions. A very simple particular solution may be obtained by substituting the trial function

$$\mathbf{E} = \mathbf{E}_0 \cos \omega \left(\frac{z}{v} - t \right) \tag{12.50}$$

where ω and v are scalar constants and $\mathbf{E}_0$ is a vector constant. The result of the substitution is

$$-\omega^2 \left(\frac{1}{v^2} - \mu\epsilon \right) \mathbf{E} = 0 \tag{12.51}$$

It is thus evident that Eq. (12.50) is a solution of (12.48), provided the constant v is given the value

$$v = \frac{1}{\sqrt{\mu\epsilon}} \tag{12.52}$$

The other constants in solution (12.50) remain arbitrary.

Now Eq. (12.50) represents a plane, harmonic wave of vector amplitude $\mathbf{E}_0$ and frequency $\omega/2\pi$ advancing along the z axis with velocity v. The velocity is characteristic of the medium in which the wave moves. In particular, the Maxwell equations thus predict the existence of electromagnetic waves in empty space, having velocity

$$c = \frac{1}{\sqrt{\mu_0\epsilon_0}} \tag{12.53}$$

Both μ_0 and ϵ_0 enter into simple electromagnetic relationships. Actually, we took one of these quantities arbitrarily:

$$\mu_0 \equiv 4\pi \times 10^{-7} \text{ newton/amp}^2 \tag{12.54}$$

(See Sec. 7.3.) Fixing μ_0 determines the unit of electric charge and this in turn fixes the value of ϵ_0. In principle, ϵ_0 may then be determined by electrostatic experiments. The result of purely electromagnetic determination of the velocity of Eq. (12.53) is

$$c_{em} = (2.99784 \pm 0.0001) \times 10^8 \text{ m/sec} \tag{12.55}$$

The striking feature of this result is that within experimental error it is identical with the velocity of light *in vacuo*, whose optically measured value is

$$c_{opt} = (2.997927 \pm 0.00002) \times 10^8 \text{ m/sec} \tag{12.56}$$

The immediate conclusion is that light is electromagnetic wave motion, and this conclusion is verified in many other ways. The identification of optical phenomena with electromagnetism was the spectacular achievement of Maxwell.

The velocity of electromagnetic waves in dielectric material as given by Eq. (12.52) may be checked by optical experiments also. The index of refraction which appears in Snell's law of refraction is related by all wave theories of light to the velocity v in the medium and the velocity c in space by

$$n = \frac{c}{v} \tag{12.57}$$

Using Eqs. (12.52) and (12.53), the electromagnetic prediction for the index of refraction is

$$n = \sqrt{\frac{\mu \epsilon}{\mu_0 \epsilon_0}} = \sqrt{K_m K_e} \tag{12.58}$$

where K_m and K_e are the relative values of permeability and dielectric constant. For most dielectric materials, K_m is so close to unity that it may be neglected, so that it is sufficient to use the approximate relation

$$n = \sqrt{K_e} \tag{12.59}$$

Equation (12.59) is experimentally verified. It is often necessary, however, to take into account the fact that K_e may depend upon the frequency of the electromagnetic wave. Dependence of n upon frequency is called dispersion.

Up to this point we have been ignoring the fact that if Eq. (12.50) is to represent an electromagnetic wave in isotropic homogeneous material where there is no charge density, it must satisfy not only the wave equation (12.48) but also

$$\text{div } \mathbf{E} = 0 \tag{12.60}$$

Substitution of Eq. (12.50) into (12.60) yields

$$\frac{\partial E_z}{\partial z} = 0 \tag{12.61}$$

The most general electric field of form (12.50) obeying (12.61) has a constant z component:

$$E_z = E_{0z} \tag{12.62}$$

Thus the z component of the electric field takes no part in the wave motion, although it may exist independently of the wave. So far as the electric field is concerned, the wave motion is transverse, that is, the dependent variable of the wave motion is a vector at right angles to the propagation direction. Polarization phenomena occur in optics and in radio-wave propagation in accordance with this prediction of electromagnetic theory. A plane-polarized plane wave is one whose electric field vector is always parallel to a given plane containing the propagation direction. For example, a wave of the type of equation (12.50) polarized parallel to the xz plane is

$$\mathbf{E}_1 = \mathbf{i} E_{0x} \cos \omega \left(\frac{z}{v} - t \right) \tag{12.63}$$

The electric field of a wave is always accompanied by a magnetic field, as is implied by the term "electromagnetic wave." Let us find the magnetic induction accompanying the electric field (12.50). This may be done by use of the Maxwell equation

$$\text{curl } \mathbf{E} = -\frac{\partial \mathbf{B}}{\partial t} \tag{12.64}$$

When Eq. (12.64) is applied to any function $\mathbf{E}$ such as (12.50) whose only space variable is z, the result is

$$\left(-\frac{\partial E_y}{\partial z} \right) \mathbf{i} + \left(\frac{\partial E_x}{\partial z} \right) \mathbf{j} = -\frac{\partial \mathbf{B}}{\partial t} \tag{12.65}$$

where $\mathbf{i}$ and $\mathbf{j}$ are unit vectors along x and y. It appears from Eq. (12.65) that the only components of $\mathbf{B}$ which change with time are the transverse ones. The longitudinal component must be constant, and thus is not a part of the wave motion; for (12.65) yields at once the scalar equation

$$\frac{\partial B_z}{\partial t} = 0 \tag{12.66}$$

A plane electromagnetic wave is therefore always transverse in its magnetic induction.

Now Eq. (12.65) may be rewritten in the form

$$\frac{\partial}{\partial z} (\mathbf{k} \times \mathbf{E}) = -\frac{\partial \mathbf{B}}{\partial t} \tag{12.67}$$

where $\mathbf{k}$ is unit vector along z. Substitution of Eq. (12.50) into (12.67) shows that the magnetic induction accompanying the electric field (12.50) satisfies the equation

$$-\frac{\omega}{v} \mathbf{k} \times \mathbf{E}_0 \sin \omega \left(\frac{z}{v} - t \right) = -\frac{\partial \mathbf{B}}{\partial t} \tag{12.68}$$

Integration now yields

$$\mathbf{B} = \frac{1}{v} (\mathbf{k} \times \mathbf{E}_0) \cos \omega \left(\frac{z}{v} - t \right) + \mathbf{B}_0(x,y,z) \tag{12.69}$$

Here $\mathbf{B}_0(x,y,z)$ is an arbitrary vector function of the space coordinates but not the time, and it enters as the constant of integration since Eq. (12.68) was a partial differential equation. This term is actually not quite arbitrary, since the magnetic induction must always satisfy

$$\text{div } \mathbf{B} = 0 \tag{12.70}$$

We shall not be concerned with $\mathbf{B}_0$ at all, however, since it is constant in time and hence is not associated with the electromagnetic wave. The term of Eq. (12.69) which is part of the wave can be rewritten in terms of the electric field (12.50):

$$\mathbf{B} = \frac{1}{v}\,\mathbf{k} \times \mathbf{E} \tag{12.71}$$

This shows that the magnetic induction is perpendicular not only to the propagation direction, but also to $\mathbf{E}$. In a plane-polarized wave, the planes of polarization of $\mathbf{E}$ and $\mathbf{B}$ are mutually perpendicular. In particular, for the plane-polarized wave (12.63), the magnetic induction is

$$\mathbf{B}_1 = \mathbf{j}\,\frac{E_{0x}}{v}\cos\omega\left(\frac{z}{v} - t\right) \tag{12.72}$$

It is to be noticed from Eq. (12.71) that the electric and magnetic fields are in phase with one another. It is also worth remarking that of course the magnetic field (12.71) of the electromagnetic wave satisfies its own wave equation:

$$\frac{\partial^2 \mathbf{B}}{\partial x^2} + \frac{\partial^2 \mathbf{B}}{\partial y^2} + \frac{\partial^2 \mathbf{B}}{\partial z^2} - \mu\epsilon\,\frac{\partial^2 \mathbf{B}}{\partial t^2} = 0 \tag{12.73}$$

There is much more that can be said about plane waves. For example, arbitrary phase constants may be introduced into Eq. (12.50); and if the phases of the x and y components of the electric field are allowed to differ, the resulting function describes the field of an elliptically polarized wave. The phenomena of elliptic polarization are well known in optics. Another fruitful topic concerns the superposition of harmonic waves of different frequency. A Fourier analysis shows that a wave in which the transverse components of electric field are arbitrary functions of $(z/v - t)$ can be represented in this way. The term "spectrum," or "spectral distribution," is used for the set of harmonic components whose resultant constitutes a given wave.

It is easy to verify directly that the transverse field components of an electromagnetic wave may be arbitrary functions of $(z/v - t)$, or of $(z/v + t)$. Suppose that the arbitrary vector function $\mathbf{f}(u)$ has first and second derivatives $\mathbf{f}'(u)$ and $\mathbf{f}''(u)$, respectively, and let $u = (z/v \mp t)$. Then

$$\frac{\partial^2 \mathbf{f}(z/v \mp t)}{\partial z^2} = \frac{1}{v^2}\,\mathbf{f}''\left(\frac{z}{v} \mp t\right) \tag{12.74}$$

and

$$\frac{\partial^2 \mathbf{f}(z/v \mp t)}{\partial t^2} - = \mathbf{f}''\left(\frac{z}{v} \mp t\right) \tag{12.75}$$

Substitution now shows immediately that

$$\mathbf{E} = \mathbf{f}\left(\frac{z}{v} \mp t\right) \tag{12.76}$$

is a solution of Eq. (12.48), provided the constant v is given by Eq. (12.52). Equation (12.60) is satisfied if $\mathbf{f}$ is entirely transverse to the propagation direction, which is the z axis. Thus Eq. (12.76) gives a possible electric field regardless of its functional form $\mathbf{f}(u)$, so long as this vector is transverse. It is to be noted that if $u = (z/v - t)$, a given phase of the wave (*i.e.*, a given value of the field) travels in the $+z$ direction with velocity v, while if $u = (z/v + t)$ the propagation is in the $-z$ direction. The wave at time $t + \Delta t$ has the same form in space as the wave at time t except that it has moved along the z axis through a distance $\Delta z = \pm v\,\Delta t$. The accompanying magnetic field may be determined by use of Eq. (12.64), just as was done for the harmonic wave, and the result, exclusive of the possibility of an independent and constant longitudinal field, is

$$\mathbf{B} = \frac{1}{v}\mathbf{k} \times \mathbf{E} = \frac{1}{v}\mathbf{k} \times \mathbf{f}\left(\frac{z}{v} \mp t\right) \tag{12.77}$$

12.7. Energy Flow. The Poynting Vector. Questions of energy transformation and energy flow are among the more perplexing and complex aspects of electromagnetic theory. The reader is reminded of the care necessary even in treating the subject of electrostatic energy in Chap. 4. For example, we excluded from consideration in Sec. 4.2 any energy storage due to the creation of bound charge by the piezoelectric effect. We need not therefore be ashamed of specializing our treatment of energy flow in the general electromagnetic field. Let us then consider energy flow in electromagnetic systems composed only of materials which for simplicity are isotropic, and which are linear in their dielectric and magnetic properties. It is to be realized at the outset that the restriction of linearity excludes from consideration the production of heat by magnetic or dielectric hysteresis, as well as the piezoelectricity and magnetostriction which are important in transducers for transferring energy in small amounts between electrical and mechanical systems. The remaining important mechanism by which electromagnetic energy is transferred or radiated is the flow of free current. Current flow in batteries, generators, or motors results in transfer of energy between electrical and chemical or mechanical forms by the operation of electromotive force; in resistors, it results in transfer of energy to heat; in electrical transmission lines, it results in transportation of electrical energy; in inductors and condensers it results in energy storage similar to the kinetic and potential energy of a mechanical system; and in antennas it results in radiation of energy which travels out indefinitely in the form of electro-magnetic waves. Thus the single mechanism of current flow is involved in so many important processes as to be well worth special attention.

Let us represent all free electric currents, for purposes of the present discussion, by the volume current density function $\mathbf{J}$. In Sec. 5.1 it was shown that if $\mathbf{J}$ results from the motion of a number of kinds of charge carriers, then at a point (x,y,z)

$$\mathbf{J}(x,y,z) = \sum_i n_i q_i \mathbf{v}_i \qquad (12.78)$$

where q_i is the charge on the ith type of carrier, n_i is the macroscopic density function giving the average number of carriers of this type per unit volume in the vicinity of the point (x,y,z), and $\mathbf{v}_i$ is the average velocity of these carriers in this vicinity. Now on the supposition that each carrier has the velocity of an average carrier for its position (x,y,z), and experiences on the average the macroscopic fields $\mathbf{E}(x,y,z,t)$ and $\mathbf{B}(x,y,z,t)$ at that position, the electromagnetic force of the field on the carrier is

$$\mathbf{F}_i = q_i(\mathbf{E} + \mathbf{v}_i \times \mathbf{B}) \qquad (12.79)$$

This is the Lorentz force law as stated in Eq. (7.12), Sec. 7.2. Work is done by the electromagnetic field on this carrier at the rate

$$\mathbf{F}_i \cdot \mathbf{v}_i = q_i \mathbf{v}_i \cdot \mathbf{E}$$

For all the kinds of carriers, the power P_1 transferred out of the field per unit volume is consequently

$$P_1 = \sum_i n_i \mathbf{F}_i \cdot \mathbf{v}_i = \mathbf{E} \cdot \sum_i n_i q_i \mathbf{v}_i \qquad (12.80)$$

Therefore

$$P_1 = \mathbf{E} \cdot \mathbf{J} \qquad (12.81)$$

The quantity $\mathbf{E} \cdot \mathbf{J}$ sometimes measures Joule heat. In a conducting region where $\mathbf{J}$ is produced solely by an electric field, it is useful to define a conductivity g such that

$$\mathbf{J} = g\mathbf{E} \qquad (12.82)$$

Substitution of Eq. (12.82) into (12.81) yields the result

$$P_{1\,\text{Joule}} = gE^2 \qquad (12.83)$$

It was for this application that Eq. (12.81) was derived in Sec. 5.5. But now in general Eq. (12.82) does not yield the current density, since other forces may act on a charge carrier besides those described by the macroscopic electric field. For example, in the armature of a motor or generator the current carriers (electrons) are constrained to share the velocity of the wire in which they flow, and because of this velocity the magnetic field in the machine produces a force on the electrons in the direction of the axis of the wire, so producing or modifying the current flow $\mathbf{J}$. Likewise, in the boundary layer between the electrolytic solution and electrode of a battery there are acting on the charge carriers forces of a chemical or quantum-mechanical nature. Such forces may sometimes cause $\mathbf{J}$ to have a direction opposite to $\mathbf{E}$. When this is the case, the product $\mathbf{J} \cdot \mathbf{E}$ is negative, and represents a net flow of power into the electromagnetic system at the expense of mechanical, chemical, or other nonelectromagnetic energy.

It appears therefore that $\mathbf{J} \cdot \mathbf{E}$ is a quantity of very general significance correctly describing the net transfer of power per unit volume between electromagnetic and other forms of energy, wherever the agent producing the transfer is the motion of free electric charge. We proceed to show how this function may be related to the electromagnetic fields. From one of Maxwell's equations,

$$\mathbf{J} = \operatorname{curl} \mathbf{H} - \frac{\partial \mathbf{D}}{\partial t} \tag{12.84}$$

Therefore

$$\mathbf{E} \cdot \mathbf{J} = \mathbf{E} \cdot \operatorname{curl} \mathbf{H} - \mathbf{E} \cdot \frac{\partial \mathbf{D}}{\partial t} \tag{12.85}$$

This expression can be made more useful and symmetrical by first using a vector identity:

$$\mathbf{E} \cdot \operatorname{curl} \mathbf{H} = - \operatorname{div} (\mathbf{E} \times \mathbf{H}) + \mathbf{H} \cdot \operatorname{curl} \mathbf{E} \tag{12.86}$$

Equation (12.86) is readily shown to be true by writing out each term in cartesian coordinates. Now, by another of the Maxwell equations,

$$\operatorname{curl} \mathbf{E} = - \frac{\partial \mathbf{B}}{\partial t} \tag{12.87}$$

Therefore

$$\mathbf{H} \cdot \operatorname{curl} \mathbf{E} = -\mathbf{H} \cdot \frac{\partial \mathbf{B}}{\partial t} \tag{12.88}$$

Combining Eqs. (12.86) and (12.88) with Eq. (12.85), we obtain the symmetrical form

$$-\mathbf{E} \cdot \mathbf{J} = \operatorname{div} \mathbf{E} \times \mathbf{H} + \left(\mathbf{E} \cdot \frac{\partial \mathbf{D}}{\partial t} + \mathbf{H} \cdot \frac{\partial \mathbf{B}}{\partial t} \right) \tag{12.89}$$

If Eq. (12.89) is integrated over a volume V of space, the left-hand member then gives the power P_V transferred into the electromagnetic field by the mechanism of motion of free charge within V:

$$P_V = - \int_V \mathbf{E} \cdot \mathbf{J} \, dV = \int_V \operatorname{div} (\mathbf{E} \times \mathbf{H}) \, dV$$

$$+ \int_V \left(\mathbf{E} \cdot \frac{\partial \mathbf{D}}{\partial t} + \mathbf{H} \cdot \frac{\partial \mathbf{B}}{\partial t} \right) dV \tag{12.90}$$

Before interpreting this expression, we may apply the divergence theorem (cf. Sec. 7.6) to the first integral on the right to obtain

$$P_V = \oint_S \mathbf{E} \times \mathbf{H} \cdot \mathbf{n} \, da + \int_V \left(\mathbf{E} \cdot \frac{\partial \mathbf{D}}{\partial t} + \mathbf{H} \cdot \frac{\partial \mathbf{B}}{\partial t} \right) dV \qquad (12.91)$$

Here $\mathbf{n}$ is the unit outward normal to the surface S enclosing the volume V. One more change in this equation may be made for linear isotropic media, where the permittivity and permeability ϵ and μ are independent of field strengths and hence of time:

$$P_V = \oint_S \mathbf{E} \times \mathbf{H} \cdot \mathbf{n} \, da + \frac{d}{dt} \tfrac{1}{2} \int_V (\epsilon E^2 + \mu H^2) \, dV \qquad (12.92)$$

The second term of the right-hand member of this equation may be compared with the expressions developed earlier (Secs. 4.5 and 9.17) for electrostatic and magnetostatic energies in linear systems:

$$W_{es} = \tfrac{1}{2} \int_{\text{all space}} \epsilon E^2 \, dV \qquad W_{ms} = \tfrac{1}{2} \int_{\text{all space}} \mu H^2 \, dV \qquad (12.93)$$

It is now natural to postulate that for linear systems the function

$$W_V = \tfrac{1}{2} \int_V (\epsilon E^2 + \mu H^2) \, dV \qquad (12.94)$$

represents energy stored by the time-varying electromagnetic field and localized within the volume V. It must be realized that this is a postulate, not a deduction, even though it makes good sense when applied to the fields of a traveling electromagnetic wave. However, it can be said more rigorously that the integral over all space,

$$W \equiv \tfrac{1}{2} \int_{\text{all space}} (\epsilon E^2 + \mu H^2) \, dV \qquad (12.95)$$

represents the total electromagnetic energy of a finite linear system, and this we proceed to prove. When the limits of integration in Eq. (12.92) extend over all space, the surface integral approaches zero:

$$\oint_{\substack{\text{infinite surface} \\ \text{enclosing all space}}} \mathbf{E} \times \mathbf{H} \cdot \mathbf{n} \, da = 0 \qquad (12.96)$$

Equation (12.92) therefore yields for the total power input P:

$$P = \frac{1}{dt} \tfrac{1}{2} \int_{\text{all space}} (\epsilon E^2 + \mu H^2) \, dV \equiv \frac{dW}{dt} \qquad (12.97)$$

Conservation of energy then requires that W represent the energy of the system, at least within a constant; and it is only natural to choose the constant so that $W = 0$ when all fields vanish. Thus the significance of the integral (12.95) is established. The proof of Eq. (12.96) may be made by taking for S a sphere of radius R about the origin and considering the limit as $R \to \infty$. All steady fields fall off at least as fast as the inverse square of R when R is large compared with the size of the charge and current system. Steady fields therefore produce an integral falling off as $1/R^4$, while the surface of integration only increases as R^2. As for the radiation fields, parts of which fall off only as $1/R$, these are propagated with finite speed (that of light) and thus cannot reach the surface of integration as $R \to \infty$.

Let us now return to the interpretation of Eq. (12.92). If the postulate of energy localization is accepted, so that Eq. (12.94) is given physical meaning, the conservation of energy requires that the surface integral in (12.92) represent power flow P_S across the closed surface S; for this integral is then the difference between the rates of production and of storage of the electromagnetic energy within V. Thus we make the interpretation

$$\oint_S \mathbf{E} \times \mathbf{H} \cdot \mathbf{n} \, da = P_S \tag{12.98}$$

The vector $\mathbf{E} \times \mathbf{H}$ is called the Poynting vector.[1] We shall call it $\mathbf{N}$:

$$\mathbf{N} \equiv \mathbf{E} \times \mathbf{H} \tag{12.99}$$

In words, Eq. (12.98) states that $\mathbf{N}$ is such a vector that its flux through a closed surface S yields the power flowing across S in the electromagnetic field.

When electromagnetic fields vary periodically or quasi-periodically in time, as for instance light or radio waves, it is the time average power flow which is physically significant. Consider the case of waves of period T, so that the time average of the power put into the electromagnetic system by conduction processes is

$$\bar{P}_V = \frac{1}{T} \int_0^T P_V \, dt \tag{12.100}$$

When this is applied to Eq. (12.92), the result is

$$\bar{P}_V = \frac{1}{T} \int_0^T dt \oint_S \mathbf{N} \cdot \mathbf{n} \, da + \frac{1}{2T} \int_V (\epsilon E^2 + \mu H^2) \, dV \Big|_{t=0}^T \tag{12.101}$$

Suppose for the present that a steady state has been reached throughout V, so that the second integral on the right has the same value at $t = T$ as at $t = 0$, by definition of a period. The last term of Eq. (12.101) then vanishes. By interchange of the order of integration in the other term

[1] Named after its discoverer, J. H. Poynting (1852–1914).

of the right member of Eq. (12.101), we obtain

$$\bar{P}_V = \oint_S \bar{\mathbf{N}} \cdot \mathbf{n} \, da \tag{12.102}$$

where $\bar{\mathbf{N}}$ is the time average of the Poynting vector:

$$\bar{\mathbf{N}} \equiv \frac{1}{T} \int_0^T \mathbf{N} \, dt \tag{12.103}$$

Equation (12.102) states that in a steady-state oscillating system, the average Poynting vector $\bar{\mathbf{N}}$ when integrated over a closed surface S does give the average power entering the electromagnetic system by conduction processes in V. Note that this is a rigorous deduction from Eq. (12.92) without any supplementary hypothesis like (12.94) about the distribution of stored energy. This theorem is useful in computing radiation from a system of oscillating charges and currents by a knowledge of the fields at a distance from the system.

Equation (12.102) does not require that $\bar{\mathbf{N}}$ should correctly specify the distribution of energy flow over the closed surface S. However, the concept that a traveling electromagnetic wave represents transportation of energy leads to the definition of a vector intensity function representing at each point of the field the energy flow per unit time per unit cross-section area. It is natural to postulate that $\bar{\mathbf{N}}$ itself, which has the proper dimensions and is a possible energy flow function for a closed surface, is this intensity function. This postulate is satisfactory for an electromagnetic wave. It should be noted, however, that interpreting $\bar{\mathbf{N}}$ in this fashion for a static system of fields leads to an unobservable and hence meaningless circulation of energy. Accepting $\bar{\mathbf{N}}$ as the intensity function for an electromagnetic wave, we may write for the average power flow $d\bar{P}$ across an infinitesimal area da with positive unit normal $\mathbf{n}$

$$d\bar{P} = \bar{\mathbf{N}} \cdot \mathbf{n} \, da \tag{12.104}$$

Thus across a finite but unclosed surface A the average power flow in an electromagnetic wave is

$$\bar{P}_A = \int_A \bar{\mathbf{N}} \cdot \mathbf{n} \, da \tag{12.105}$$

As an example, let us find the Poynting vector for the plane, harmonic electromagnetic wave of Sec. 12.6. From Eqs. (12.63) and (12.72) of that section, we obtain

$$\mathbf{E} = \mathbf{i} E_{0x} \cos \omega(z \sqrt{\mu\epsilon} - t) \tag{12.106}$$

$$\mathbf{H} = \mathbf{j} \frac{\sqrt{\mu\epsilon}}{\mu} E_{0x} \cos \omega(z \sqrt{\mu\epsilon} - t) \tag{12.107}$$

In these equations the velocity v of the wave has been expressed as $1/\sqrt{\mu\epsilon}$. The average Poynting vector is thus

$$\bar{\mathbf{N}} = \mathbf{k} \sqrt{\frac{\epsilon}{\mu}} E_{0x}{}^2 \left\langle \cos^2 \omega(z \sqrt{\mu\epsilon} - t) \right\rangle_{\text{av}} \tag{12.108}$$

The average of the cosine squared function is $\frac{1}{2}$ as is seen at once from the trigonometric identity $\cos^2 u = \frac{1}{2} + \frac{1}{2} \cos 2u$.   Therefore

$$\bar{\mathbf{N}} = \mathbf{k} \frac{1}{2} \sqrt{\frac{\epsilon}{\mu}} E_{0x}{}^2 \tag{12.109}$$

It is to be observed that $\bar{\mathbf{N}}$ has here the direction of propagation of the wave, namely, that of the $+z$ axis, and that the magnitude of $\bar{\mathbf{N}}$, or the scalar intensity of the wave, is proportional to the square of the amplitude of the electric field vector.

It is interesting to note that the postulate which makes $\bar{\mathbf{N}}$ the correct average energy flow function for a harmonic electromagnetic wave is consistent with a model in which an average energy density

$$\bar{w} = \frac{1}{2}\epsilon\langle E^2\rangle_{\text{av}} + \frac{1}{2}\mu\langle H^2\rangle_{\text{av}} \tag{12.110}$$

travels like a fluid with the speed $v = 1/\sqrt{\mu\epsilon}$ of the electromagnetic wave in the direction of propagation of the wave.   In such a model the relation of the various quantities is

$$\bar{\mathbf{N}} = \bar{w}\mathbf{v} \tag{12.111}$$

where $\mathbf{v}$ is the vector velocity of the propagation of the wave.   This may be seen from Fig. 12.1.   Consider the energy which crosses an area da with unit normal $\mathbf{n}$, in a time T equal to a period of the wave.   By the intensity function $\bar{\mathbf{N}}$ this should be

$$dE = T\bar{\mathbf{N}} \cdot \mathbf{n} \, da \tag{12.112}$$

But if energy density $\bar{w}$ is flowing past da with velocity $\mathbf{v}$, it fills a volume

$$dV = \mathbf{v} \cdot \mathbf{n}T \, da \tag{12.113}$$

whence the energy that has crossed da is

$$dE = \bar{w}\mathbf{v} \cdot \mathbf{n}T \, da \tag{12.114}$$

Equations (12.112) and (12.114) hold for any orientation of the surface da.   Equating these two expressions then leads to Eq. (12.111).   Q.E.D. It is left as a problem for the reader to show that Eqs. (12.110) and (12.111) when applied to the plane wave of our example result in the expression (12.109) for the intensity function.

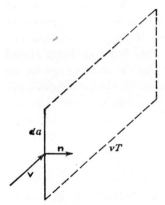

Fig. 12.1. Energy flow across a surface element.

12.8. Radiation of a Harmonically Oscillating Electric Dipole.   The term radiation is applied to a traveling electromagnetic field which carries energy away from a time-varying system of charge and current, or to the process by which such a field is produced.   A thorough discussion of the radiation process belongs to an advanced treatment of electromagnetic theory.   Nevertheless, as a sequel to the preceding sections on electromagnetic waves, we shall give without complete proof a simple description of the simplest kind of radiating system, which is called a harmonically oscillating dipole.   A system of electric charges and

currents will be said to be a harmonically oscillating dipole under the following conditions:

1. The system has an electric dipole moment **p** in a fixed direction, whose magnitude varies harmonically with time, having a given frequency f. The symbol ω will be used for $2\pi f$.

2. The space occupied by the system is finite, and has a maximum length L which is much less than the distance R from an origin in the system to the observer:

$$L \ll R \qquad (12.115)$$

3. The wavelength

$$\lambda = \frac{c}{f} \qquad (12.116)$$

of electromagnetic waves in empty space, in which for simplicity the system is to be located, is very much greater than the size of the system. Here c is the velocity of light *in vacuo*, which we have seen to be $1/\sqrt{\mu_0\epsilon_0}$. The exact form of inequality that will be needed includes a factor of 2π:

$$L \ll \frac{\lambda}{2\pi} \qquad (12.117)$$

This restriction means also that the time $t_1 = L/c$ required for an electromagnetic wave to cross the system is much smaller than the period $1/f$ of oscillation. If this were not the case, the system could not be said to be "small" for the radiation process, and thus would not be called a dipole.

To be precise as to the meaning of the inequalities (12.115) and (12.117), we are undertaking an approximation for the radiation of any system involving the neglect of the ratios L/R and $2\pi L/\lambda$ compared with unity. It may be instructive to observe that the most elementary source of static electric fields is a point charge, and the lowest approximation to the field at a distance from a static system is the field of a point charge. There is no point-charge field for any complete magnetostatic system, because of the nonexistence of free magnetic charge; and consequently the simplest magnetostatic field for a complete system is the magnetic dipole field. Accordingly we noticed in Chap. 7 that the magnetic dipole field is the lowest nonvanishing approximation to the field at a distance from a current circuit. Likewise, there is no radiating system consisting of an oscillating point charge: such a system is impossible because it would violate the conservation of electric charge. Thus the simplest radiating system is the oscillating dipole. A superposition of fields of oscillating electric dipoles is the lowest significant approximation to the distant field of any radiating system which is not too large compared with λ and which has a time-varying electric dipole moment at all.

In order to simplify our work, we shall compute the radiation from a particular system consisting of a straight piece of wire of length L in which we shall suppose a current

$$I = I_0 \cos \omega t \qquad (12.118)$$

to flow.   This current is to be uniform along the length of the wire. In order to satisfy the conservation of charge, we may suppose that the current builds up charges of opposite signs on the ends of the wire. Suppose the wire is at the origin of coordinates, as shown in Fig. 12.2, and has the direction of the z axis.

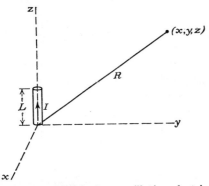

Take the positive sense for I as that of the $+z$ axis, and let the charge on the positive end of the wire be called q.   By conservation of charge, q is that which is transported by the current I, and hence

$$q = \int I\, dt = \frac{I_0}{\omega} \sin \omega t \qquad (12.119)$$

Since no steady charges contribute to the time-varying electromagnetic field which is our only present concern, the constant of integration in Eq. (12.119) has been set to zero.   Similarly, within an irrelevant constant, the charge on the lower end of the wire is $-q$.   The dipole moment of the wire is therefore

Fig. 12.2. Model of an oscillating electric dipole.

$$\mathbf{p} = qL\mathbf{k} = \frac{I_0}{\omega} L\mathbf{k} \sin \omega t \equiv p_0\mathbf{k} \sin \omega t \qquad (12.120)$$

where $\mathbf{k}$ is unit vector in the $+z$ direction and the symbol p_0 is used for the amplitude of the varying dipole movement.   This is seen to satisfy postulate (1) above.   The system is therefore an oscillating dipole, provided the inequalities (12.115) and (12.117) apply.   Notice the relation between the amplitudes I_0 and p_0:

$$I_0 L = p_0 \omega \qquad (12.121)$$

Now to provide a basis on which to compute the field of the wire element, we shall state without proof a theorem from radiation theory. See Sec. 12.11 for further discussion of this theorem.   First of all, any magnetic field $\mathbf{B}$ can be described by a vector potential function $\mathbf{A}$ such as was introduced in Chap. 7 for the magnetostatic field.   In abbreviated notation,

$$\mathbf{B} = \operatorname{curl} \mathbf{A} \qquad (12.122)$$

This is valid because the divergence of a curl is identically zero, as is required of the divergence of $\mathbf{B}$ by the Maxwell equations. A convenient integral formula for a vector potential which yields the magnetostatic field is found in Sec. 7.5 to be

$$\mathbf{A}(x,y,z) = \frac{\mu_0}{4\pi} \oint_C \frac{I(x',y',z')\,d\mathbf{l}}{r} \qquad (12.123)$$

The quantity r is the distance between the element of integration at (x',y',z'), which is an element $d\mathbf{l}$ of wire carrying current I, and the observer at (x,y,z). Equation (12.123) is written for space empty except for the current I. Now the theorem which we wish to use states that a correct vector potential for the magnetic field of time-varying currents, when all space is otherwise empty, is

$$\mathbf{A}(x,y,z,t) = \frac{\mu_0}{4\pi} \int_{\text{system}} \frac{I(x',y',z'\,;\,t - r/c)}{r}\,d\mathbf{l} \qquad (12.124)$$

This is called a *retarded potential*, and the current or current density is to be evaluated at the *retarded time* $t - r/c$ appropriate to each element of integration, where c is the velocity $1/\sqrt{\mu_0\epsilon_0}$ of electromagnetic waves in space. Equation (12.124) is plausible, since an interval of time r/c must elapse before a change of current at a given point of the system can have its effect on the field at the observer. One can describe the retarded integral (12.124) as the result of integrating in accordance with the state of the system as "seen" by the observer, it being understood that "seeing" takes the time r/c for a light ray to traverse the distance between the observer and each point of the system. To derive Eq. (12.124) rigorously requires first setting up a partial differential equation, which is satisfied by the vector potential $\mathbf{A}$, and then working out its solution.

Equation (12.124) is general and in no way limited in application to oscillating dipoles. It leads to a particularly simple result, however, for the oscillating dipole. The variable distance r then differs from the fixed distance R between observer and origin at most by the length L of the system, and in view of inequality (12.115) we take as the dipole approximation

$$\frac{1}{r} \doteq \frac{1}{R} \qquad (12.125)$$

Thus the denominator of the integrand of Eq. (12.124) comes outside the integral sign. Before substituting Eq. (12.125) into (12.124), notice that for the wire along the z axis

$$d\mathbf{l} = \mathbf{k}\,dz' \qquad (12.126)$$

Now when Eqs. (12.125), (12.126), and (12.118) are put into Eq. (12.124), the vector potential of the wire of length L becomes

$$\mathbf{A}(x,y,z,t) \doteq \frac{\mu_0 I_0 \mathbf{k}}{4\pi R} \int_0^L \cos\left[\omega\left(t - \frac{r}{c}\right)\right] dz' \qquad (12.127)$$

Inequality (12.117), which has not yet been used, simplifies this result further. Since r differs from R at most by L, the argument of the cosine function differs from $\omega(t - R/c)$ at most by

$$\frac{\omega L}{c} = \frac{2\pi L}{\lambda} \qquad (12.128)$$

By inequality (12.117) this is only a small fraction of a radian, so that to the dipole approximation we shall write $\cos \omega(t - R/c)$ as the integrand of Eq. (12.127). Thus

$$\mathbf{A} \doteq \frac{\mu_0 I_0 \cos \omega(t - R/c)\mathbf{k}}{4\pi R} \int_0^L dz' \qquad (12.129)$$

This integration may be performed at once. To avoid continued use of the sign for approximate equality, expression (12.129) will be defined as the dipole approximation $\mathbf{A}_0$ to the vector potential of the radiating wire. Thus

$$\mathbf{A}_0 = \frac{\mu_0 I_0 L \cos \omega(t - R/c)}{4\pi R} \mathbf{k} \qquad (12.130)$$

In terms of the amplitude p_0 of the dipole moment of the wire, as given in Eq. (12.121),

$$\mathbf{A}_0 = \frac{\mu_0 \omega p_0 \cos \omega(t - R/c)}{4\pi R} \mathbf{k} \qquad (12.131)$$

Without proof, it may be stated that Eq. (12.131) is more general than the particular system of the straight wire which we have used in the derivation. It may in fact be shown to apply to any harmonically oscillating dipole whose moment lies in the $\mathbf{k}$ direction.

The problem of determining the dipole radiation fields may now be carried through in two steps. First, the magnetic induction $\mathbf{B}$ may be found by taking the curl of the potential $\mathbf{A}_0$. The electric field $\mathbf{E}$ may then be found from $\mathbf{B}$ by using the Maxwell equation

$$\text{curl } \mathbf{H} = \mathbf{J} + \frac{\partial \mathbf{D}}{\partial t} \qquad (12.132)$$

For the empty space at the observer's position, where $\mathbf{J} = 0$, Eq. (12.132) can be rewritten in the form

$$\frac{\partial \mathbf{E}}{\partial t} = \frac{1}{\mu_0 \epsilon_0} \text{ curl } \mathbf{B} \qquad (12.133)$$

Integration then yields the electric field:

$$\mathbf{E} = \frac{1}{\mu_0\epsilon_0} \int \operatorname{curl} \mathbf{B} \, dt \qquad (12.134)$$

Since Eq. (12.133) involves a partial time derivative of $\mathbf{E}$, it leaves unspecified any static electric field, which is the constant of integration for (12.134). No static field is associated with the radiation; therefore this constant has been set to zero. In principle, the cartesian components of the radiation fields may now be found by straightforward differentiations and an integration, starting with Eq. (12.131). The work is made much simpler, however, and the results take a simpler and more meaningful form, if spherical coordinates are used. Figure 12.3 shows how these coordinates, radius R, polar angle θ, and azimuth ϕ, are related to cartesian coordinates. A vector in cartesian form,

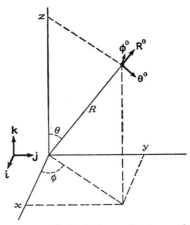

Fig. 12.3. Spherical coordinates and unit vectors.

$$\mathbf{a} = a_x\mathbf{i} + a_y\mathbf{j} + a_z\mathbf{k}$$

may be rewritten in terms of unit vectors $\mathbf{R}^0$, $\mathbf{\theta}^0$, and $\mathbf{\phi}^0$:

$$\mathbf{a} = a_R\mathbf{R}^0 + a_\theta\mathbf{\theta}^0 + a_\phi\mathbf{\phi}^0$$

$\mathbf{R}^0$ at any point of space has the direction and sense of the infinitesimal displacement corresponding to an increment of R alone; and similarly for the other unit vectors. It is to be noted that the spherical unit vectors are not constants like $\mathbf{i}$, $\mathbf{j}$, and $\mathbf{k}$, but depend on the point of space. The vector potential (12.131) of the oscillating dipole has for a general observer both R and θ components:

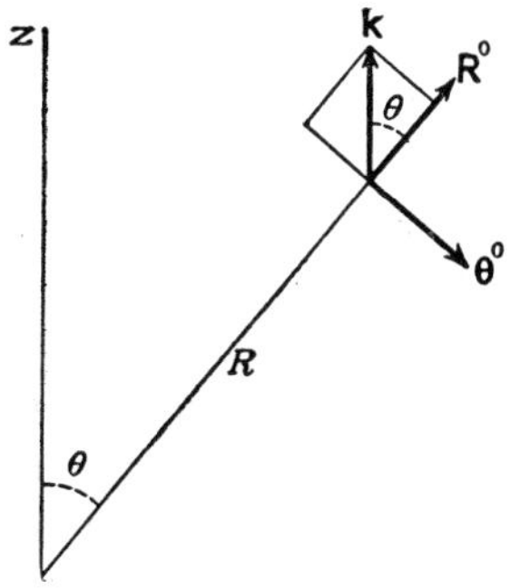

$$\mathbf{A}_0 = \left[\frac{\mu_0\omega p_0}{4\pi R} \cos \omega \left(t - \frac{R}{c} \right) \right] (\mathbf{R}^0 \cos \theta - \mathbf{\theta}^0 \sin \theta) \qquad (12.135)$$

Fig. 12.4. Resolution of the k unit vector in the $\mathbf{R}^0$ and $\mathbf{\theta}^0$ directions.

This is readily seen from Fig. 12.4, which shows the vectors $\mathbf{k}$, $\mathbf{R}^0$, and $\mathbf{\theta}^0$ in their common plane, the zR plane. The spherical formula for the curl operation is

$$\textbf{curl a} = \frac{1}{R \sin \theta} \left[\frac{\partial}{\partial \theta} \left(a_\phi \sin \theta \right) - \frac{\partial a_\theta}{\partial \phi} \right] \textbf{R}^0$$

$$+ \frac{1}{R} \left[\frac{1}{\sin \theta} \frac{\partial a_R}{\partial \phi} - \frac{\partial}{\partial R} \left(R a_\phi \right) \right] \boldsymbol{\theta}^0 + \frac{1}{R} \left[\frac{\partial}{\partial R} \left(R a_\theta \right) - \frac{\partial a_R}{\partial \theta} \right] \boldsymbol{\phi}^0 \quad (12.136)$$

The reader may find this derived in a text on vector analysis or advanced engineering mathematics. Application of Eq. (12.136) to (12.135) leads quickly to

$$\textbf{B} = \frac{\mu_0 \omega p_0 \sin \theta}{4\pi} \left[-\frac{\omega}{cR} \sin \omega \left(t - \frac{R}{c} \right) + \frac{1}{R^2} \cos \omega \left(t - \frac{R}{c} \right) \right] \boldsymbol{\phi}^0 \quad (12.137)$$

Thus the lines of **B** are circular about the z axis, and **B** is everywhere azimuthal in direction. When formula (12.136) is applied to the **B** function, the result is

$$\textbf{curl B} = \frac{2\mu_0 \omega p_0 \cos \theta}{4\pi} \left[-\frac{\omega}{cR^2} \sin \omega \left(t - \frac{R}{c} \right) + \frac{1}{R^3} \cos \omega \left(t - \frac{R}{c} \right) \right] \textbf{R}^0$$

$$+ \frac{\mu_0 \omega p_0 \sin \theta}{4\pi} \left[-\frac{\omega^2}{c^2 R} \cos \omega \left(t - \frac{R}{c} \right) - \frac{\omega}{cR^2} \sin \omega \left(t - \frac{R}{c} \right) \right.$$

$$\left. + \frac{1}{R^3} \cos \omega \left(t - \frac{R}{c} \right) \right] \boldsymbol{\theta}^0 \quad (12.138)$$

The time integration indicated in Eq. (12.134) is easy, and yields

$$\textbf{E} = \frac{2p_0 \cos \theta}{4\pi\epsilon_0} \left[\frac{\omega}{cR^2} \cos \omega \left(t - \frac{R}{c} \right) + \frac{1}{R^3} \sin \omega \left(t - \frac{R}{c} \right) \right] \textbf{R}^0$$

$$+ \frac{p_0 \sin \theta}{4\pi\epsilon_0} \left[-\frac{\omega^2}{c^2 R} \sin \omega \left(t - \frac{R}{c} \right) + \frac{\omega}{cR^2} \cos \omega \left(t - \frac{R}{c} \right) \right.$$

$$\left. + \frac{1}{R^3} \sin \omega \left(t - \frac{R}{c} \right) \right] \boldsymbol{\theta}^0 \quad (12.139)$$

Equations (12.137) and (12.139) describe the electromagnetic field of the oscillating dipole. Notice that this field contains inverse first-, second-, and third-power terms in the distance R between dipole and observer and that the magnitudes of successive terms are in the ratio $c/\omega R = \lambda/2\pi R$. Thus for $R \gg \lambda/2\pi$, the terms having higher inverse powers of R become negligible compared with the inverse first power, while for $R \ll \lambda/2\pi$ the reverse is true. The inverse first-power terms are peculiar to radiation, since no such terms appear in electrostatic or magnetostatic fields. These radiation terms are responsible for the transportation of energy away from the dipole. The inverse-square term in **B** resembles the magnetostatic field of a current element, but differs in a very important respect: it is in phase with the current at retarded time, so that the distance R appears in the argument of the cosine function.   Inverse-square terms appear also in the two components of the electric field.   The inverse-cube terms in the electric field resemble those in the field of an electrostatic dipole, but are in phase with the' dipole moment at retarded time.

It is instructive to form Poynting's vector for these radiation fields. We shall do this only for the field at large distances, since for the local fields Poynting's vector, if it means anything, is concerned only with redistribution of energy near the dipole.   The radiation terms in the field are

$$\mathbf{E}_1 = -\frac{p_0\omega^2 \sin \theta}{4\pi\epsilon_0 c^2 R} \sin \omega\left(t - \frac{R}{c}\right)\theta^0 \tag{12.140}$$

$$\mathbf{B}_1 = -\frac{\mu_0 p_0\omega^2 \sin \theta}{4\pi c R} \sin \omega\left(t - \frac{R}{c}\right)\phi^0 \tag{12.141}$$

Notice that these fields are transverse to the direction of propagation $\mathbf{R}^0$ The radiative Poynting vector $\mathbf{N}_1 = \mathbf{E}_1 \times \mathbf{H}_1$ is therefore

$$\mathbf{N}_1 = \frac{p_0^2\omega^4 \sin^2 \theta}{16\pi^2\epsilon_0 c^3 R^2} \sin^2 \omega\left(t - \frac{R}{c}\right)\mathbf{R}^0 \tag{12.142}$$

The time average Poynting vector is

$$\bar{\mathbf{N}}_1 = \frac{\mu_0 p_0^2\omega^4 \sin^2 \theta}{32\pi^2 c R^2}\mathbf{R}^0 \tag{12.143}$$

Here we have used $c^2 = 1/\mu_0\epsilon_0$ to simplify the constants.   For the average, see the preceding section in the context of Eqs. (12.108) and (12.109).

Equation (12.143) indicates the angular distribution of the power radiated from a dipole, provided the Poynting vector is postulated to be the correct energy flow function.   The total average radiated power $\bar{P}$ is found by integrating (12.143) over a spherical surface of radius R about the origin.   A zonal element of area on such a surface is

$$da = 2\pi R^2 \sin \theta \, d\theta$$

so that

$$\bar{P} = \int_0^\pi \bar{\mathbf{N}}_1 \cdot \mathbf{R}^0 2\pi R^2 \sin \theta \, d\theta \tag{12.144}$$

Performing the integration, we obtain

$$\bar{P} = \frac{\mu_0 p_0^2\omega^4}{12\pi c} \tag{12.145}$$

In terms of the peak current,

$$\bar{P} = \frac{\mu_0 I_0^2 L^2\omega^2}{12\pi c} \tag{12.146}$$

The power $\bar{P}$ rises rapidly with frequency: as the fourth power for a given amplitude p_0 of dipole moment, or as the square for a given current amplitude I_0. It is evident therefore why radiation effects are small at power line frequencies, and why radio communications frequencies are high. Notice that the power is independent of the radius R of the surface through which it passes. This power is therefore propagated away from the dipole without suffering loss on the way.

It may be helpful in conclusion to use the results of this section to illustrate the general theory of the preceding section. Suppose the terminals of an old-fashioned high-frequency generator to be connected to the terminals of an antenna which satisfies the dipole approximations of this section. From the viewpoint of the Poynting theorem, it is only within the armature windings of the generator that the power transfer per unit volume, $P_1 = \mathbf{J} \cdot \mathbf{E}$, is negative. It is here that the currents flow by which the mechanical power driving the generator is transferred into the electromagnetic system. The word system here includes the generator-antenna electric circuit as well as the electromagnetic field. In the antenna wire itself, $\mathbf{J} \cdot \mathbf{E}$ is positive and in fact is just the Joule heat gE^2 which leaves the electromagnetic system due to current flow in this region. The time average of the integral of $-\mathbf{J} \cdot \mathbf{E}$ over the entire conducting path is by the Poynting theorem equal to the radiated power (12.145). Now it is always dangerous to limit oneself to one point of view; and in this case, the strange conclusion might be reached that the antenna is not necessary for the radiation, but is in fact worse than useless because it dissipates power. Such a conclusion is not a result of Poynting's theorem but of its misapplication. Poynting's theorem is a correct and useful mathematical relation, but it is not intended for describing the entire function of all parts of a system. The antenna is of course necessary in producing the radiation field, and its dimensions affect the radiated power. It is also necessary as a load for the generator, which could not function to transfer power from mechanical to electrical form without the flow of current made possible by attaching a load. Furthermore, had the load been merely a laboratory resistor, the Joule heat in the resistor would have absorbed almost all the power produced by the generator. This would mean, in terms of Poynting's theorem, that $-\mathbf{J} \cdot \mathbf{E}$ integrated over the resistor would have practically canceled $-\mathbf{J} \cdot \mathbf{E}$ integrated over the generator, leaving hardly any net power received by the electromagnetic system. This is not the case for the antenna load.

An alternative point of view is that of the electric circuit only. Here the accounts are kept in a different way, the requirement being that the average input and output to the circuit must be equal in steady state. Let us neglect the practical complication that the current at a given time is not necessarily the same at all points of a high-frequency circuit, for such a condition is minimized by the dipole assumption that the wavelength λ of radiation is much larger than the size of the radiating system. The power entering the circuit is then the average $\langle \mathcal{E}I \rangle_{av}$, where $\mathcal{E}$ is the total emf. In our system, an emf exists in the generator, accounting for energy transfer into the circuit from the engine driving the generator. This emf has, by our convention, a positive sign relative to the current. In the antenna, however, the changing magnetic fields induce an emf of opposite sign to the current accounting for the energy transferred out of the circuit by radiation. This emf contributes to the potential difference across the antenna in such a sense as to cause the current to enter the antenna at the higher potential terminal. This contribution to the antenna potential difference is in the same sense as that produced by the ohmic resistance R_j. Furthermore, just as the average power lost to Joule heat in the antenna is $\frac{1}{2}I_0^2 R_j$ so the radiated power $\bar{P}$ is, by Eq. (12.146), proportional to $\frac{1}{2}I_0^2$ with the factor

$$R_r = \frac{\mu_0 L^2 \omega^2}{6\pi c} \tag{12.147}$$

It appears then that the emf producing the radiation loss to the circuit can be replaced, so far as circuit analysis goes, by the effective resistance R_r, which is called the radiation resistance. The total or apparent antenna resistance is then $R_j + R_r$. An alternative form of Eq. (12.147), written in terms of the wavelength λ of the radiation, is

$$R_r = \frac{2\pi}{3} \sqrt{\frac{\mu_0}{\epsilon_0}} \left(\frac{L}{\lambda}\right)^2 \tag{12.148}$$

Evaluation of the constants in this expression leads to an interesting practical formula,

$$R_r = 790 \left(\frac{L}{\lambda}\right)^2 \quad \text{ohms} \tag{12.149}$$

12.9. General Boundary Conditions. Many problems in electromagnetism are concerned with the effects of boundary surfaces on electromagnetic waves. Such problems are the behavior of resonant cavities and wave guides in microwave theory, propagation of radio waves between the surface of the earth and of the ionized Heaviside layer in the atmosphere, and the reflection, refraction, and polarization of light at optical surfaces. It is important therefore to develop general boundary conditions based on the complete Maxwell equations. For mathematical details in what follows, the reader is referred to Sec. 3.9, where electrostatic boundary conditions were carefully discussed.

The treatment of a boundary as a regular mathematical surface of discontinuity in the properties of matter is of course macroscopic in viewpoint. From the microscopic view, a physical boundary surface is simply a transition region where the molecular population changes kind or average density, and in which free electric charge or even current may be concentrated. The macroscopic picture is possible because this transition region may be thin, and may have irregularities of form which are on a small scale, compared with the wavelength of the radiation.

Consider the two Maxwell equations

$$\text{curl } \mathbf{E} = -\frac{\partial \mathbf{B}}{\partial t} \tag{12.150}$$

$$\text{curl } \mathbf{H} = \mathbf{J} + \frac{\partial \mathbf{D}}{\partial t} \tag{12.151}$$

We may deduce tangential boundary conditions from these by considering the line integral of a field vector taken about a small rectangle $abcd$, having a pair of sides ab and cd of equal length l parallel to the boundary

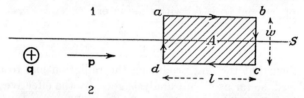

FIG. 12.5. Construction leading to tangential boundary conditions at an interface.

S and on opposite sides of it (see Fig. 12.5). Quantities with subscripts 1 and 2 will refer, respectively, to the regions above and below S. Unit vector $\mathbf{p}$ in the boundary is parallel to the sides ab and cd of the rectangle, while unit vector $\mathbf{q}$ in the boundary is normal to the plane area A of the rectangle, in the positive sense relative to the sense of integration which will be clockwise. Thus $\mathbf{q}$ is into the paper in Fig. 12.5.

Now the integrated forms of these Maxwell equations as applied to the rectangle and its plane area are

$$\oint_{abcd} \mathbf{E} \cdot d\mathbf{l} = -\int_A \frac{\partial \mathbf{B}}{\partial t} \cdot \mathbf{q} \, da \tag{12.152}$$

$$\oint_{abcd} \mathbf{H} \cdot d\mathbf{l} = \int_A \left(\mathbf{J} + \frac{\partial \mathbf{D}}{\partial t} \right) \cdot \mathbf{q} \, da \tag{12.153}$$

The line integrals take a simple form when the length l is finite but small compared with the macroscopic variations of the fields and when the width w of the rectangle $abcd$ approaches zero. From the context of Eqs. (3.86) to (3.88), Sec. 3.9, we have as the results

$$\lim_{w \to 0} \oint_{abcd} \mathbf{E} \cdot d\mathbf{l} = (\mathbf{E}_1 - \mathbf{E}_2) \cdot \mathbf{p} l \tag{12.154}$$

$$\lim_{w \to 0} \oint_{abcd} \mathbf{H} \cdot d\mathbf{l} = (\mathbf{H}_1 - \mathbf{H}_2) \cdot \mathbf{p} l \tag{12.155}$$

The surface integrals in Eqs. (12.152) and (12.153) approach zero as $w \rightarrow 0$, provided their integrands are finite, since $w \rightarrow 0$ means that $A \rightarrow 0$. In all real problems, $\mathbf{B}$ and $\mathbf{D}$ are always finite and continuous in their time variation; thus the terms $\partial\mathbf{B}/\partial t$ and $\partial\mathbf{D}/\partial t$ are finite. The current density $\mathbf{J}$, which may be written $g\mathbf{E}$ in the absence of electromotive force, is finite since $\mathbf{E}$ is finite, provided the conductivity g is finite. This in turn is always the case unless perhaps in superconductivity or in an ideal problem. Thus both surface integrals vanish:

$$\lim_{w \to 0} \int_A \frac{\partial\mathbf{B}}{\partial t} \cdot \mathbf{q}\, da = 0 \qquad \lim_{w \to 0} \int_A \left(\mathbf{J} + \frac{\partial\mathbf{D}}{\partial t}\right) \cdot \mathbf{q}\, da = 0 \qquad (12.156)$$

Substitution into Eqs. (12.152) and (12.153) now yields

$$(\mathbf{E}_1 - \mathbf{E}_2) \cdot \mathbf{p} = 0 \qquad\qquad (12.157)$$
$$(\mathbf{H}_1 - \mathbf{H}_2) \cdot \mathbf{p} = 0 \qquad\qquad (12.158)$$

Finally, since these results must hold for any orientation of the rectangle with its associated unit vector $\mathbf{p}$, we deduce the required boundary conditions:

$$\mathbf{E}_{1p} = \mathbf{E}_{2p} \qquad\qquad (12.159)$$
$$\mathbf{H}_{1p} = \mathbf{H}_{2p} \qquad\qquad (12.160)$$

The notation here is like that of Sec. 3.9. The vectors with subscript p are the vector components of the respective fields tangential to the boundary S. For example, if n is a normal to the boundary S, the normal vector component $\mathbf{E}_{2n}$ of a vector $\mathbf{E}_2$ is

$$\mathbf{E}_{2n} = (\mathbf{E}_2 \cdot \mathbf{n})\mathbf{n} \qquad\qquad (12.161)$$

The vector component $\mathbf{E}_{2p}$ is then such that

$$\mathbf{E}_{2n} + \mathbf{E}_{2p} = \mathbf{E}_2 \qquad\qquad (12.162)$$

It is understood that the fields (12.159) and (12.160) are evaluated at corresponding points on opposite sides of the boundary but infinitely near to it.

The remaining pair of Maxwell equations is

$$\text{div } \mathbf{D} = \rho \qquad\qquad (12.163)$$
$$\text{div } \mathbf{B} = 0 \qquad\qquad (12.164)$$

Equation (12.163) holds in the general case just as it does in electrostatics. It thus leads to the same boundary condition as in electrostatics, which we quote from Eq. (3.97), Sec. 3.9,

$$D_{2n} - D_{1n} = \sigma \qquad\qquad (12.165)$$

Here D_{2n} and D_{1n} are the normal components of the electric displacement at corresponding points on opposite sides of a boundary on which the surface density of free charge is σ. In the general case, of course σ is a function of time as well as of space coordinates in the boundary. Now Eq. (12.164) is of the same form as (12.163) except for the nonexistence of free magnetic charge; and hence (12.164) implies the boundary condition that the normal component of magnetic induction is continuous across any boundary:

$$B_{2n} = B_{1n} \qquad (12.166)$$

We might have written these normal components of **B** and **D** as vector components, but it is not necessary to do so as it was for the parallel

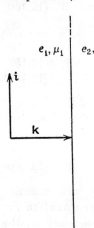

components of **H** and **E**; for there are infinitely many parallel directions to a boundary, but only one perpendicular direction.

The foregoing boundary conditions are general in that no reference (other than the restriction that the conductivity be finite) has been made to the properties of the media on the two sides of the boundary. If the media are isotropic and linear, the simple constitutive equations

$$\mathbf{D} = \epsilon\mathbf{E} \qquad (12.167)$$
$$\mathbf{B} = \mu\mathbf{H} \qquad (12.168)$$

may be conveniently employed to yield tangential conditions of **D** and **B** and normal conditions on **E** and **H**.

12.10. Reflection and Transmission of a Plane Wave at a Dielectric Interface. Normal Incidence. Let us now consider one of the simplest boundary problems, in which a plane harmonic wave is incident perpendicularly upon a plane boundary between two dielectric media. Suppose the media are isotropic, linear, and homogeneous, with permittivities and

Fig. 12.6. A dielectric interface for the problem of normally incident electromagnetic radiation.

permeabilities ϵ_1, μ_1, and ϵ_2, μ_2, respectively (see Fig.12.6). Take the boundary as the xy plane, and let the incident wave travel in the positive z or **k** direction with its electric vector polarized in the x or **i** direction. The electric field of the incident wave is then represented by

$$\mathbf{E} = E_0\mathbf{i}\cos\omega\left(t - \frac{z}{v_1}\right) \qquad (12.169)$$

[See Eq. (12.63), Sec. 12.6.] Here the choice of phase represented by the use of the cosine function is arbitrary. The symbol ω as usual is 2π times the frequency of the wave, and the velocity of the wave is

$$v_1 = \frac{1}{\sqrt{\mu_1\epsilon_1}} \qquad (12.170)$$

The accompanying magnetic field $\mathbf{H}$ is, from Eq. (12.72),

$$\mathbf{H} = \frac{E_0}{\mu_1 v_1}\, \mathbf{j}\, \cos \omega \left(t - \frac{z}{v_1} \right) \tag{12.171}$$

The problem at hand is to determine the effect of the boundary on the incident wave.   From the microscopic viewpoint, the molecules in the interface, like all the molecules of a material medium, interact with the incident wave in a manner which may be described as the receiving and reradiating of electromagnetic energy.   Within a body of material, this interaction serves to modify the propagation of a steady-state wave by affecting its phase velocity; but the molecules at an interface, by virtue of their privileged location, may not only modify the wave as it advances, but may also reradiate in the backward direction, that is, produce reflection.   Thus at an interface an incident wave will generally produce both a reflected and a transmitted or refracted wave, and these two together carry away from the boundary the energy carried toward it by the incident wave.   The macroscopic, boundary-value solution of a given problem does not refer to the processes involved in reflection and refraction, but seeks merely to find the transmitted and reflected waves which combine with the incident wave to satisfy the boundary conditions.

For the given problem, it is reasonable to try to satisfy the boundary conditions with reflected and transmitted waves propagated normally to the boundary, polarized in the same plane as the incident wave, and having the same frequency as the incident wave.   Let us write for the transmitted wave

$$\mathbf{E}' = E_0' \mathbf{i}\, \cos \omega \left(t - \frac{z}{v_2} \right) \tag{12.172}$$

using the velocity

$$v_2 = \frac{1}{\sqrt{\mu_2 \epsilon_2}} \tag{12.173}$$

appropriate to medium 2.   The associated magnetic field is then

$$\mathbf{H}' = \frac{E_0'}{\mu_2 v_2}\, \mathbf{j}\, \cos \omega \left(t - \frac{z}{v_2} \right) \tag{12.174}$$

Let us try a reflected wave having the form

$$\mathbf{E}'' = E_0'' \mathbf{i}\, \cos \omega \left(t + \frac{z}{v_1} \right) \tag{12.175}$$

The accompanying magnetic field is found, by the methods used in Sec. 12.6, to be

$$\mathbf{H}'' = -\frac{E_0''}{\mu_1 v_1}\, \mathbf{j}\, \cos \omega \left(t + \frac{z}{v_1} \right) \tag{12.176}$$

Notice that a tentative assumption has been made about the phases of both the transmitted and the reflected waves. If E'_0 or E''_0 has the same sign as E_0, the transmitted or reflected wave is in phase with the incident wave at $z = 0$, that is, on the boundary, while an opposite sign indicates a phase shift of 180 degrees or half a cycle. General forms can easily be written, allowing for arbitrary phase shifts, but it turns out that the shifts required to satisfy the boundary conditions are either zero or 180 degrees.

The incident wave and the postulated transmitted and reflected waves have their fields entirely parallel to the boundary. The only boundary conditions concerned are therefore the parallel ones.

$$\mathbf{E}_{1p} = \mathbf{E}_{2p} \tag{12.177}$$
$$\mathbf{H}_{1p} = \mathbf{H}_{2p} \tag{12.178}$$

These equations are to hold at all points of the boundary, that is, at $z = 0$, and at all times. Let us see by substitution whether the postulated fields can satisfy the boundary conditions identically:

$$(E_0 + E''_0)\mathbf{i} \cos \omega t = E'_0 \mathbf{i} \cos \omega t \tag{12.179}$$

$$\left(\frac{E_0}{\mu_1 v_1} - \frac{E''_0}{\mu_1 v_1} \right) \mathbf{j} \cos \omega t = \frac{E'_0}{\mu_2 v_2} \mathbf{j} \cos \omega t \tag{12.180}$$

Evidently these are identities, provided the scalar amplitudes of the fields satisfy

$$E_0 + E''_0 = E'_0 \tag{12.181}$$

$$E_0 - E''_0 = \frac{\mu_1 v_1}{\mu_2 v_2} E'_0 \tag{12.182}$$

Notice that without the reflected wave amplitude E''_0 it would be impossible to satisfy these relations in general. They are satisfied, however, by the presence of both transmitted and reflected waves of the assumed form whose electric field amplitudes are, respectively,

$$E'_0 = \frac{2E_0}{1 + \mu_1 v_1/\mu_2 v_2} \tag{12.183}$$

$$E''_0 = \frac{1 - \mu_1 v_1/\mu_2 v_2}{1 + \mu_1 v_1/\mu_2 v_2} E_0 \tag{12.184}$$

It will be assumed, without formulating or proving a uniqueness theorem, that these waves are the solution of the given problem. More general forms of the reflected and transmitted waves lead to the same results.

Dielectric materials are never highly magnetic, and therefore it is not necessary to carry along the permeabilities μ_1 and μ_2 in Eqs. (12.183) and (12.184). For optical problems, it is usual to use the index of refraction of the materials, defined as

$$n_1 \equiv \frac{c}{v_1} \qquad n_2 \equiv \frac{c}{v_2} \tag{12.185}$$

where c is the velocity of the light *in vacuo* and v_1 or v_2 is the wave velocity for the material. Equations (12.183) and (12.184) may therefore be written

$$E_0' = \frac{2E_0}{1 + n_2/n_1} \tag{12.186}$$

$$E_0'' = \frac{1 - n_2/n_1}{1 + n_2/n_1} E_0 \tag{12.187}$$

A medium for which n is large is called optically dense. It may be noticed from these equations that the transmitted wave is always in phase with the incident wave at the boundary. The reflected wave, on the other hand, is reversed in phase if $n_2 > n_1$, that is, when the second material is more dense than the first. It is in phase with the incident wave when $n_2 < n_1$. These conclusions are important in interference phenomena. The relative phase shift between waves reflected under the two conditions is immediately verified by experiment.

Another matter of interest is the proportion of energy reflected at the boundary. The intensity of the incident wave, in terms of the time-average Poynting vector, may be found from the definition $\bar{\mathbf{N}} = \langle \mathbf{E} \times \mathbf{H} \rangle_{\text{av}}$:

$$\bar{\mathbf{N}} = \mathbf{k} \frac{E_0{}^2}{\mu_1 v_1} \left\langle \cos^2 \omega \left(t - \frac{z}{v_1} \right) \right\rangle_{\text{av}} \tag{12.188}$$

(See Sec. 12.7.)   Thus

$$\bar{\mathbf{N}} = \mathbf{k} \frac{E_0{}^2}{2\mu_1 v_1} \tag{12.189}$$

For the reflected wave

$$\bar{\mathbf{N}}'' = -\mathbf{k} \frac{E_0''{}^2}{2\mu_1 v_1} \tag{12.190}$$

The fraction of the incident energy which is reflected is called the reflection coefficient R. Therefore

$$R \equiv \frac{\bar{\mathbf{N}}''}{\bar{\mathbf{N}}} = \left(\frac{E_0''}{E_0} \right)^2 \tag{12.191}$$

Thus, from Eq. (12.187),

$$R = \left(\frac{1 - n_2/n_1}{1 + n_2/n_1} \right)^2 \tag{12.192}$$

This is sometimes rewritten

$$R = \left(\frac{n_1/n_2 - 1}{n_1/n_2 + 1} \right)^2 \tag{12.193}$$

The symmetry of these expressions shows that the reflection coefficient is unaltered by interchanging the two media or reversing the sense of propagation of the incident radiation.

The more general problem of reflection and refraction of waves of any polarization and any angle of incidence at a dielectric interface is no more difficult in principle than that of normal incidence but requires much more space for its complete presentation and discussion. Still more complex are problems of reflection at metallic surfaces. The reader who cares to pursue the subject can find it treated in texts on advanced electromagnetism or physical optics. Detailed comparison of theory with experiment is possible; and the conclusion from such comparison is that the laws of electromagnetism form the correct basis for physical optics.

12.11. Electromagnetic Potentials. In the earlier chapters of our work, considerable use has been made of potential functions. A scalar potential U was used in electrostatics, and a scalar potential U^* as well as a vector potential $\mathbf{A}$ in magnetostatics. These are special cases of certain potential functions which are valid in the more general case of time-varying electromagnetic fields. We may define a potential function generally as any scalar or vector point function from which electric or magnetic fields are obtainable by processes of differentiation. Under such a definition is included a variety of useful potential functions, the full discussion of which is appropriate to a more advanced treatment of electromagnetism. The reader at the intermediate level is entitled, however, to an introductory discussion of the most commonly used electromagnetic potentials. Their use will permit clarification and unification of the treatment of the many important electromagnetic problems which fall into special cases: the electrostatic problems, the steady-current and steady-state problems, and the field problems associated with relatively slow variations of electric current and charge. In addition, the reader will be prepared for use of these potentials in handling radiation problems.

The particular potential functions to be discussed are a pair of functions, one a vector and one a scalar. The vector function will be denoted by $\mathbf{A}$ in accordance with general usage, and has already been used in Sec. 12.8 in the treatment of electric dipole radiation. $\mathbf{A}$ is such that its curl yields the magnetic induction $\mathbf{B}$:

$$\mathbf{B} = \operatorname{curl} \mathbf{A} \qquad (12.194)$$

Equation (12.194) may be considered a general solution of the Maxwell equation

$$\operatorname{div} \mathbf{B} = 0 \qquad (12.195)$$

Any field derived by Eq. (12.194) satisfies (12.195), as may easily be shown by substitution; and conversely any field satisfying (12.195) can be written in form (12.194), although here the proof is not so simple. It must be understood, however, that $\mathbf{A}$ is not unique for a given field $\mathbf{B}$. There are, in fact, infinitely many functions whose curl is a given function. Having found one vector potential for a given field, another may be obtained by subtracting the gradient of any scalar function.

Equation (12.194) may be substituted into another of the Maxwell equations to yield an expression for the electric field:

$$\text{curl } \mathbf{E} = -\frac{\partial \mathbf{B}}{\partial t} \tag{12.196}$$

Therefore

$$\text{curl } \mathbf{E} = -\frac{\partial}{\partial t}\text{curl } \mathbf{A} \tag{12.197}$$

The order of differentiation in Eq. (12.197) can be reversed, and collection of terms then gives

$$\text{curl}\left(\mathbf{E} + \frac{\partial \mathbf{A}}{\partial t}\right) = 0 \tag{12.198}$$

Now it is shown in vector analysis that any vector function whose curl is zero can be expressed as the gradient of a scalar function. The reader can readily check the converse, that any gradient of a scalar has a zero curl. It follows that the most general solution of Eq. (12.198) is

$$\mathbf{E} + \frac{\partial \mathbf{A}}{\partial t} = -\text{ grad }\phi \tag{12.199}$$

where ϕ is an arbitrary scalar function. The negative sign has been chosen to conform to convention. Equation (12.199) may be solved for $\mathbf{E}$:

$$\mathbf{E} = -\frac{\partial \mathbf{A}}{\partial t} - \text{ grad }\phi \tag{12.200}$$

The function ϕ is the electromagnetic scalar potential function. $\mathbf{E}$ is thus derived by differentiation from both a vector and a scalar potential function, while $\mathbf{B}$ is derived from the vector potential only. Equations (12.194) and (12.200) together form a general solution of the two Maxwell equations (12.195) and (12.196). It is to be noted that when a vector potential $\mathbf{A}$ is specified for a given electromagnetic field $(\mathbf{E,B})$, the scalar potential ϕ is determined within a space-independent, additive term; for Eq. (12.200) then specifies the gradient of ϕ and thus all the space derivatives of ϕ are determined. The same fields may, however, be described by an infinite number of other pairs of functions $\mathbf{A},\phi$. The process of changing the pair of potential functions describing a given field is called a gauge transformation. Gauge transformations are important in theoretical physics, but their details do not concern us here.

The electromagnetic potentials $\mathbf{A}$ and ϕ find an important application in the determination of the fields produced by given sources. The sources of fields are usually free charge and current distributions, although a notable exception is the case of permanent magnets. These sources appear in the two Maxwell equations which have not yet been used in this discussion:

$$\text{div } \mathbf{D} = \rho \tag{12.201}$$

$$\text{curl } \mathbf{H} = \mathbf{J} + \frac{\partial \mathbf{D}}{\partial t} \tag{12.202}$$

Let us confine our attention to charges and currents in empty space, so that the two auxiliary vectors **D** and **H** can be expressed in terms of the force fields **E** and **B** by the constitutive equations for space:

$$\mathbf{D} = \epsilon_0 \mathbf{E} \tag{12.203}$$

$$\mathbf{H} = \frac{1}{\mu_0} \mathbf{B} \tag{12.204}$$

The Maxwell equations (12.201) and (12.202) may then be written in terms of **E** and **B**; and the fields (12.194) and (12.200) may be substituted to find differential equations for the potentials **A** and ϕ of the fields of given sources **J** and ρ. This process involves some algebraic manipulations similar to those used in Sec. 12.5, and we simply quote the results:

$$\left(\frac{\partial^2 \phi}{\partial x^2} + \frac{\partial^2 \phi}{\partial y^2} + \frac{\partial^2 \phi}{\partial z^2} \right) + \frac{\partial}{\partial t} \operatorname{div} \mathbf{A} = -\frac{1}{\epsilon_0} \rho \tag{12.205}$$

$$\left(\frac{\partial^2 A_x}{\partial x^2} + \frac{\partial^2 A_x}{\partial y^2} + \frac{\partial^2 A_x}{\partial z^2} \right) - \mu_0 \epsilon_0 \frac{\partial^2 A_x}{\partial t^2} = -\mu_0 J_x$$

$$+ \frac{\partial}{\partial x} \left(\operatorname{div} \mathbf{A} + \mu_0 \epsilon_0 \frac{\partial \phi}{\partial t} \right) \tag{12.206}$$

There are two similar equations for the other cartesian components A_y and A_z of **A**. Now these equations are not only complicated in form but each contains both of the potential functions **A** and ϕ. Simultaneous solution of four scalar equations would thus be necessary in order to find potentials of the fields of given sources. This mathematical difficulty is overcome by arbitrarily requiring that the two potential functions satisfy an equation called the Lorentz condition:

$$\operatorname{div} \mathbf{A} + \mu_0 \epsilon_0 \frac{\partial \phi}{\partial t} = 0 \tag{12.207}$$

Because of the latitude of choice of the pair of potential functions for any given field, this condition can always be fulfilled, as may be shown from the theory of gauge transformations. The Lorentz condition causes the differential equations for **A** and ϕ to separate into the form of similar wave equations:

$$\left(\frac{\partial^2 \phi}{\partial x^2} + \frac{\partial^2 \phi}{\partial y^2} + \frac{\partial^2 \phi}{\partial z^2} \right) - \mu_0 \epsilon_0 \frac{\partial^2 \phi}{\partial t^2} = -\frac{1}{\epsilon_0} \rho \tag{12.208}$$

$$\left(\frac{\partial^2 A_x}{\partial x^2} + \frac{\partial^2 A_x}{\partial y^2} + \frac{\partial^2 A_x}{\partial z^2} \right) - \mu_0 \epsilon_0 \frac{\partial^2 A_x}{\partial t^2} = -\mu_0 J_x$$

$$\left(\frac{\partial^2 A_y}{\partial x^2} + \frac{\partial^2 A_y}{\partial y^2} + \frac{\partial^2 A_y}{\partial z^2} \right) - \mu_0 \epsilon_0 \frac{\partial^2 A_y}{\partial t^2} = -\mu_0 J_y \tag{12.209}$$

$$\left(\frac{\partial^2 A_z}{\partial x^2} + \frac{\partial^2 A_z}{\partial y^2} + \frac{\partial^2 A_z}{\partial z^2} \right) - \mu_0 \epsilon_0 \frac{\partial^2 A_z}{\partial t^2} = -\mu_0 J_z$$

The determination of the field of given sources is now reduced to the solution of the wave equations (12.208) and (12.209) subject to the Lorentz condition (12.207). It is outside our scope to present the details of such a solution. We may notice first that in the electrostatic case, where the time derivative $\partial\phi/\partial t$ vanishes, Eq. (12.208) reduces to the familiar Poisson equation, as given in Sec. 2.2. Thus ϕ reduces in this case to the electrostatic scalar potential U. Now a simple integral formula for U exists when static charges are situated in otherwise empty space. This formula, as given in Sec. 1.7, is

$$U(x,y,z) = \frac{1}{4\pi\epsilon_0} \int_{\text{all space}} \frac{\rho(x',y',z')\, dV}{r} \qquad (12.210)$$

when the charge distributions are represented by the volume density $\rho(x',y',z')$. Here r is the distance between the observer at (x,y,z) and the point of integration (x',y',z'). Equation (12.210) is thus a particular solution of Poisson's equation for empty space; and it is also the limiting form, as time variations of charge become slower, of a particular solution of Eq. (12.208). It is not surprising to learn then that the corresponding particular solution of Eq. (12.208) for arbitrary time variations is

$$\phi(x,y,z,t) = \frac{1}{4\pi\epsilon_0} \int_{\text{all space}} \frac{\rho(x',y',z'; t - r/c)\, dV}{r} \qquad (12.211)$$

We shall not reproduce the proof that Eq. (12.211) is a solution of (12.208), for this is tedious when carefully done. The potential (12.211) is said to be a retarded potential, for the ρ function in the integrand is to be evaluated at retarded time $t - r/c$ for each point of integration. Here r is, as always, the distance from the observer to the volume element dV; and $t - r/c$ is earlier than observer's time by the time of transit of an electromagnetic wave whose velocity is

$$c = \frac{1}{\sqrt{\mu_0\epsilon_0}} \qquad (12.212)$$

Equations (12.209) are treated in a similar way. Corresponding to the steady-current steady-state formula given in Sec. 7.5 for the magnetic vector potential,

$$\mathbf{A}(x,y,z) = \frac{\mu_0}{4\pi} \int_{\text{all space}} \frac{\mathbf{J}(x',y',z')}{r}\, dV \qquad (12.213)$$

a particular solution of Eqs. (12.209) is the vector function

$$\mathbf{A}(x,y,z,t) = \frac{\mu_0}{4\pi} \int_{\text{all space}} \frac{\mathbf{J}(x',y',z'; t - r/c)}{r}\, dV \qquad (12.214)$$

This is the retarded vector potential, as used in Sec. 12.8 in the discussion of electric dipole radiation. To complete the discussion, it is necessary to show that the retarded potentials (12.211) and (12.214) satisfy the Lorentz relation (12.207), for otherwise they are not solutions of Eqs. (12.205) and (12.206) and hence fields derived from them will not satisfy the Maxwell equations (12.201) and (12.202). This demonstration is somewhat tedious, and will be omitted; but the conclusion is that Eqs. (12.211) and (12.214) do satisfy (12.207) by virtue of the conservation of electric charge as expressed in the equation of continuity, Eq. (5.23), Sec. 5.3.

The differential equations and formulas for electromagnetic potentials can be extended to apply in systems containing dielectric and magnetic material. One way of doing this is to introduce the permittivity ϵ and permeability μ for isotropic materials. The differential equations retain the same form with ϵ replacing ϵ_0 and μ replacing μ_0 only for linear homogeneous matter; but the integral formulas with c replaced by $v = 1/\sqrt{\mu\epsilon}$ are valid only in the further special case when a single medium pervades all the space of the system. Systems which contain dielectric or magnetic interfaces between subregions must generally be solved by boundary-value methods, as we remarked for electrostatics (see Secs. 2.1 and 3.11). Another way of extending the equations for the potentials is to represent the presence of matter by using the polarization and magnetization vectors. This leads to perfectly general equations which are theoretically satisfactory but not often useful for problem solving, for the **P** and **M** vectors are usually unknowns of the problem.

12.12. Electric and Magnetic Fields in Small Systems. An important class of electromagnetic problems is that of small systems containing the point of observation. By this we shall mean that the distances between the observer and elements of charge or current in the system are all so short as to be traversed by an electromagnetic wave in times during which no appreciable changes occur in the charges or currents. If the charges and currents oscillate harmonically with frequency $\omega/2\pi$, this condition may be restated in the following form: All distances between observer and elements of the system are very short compared with a wavelength of electromagnetic radiation. This wavelength for empty space, in which the velocity of electromagnetic waves is c, is

$$\lambda = \frac{2\pi c}{\omega} \tag{12.215}$$

Now if R is the maximum distance from any part of the system to the observer, we call the system small if

$$R \ll \frac{\lambda}{2\pi} \tag{12.216}$$

An example of a small system is an a-c circuit of not too high frequency when the local fields in the near vicinity of the circuit are of interest. Notice that condition (12.216) implies also that the maximum distance L between any pairs of elements of the system, which can at most be $2R$, is still small compared with $\lambda/2\pi$. This last condition was laid down in the definition of an oscillating dipole; but in the dipole approximation we considered a very distant observer in comparison with the size of the system and without regard to the wavelength, whereas now the observer is required to be close in comparison with the wavelength without regard to the size of the system.

The retarded potentials of Sec. 12.11 may be used to clarify the remarks which have been made from time to time in our work, e.g., Sec. 5.7, about small systems. For simplicity, consider only charges and currents in empty space, for which the retarded potentials are given by the integrals

$$\phi(x,y,z,t) = \frac{1}{4\pi\epsilon_0} \int_{\text{all space}} \frac{\rho(x',y',z';t-r/c)}{r} \, dV \qquad (12.211)$$

$$\mathbf{A}(x,y,z,t) = \frac{\mu_0}{4\pi} \int_{\text{all space}} \frac{\mathbf{J}(x',y',z';t-r/c)}{r} \, dV \qquad (12.214)$$

The presence of the distance $r = \sqrt{(x-x')^2 + (y-y')^2 + (z-z')^2}$ in the retarded time causes more mathematical complexity than might be supposed, both in integration and in taking derivatives to find the fields. If the system is small, however, we shall simply assume that the functions ρ and $\mathbf{J}$ at retarded time $t - r/c$ and for any point within the system differ negligibly from their values at observer's time t. The potentials resulting from this approximation we shall call quasi-static, and shall designate them by the subscript s:

$$\phi_s(x,y,z,t) = \frac{1}{4\pi\epsilon_0} \int_{\text{all space}} \frac{\rho(x',y',z',t)}{r} \, dV \qquad (12.217)$$

$$\mathbf{A}_s(x,y,z,t) = \frac{\mu_0}{4\pi} \int_{\text{all space}} \frac{\mathbf{J}(x',y',z',t)}{r} \, dV \qquad (12.218)$$

Within the validity of this approximation, the fields in a small system are then

$$\mathbf{B} = \text{curl } \mathbf{A}_s \qquad (12.219)$$

$$\mathbf{E} = -\frac{\partial \mathbf{A}_s}{\partial t} - \text{grad } \phi_s \qquad (12.220)$$

Before examining these fields, a word should be said about the nature of their approximation to the true fields of the system. It is not sure that the percentage difference between Eqs. (12.219) and (12.220) and the true fields is always negligible; for at certain instants and points of space one of the approximate fields may vanish while the true field may remain finite. It is true, however, that in the case of harmonically varying sources, the true fields differ negligibly from these approximate fields in amplitude and phase.

Consider first the magnetic field (12.219). This is evidently derived from the currents in the same way as the field of steady currents, and therefore has all the properties of steady fields at any particular time; it only differs in being time-dependent. Thus we may write a quasi-static Ampère law for small current systems *in vacuo:*

$$\mathbf{B}(x,y,z,t) = \frac{\mu_0}{4\pi} \int_{\text{all space}} \frac{\mathbf{J}(x',y',z',t) \times \mathbf{r}^0}{r^2} \, dV \qquad (12.221)$$

This needs to be generalized in order to apply to systems containing magnetic matter. The concept of the quasi-static magnetic field remains valid for such systems, and it formed the basis of the work on magnetic circuits in Sec. 9.12.

The electric field (12.220) is expressed as a sum of two terms which we shall call the partial fields $\mathbf{E}_m$ and $\mathbf{E}_s$, respectively,

$$\mathbf{E} = \mathbf{E}_m + \mathbf{E}_s \qquad (12.222)$$

$$\mathbf{E}_m \equiv -\frac{\partial \mathbf{A}_s}{\partial t} \qquad (12.223)$$

$$\mathbf{E}_s \equiv -\operatorname{grad} \phi_s \qquad (12.224)$$

The field $\mathbf{E}_s$ evidently bears the same relation to electric charge, at any given instant, as the electrostatic field bears to static charge. It is therefore possible to write a quasi-static Coulomb integral for space

$$\mathbf{E}_s\,(x,y,z,t) = \frac{1}{4\pi\epsilon_0} \int_{\text{all space}} \frac{\rho(x',y',z',t)\mathbf{r}^0}{r^2} \, dV \qquad (12.225)$$

This implies Gauss' law, whose differential expression is

$$\operatorname{div} \mathbf{E}_s = \frac{1}{\epsilon_0} \rho \qquad \text{space} \qquad (12.226)$$

(See Secs. 1.9 and 2.2.) The **curl** of $\mathbf{E}_s$, like that of the electrostatic field, vanishes identically, and with it the line integral of $\mathbf{E}_s$ about any closed curve; for $\mathbf{E}_s$ is expressed as a gradient, and the curl of any gradient is identically zero:

$$\operatorname{curl} \mathbf{E}_s \equiv 0 \qquad (12.227)$$

$$\oint_C \mathbf{E}_s \cdot d\mathbf{l} = 0 \qquad (12.228)$$

(See Sec. 1.5.) The partial field $\mathbf{E}_s$ thus shares all the properties of the electrostatic field, and is properly called quasi-electrostatic. It is identical with the quasi-electrostatic field $\mathbf{E}_s$ of Sec. 5.7 and other parts of our earlier work.

Finally, let us consider the partial field $\mathbf{E}_m$ of Eq. (12.223). This field is derived from the time rate of change of the vector whose **curl** gives the magnetic field, and thus it is associated with a changing magnetic field. Another way of justifying this description is to consider the Maxwell expression of Faraday's law:

$$\text{curl } \mathbf{E} = -\frac{\partial \mathbf{B}}{\partial t} \tag{12.229}$$

Substituting from Eqs. (12.222) and (12.227), we find that

$$\text{curl } \mathbf{E}_m = -\frac{\partial \mathbf{B}}{\partial t} \tag{12.230}$$

Thus only the partial field $\mathbf{E}_m$ is involved in Faraday's law, and its source may be considered to be the changing magnetic field. Another way of characterizing $\mathbf{E}_m$ would be as that electric field due to changing current density, for, from Eqs. (12.218) and (12.223),

$$\mathbf{E}_m = \frac{\mu_0}{4\pi} \int_{\text{all space}} \frac{1}{r} \frac{\partial}{\partial t} \mathbf{J}(x',y',z',t) \, dV \tag{12.231}$$

This expression is only true for otherwise empty space, and needs to be generalized in order to include the effects of moving magnets or moving bound charges in dielectrics. The former characterization of $\mathbf{E}_m$ as the electric field due to a changing magnetic field is the one used in Sec. 5.7 and other parts of our work. We have now justified the references to quasi-static magnetic and electric fields, and to the electric field of a changing magnetic field, made in previous discussions of small systems.

A word of warning should be given in conclusion. It is tempting to divide the electric field into two partial fields for general systems, because of Eq. (12.200), Sec. 12.11. While this may be done formally once a particular choice of gauge (that is, of particular potential functions) has been made, it does not seem to be fruitful except for small systems. If the radiation field of an electric dipole be worked out by the retarded potentials (12.211) and (12.214), the terms $-\partial \mathbf{A}/\partial t$ and $-\text{ grad } \phi$ have no distinctive meaning. While $-\text{ grad } \phi$ does yield the inverse-cube field (see Sec. 12.8), this is not a quasi-electrostatic field because of the distance R in the retarded time, and does not of itself satisfy the Maxwell equation for the observer's position where there is no charge:

$$\text{div } \mathbf{E} = 0 \tag{12.232}$$

Furthermore, $-\text{ grad } \phi$ for the electric dipole yields other terms also, including an inverse first-power term which is canceled by a corresponding term in $-\partial \mathbf{A}/\partial t$. Thus in general electromagnetic fields, $-\text{ grad } \phi$ is not properly called quasi-electrostatic. Furthermore, there is no more reason to ascribe part of a general electric field to a changing magnetic field than the converse. This kind of division of $\mathbf{E}$ into $\mathbf{E}_s$ and $\mathbf{E}_m$ is therefore not appropriate to general systems.

PROBLEMS

12.1. Suppose that in an apparatus having rotational symmetry about the x axis, the magnetic induction in air is

$$\mathbf{B} = \mathbf{i} B_0 \cos \omega t$$

where $\mathbf{i}$ is a unit vector along the x axis and B_0 and ω are constant.

Use Faraday's law to find the induced electric field symmetric about the same axis. Express this field in cartesian coordinates, and check it into Maxwell's equation equivalent to Faraday's law.

12.2. Show that the electric field deduced in the preceding problem is not consistent with the Maxwell equation involving displacement current. What do you conclude?

12.3. Find the peak contribution of the electric polarization to the displacement current in ethyl alcohol of specific permittivity 25 for an alternating electric field whose peak intensity is 5,000 volts/cm and whose frequency is 600 kc/sec.

12.4. A parallel-plate air condenser has a plate area of 500 cm² and a separation of ½ mm (cf. Sec. 4.9). Suppose the condenser in series with a 100-ohm resistor to be connected across a 1,000-volt power supply with negligible internal impedance. At the instant of connection, find the conduction current into the condenser by the transient analysis of Sec. 10.4, and find from its definition the total displacement current in the condenser. Compare these two currents, and show why the result is to be expected.

12.5. Suppose there were such a thing as charge and current of free magnetic poles. Show how the Maxwell equations would need to be amended and an additional equation of continuity would arise.

12.6. Suppose there were such a thing as a current of free magnetic poles, as in Prob. 12.5, and consider a closed loop carrying magnetic current. Transfer the concept of self-inductance to such a magnetic circuit, and examine particularly the sign of the self-induced mmf and current. What corresponds to Lenz's law for this hypothetical system?

12.7. Follow through the steps in deducing the wave equation (12.47) for the z component of the magnetic induction.

12.8. Show that in an isotropic, linear, and homogeneous conducting medium, in the absence of net charge density, the wave equation for the x component of the electric field is

$$\frac{\partial^2 E_x}{\partial x^2} + \frac{\partial^2 E_x}{\partial y^2} + \frac{\partial^2 E_x}{\partial z^2} - \mu g \frac{\partial E_x}{\partial t} - \mu \epsilon \frac{\partial^2 E_x}{\partial t^2} = 0$$

12.9. Find how the inclusion of a charge density ρ and free current density $\mathbf{J}$ alters the wave equation (12.46) for the x component of the electric field. Do not use the conductivity g, but let $\mathbf{J}$ appear explicitly.

12.10. Assume that some of the solutions of the wave equation in an isotropic, linear, homogeneous dielectric, where there is no net charge, may be written in the form of a product of functions:

$$\mathbf{E} = \mathbf{E}_0(z) f(t)$$

Show that this substitution leads to the ordinary differential equations

$$\frac{d^2 \mathbf{E}_0}{dz^2} + k \mathbf{E}_0 = 0 \qquad \mu \epsilon \frac{d^2 f}{dt^2} + k f = 0$$

where k is an arbitrary constant.

12.11. Show that a combination of particular solutions of the ordinary differential equations of Prob. 12.10 yields the wave described by Eq. (12.63), Sec. 12.6. See Sec. 10.5 for a method of obtaining the solutions.

12.12. Suppose that the wave equation in uncharged, conducting material (cf. Prob. 12.8) has solutions of the form

$$\mathbf{E} = \mathbf{E}_0(x,y,z) \cos (\omega t + \phi)$$

where $\mathbf{E}_0$ is a space-dependent vector amplitude and ω and ϕ are constants.

a. Interpret ω, and find in terms of ω the ratio of the amplitude of the second time-derivative term of the differential equation to that of the first time-derivative term. Show that this is the same as the ratio of the Maxwell displacement current density to the free conduction current density.   Show that the mks units in this ratio check out to yield a pure number.   *Ans. $\epsilon\omega/g$.*

12.13. Find for what frequency each of the following materials has unity for the ratio $\epsilon\omega/g$ of displacement to conduction current (cf. Prob. 12.12).

a. Copper: conductivity 5.80×10^7 mho/m; permittivity that of space

b. Ordinary water: conductivity 4.00×10^{-3} mho/m; specific permittivity 81

c. Marble: resistivity 10^8 ohm-m; specific permittivity 8.0

12.14. A certain plane wave has for its electric field

$$\mathbf{E} = \mathbf{E}_0 \cos \omega \left(\frac{a_1 x + a_2 y + a_3 z}{v} \mp t \right)$$

where $v = 1/\sqrt{\mu\epsilon}$ is the phase velocity for the isotropic, homogeneous, linear medium in which the wave travels.

a. Find the condition on the constants a_1, a_2, and a_3 if this is to be a solution of the wave equation.

b. Interpret these constants and this formula.

c. Show by use of a Maxwell equation that if the wave travels in charge-free space, then $\mathbf{E}$ is necessarily normal to the direction of propagation.

12.15. *a.* Apply the substitution used in Prob. 12.10 to the wave equation for conducting media, as given in Prob. 12.8, and thus obtain two ordinary differential equations.

b. Solve these ordinary differential equations, assuming the separation constant is real and has the sign which makes the equations resemble the ones solved in Secs. 10.5 and 10.6.

Ans. $\mathbf{E} = a \cos (\sqrt{k}z - \phi)e^{-(g/2\epsilon)t} \cos \left(\sqrt{\dfrac{k}{\epsilon} - \dfrac{g^2}{4\epsilon^2}}\, t - \psi \right).$

12.16. Consider the wave *in vacuo*

$$\mathbf{E} = \mathbf{i}E_{0x} \cos \omega \left(\frac{z}{c} - t \right) + \mathbf{j}E_{0y} \sin \omega \left(\frac{z}{c} - t \right)$$

where E_{0x} and E_{0y} are constants.

a. Describe the behavior of the $\mathbf{E}$ vector with change of time at a given point of space.

b. Find the corresponding magnetic field, and investigate its behavior at the same point of space.

12.17. The specific dielectric constant of air at 0°C and 1 atm has been observed to be 1.000590, while the refractive index of air under the same conditions has been observed to approach 1.0002876 asymptotically as the wavelength increases. Compare these two figures with theory.

12.18. Show for a plane-polarized plane sinusoidal electromagnetic wave traveling in an isotropic linear and homogeneous dielectric that the quantities interpreted as the average electric and magnetic energies per unit volume are equal.

12.19. Compute the average energy density per unit volume in the plane electromagnetic wave described by Eqs. (12.106) and (12.107), Sec. 12.7, and show that this density, used in Eq. (12.111), yields the intensity (12.109).

12.20. *a.* A straight, isolated, copper wire of conductivity g and diameter D carries a steady current I. Integrate Poynting's vector over the entire boundary of a piece of the wire of length L, and compare with the Joule heat developed in this section.

b. Evaluate the Poynting vector at the wire's surface if $g = 5.80 \times 10^7$ mho/m, $D = 0.102$ cm (No. 18 wire), and $I = 5$ amp.

12.21. A coaxial cable of circular section has an outer conductor of inside diameter 2 cm and a central wire whose diameter is $\frac{1}{2}$ cm, the space between being filled with insulating material. The outer conductor is grounded while the inner is at a potential of $+330$ volts, and the cable carries 50 amp. Find (*a*) the axial component of the Poynting vector between conductors; (*b*) the integral of this vector over the cross-sectional area between conductors. Compare this with the power transmitted by the cable.

Note: The integration is easy if the electric field involved is expressed as the radial derivative of the electrostatic potential function.

12.22. The radiant energy from the sun is about 8 joules in 1 min on 1 cm² of cross section. Assuming this to be in the form of a plane wave traveling in the x direction *in vacuo*, plane-polarized with its electric field in the zx plane, and having a wavelength of 0.555×10^{-3} mm, find expressions for the electric and magnetic fields with all constants (except phase) evaluated and units given.

12.23. An electron moves with drift velocity $\mathbf{v}_1$ along an armature conductor in a generator. The constant magnetic induction $\mathbf{B}$, conductor velocity $\mathbf{v}_0$, and conductor length are all mutually perpendicular. Sketch the situation, and consider the energy balance. In particular, investigate the source of the power $-\mathbf{J} \cdot \mathbf{E}$ (see Sec. 5.8).

12.24. *a.* Obtain the magnetic field components of an oscillating electric dipole in cartesian coordinates by direct differentiation of the magnetic vector potential function.

b. Check this result against Eq. (12.137).

Ans. (a) $B_x = \dfrac{\mu_0 \omega p_0}{4\pi} \left[\dfrac{\omega y}{cR^2} \sin \omega \left(t - \dfrac{R}{c} \right) - \dfrac{y}{R^3} \cos \omega \left(t - \dfrac{R}{c} \right) \right]$

$B_y = \dfrac{\mu_0 \omega p_0}{4\pi} \left[-\dfrac{\omega x}{cR^2} \sin \omega \left(t - \dfrac{R}{c} \right) + \dfrac{x}{R^3} \cos \omega \left(t - \dfrac{R}{c} \right) \right]$

12.25. From the results of Prob. 12.24, find the z component of the electric field of the oscillating dipole, using a Maxwell equation as in Sec. 12.8. Work in cartesian coordinates.

12.26. Given a magnetic field in empty space where there is neither charge nor current density:

$$\mathbf{B} = \mathbf{i}a \sin (\omega t - nx) + \mathbf{j}any \cos (\omega t - nx)$$

where a, n, and ω are constants.

a. Use a Maxwell equation to derive the time-dependent part $\mathbf{E}$ of the electric field.

b. Show that this $\mathbf{E}$ and $\mathbf{B}$ satisfy all the Maxwell equations, provided ω and n satisfy a certain condition.

12.27. A circuit oscillating at a frequency of 2 megacycles/sec has an air condenser consisting of two circular, parallel plates of 10 cm² area with a separation of 1 mm.

a. Show that the condenser may be considered an oscillating electric dipole if the observer is far enough away, giving by an inequality the range of observer distance.

b. Give the range of observer distance if the near fields (inverse square and cube) are to be negligible compared with the radiation field.

c. Give the range of observer distance if the inverse cube is to predominate over the other terms in the electric field.

12.28. Compute the radiation resistance of the condenser in the preceding problem, and compare it with the reactance at the frequency of oscillation.

12.29. Suppose that the peak potential difference across the condenser of Prob. 12.27 is 3,000 volts. Find, to the electric dipole approximation, (*a*) the average radiated power; (*b*) the vector potential, magnetic induction, and electric field at a point 5 m from the condenser, in its plane and at the time when the condenser potential difference is zero but increasing in the sense of the positive z axis.

12.30. *a.* Find the Poynting vector arising from the nonradiative terms of the field of an oscillating electric dipole.

b. Show that the time average of the surface integral of this vector on a sphere about the dipole is zero.   What significance does this have?

12.31. Write tangential boundary conditions for **D** and **B** and normal conditions for **E** and **H**, assuming isotropic media on the two sides of a boundary.

12.32. Revise the tangential boundary condition on the magnetizing force **H** to apply when a surface current of density **K** flows in the boundary.   Use the unit vectors defined in Sec. 12.9.

12.33. If an electromagnetic wave impinges normally on a polished surface of material whose conductivity is infinite, there can be no electric field in the body of the material.   Show therefore (*a*) that there is 100 per cent reflection and (*b*) that a surface density of current must be permitted in the application of boundary conditions.

12.34. At a boundary between air and a certain kind of glass, $5\frac{1}{3}$ per cent of normally incident light is reflected.   For this light, find (*a*) the index of refraction of the glass; (*b*) the amplitude ratios of the reflected and the transmitted electric fields to the incident electric field.

12.35. Let the boundary of two isotropic transparent dielectrics be the yz plane, and let light polarized with its electric vector in the z direction be incident in the xy plane at angle θ to the x axis.

a. Assuming the same polarization but arbitrary angles θ' and θ'' of refraction and reflection, write equations giving the form of the incident, reflected, and refracted electric fields (see Prob. 12.14).

b. By reference to the parallel boundary condition for electric fields, prove the optical laws of reflection and refraction.

Take frequency $\omega/2\pi$, and phase velocities v_1 and v_2, respectively, in the two media.
Ans. (*b*) $\theta = \theta''$, if θ'' is properly defined, and

$$\frac{\sin \theta}{v_1} = \frac{\sin \theta'}{v_2}$$

12.36. Work out the details in the deduction of Eqs. (12.205) and (12.206), Sec. 12.11.

12.37. Find a scalar potential function which together with the vector potential (12.131) of an oscillating dipole satisfies the Lorentz condition.   To what extent is this result arbitrary?

12.38. Investigate the vector potential function in empty space devoid of current

$$\mathbf{A} = \mathbf{i} A_1 \cos \omega \left(\frac{x}{c} - t\right)$$

where A_1 and ω are constant and **i** is the unit vector in the x direction.

a. Show that this function satisfies its wave equation, provided the constant c is correctly chosen.

b. Notice that this function yields a zero magnetic field. Show that it also implies that the electric field, if any, is independent of time by finding the corresponding scalar potential and then deriving the electric field.

12.39. Find a pair of potential functions $\mathbf{A}$ and ϕ satisfying the Lorentz condition and the wave equations in empty space, to yield the fields of the plane wave described by Eqs. (12.63) and (12.72), Sec. 12.6.

12.40. Show how the Lorentz condition together with the wave equations for the potentials, for a region where charge and current may exist but the permeability and permittivity are those of empty space, implies the equation of continuity. *Hint:* Differentiate the wave equations, and interchange order of differentiation.

12.41. Consider a steady-state system having charges and currents that do not vary with time, and having no dielectric or magnetic matter.

a. Show that the electrostatic scalar potential and the magnetostatic vector potential integrals are special cases of the retarded potentials.

b. The Lorentz condition was stated to hold for the retarded potential integrals. Show that this implies, for the steady-state system, that

$$\mathrm{div} \int\limits_{\text{all space}} \frac{\mathbf{J}(x,y,z)}{r} \, dV = 0$$

12.42. Suppose that the displacement current is omitted from the Maxwell equations and that vector and scalar potential functions are introduced as in Sec. 12.11.

a. Find the wave equations, in a system where there is no dielectric or magnetic matter, which the potentials would then satisfy.

b. Show how these equations separate if, instead of the Lorentz condition, it is required that div $\mathbf{A} = 0$.

Ans. (b) $\dfrac{\partial^2 \phi}{\partial x^2} + \dfrac{\partial^2 \phi}{\partial y^2} + \dfrac{\partial^2 \phi}{\partial z^2} = -\dfrac{\rho}{\epsilon_0}$

$\dfrac{\partial^2 A_x}{\partial x^2} + \dfrac{\partial^2 A_x}{\partial y^2} + \dfrac{\partial^2 A_x}{\partial z^2} = -\mu_0 J_x$, etc.

12.43. *a.* Show that the small-system potential integrals are exact solutions of the system of equations derived by omission of the Maxwell displacement current in Prob. 12.42, and consequently that the small-system approximation simply means omission of displacement current. *Hint:* Compare steady-state equations and solutions, and see Prob. 12.41.

Note: Compare Probs. 12.1 and 12.2, where the fields are consistent with the small-system approximation but not with the complete Maxwell equations.

12.44. A circuit including a pair of parallel wires $\frac{1}{2}$ cm apart and 2 m long carries an a-c current of 100 ma with a frequency of 1 megacycle/sec. The wires carry the current in opposite senses. At a point $\frac{1}{2}$ cm from one wire and 1 cm from the other, and far from their ends, find as a function of time (*a*) the vector potential, and (*b*) the electric field due to the change of current in the wires. Justify the use of any approximations involved in the problem.

12.45. *a.* Express the inverse-cube electric field of an oscillating electric dipole in cartesian coordinates.

b. Show that this part of the field by itself does not satisfy div $\mathbf{E} = 0$, which holds at the observer's position.

12.46. Find the small-system approximation to the retarded vector and scalar potential functions of the oscillating electric dipole of Sec. 12.8.

a. For what range of observer distances should this approximation be valid?

b. Derive the electric and magnetic fields, to the small-system approximation; and compare with corresponding terms of the general dipole fields found in Sec. 12.8.

INDEX